THE PERIODIC TABLE OF THE ELEMENTS
WITH ATOMIC WEIGHTS[a]

[a]Based on $^{12}C = 12.000$, for elements in materials of terrestrial origin.
[b]Variation in natural isotopic abundance limits precision.
[c]Variations are possible, owing to artificial isotopic separations.
[d]For the most commonly available long-lived isotope.

I A (1)	II A (2)	III A (3)	IV A (4)	V A (5)	VI A (6)	VII A (7)	VIII A (8)	VIII A (9)
1 H 1.00797[b] Hydrogen								
3 Li 6.941[b,c] Lithium	4 Be 9.01218 Beryllium							
11 Na 22.98977 Sodium	12 Mg 24.305 Magnesium							
19 K 39.0983 Potassium	20 Ca 40.08 Calcium	21 Sc 44.9559 Scandium	22 Ti 47.90 Titanium	23 V 50.941 Vanadium	24 Cr 51.996 Chromium	25 Mn 54.9380 Manganese	26 Fe 55.847 Iron	27 Co 58.9332 Cobalt
37 Rb 85.467 Rubidium	38 Sr 87.62 Strontium	39 Y 88.9059 Yttrium	40 Zr 91.22 Zirconium	41 Nb 92.9064 Niobium	42 Mo 95.94 Molybdenum	43 Tc 98.9062[d] Technetium	44 Ru 101.07 Ruthenium	45 Rh 102.9055 Rhodium
55 Cs 132.9054 Cesium	56 Ba 137.34 Barium	57 La 138.905 Lanthanum	72 Hf 178.49 Hafnium	73 Ta 180.948 Tantalum	74 W 183.85 Tungsten	75 Re 186.2 Rhenium	76 Os 190.2 Osmium	77 Ir 192.2 Iridium
87 Fr Francium	88 Ra 226.0254[d] Radium	89 Ac 227.0278 Actinium	104	105	106	107	108	109

58 Ce 140.12 Cerium	59 Pr 140.907 Praseodymium	60 Nd 144.24 Neodymium	61 Pm Promethium	62 Sm 150.35 Samarium
90 Th 232.0381 Thorium	91 Pa 231.0359 Protactinium	92 U 238.029[c] Uranium	93 Np 237.0482 Neptunium	94 Pu Plutonium

GROUP DESIGNATIONS
Traditional
(IUPAC)

VIII A (10)	I B (11)	II B (12)	III B (13)	IV B (14)	V B (15)	VI B (16)	VII B (17)	VIII B (18)
								2 He 4.00260 Helium
			5 B 10.811[b] Boron	6 C 12.01115 Carbon	7 N 14.0067 Nitrogen	8 O 15.9994[b,c] Oxygen	9 F 18.9984 Fluorine	10 Ne 20.179 Neon
			13 Al 26.98154[b] Aluminum	14 Si 28.086 Silicon	15 P 30.97376 Phosphorus	16 S 32.064[b] Sulfur	17 Cl 35.453 Chlorine	18 Ar 39.948 Argon
28 Ni 58.69 Nickel	29 Cu 63.546[b] Copper	30 Zn 65.377 Zinc	31 Ga 69.72 Gallium	32 Ge 72.59 Germanium	33 As 74.9216 Arsenic	34 Se 78.96 Selenium	35 Br 79.904 Bromine	36 Kr 83.80 Krypton
46 Pd 106.4 Palladium	47 Ag 107.868 Silver	48 Cd 112.40 Cadmium	49 In 114.82 Indium	50 Sn 118.69 Tin	51 Sb 121.75 Antimony	52 Te 127.60 Tellurium	53 I 126.9045 Iodine	54 Xe 131.30 Xenon
78 Pt 195.09 Platinum	79 Au 196.9665 Gold	80 Hg 200.59 Mercury	81 Tl 204.38 Thallium	82 Pb 207.19[b] Lead	83 Bi 208.9804 Bismuth	84 Po Pollonium	85 At Astatine	86 Rn Radon

63 Eu 151.96 Europium	64 Gd 157.25 Gadolinium	65 Tb 158.9254 Terbium	66 Dy 162.50 Dysprosium	67 Ho 164.9304 Holmium	68 Er 167.26 Erbium	69 Tm 168.9342 Thulium	70 Yb 173.04 Ytterbium	71 Lu 174.97 Lutetium
95 Am Americium	96 Cm Curium	97 Bk Berkelium	98 Cf Californium	99 Es Einsteinium	100 Fm Fermium	101 Md Mendelevium	102 No Nobelium	103 Lw Lawrencium

BASIC
INORGANIC CHEMISTRY
second edition

second edition

BASIC INORGANIC CHEMISTRY

F. Albert Cotton

W. T. Doherty-Welch Foundation Distinguished Professor of Chemistry
Texas A and M University
College Station, Texas, USA

Geoffrey Wilkinson

Sir Edward Frankland Professor of Inorganic Chemistry
Imperial College of Science and Technology
University of London, England

Paul L. Gaus

Associate Professor of Chemistry
The College of Wooster
Wooster, Ohio, USA

(Formerly *Basic Inorganic Chemistry*, by Cotton and Wilkinson)

John Wiley & Sons

New York   Chichester   Brisbane   Toronto   Singapore

Cover photograph by Paul Silverman

Copyright © 1976, 1987, by John Wiley & Sons, Inc.

All rights reserved. Published simultaneously in Canada.

Library of Congress Cataloging in Publication Data:

Cotton, F. Albert (Frank Albert), 1930–
  Basic inorganic chemistry.

  Includes index.
  1. Chemistry, Inorganic.   I. Wilkinson, Geoffrey, Sir,
1921–   II. Gaus, Paul L.   III. Title.
QD151.2.C69   1987   546   86-22403

10 9 8 7 6 5

Printed in Singapore

The principal goals in *Basic Inorganic Chemistry, Second Edition* are to set down the primary facts of inorganic chemistry in a clear and accurate manner, and to organize the facts of chemical structure and reactivity (while presenting the pertinent theories) in a way that emphasizes the descriptive approach to the subject. The chemistry of the elements and their compounds is organized by classes of substances and types of reactions, and periodicity in structure and reactivity is emphasized.

This text can be used in a one-semester course that does not require physical chemistry (as taught traditionally in the United States) as a prerequisite. The principles generally encountered in the first year of college are reviewed in Chapter 1, and the book could be used in any inorganic course for which at least concurrent enrollment in sophomore organic chemistry was anticipated. A glossary has been added to help make this second edition more useful in interdisciplinary settings.

Although the organization of the second edition is essentially unchanged from the first edition, some chapters have been revised considerably, and others have been rewritten entirely. There are, for instance, new sections on geometry and bonding in molecules and complex ions, boron chemistry, mechanisms of reactions of coordination compounds, electronic spectroscopy, and catalysis. The chapter on bioinorganic chemistry has been thoroughly revised and updated. The topics of structure, reactivity, and periodicity have been uniformly emphasized throughout the descriptive chapters. Bonding theories are developed in Chapter 3 (including an intuitive treatment of delocalized molecular orbital approaches), and these are applied in subsequent chapters wherever useful, and especially in the end-of-chapter exercises.

The end-of-chapter exercises have been revised and organized into three groups. *Review* questions are straightforward, and require only that the student recall the material in the chapter. *Additional Exercises* generally require application of important principles or additional thought by the student. *Questions from the Literature of Inorganic Chemistry* refer the student to specific journal articles that are germane to the topic at hand. Thus the study guides, supplementary readings, and study questions range in scope from a straightforward review of the chapter to the sort of professional literature on which the science is based. A separate solutions manual, containing detailed answers for each of the study questions, is also available.

The study guides at the end of certain chapters give some idea, to the student and the instructor, of the goals of, organization in, and prerequisites for a given chapter. Chapter 1 constitutes a review of the principles that are normally encountered in the first college year, and that are of use in the present text. Chapters 2 through 8 contain much of what is essential for complete comprehension of later chapters. Chapters 9 through 22 may be covered selectively, at the instructor's discretion, depending on the constraints of time. Chapter 23 is an important prerequisite for the material in Chapters

24 through 27, which are optional. Chapters 28 and 29 will be helpful to the discussion of the material in Chapter 30.

We are grateful for the efforts of those who reviewed the first edition, prior to its revision: Dr. Robert Parry, University of Utah; Dr. Richard Treptow, Chicago State University; and Prof. Glen Rodgers, Allegheny College.

We also gratefully acknowledge the very fine efforts of those who critiqued the revised edition: David Goodgame, Margaret Goodgame, Richard Treptow, Glen Rodgers, and Robert Parry. These reviewers made useful and substantial comments on the text, and have contributed significantly to its accuracy and clarity. Jeannette Stiefel was very helpful in editing the manuscript.

We would be pleased to correspond with teachers and to receive comments regarding the text. Suggestions for new journal articles to be used in *Questions from the Literature of Inorganic Chemistry* would be welcomed. Please address correspondence to P. L. Gaus.

Finally, P. L. G. wishes especially to acknowledge the help, encouragement, and support of his family: Madonna, Laura, and Amy, and to dedicate the revised edition to his parents.

F. Albert Cotton
College Station, Texas

Geoffrey Wilkinson
London, England

Paul L. Gaus
Wooster, Ohio

October , 1986

preface to the first edition

Those who aspire not to guess and divine, but to discover and know, who propose not to devise mimic and fabulous worlds of their own, but to examine and dissect the nature of this very world itself, must go to facts themselves for everything.

F. Bacon, 1620

There are already several textbooks of inorganic chemistry that treat the subject in considerably less space than our comprehensive text, *Advanced Inorganic Chemistry*. Moreover, most of them include a great deal of introductory theory, which we omitted from our larger book because of space considerations. The net result is that these books contain very little of the real content of inorganic chemistry—namely, the actual facts about the properties and behavior of inorganic compounds.

Our purpose in *Basic Inorganic Chemistry*, is to meet the needs of teachers who present this subject to students who do not have the time or perhaps the inclination to pursue it in depth, but who may also require explicit coverage of basic topics such as the electronic structure of atoms and elementary valence theory. We therefore introduce material of this type, in an elementary fashion, and present only the main facts.

The point, however, is that this book does present the facts, in a systematic way. We have a decidedly Baconian philosophy about all chemistry, but particularly inorganic chemistry. We are convinced that inorganic chemistry *sans* facts (or nearly so), as presented in other books, is like a page of music with no instrument to play it on. One can appreciate the sound of music without knowing anything of musical theory, although of course one's appreciation is enhanced by knowing some theory. However, a book of musical theory, even if it is illustrated by audible snatches of themes and a few chord progressions, is quite unlike the hearing of a real composition in its entirety.

We believe that a student who has read a book on "inorganic chemistry" that consists almost entirely of theory and so-called principles, with but sporadic mention of the hard facts (only when they "nicely" illustrate the "principles") has not, in actual fact, had a course in inorganic chemistry. We deplore the current trend toward this way of teaching students who are not expected to specialize in the subject, and believe that even the nonspecialist ought to get a straight dose of the subject as it really is—"warts and all." This book was written to encourage the teaching of inorganic chemistry in a Baconian manner.

At the end of each chapter, there is a study guide. Occasionally this includes a few remarks on the scope and purpose of the chapter to help the student place it in the context of the entire book. A supplementary reading list is included in all chapters. This consists of relatively recent articles in the secondary (monograph and review) literature, which will be of interest to those who wish to pursue the subject matter in more detail. In some instances there is little literature of this kind available. However, the student—and the instructor—will find more detailed treatments of all the elements and classes of compounds, as well as further references, in our *Advanced Inorganic Chemistry*, fourth edition, Wiley, 1984, and in *Comprehensive Inorganic Chemistry*, J. C. Bailar, Jr., H. J. Emeléus, R. S. Nyholm, and A. F. Trotman-Dickinson, Eds., Pergamon, 1973.

F. Albert Cotton
Geoffrey Wilkinson

contents

BASIC
INORGANIC CHEMISTRY
second edition

FIRST
PRINCIPLES

chapter 1

SOME PRELIMINARIES

1-1　A Description of Inorganic Chemistry

Inorganic chemistry embraces the chemistry of all of the elements. Consequently it ranges from the border of what is called organic chemistry (primarily the chemistry of carbon bound to hydrogen, nitrogen, oxygen, sulfur, phosphorus, halogens, and possibly a few other elements such as selenium and arsenic) to the border of physical chemistry, which is the study of the physical properties and quantitative behavior of matter. Inorganic chemistry is concerned with substances similar to those encountered in organic chemistry, but additionally with gases, insoluble solids, air sensitive (and hydrolytically sensitive) compounds, and with compounds that are soluble in water, as well as those that are soluble in organic solvents.

A further difference is that while organic substances principally have a maximum coordination number of 4 (e.g., CH_4 and NR_4^+), inorganic substances feature elements with coordination numbers frequently exceeding 4 (indeed as high as 14), and having a variety of oxidation states. Some simple examples are PF_5, $W(CH_3)_6$, and $[Nd(H_2O)_9]^{3+}$.

We must hence be concerned with a great many methods of synthesis and manipulation of inorganic compounds, with the problem of ascertaining the structures of a broad range of materials with widely differing properties, and finally with exceedingly complicated patterns of reactivity. In accounting for the existence and in describing the behavior of inorganic materials, we shall need to use certain aspects of physical chemistry, notably thermodynamics, atomic and molecular bonding theories, kinetics, and the like. Some of these topics are reviewed in later portions of this chapter. The remainder of Part I will deal with atomic and molecular structure, chemical bonding, and other principles that allow an understanding of the structures and properties of inorganic substances of all classes.

Classes of Substances

The main classes of materials that we shall discuss are

    A. The elements themselves, which may be
        (i) Atomic (Ar, Kr) or molecular (H_2, O_2) gases.
        (ii) Molecular solids (P_4, S_8).
        (iii) Extended molecules or network solids (diamond, graphite).
        (iv) Solid or liquid (Hg, Ga) metals.

B. Ionic compounds (solids), including
   (i) Simple ionic compounds such as NaCl that are soluble in water or other polar solvents.
   (ii) Ionic oxides that are insoluble in water, for example, ZrO_2, and mixed oxides such as spinels, silicates, and so on.
   (iii) Halides, carbides, sulfides, and similar materials, examples being, SiC, GaAs, and BN.
   (iv) Compounds containing solvated or complex ions such as $[SiF_6]^{2-}$, $[Co(NH_3)_6]^{3+}$, $[Fe(CN)_6]^{3-}$, and $[Ni(H_2O)_6]^{2+}$.

C. Molecular compounds (solids, liquids, or gases) including:
   (i) Simple compounds such as PF_3, SO_2, OsO_4, and UF_6.
   (ii) Complex metal-containing compounds such as $PtCl_2(PMe_3)_2$ and $RuH(CO_2Me)$ $(PPh_3)_3$.
   (iii) Organometallic compounds that have metal–carbon bonds, examples being, $Ni(CO)_4$, $Zr(CH_2C_6H_5)_4$, and $(C_8H_8)_2U$.

Classes of Reactions

Most inorganic reactions fit into one or more of the following classes, which are defined in the glossary or in context at the appropriate point in the text:

1. Acid–Base or neutralization
2. Addition
3. Elimination
4. Oxidation–reduction
5. Insertion
6. Substitution or Displacement
7. Rearrangement or isomerization
8. Metathesis or exchange
9. Solvolysis
10. Chelation
11. Cyclization
12. Nuclear

At the most detailed level in the description of an inorganic reaction, we seek to prepare a complete reaction profile, from reactants (through any intermediates or transition states) to products. This requires intimate knowledge of the kinetics and thermodynamics of the reaction, and it requires that we understand the influence of structure and bonding on reactivity. These are the topics to be covered.

1-2   Thermochemistry

Standard States

To have universally recognized and understood values for energy changes in chemical processes, it is first necessary to define standard states for all substances.

The standard state for any substance is that phase in which it exists at 25 °C (298.15 K) and 1 atm (101.325 N/m^2) pressure. Substances in solution are at unit concentration.

Heat Content or Enthalpy

Virtually all physical and chemical changes either produce or consume energy, and generally this energy takes the form of heat. The gain or loss of heat may be attributed to a change in the "heat content" of the substances taking part in the process. *Heat content* is called **enthalpy,** symbolized H. The change in heat content is called the **enthalpy change,** ΔH, defined in Eq. 1-2.1:

$$\Delta H = (H \text{ of products}) - (H \text{ of reactants}) \tag{1-2.1}$$

For the case in which all products and reactants are in their standard states, the enthalpy change is designated $\Delta H°$, the **standard enthalpy change** of the process. For example, although the formation of water from H_2 and O_2 cannot actually be carried out at an appreciable rate at standard conditions, it is nevertheless useful to know, through indirect means, that the standard enthalpy change for reaction 1-2.2 is highly negative:

$$H_2(g, 1 \text{ atm}, 25 \text{ °C}) + \tfrac{1}{2} O_2(g, 1 \text{ atm}, 25 \text{ °C}) = H_2O(\ell, 1 \text{ atm}, 25 \text{ °C})$$
$$\Delta H° = -285.7 \text{ kJ mol}^{-1} \tag{1-2.2}$$

The heat contents of all elements in their standard states are arbitrarily defined to be zero for thermochemical purposes.

The Signs of ΔH's

In Eq. 1-2.2, $\Delta H°$ has a negative value. The heat content of the products has a lower value than that of the reactants, and heat is released to its surroundings by the process. This constitutes an **exothermic** process ($\Delta H < 0$). When heat is absorbed from the surroundings by the process ($\Delta H > 0$), it is called **endothermic.** The same convention will apply to changes in free energy, ΔG, to be discussed shortly.

Standard Heats (Enthalpies) of Formation

The standard enthalpy change for any reaction can be calculated if the **standard heat of formation,** $\Delta H_f°$, of each reactant and product is known. It is therefore useful to have tables of $\Delta H_f°$ values, in units of kilojoules per mole (kJ mol^{-1}). The $\Delta H_f°$ value for a substance is the $\Delta H°$ value for the process in which 1 mol of that substance is produced in its standard state from elements, each in its standard state. Equation 1-2.2 describes such a process, and the $\Delta H°$ given for that reaction is actually the standard enthalpy of formation of liquid water, $\Delta H_f°[H_2O(\ell)]$.

Take, as an example, the reaction shown in Eq. 1-2.3:

$$LiAlH_4(s) + 4H_2O(\ell) = LiOH(s) + Al(OH)_3(s) + 4H_2(g)$$
$$\Delta H = -599.6 \text{ kJ} \tag{1-2.3}$$

The standard enthalpy change for reaction 1-2.3 may be calculated from Eq. 1-2.4:

$$\Delta H^\circ = \Delta H_f^\circ[\text{LiOH(s)}] + \Delta H_f^\circ[\text{Al(OH)}_3\text{(s)}]$$
$$- 4\Delta H_f^\circ[\text{H}_2\text{O}(\ell)] - \Delta H_f^\circ[\text{LiAlH}_4\text{(s)}] \quad (1\text{-}2.4)$$

Other Special Enthalpy Changes

Aside from formation of compounds from the elements, there are several other physical and chemical processes of special importance for which the ΔH or ΔH° values are frequently required. Among these are the process of melting (for which we specify the enthalpy of fusion, ΔH_{fus}°), the process of vaporization (for which we specify the enthalpy of vaporization, ΔH_{vap}°), and the process of sublimation (for which we specify the enthalpy of sublimation, ΔH_{sub}°).

We also specially designate the enthalpy changes for ionization processes that produce cations or anions by loss or gain of electrons, respectively.

Ionization Enthalpies

Of particular interest is the process of ionization by loss of electron(s), as in reaction 1-2.5:

$$\text{Na(g)} = \text{Na}^+\text{(g)} + e^-\text{(g)} \qquad \Delta H_{ion}^\circ = 502 \text{ kJ mol}^{-1} \qquad (1\text{-}2.5)$$

For many atoms, the enthalpies of removal of a second, third, and so on, electron are also of chemical interest, and for most elements, these enthalpies are known. For example, the first three ionization enthalpies of aluminum are given in reactions 1-2.6 to 1-2.8:

$$\text{Al(g)} = \text{Al}^+\text{(g)} + e^- \qquad \Delta H^\circ = 577.5 \text{ kJ mol}^{-1} \qquad (1\text{-}2.6)$$

$$\text{Al}^+\text{(g)} = \text{Al}^{2+}\text{(g)} + e^- \qquad \Delta H^\circ = 1817 \text{ kJ mol}^{-1} \qquad (1\text{-}2.7)$$

$$\text{Al}^{2+}\text{(g)} = \text{Al}^{3+}\text{(g)} + e^- \qquad \Delta H^\circ = 2745 \text{ kJ mol}^{-1} \qquad (1\text{-}2.8)$$

The overall ionization enthalpy for formation of the $\text{Al}^{3+}\text{(g)}$ ion is then the sum of the single ionization enthalpies, as shown in reaction 1-2.9:

$$\text{Al(g)} = \text{Al}^{3+}\text{(g)} + 3e^- \qquad \Delta H^\circ = 5140 \text{ kJ mol}^{-1} \qquad (1\text{-}2.9)$$

Ionization enthalpies may also be defined for molecules, as in Eq. 1-2.10:

$$\text{NO(g)} = \text{NO}^+\text{(g)} + e^- \qquad \Delta H^\circ = 890.7 \text{ kJ mol}^{-1} \qquad (1\text{-}2.10)$$

It is to be noted that for molecules and atoms the ionization enthalpies are always positive; energy must be expended to detach electrons. Also, the increasing magnitudes of successive ionization steps, as shown previously for aluminum, is completely general; the more positive the system becomes, the more difficult it is to ionize it further.

Electron Attachment Enthalpies

Consider reactions 1-2.11 to 1-2.13:

$$Cl(g) + e^- = Cl^-(g) \qquad \Delta H^\circ = -349 \text{ kJ mol}^{-1} \qquad (1\text{-}2.11)$$

$$O(g) + e^- = O^-(g) \qquad \Delta H^\circ = -142 \text{ kJ mol}^{-1} \qquad (1\text{-}2.12)$$

$$O^-(g) + e^- = O^{2-}(g) \qquad \Delta H^\circ = 844 \text{ kJ mol}^{-1} \qquad (1\text{-}2.13)$$

The $Cl^-(g)$ ion forms exothermically. The same is true of the other halide ions. Observe that the formation of the oxide ion, $O^{2-}(g)$, requires first an exothermic and then an endothermic step. This is understandable because the O^- ion, which is already negative, will tend to resist the addition of another electron.

In most of the chemical literature, the negative of the enthalpy change for processes such as Eqs. 1-2.11 to 1-2.13 is called the electron affinity, A, for the atom. In this book, however, we shall use only the systematic notation illustrated previously: we shall speak of the enthalpy changes (ΔH_{EA}) that accompany the attachment of electrons to form specific ions.

Direct measurement of ΔH_{EA}'s is difficult, and indirect methods tend to be inaccurate. To give an idea of their magnitudes, some of those that are known (with those that are estimates in parentheses) are listed in kilojoules per mole:

H	−73									
Li	−58	Be	(+60)	B	(−30)	C	−120	N	(+10)	O	−142	F	−328
Na	(−50)					Si	(−135)	P	(−75)	S	−200	Cl	−349
										Se	(−160)	Br	−324
												I	−295

Bond Energies

Consider homolytic cleavage of the HF molecule as in reaction 1-2.14:

$$HF(g) = H(g) + F(g) \qquad \Delta H_{298} = 566 \text{ kJ mol}^{-1} \qquad (1\text{-}2.14)$$

The enthalpy requirement of this process has a simple, unambiguous significance. It is the energy required to break the H—F bond. It can be called the "H—F bond energy," and we can, if we prefer, think of 566 kJ mol^{-1} as the energy released when the H—F bond is formed—a perfectly equivalent and equally unambiguous statement.

Consider, however, the stepwise cleavage of the two O—H bonds in water, as in Eqs. 1-2.15 and 1-2.16:

$$H_2O(g) = H(g) + OH(g) \qquad \Delta H_{298} = 497 \text{ kJ mol}^{-1} \qquad (1\text{-}2.15)$$

$$OH(g) = H(g) + O(g) \qquad \Delta H_{298} = 421 \text{ kJ mol}^{-1} \qquad (1\text{-}2.16)$$

These two processes of breaking the O—H bonds one after the other have different energies. Furthermore, the overall homolytic cleavage of the two

O—H bonds as in Eq. 1-2.17:

$$H_2O(g) = 2H(g) + O(g) \qquad \Delta H_{298} = 918 \text{ kJ mol}^{-1} \qquad (1\text{-}2.17)$$

has an associated enthalpy change that is the sum of those for the individual steps (Eq. 1-2.15 + Eq. 1-2.16). How then can we define the O—H bond energy? It is customary to take the mean of the two values for reactions 1-2.15 and 1-2.16, which is one half of their sum: $918/2 = 459 \text{ kJ mol}^{-1}$. We then speak of a mean O—H bond energy, a quantity that we must remember is somewhat artificial; we cannot know the actual enthalpies of either step if we know only their mean.

When we consider molecules containing more than one kind of bond, the problem of defining bond energies becomes even more subtly troublesome. For example, we can consider that the total enthalpy change for reaction 1-2.18:

$$H_2N—NH_2(g) = 2N(g) + 4H(g) \qquad \Delta H_{298} = 1724 \text{ kJ mol}^{-1} \qquad (1\text{-}2.18)$$

consists of the sum of the N—N bond energy, E_{N-N}, and four times the mean N—H bond energy, E_{N-H}. But is there any unique and rigorous way to divide the total enthalpy needed for reaction 1-2.18 (1742 kJ mol^{-1}) into these component parts? The answer is no. Instead we take the following practical approach.

We know, from experiment, the enthalpy change for reaction 1-2.19:

$$NH_3(g) = N(g) + 3H(g) \qquad \Delta H_{298} = 1172 \text{ kJ mol}^{-1} \qquad (1\text{-}2.19)$$

Thus we can determine that the mean N—H bond energy (E_{N-H}) is

$$E_{N-H} = \frac{1172}{3} = 391 \text{ kJ mol}^{-1} \qquad (1\text{-}2.20)$$

If we make the *assumption* that this value can be transferred to H_2NNH_2, then we can evaluate the N—N bond energy according to Eq. 1-2.21:

$$
\begin{aligned}
E_{N-N} + 4E_{N-H} &= 1724 \text{ kJ mol}^{-1} \\
E_{N-N} &= 1724 - 4E_{N-H} \\
&= 1724 - 4(391) \\
&= 160 \text{ kJ mol}^{-1}
\end{aligned}
\qquad (1\text{-}2.21)
$$

By proceeding in this way it is possible to build up a table of bond energies. These can then be used to calculate the enthalpies of *forming* molecules from their constituent gaseous atoms. That this approach is successful shows that the energy of the bond between a given pair of atoms is somewhat independent of the molecular environment in which that bond occurs. This is only approximately true, but true enough that the approach can be used in understanding and interpreting many chemical processes.

Figure 1-1 The variation of the bond energy with bond order for CC, NN, CN, and CO bonds.

Table 1-1 Some Average Thermochemical Bond Energies at 25 °C (in kilojoules per mole)

A. Single bond energies

	H	C	Si	Ge	N	P	As	O	S	Se	F	Cl	Br	I
H	436	416	323	289	391	322	247	467	347	276	566	431	366	299
C		356	301	255	285	264	201	336	272	243	485	327	285	213
Si			226	—	335	—	—	368	226	—	582	391	310	234
Ge				188	256	—	—	—	—	—	—	342	276	213
N					160	~200	—	201	—	—	272	193	—	—
P						209	—	~340	—	—	490	319	264	184
As							180	331	—	—	464	317	243	180
O								146	—	—	190	205	—	201
S									226	—	326	255	213	—
Se										172	285	243	—	—
F											158	255	238	—
Cl												242	217	209
Br													193	180
I														151

B. Multiple bond energies

$C{=}C$ 598	$C{=}N$ 616	$C{=}O$ 695	$N{=}N$ 418
$C{\equiv}C$ 813	$C{\equiv}N$ 866	$C{\equiv}O$ 1073	$N{\equiv}N$ 946

Thus far only single bonds have been considered. What about double and triple bonds? The bond energy increases as the bond order increases, in all cases. The increase is not linear, however, as shown in Fig. 1-1. A list of some generally useful bond energies is given in Table 1-1.

1-3   Free Energy and Entropy

The direction in which a chemical reaction will go, and the point at which equilibrium will be reached depend on two factors: (1) The tendency to give off energy; exothermic processes are favored. (2) The tendency to attain a state that is statistically more probable, crudely describable as a "more disordered" state.

We already have a measure of the energy change of a system, namely, the magnitude and sign of ΔH.

The statistical probability of a given state of a system is measured by its *entropy,* denoted S. The greater the value of S, the more probable (and, generally, more disordered) is the state. Thus we can rephrase the two statements made in the first paragraph as follows. The likelihood of a process occurring increases as (1) ΔH becomes more negative, or (2) ΔS becomes more positive.

Only in rare cases, an example being racemization,

$$2d\text{-}[Co(en)_3]^{3+} = d\text{-}[Co(en)_3]^{3+} + \ell\text{-}[Co(en)_3]^{3+} \qquad (1\text{-}3.1)$$
$$(en = ethylenediamine)$$

does a reaction have $\Delta H = 0$. In such a case, the direction and extent of reaction depends solely on ΔS. In the case where $\Delta S = 0$, ΔH would alone determine the extent and direction of reaction. However, both cases are exceptional and it is, therefore, necessary to know how these two quantities combine to influence the direction and extent of a reaction. Thermodynamics provides the necessary relationship, which is

$$\Delta G = \Delta H - T\,\Delta S \qquad (1\text{-}3.2)$$

in which T represents the absolute temperature in kelvins (K).

The letter G stands for the *free energy,* which is measured in kilojoules per mole (kJ mol^{-1}). The units of entropy are joules per kelvin (JK^{-1}), but for use with ΔG and ΔH in kilojoules per mole (kJ mol^{-1}), ΔS must be expressed as kilojoules per kelvin (kJ K^{-1}).

1-4   Chemical Equilibrium

For any chemical reaction,

$$a\text{A} + b\text{B} + c\text{C} + \cdots = k\text{K} + l\text{L} + m\text{M} + \cdots \qquad (1\text{-}4.1)$$

the position of equilibrium, for given temperature and pressure, is expressed by the equilibrium constant, K. This is defined as follows:

$$K = \frac{[K]^k[L]^l[M]^m \cdots}{[A]^a[B]^b[C]^c \cdots}$$ (1-4.2)

where [A], [B], and so on, represent the thermodynamic *activities* of A, B, and so on. For reactants in solution, the activities are approximated by the concentrations in moles per liter so long as the solutions are not too concentrated. For gases, the activities are approximated by the pressures. For a pure liquid or solid phase, X, the activity is defined as unity and $[X]^x$ can, therefore, be omitted from the expression for the equilibrium constant.

1-5   ΔG° As a Predictive Tool

For any reaction, the position of the equilibrium at 25 °C is determined by the value of $\Delta G°$. $\Delta G°$ is defined in a manner similar to that for $\Delta H°$, namely, Eq. 1-5.1,

$$\Delta G° = \sum \Delta G_f°(\text{products}) - \sum \Delta G_f°(\text{reactants})$$ (1-5.1)

which similarly applies only at 25 °C (298.15 K). In terms of enthalpy and entropy we also have, at 25 °C, Eq. 1-5.2:

$$\Delta G° = \Delta H° - 298.15 \, \Delta S°$$ (1-5.2)

where $\Delta S°$, the standard entropy change for the reaction, is defined as the difference between the sum of the absolute entropies of the products and the sum of the absolute entropies of the reactants:

$$\Delta S° = \sum S°(\text{products}) - \sum S°(\text{reactants})$$ (1-5.3)

The standard against which we tabulate entropy for any substance is the perfect crystalline solid at 0 K, for which the absolute entropy is taken to be zero.

The following relationship exists between ΔG and the equilibrium constant, K:

$$\Delta G = -RT \ln K$$ (1-5.4)

where R is the gas constant and has the value

$$R = 8.314 \, \text{JK}^{-1} \, \text{mol}^{-1}$$ (1-5.5)

in units appropriate to this equation. At 25 °C we have

$$\Delta G° = -5.69 \log K_{298.15}$$ (1-5.6)

For a reaction with $\Delta G° = 0$, the equilibrium constant is unity. The more negative the value of $\Delta G°$ the more the reaction proceeds in the direction written, that is, to produce substances on the right and consume those on the left.

When $\Delta G°$ is considered as the net result of enthalpy ($\Delta H°$) and entropy ($\Delta S°$) contributions, a number of possibilities must be considered. Reactions which proceed as written, that is, from left to right, have $\Delta G° < 0$. There are three main ways that this can happen.

1. Both $\Delta H°$ and $\Delta S°$ favor the reaction. That is, $\Delta H° < 0$ and $\Delta S° > 0$.
2. $\Delta H°$ favors the reaction while $\Delta S°$ does not, but $\Delta H°$ (<0) has a greater absolute value than $T \Delta S°$ and thus gives a net negative $\Delta G°$.
3. $\Delta H°$ disfavors the reaction (is > 0) but $\Delta S°$ is positive and sufficiently large that $T \Delta S°$ has a larger absolute magnitude than $\Delta H°$.

There are actual chemical reactions that belong to each of these categories. Case 1 is fairly common. The formation of CO from the elements is an example:

$$\tfrac{1}{2} O_2(g) + C(s) = CO(g)$$

$$\Delta G° = -137.2 \text{ kJ mol}^{-1}$$

$$\Delta H° = -110.5 \text{ kJ mol}^{-1}$$

$$T \Delta S° = 26.7 \text{ kJ mol}^{-1}$$

(1-5.7)

as are a host of combustion reactions, for example,

$$S(s) + O_2(g) = SO_2(g)$$

$$\Delta G° = -300.4 \text{ kJ mol}^{-1}$$

$$\Delta H° = -292.9 \text{ kJ mol}^{-1}$$

$$T \Delta S° = 7.5 \text{ kJ mol}^{-1}$$

(1-5.8)

$$C_4H_{10}(g) + \tfrac{13}{2} O_2(g) = 4CO_2(g) + 5H_2O(g)$$

$$\Delta G° = -2705 \text{ kJ mol}^{-1}$$

$$\Delta H° = -2659 \text{ kJ mol}^{-1}$$

$$T \Delta S° = 46 \text{ kJ mol}^{-1}$$

(1-5.9)

The reaction used in industrial synthesis of ammonia is an example of case 2:

$$N_2(g) + 3H_2(g) = 2NH_3(g)$$

$$\Delta G° = -16.7 \text{ kJ mol}^{-1}$$

$$\Delta H° = -46.2 \text{ kJ mol}^{-1}$$

$$T \Delta S° = -29.5 \text{ kJ mol}^{-1}$$

(1-5.10)

The negative entropy term can be attributed to the greater "orderliness" of a product system that contains only 2 mol of independent particles compared with the reactant system in which there are 4 mol of independent molecules.

Case 3 is the rarest. Examples are provided by substances that dissolve endothermically to give a saturated solution greater than $1\ M$ in concentration. This happens with sodium chloride:

$$NaCl(s) = Na^+(aq) + Cl^-(aq)$$

$$\Delta G° = -2.7$$
$$\Delta H° = +1.9$$
$$T\ \Delta S° = +4.6$$

(1-5.11)

It must be stressed that the $\Delta G°$ value does not *necessarily* predict the *actual result* of a reaction, but only the result that corresponds to the attainment of equilibrium at 25 °C. It tells what is *possible*, but not what will actually *occur*. Thus, none of the first four reactions cited, which all have $\Delta G° < 0$, actually occurs to a detectable extent at 25 °C simply on mixing the reactants. Activation energy and/or a catalyst (see page 22) must be supplied. Moreover, there are many compounds that are perfectly stable in a practical sense with positive values of $\Delta G_f°$. They do not spontaneously decompose into the elements, although that would be the equilibrium situation. Common examples are benzene, CS_2, and hydrazine (H_2NNH_2).

The actual occurrence of a reaction requires not only that $\Delta G°$ be negative but that the *rate* of the reaction be appreciable.

1-6   Temperature Dependence of the Equilibrium Constant

The equilibrium constant for a reaction depends on temperature. That dependence is determined by $\Delta H°$, and the dependence can be used to determine $\Delta H°$ in the following way. If the value of the equilibrium constant is known to be K_1 at T_1 and K_2 at T_2, then we have Eqs. 1-6.1 and 1-6.2:

$$\ln K_1 = -\frac{\Delta H°}{RT_1} + \frac{\Delta S°}{R}$$

(1-6.1)

$$\ln K_2 = -\frac{\Delta H°}{RT_2} + \frac{\Delta S°}{R}$$

(1-6.2)

By subtracting Eqs. 1-6.1 and 1-6.2 we have Eq. 1-6.3:

$$\ln K_1 - \ln K_2 = \ln \frac{K_1}{K_2} = -\frac{\Delta H°}{R}\left(\frac{1}{T_1} - \frac{1}{T_2}\right)$$

(1-6.3)

which allows us to calculate $\Delta H°$ if we can measure the equilibrium constant at two different temperatures. In practice, one secures greater accuracy by measuring the equilibrium constant at several different temperatures and plotting $\ln K$ versus $1/T$. Such a plot should be a straight line with a slope of

$-(\Delta H^{\circ}/R)$, assuming that ΔH° is constant over the temperature range employed.

1-7   Electrochemical Cell Potentials

Although it is true that the direction and extent of a reaction are indicated by the sign and magnitude of ΔG°, this is not generally an easy quantity to measure. There is one class of reactions, redox reactions in solution, that frequently allows straightforward measurement of ΔG°. The quantity actually measured is the potential difference, ΔE, in volts, between two electrodes. Under the proper conditions, this can be related to ΔG° beginning with the following equation:

$$\Delta E = \Delta E^{\circ} - \frac{RT}{nF} \log Q \qquad (1\text{-}7.1)$$

ΔE° is the so-called standard potential, which will be discussed more fully. The number of electrons in the redox reaction as written is n, and F is the faraday, 96,486.7 Coulombs per mole.

Q is an expression with the same algebraic form as the equilibrium constant for the reaction, into which the actual activities that exist when ΔE is measured are inserted. Clearly, when each concentration equals unity, $\log Q = \log 1 = 0$ and the measured ΔE equals ΔE°, the standard potential for the cell.

To illustrate, the reaction between zinc and hydrogen ions may be used

$$Zn(s) + 2H^{+}(aq) = Zn^{2+}(aq) + H_2(g) \qquad (1\text{-}7.2)$$

For this, $n = 2$ and Q has the form:

$$\frac{A_{H_2} \cdot A_{Zn^{2+}}}{A_{H^+}^2} \qquad (A_{Zn} = 1) \qquad (1\text{-}7.3)$$

The symbol A_X stands for the thermodynamic activity of X. For dilute gases, the activity is equal to the pressure, and for dilute solutions, the activity is equal to the concentration. At higher pressures or concentrations, correction factors (called activity coefficients) are necessary, because activity is not then equal to pressure or concentration. We shall assume here that the activity coefficients can be ignored, so that the actual pressures and concentrations may be used.

Now, suppose the reaction of interest is allowed to run until equilibrium is reached. The numerical value of Q is then equal to the equilibrium constant, K. Moreover, at equilibrium there is no longer any tendency for electrons to flow from one electrode to the other: $\Delta E = 0$. Thus, we have

$$0 = \Delta E^{\circ} - \frac{RT}{nF} \ln K \qquad (1\text{-}7.4)$$

or

$$\Delta E° = \frac{RT}{nF} \ln K \qquad (1\text{-}7.5)$$

However, we already know that

$$\Delta G° = -RT \ln K \qquad (1\text{-}7.6)$$

We, therefore, have a way of relating cell potentials to $\Delta G°$ values, that is,

$$\frac{nF}{RT} \Delta E° = -\frac{1}{RT} \Delta G° \qquad (1\text{-}7.7)$$

or

$$\Delta G° = -nF \Delta E° \qquad (1\text{-}7.8)$$

Just as $\Delta G°$ values for a series of reactions may be added algebraically to give $\Delta G°$ for a reaction that is the sum of those added so, too, may $\Delta E°$ values be combined. But, remember that it is $n \Delta E°$, not simply $\Delta E°$, which must be used for each reaction. The factor F will, of course, cancel out in such a computation. For example, take the sum of Eqs. 1-7.9 and 1-7.10:

$(n = 2)$
$$\text{Zn(s)} + 2\text{H}^+(\text{aq}) \;\; = \text{Zn}^{2+}(\text{aq}) + \text{H}_2(\text{g}) \qquad \Delta E_1° = +0.763 \qquad (1\text{-}7.9)$$

$(n = 2)$
$$2\text{Cr(aq)}^{3+} + \text{H}_2(\text{g}) = 2\text{Cr}^{2+}(\text{aq}) + 2\text{H}^+(\text{aq}) \quad \Delta E_2° = -0.408 \qquad (1\text{-}7.10)$$

$(n = 2)$
$$\text{Zn(s)} + 2\text{Cr}^{3+}(\text{aq}) = \text{Zn}^{2+}(\text{aq}) + 2\text{Cr}^{2+}(\text{aq}) \quad \Delta E_3° = +0.355 \qquad (1\text{-}7.11)$$

The correct relationship for the potential of the net reaction 1-7.11 is

$$2 \Delta E_3° = 2 \Delta E_1° + 2 \Delta E_2° \qquad (1\text{-}7.12)$$

In this example, we have added balanced equations to give a balanced equation. This automatically ensures that the coefficient n is the same for each $\Delta E°$. However, in dealing with electrode potentials (see the next section) instead of potentials of balanced reactions the cancellation is not automatic, as we shall learn presently.

Signs of $\Delta E°$ Values

Physically, there is no absolute way to associate algebraic signs with measured $\Delta E°$ values. Yet a convention must be adhered to since, as illustrated previously, the signs of some are opposite to those of others.

Negative values of $\Delta G°$ correspond to reactions for which the equilibrium state favors products, that is, reactions that proceed in the direction written. Therefore, reactions that "go" also have positive $\Delta E°$ values. The reduction of Cr^{3+} by elemental zinc $(E° = +0.355)$ therefore goes as written in the previous example.

Half-Cells and Half-Cell (or Electrode) Potentials

Any complete, balanced chemical reaction can be artificially separated into two "half-reactions." Correspondingly, any complete electrochemical cell can be separated into two hypothetical half-cells. The potential of the actual cell, $\Delta E°$, can then be regarded as the algebraic sum of the two half-cell potentials. In the three reactions cited previously, there are a total of three distinct half-cells. Let us consider first the reaction of zinc and $H^+(aq)$:

$$Zn(s) = Zn^{2+}(aq) + 2e^- \qquad E_1° = +0.763 \text{ V}$$
$$2H^+(aq) + 2e^- = H_2(g) \qquad E_2° = 0.000 \text{ V}$$
$$\overline{Zn(s) + 2H^+(aq) = Zn^{2+}(aq) + H_2(g) \qquad E° = +0.763 \text{ V}} \qquad (1\text{-}7.13)$$

$E_1°$ and $E_2°$ must be chosen to give the sum $+0.763$ V. The only solution to this or any similar problem is to assign an arbitrary *conventional* value to one such half-cell potential. All others will then be determined. The conventional choice is to assign the hydrogen half-cell a standard potential of zero. The zinc half-cell reaction as written then has $E° = +0.763$ V. In an exactly analogous way we get

$$Cr^{3+}(aq) + e^- = Cr^{2+}(aq) \qquad E° = -0.408 \text{ V} \qquad (1\text{-}7.14)$$

These two half-cell potentials may then be used directly to calculate the standard potential for reduction of Cr^{3+} by $Zn(s)$:

$$Zn(s) = Zn^{2+}(aq) + 2e^- \qquad E° = +0.763 \text{ V}$$
$$2e^- + 2Cr^{3+}(aq) = 2Cr^{2+}(aq) \qquad E° = -0.408 \text{ V}$$
$$\overline{Zn(s) + 2Cr^{3+}(aq) = Zn^{2+}(aq) + 2Cr^{2+}(aq) \qquad E° = +0.355 \text{ V}} \qquad (1\text{-}7.15)$$

Since each reaction involves the same number of electrons, the factor n in the expression $\Delta G° = -nFE°$ is the same in this case and cancels out.

When two half-cell reactions are added to give a third half-cell reaction, then the n's cannot cancel out and must be explicitly employed in the computation. For example:

$$Cl^- + 3H_2O = ClO_3^- + 6H^+ + 6e^- \qquad E° = -1.45 \qquad 6E_1° = -8.70 \text{ V}$$
$$e^- + \tfrac{1}{2}Cl_2 = Cl^- \qquad E° = +1.36 \qquad 1E_2° = +1.36 \text{ V}$$
$$\overline{\tfrac{1}{2}Cl_2 + 3H_2O = ClO_3^- + 6H^+ + 5e^- \qquad E° = -1.47 \qquad 5E_3° = -7.34 \text{ V}}$$

where it should be emphasized that the correct relationship between the half-cell potentials is given in Eq. 1-7.16:

$$5E_3^\circ = 6E_1^\circ + 1E_2^\circ$$

$$E_3^\circ \neq E_1^\circ + E_2^\circ$$

$$(1\text{-}7.16)$$

Thus, the correct value of E_3° (-1.47 V) is nowhere near the simple sum of $E_1^\circ + E_2^\circ$ (-0.09 V).

Table 1-2 Some Half-Cell Reduction Potentials

Reaction Equation	E°(V)
$Li^+ + e^- = Li$	-3.04
$Cs^+ + e^- = Cs$	-3.02
$Rb^+ + e^- = Rb$	-2.99
$K^+ + e^- = K$	-2.92
$Ba^{2+} + 2e^- = Ba$	-2.90
$Sr^{2+} + 2e^- = Sr$	-2.89
$Ca^{2+} + 2e^- = Ca$	-2.87
$Na^+ + e^- = Na$	-2.71
$Mg^{2+} + 2e^- = Mg$	-2.34
$\frac{1}{2}H_2 + e^- = H^-$	-2.23
$Al^{3+} + 3e^- = Al$	-1.67
$Zn^{2+} + 2e^- = Zn$	-0.76
$Fe^{2+} + 2e^- = Fe$	-0.44
$Cr^{3+} + e^- = Cr^{2+}$	-0.41
$H_3PO_4 + 2H^+ + 2e^- = H_3PO_3 + H_2O$	-0.20
$Sn^{2+} + 2e^- = Sn$	-0.14
$H^+ + e^- = \frac{1}{2}H_2$	0.00
$Sn^{4+} + 2e^- = Sn^{2+}$	0.15
$Cu^{2+} + e^- = Cu^+$	0.15
$S_4O_6^{2-} + 2e^- = 2S_2O_3^{2-}$	0.17
$Cu^{2+} + 2e^- = Cu$	0.34
$Cu^+ + e^- = Cu$	0.52
$\frac{1}{2}I_2 + e^- = I^-$	0.53
$H_3AsO_4 + 2H^+ + 2e^- = H_3AsO_3 + H_2O$	0.56
$O_2 + 2H^+ + 2e^- = H_2O_2$	0.68
$Fe^{3+} + e^- = Fe^{2+}$	0.76
$\frac{1}{2}Br_2 + e^- = Br^-$	1.09
$IO_3^- + 6H^+ + 6e^- = I^- + 3H_2O$	1.09
$IO_3^- + 6H^+ + 5e^- = \frac{1}{2}I_2 + 3H_2O$	1.20
$\frac{1}{2}Cl_2 + e^- = Cl^-$	1.36
$\frac{1}{2}Cr_2O_7^{2-} + 7H^+ + 3e^- = Cr^{3+} + \frac{7}{2}H_2O$	1.36
$MnO_4^- + 8H^+ + 5e^- = Mn^{2+} + 4H_2O$	1.52
$Ce^{4+} + e^- = Ce^{3+}$	1.61
$H_2O_2 + 2H^+ + 2e^- = 2H_2O$	1.77
$\frac{1}{2}S_2O_8^{2-} + e^- = SO_4^{2-}$	2.05
$O_3 + 2H^+ + 2e^- = O_2 + H_2O$	2.07
$\frac{1}{2}F_2 + e^- = F^-$	2.85
$\frac{1}{2}F_2 + H^+ + e^- = HF$	3.03

Tables of Half-Cell or Electrode Potentials

The International Union of Pure and Applied Chemistry has agreed that half-cell and electrode potentials shall be written as reductions and the terms "half-cell potential" or "electrode potential" shall mean values carrying the sign appropriate to the reduction reaction. For example, the zinc electrode reaction is tabulated as

$$Zn^{2+}(aq) + 2e^- = Zn(s) \qquad E° = -0.763 \text{ V} \qquad (1\text{-}7.17)$$

Zinc is said to have an electrode potential of *minus* 0.763 V.

This convention is most easily remembered by noting that a half-cell reaction with a *negative* potential is *electron* rich. When two half-cells are combined to produce a complete electrolytic cell, the electrode having the more negative standard half-cell potential will be, physically, the negative electrode (electron source) if the cell is to be operated as a battery.

A list of some important standard half-cell or electrode potentials is given in Table 1-2.

1-8   Kinetics

It is primarily through the study of the kinetics of a reaction that one gains insight into the mechanism of the reaction. In kinetics experiments, the rate of a reaction is studied as a function of the concentrations of each of the reactants and products. Activities or pressures may be employed in place of concentration. The rate of a reaction is also studied as a function of reaction conditions: temperature, solvent polarity, catalysis, and the like. A kinetic study begins with the determination of the rate law for the reaction. It is assumed that the correct stoichiometry has already been determined.

The Rate Law

This is an algebraic equation, determined experimentally for each reaction, which tells how the rate of reaction (units = concentration $\times$ time^{-1}) depends on the concentrations of reactants and products, other things such as temperature being fixed. For example, it has been shown that reaction 1-8.1:

$$4HBr(g) + O_2(g) = 2H_2O(g) + 2Br_2(g) \qquad (1\text{-}8.1)$$

has the rate law Eq. 1-8.2:

$$\frac{d[O_2]}{dt} = -k[HBr][O_2] \qquad (1\text{-}8.2)$$

The rate of reaction 1-8.1 (expressed as the decrease in the concentration of O_2 as a function of time) is proportional to the first power of the HBr concentration and to the first power of the oxygen concentration. Note that the rate law is not derived from the stoichiometry of the reaction; four equivalents of HBr are consumed in the stoichiometric equation, but the HBr concentration is only featured to the first power in the rate law. Although a total of five molecules must react to complete the process of reaction 1-8.1, the rate law implies that the slowest or rate-determining step in the process is one that engages only one O_2 molecule and one HBr molecule.

This reaction is called a second-order reaction because the sum of the exponents on the concentration terms of the rate law is two. The reaction is further said to be first order in each reactant.

The other common type of reaction, kinetically speaking, is the first-order reaction. The decomposition of N_2O_5 according to Eq. 1-8.3 is an example:

$$2N_2O_5(g) = 4NO_2(g) + O_2(g) \qquad (1\text{-}8.3)$$

$$\frac{d[N_2O_5]}{dt} = -k[N_2O_5] \qquad (1\text{-}8.4)$$

The first-order rate law implies certain useful regularities. Equation 1-8.4 can be rearranged and integrated as follows:

$$\frac{d[N_2O_5]}{[N_2O_5]} = -kdt$$

$$d\{\ln[N_2O_5]\} = -kdt \qquad (1\text{-}8.5)$$

$$\ln \frac{[N_2O_5]_t}{[N_2O_5]_0} = -kt$$

where $[N_2O_5]_0$ denotes the initial reactant concentration that is employed at the start of a kinetics experiment, and $[N_2O_5]_t$ denotes the concentration that is found after some time, t.

An equivalent expression can be given for any substance that disappears in first-order fashion, namely, Eq. 1-8.6:

$$\frac{[X]_t}{[X]_0} = e^{-kt} \qquad (1\text{-}8.6)$$

For the particular case where half of the original quantity of reactant has disappeared, we have

$$[X]_t = \tfrac{1}{2}[X]_0 \qquad (1\text{-}8.7)$$

so that Eq. 1-8.5 becomes

$$\ln \tfrac{1}{2} = -kt_{1/2} \qquad (1\text{-}8.8)$$

or

$$t_{1/2} = \frac{1}{k}\ln 2 = \frac{0.693}{k} \qquad (1\text{-}8.9)$$

Thus the half-life, $t_{1/2}$, of a first-order process is inversely proportional to the rate constant, k. The higher the rate constant, the faster is the reaction, and the shorter is the half-life.

The Effect of Temperature on Reaction Rates

The rates of chemical reactions increase with increasing temperature. Generally, the dependence of the rate constant, k, on temperature, T (in kelvins), follows the Arrhenius equation, at least over moderate temperature ranges (ca. 100 K):

$$k = Ae^{-E_a/RT} \qquad (1\text{-}8.10)$$

The coefficient A is called the frequency factor and E_a is called the activation energy. The higher the activation energy the slower the reaction at any given temperature. By plotting log k against T the value of E_a (as well as A) can be determined. These E_a values are often useful in interpreting the reaction mechanism.

An alternative approach to interpreting the temperature dependence of reaction rates, especially for reactions in solution, is based on the so-called absolute reaction rate theory. In essence, this theory postulates that in the rate-determining step, the reacting species, A and B, combine reversibly to form an "activated complex," $AB^{\ddagger}$, which can then decompose to products. Thus the following pseudoequilibrium constant is written

$$K^{\ddagger} = \frac{[AB^{\ddagger}]}{[A][B]} \qquad (1\text{-}8.11)$$

The activated complex, $AB^{\ddagger}$, is treated as a normal molecule except that one of its vibrations is considered to have little or no restoring force and to allow dissociation into products. The frequency, v, with which dissociation to products takes place is assumed to be given by equating the "vibrational" energy, hv, to thermal energy, $\mathbf{k}T$. Thus we write

$$-\frac{d[A]}{dt} = v[AB^{\ddagger}] = \left(\frac{\mathbf{k}T}{h}\right)[AB^{\ddagger}] \qquad (1\text{-}8.12)$$

The measurable rate constant is defined by

$$-\frac{d[A]}{dt} = k[A][B] \qquad (1\text{-}8.13)$$

so that we have

$$k = \left(\frac{\mathbf{k}T}{h}\right)\frac{[AB^{\ddagger}]}{[A][B]} = \frac{\mathbf{k}T}{h}K^{\ddagger} \qquad (1\text{-}8.14)$$

The formation of this activated complex is governed by the thermodynamic considerations similar to those of ordinary chemical equilibria. Thus we have

$$\Delta G^{\ddagger} = -RT \ln K^{\ddagger} \tag{1-8.15}$$

and, therefore,

$$k = \left(\frac{\mathbf{k}T}{h}\right) e^{-\Delta G^{\ddagger}/RT} \tag{1-8.16}$$

Furthermore, since

$$\Delta G^{\ddagger} = \Delta H^{\ddagger} - T \Delta S^{\ddagger} \tag{1-8.17}$$

we obtain

$$k = \left(\frac{\mathbf{k}T}{h}\right) e^{\Delta S^{\ddagger}/R} e^{-\Delta H^{\ddagger}/RT} \tag{1-8.18}$$

By taking the logarithm of both sides of Eq. 1-8.18, we obtain Eq. 1-8.19:

$$\ln k = \text{constant} + \Delta S^{\ddagger}/R - \Delta H^{\ddagger}/RT \tag{1-8.19}$$

A graph of $\ln k$ versus $1/T$ should be a straight line with a slope related to $\Delta H^{\ddagger}$ and an intercept related to $\Delta S^{\ddagger}$. Thus the activation enthalpies and entropies can be determined from a study of the dependence of the rate constant on temperature.

This absolute rate theory approach is entirely consistent with the Arrhenius approach. From standard classical thermodynamics, we have Eq. 1-8.20:

$$E = \Delta H + RT \tag{1-8.20}$$

Making the appropriate substitution into Eq. 1-8.18, we get Eq. 1-8.21:

$$k = (\mathbf{k}T/h)\, e^{\Delta S^{\ddagger}/R} e^{-(E-RT)/RT}$$
$$= \left(\frac{e\mathbf{k}T}{h}\right) e^{\Delta S^{\ddagger}/R} e^{-E_a/RT} \tag{1-8.21}$$

Thus we see that the Arrhenius factor is a function of the entropy of activation.

Reaction Profiles

The course of a chemical reaction as described in the absolute reaction rate theory can be conveniently depicted in a graph of free energy versus the *reaction coordinate*. The latter is simply the pathway along which the changes in various interatomic distances progress as the system passes from reactants to activated

Figure 1-2   The free energy profile for the decomposition of formic acid. $\Delta G^{\ddagger}$ is the free energy of activation. ΔG^0 is the standard free energy change for the overall reaction.

complex to products. A representative graph is shown in Fig. 1-2 for the unimolecular decomposition of formic acid.

The Effect of Catalysts

A catalyst is a substance that causes a reaction to proceed more rapidly to equilibrium. It does not change the value of the equilibrium constant, and it does not itself undergo any net change. In terms of the absolute reaction rate theory, the role of a catalyst is to lower the free energy of activation, $\Delta G^{\ddagger}$. Some catalysts do this by simply assisting the reactants to attain basically the

Figure 1-3   The free energy profile for the acid catalyzed decomposition of formic acid. ΔG^0 is the same as in Fig. 1-2, but $\Delta G^{\ddagger}$ is now smaller.

Figure 1-4 A sketch of how a suitable platinum surface can catalyze alkene hydrogenation by binding and bringing together the reactants.

same activated complex as they do in the absence of a catalyst, but most of them appear to provide a different sort of pathway, in which they are temporarily bound, which has a lower free energy.

An example of acid catalysis, in which protonated intermediates play a role, is provided by the catalytic effect of protonic acids on the decomposition of formic acid. Figure 1-3, when compared with Fig. 1-2 (the uncatalyzed reaction pathway) shows how the catalyst modifies the reaction pathway so that the highest value of the free energy that must be reached is diminished.

Catalysis may be either homogeneous or heterogeneous. In the example just cited, it is homogeneous. The strong acid is added to the solution of formic acid and the whole process proceeds in the one liquid phase. On the other hand, especially in the majority of industrially important reactions, the catalyst is a solid surface and the reactants, either as gases or in solution, flow over the surface. Many reactions can be catalyzed in more than one way, and in some cases both homogeneously and heterogeneously.

The hydrogenation of alkenes affords an example where both heterogeneous and homogeneous catalyses are effective. The simple, uncatalyzed reaction shown in Eq. 1-8.22

$$RCH{=}CH_2 + H_2 \longrightarrow RCH_2CH_3 \tag{1-8.22}$$

is impractically slow unless very high temperatures are used, and that gives rise to other difficulties, such as the expense and difficulty of maintaining the temperature and the occurrence of other, undesired reactions. If the gases are allowed to come in contact with certain forms of noble metals, for example, platinum, supported on high surface area materials such as silica or alumina, catalysis occurs. It is believed that both reactants are absorbed by the metal surface, possibly with dissociation of the hydrogen, as indicated in Fig. 1-4. Homogeneous catalysis (one of many examples to be discussed in detail in Chapter 30) proceeds somewhat similarly but entirely on one metal ion that is present in solution as a complex.

1-9   Nuclear Reactions

Although chemical processes depend essentially on how the electrons in atoms and molecules interact with each other, the internal nature of nuclei, and changes in nuclear composition (nuclear reactions) play an important role in the study and understanding of chemical processes. Conversely, the study of nuclear processes constitutes an important area of applied chemistry, particularly inorganic chemistry.

Atomic nuclei consist of a certain number, N, of protons (p) called the *atomic number*, and a certain number of neutrons (n). The masses of these particles are each approximately equal to one mass unit and the total number of nucleons (protons and neutrons) is called the *mass number*, A. The two numbers, N and A, completely designate a given nuclear species (neglecting the excited states of nuclei). It is the number of protons, that is, the atomic number that tells us which *element* we are dealing with, and for a given N, the different values of A, resulting from different numbers of neutrons, are responsible for the existence of different *isotopes* of that element.

When it is necessary to specify a particular isotope of an element, the mass number is placed as a left superscript. Thus the isotopes of hydrogen are ^1H, ^2H, and ^3H. In this one case, there are generally used separate symbols and names for the less common isotopes $^2H = D$ (deuterium) and $^3H = T$ (tritium).

All isotopes of an element have the same chemical properties except insofar as the mass differences may alter the exact magnitudes of reaction rates and thermodynamic properties. These mass effects are virtually insignificant for elements other than hydrogen where the percentage variation in the masses of the isotopes is uniquely large.

Most elements are found in nature as a mixture of two or more isotopes. Tin occurs as a mixture of nine, from ^{112}Sn (0.96%) through the most abundant ^{118}Sn (24.03%) to ^{124}Sn (5.94%). A few common elements that are terrestrially monoisotopic are ^{27}Al, ^{31}P, and ^{55}Mn. Because the exact masses of protons and neutrons differ, and neither is precisely equal to 1 amu, and for other reasons to be mentioned later, the masses of nuclei are not equal to their mass numbers. The actual atomic mass of ^{55}Mn, for example, is 54.9381 amu.

Usually, the isotopic composition of an element is constant all over the earth and thus its practical atomic weight, as found in the usual tables, is invariant. In a few instances, lead being most conspicuous, isotopic composition varies from place to place because of different parentage of the element in radioactive species of higher atomic number. Also, for elements that do not occur in nature, the atomic weight depends on which isotope, or isotopes, are made in nuclear reactions. In tables, it is customary to give these the mass number of the longest-lived isotope known.

Spontaneous Decay of Nuclei

Only certain nuclear compositions are stable indefinitely. All others spontaneously decompose by emitting α particles ($2p2n$) or β particles (positive or negative electrons) or by capture of a $1s$ electron. Emission of high energy photons (γ rays) generally accompanies nuclear decay. Alpha emission reduces the atomic number by two and the mass number by four. An example is

$$^{238}U \longrightarrow {}^{234}Th + \alpha \qquad (1\text{-}9.1)$$

β decay advances the atomic number by one unit without changing the mass

number. Effectively, a neutron becomes a proton. An example is

$$^{60}\text{Co} \longrightarrow {}^{60}\text{Ni} + \beta^- \tag{1-9.2}$$

These decay processes follow first-order kinetics (page 19) and are insensitive to the physical or chemical conditions surrounding the atom. The half-lives are unaffected by temperature, which is an important distinction from first-order chemical reactions. In short, the half-life of an unstable isotope is one of its fixed, characteristic properties.

All elements have some unstable (i.e., radioactive) isotopes. Of particular importance is the fact that some elements have no stable isotopes. No element with atomic number 84 (polonium) or higher has *any* stable isotope. Some, for instance, uranium and thorium, are found in substantial quantities in nature because they have, at least, one very long-lived isotope. Others, for instance, Ra, Rn, are found only in small quantities in a steady state as intermediates in radioactive decay chains. Others, for instance, At, Fr, have no single isotope stable enough to be present in macroscopic quantities. There are also two other elements, Tc and Pm, which not only have no stable isotope but none sufficiently long lived that any detectable quantities of these elements occur in nature. Both are recovered from fission products.

Nuclear Fission

Many of the heaviest nuclei can be induced to break up into two fragments of intermediate size, a process called nuclear fission. The stimulus for this is the capture of a neutron by the heavy nucleus. This creates an excited state that splits. In the process, several neutrons and a great deal of energy are released. Because the process generates more neutrons than are required to stimulate it, a chain reaction is possible. Each individual fission can lead to an average of more than one subsequent fission. Thus, the process can become self-sustaining (nuclear reactor) or even explosive (atomic bomb). A representative example of a nuclear fission process (shown schematically in Fig. 1-5) is the following:

	^{235}U	+ n →	^{141}Ba	+ ^{92}Kr	+ $3n$	
Mass number	235	1	141	92	3	
Atomic number	92	0	56	36	0	(1-9.3)
Neutrons	143	1	85	56	3	

Nuclear Fusion

In principle, very light nuclei can combine to form heavier ones and release energy as they do so. Such processes are the main source of the energy generated in the sun and other stars. They also form the basis of the hydrogen bomb. At present, engineering research is underway to adapt nuclear fusion processes to the controlled, sustained generation of energy, but practical results cannot be expected in the near future.

Figure 1-5 A schematic equation for a typical nuclear fission process.

Nuclear Binding Energies

The reasons why fission and fusion processes are sources of nuclear energy can be understood by reference to a plot of the binding energy per nucleon as a function of mass number (Fig. 1-6). Binding energy is figured by subtracting the actual nuclear mass from the sum of the individual masses of the constituent neutrons and protons and converting that mass difference into energy using Einstein's equation, $E = mc^2$. The usual unit for nuclear energies is 1 million electron volts (MeV), which is equal to 96.5×10^6 kJ mol^{-1}.

For example, for ^{12}C we have

1.	Actual mass	12.000000 amu
2.	6 × proton mass	6.043662 amu
3.	6 × neutron mass	6.051990 amu
	(2) + (3) − (1) =	0.095652 amu

One amu = 931.4 MeV. Hence:

Total binding energy = (931.4)(0.095652) = 89.09 MeV.
Binding energy per nucleon = (89.09)/12 = 7.42 MeV.

Figure 1-6 The binding energy of nucleons as a function of mass number.

Since the formation of nuclei of intermediate masses releases more energy per nucleon than the formation of very light or very heavy ones, energy will be released when very heavy nuclei split (fission) or when very light ones coalesce (fusion).

Nuclear Reactions

For many purposes the chemist often requires particular isotopes not available in nature, or even elements not found in nature. These can be made in nuclear reactors. In general, they are formed when the nucleus of a particular isotope of one element captures one or more particles (α-particles or neutrons) to form an unstable intermediate. This decays, ejecting one or more particles, to give the product. The more common changes are indicated in Fig. 1-7.

A convenient shorthand for writing nuclear reactions is illustrated by the following for the process used to prepare an isotope of astatine.

$$^{209}\text{Bi}\ (\alpha,\ 2n)^{211}\text{At}$$

This equation says that ^{209}Bi captures an α-particle, and the resulting nuclear species, which is not isolable, promptly emits two neutrons to give the astatine isotope of mass number 211. The mass number increases by 4 (for α) minus 2 (for $2n$) = 2 units and the atomic number increases by 2 units due to the

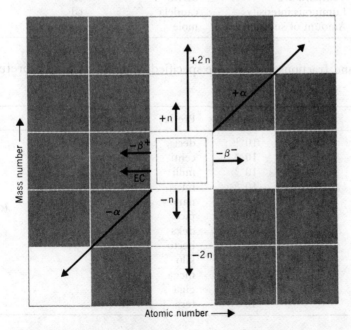

Figure 1-7 A chart showing how the more important processes of capture and ejection of particles change the nuclei (EC = electron capture).

two protons in the α-particle. Another representative nuclear reaction is

$$^{209}\text{Bi}\ (n,\ \gamma)^{210}\text{Bi} \longrightarrow {}^{210}\text{Po} + \beta \qquad (1\text{-}9.4)$$

1-10 Units

There is now an internationally accepted set of units for the physical sciences. It is called the SI (for *Système International*) units. Based on the metric system, it is designed to achieve maximum internal consistency. However, since it requires the abandonment of many familiar units and numerical constants in favor of new ones, its adoption in practice will take time. In this book, we shall take a middle course, adopting some SI units (e.g., joules for calories) but retaining some non-SI units (e.g., angstroms).

The SI Units

The SI system is based on the following set of defined units:

Physical Quantity	Name of Unit	Symbol for Unit
Length	meter	m
Mass	kilogram	kg
Time	second	s
Electric current	ampere	A
Temperature	kelvin	K
Luminous intensity	candela	cd
Amount of substance	mole	mol

Multiples and fractions of these are specified using the following prefixes:

Multiplier	Prefix	Symbol
10^{-1}	deci	d
10^{-2}	centi	c
10^{-3}	milli	m
10^{-6}	micro	μ
10^{-9}	nano	n
10^{-12}	pico	p
10	deka	da
10^{2}	hecto	h
10^{3}	kilo	k
10^{6}	mega	M
10^{9}	giga	G
10^{12}	tera	T

In addition to the defined units, the system includes a number of derived units, of which the following are the main ones.

Physical Quantity	Name of Unit	Symbol		Basic Units
Force	newton	N	=	kg m s^{-2}
Work, energy, quantity of heat	joule	J	=	N m or kg m^2 s^{-2}
Power	watt	W	=	J s^{-1}
Electric charge	coulomb	C	=	A s
Electric potential	volt	V	=	WA^{-1}, kg m^2 s^{-3} A^{-1}, or J/C
Electric capacitance	farad	F	=	A s V^{-1}
Electric resistance	ohm	Ω	=	V A^{-1}
Frequency	hertz	Hz	=	s^{-1}
Magnetic flux	weber	Wb	=	V s
Magnetic flux density	tesla	T	='	Wb m^{-2}
Inductance	henry	H	=	V s A^{-1}

Units to Be Used in This Book

Energy

Joules and kilojoules will be used exclusively. Most of the chemical literature to date employs calories, kilocalories, electron volts and, to a limited extent, wave numbers (cm^{-1}). Conversion factors are given below.

Bond Lengths

The angstrom (Å) will be used. This is defined as 10^{-8} cm. The nanometer (10 Å) and picometer (10^{-2} Å) are to be found in recent literature. The C—C bond length in diamond has the value:

$$1.54 \text{ angstrom}$$
$$0.154 \text{ nanometers}$$
$$154 \text{ picometers}$$

Pressure

Atmospheres (atm) and Torr (1/760 atm) will be used.

Some Useful Conversion Factors and Numerical Constants

Conversion Factors

1 calorie (cal)	= 4.184 joules (J)
1 electron volt per molecule (eV/molecule)	= 96. 485 kilojoules per mole (kJ mol^{-1}) = 23.06 kilocalories per mole (kcal mol^{-1})
1 kilojoule per mole (kJ/mol^{-1})	= 83.54 wave numbers (cm^{-1})
1 atomic mass unit (amu)	= 1.6605655 × 10^{-27} kilogram (kg) = 931.5016 mega electron volt (MeV)

Important Constants

Avogadro's number	N_A	= 6.022045 × 10^{23} mol^{-1}
Electron charge	e	= 4.8030 × 10^{-10} abs esu = 1.6021892 × 10^{-19} C

Important Constants (Continued)

Electron mass	m_e	$= 9.1091 \times 10^{-31}$ kg
		$= 0.5110$ MeV
Proton mass	m_p	$= 1.6726485 \times 10^{-27}$ kg
		$= 1.007276470$ amu
Gas constant	R	$= 8.31441$ J mol^{-1} K^{-1}
		$= 1.9872$ cal mol^{-1} K^{-1}
		$= 0.08206$ L atm mol^{-1} K^{-1}
Ice point		$= 273.15$ K
Molar volume		$= 22.414 \times 10^3$ cm^3 mol^{-1}
		$= 2.2414 \times 10^{-2}$ m^3 mol^{-1}
Planck's constant	h	$= 6.626176 \times 10^{-34}$ J s
		$= 6.626176 \times 10^{-27}$ erg s
Boltzmann's constant	k	$= 1.380662 \times 10^{-23}$ J K^{-1}
Rydberg constant	$\mathcal{R}$	$= 1.097373177 \times 10^{-7}$ m^{-1}
Speed of light	c	$= 2.99792458 \times 10^8$ m s^{-1}
Bohr radius	a_0	$= 0.52917706 \times 10^{-10}$ m
Other numbers	π	$= 3.14159$
	e	$= 2.7183$
	ln 10	$= 2.3026$

Coulombic Force and Energy Calculations in SI Units

Although SI units do, for the most part, lead to simplification, one computation that is important to inorganic chemistry becomes slightly more complex. We explain that point in detail here. It traces back to the concept of the dielectric constant, ϵ, which relates the intensity of an electric field induced within a substance, D, to the intensity of the field applied, E, by the equation

$$D = \epsilon E \tag{1-10.1}$$

The same parameter appears in the coulomb equation for the force, F, between two charges, q_1 and q_2, separated by a distance, d, and immersed in a medium with a dielectric constant, ϵ:

$$F = \frac{q_1 \times q_2}{\epsilon d^2} \tag{1-10.2}$$

In the old (cgs) system of units, which the SI system replaces, units and magnitudes were so defined that ϵ was a dimensionless quantity and for a vacuum we had $\epsilon_0 = 1$.

For reasons that we shall not pursue here, Coulomb's law of electrostatic force, in SI units, must be written

$$F = \frac{q_1 \times q_2}{4\pi\epsilon d^2} \tag{1-10.3}$$

The charges are expressed in coulombs (C), the distance in meters (m), and the force is obtained in newtons (N). It now develops that ϵ has units (i.e., is no longer a dimensionless quantity), namely, $C^2\,m^{-1}\,J^{-1}$. Moreover, the dielectric constant of a vacuum (the permittivity, as it should formally be called) is no longer unity. It is, instead,

$$\epsilon_0 = 8.854 \times 10^{-12}\,C^2\,m^{-1}\,J^{-1} \qquad (1\text{-}10.4)$$

Thus, to calculate a coulomb energy, E, in joules (J) we must employ the expression

$$E = \frac{q_1 \times q_2}{4\pi\epsilon d} \qquad (1\text{-}10.5)$$

with all quantities being as defined for the coulomb force.

STUDY GUIDE

Study Questions

1. Define the terms exothermic and endothermic. What are the signs of ΔH for each type of process?

2. How is the standard enthalpy of formation of a substance defined? Write the balanced chemical equation that applies to $\Delta H_f^\circ[CF_3SO_3H]$.

3. Write balanced chemical equations that apply to each of the following enthalpy changes:

   (a) $\Delta H_{sub}^\circ[H_2O]$ (b) $\Delta H_{vap}^\circ[C_6H_6]$

   (c) $\Delta H_{EA}[Cl(g)]$ (d) $\Delta H_{ion}[Na(g)]$

4. Write an equation that can be used to define the mean S—F bond energy in SF_6. How is this value likely to be related in magnitude to the energy of the process $SF_6(g) \rightarrow SF_5(g) + F(g)$

5. Prepare graphical representations of the relationships between

   (a) ΔG and T; four separate possibilities depending on the signs of ΔH and ΔS

   (b) k and T, using $\Delta H^\ddagger$ and $\Delta S^\ddagger$

6. Give a qualitative definition of entropy.

7. Against what standard are the absolute entropies of substances tabulated?

8. Prepare graphs of the concentration of reactant A as a function of time if A disappears in first-order fashion. How should the data for such a first-order reaction be plotted in order to obtain a straight line relationship?

9. Answer as in Question 8, but for a second-order disappearance of reactant A.

10. What elements might have negative electron attachment enthalpies? What is the meaning of a negative sign for the electron attachment enthalpy?

11. The N—N bond energy in F_2NNF_2 is only about 80 kJ mol^{-1} compared to 160 kJ mol^{-1} in H_2NNH_2. Suggest a reason.

12. Predict the signs of the entropy changes for the following processes:

    (a) $H_2O(\ell) \rightarrow H_2O(g)$

    (b) $P_4(g) + 10 F_2(g) \rightarrow 4 PF_5(g)$

    (c) $I_2(s) + Cl_2(g) \rightarrow 2 ICl(g)$

    (d) $BF_3(g) + NH_3(g) \rightarrow H_3NBF_3(g)$

    (e) $CO_2(g) \rightarrow CO_2(s)$

13. Use the data of Table 1-1 to estimate ΔH_f° values for the following molecules:

    (a) $HNCl_2$ (b) CF_3SF_3 (c) Cl_2NNH_2

14. What do you suppose is the main thermodynamic reason why the following reaction has an equilibrium constant > 1 ?

    $$BCl_3(g) + BBr_3(g) \longrightarrow BCl_2Br(g) + BClBr_2(g)$$

15. Use the data of Table 1-1 to predict the enthalpy change for the reaction $CO + H_2O \rightarrow CO_2 + H_2$.

16. What is the value of the equilibrium constant for a reaction that has $\Delta G^\circ = 0$? Draw the reaction profile for such a system.

17. The following data are available for the forward direction of an equilibrium system: $\Delta G^\circ = -50$ kJ mol^{-1} and $\Delta G^\ddagger = 20$ kJ mol^{-1}. What is the activation free energy for the reverse direction of the equilibrium? Prepare a reaction profile, showing the relative magnitude of each of these three quantities.

18. The conversion of diamond into graphite is a thermodynamically favorable (spontaneous) process, and yet one doesn't expect a diamond to change into graphite. Why?

19. Determine the standard cell potentials for the following redox reactions:

    (a) The oxidation of lithium by chlorine

    (b) The reduction of Ce^{4+} by iodide.

20. Use Eq. 1-6.3 to ascertain the relative values of K_1 and K_2 for an exothermic reaction, assuming that $T_1 > T_2$. Answer also for an endothermic reaction. Explain the consequences in terms of the Principle of Le Châtelier.

chapter 2

THE ELECTRONIC STRUCTURE OF ATOMS

2-1 Introduction

The term **electronic structure,** used with respect to an atom, refers to the number and the distribution of electrons about a central nucleus. The nucleus can be considered to consist of the proper number of protons and neutrons, depending on the mass number and atomic number of the isotope in question. It is reasonable, for purposes of this work, to take this simplistic view of the nucleus. Apart from electrostatic repulsions between nuclei, all of the major interactions between atoms in normal chemical reactions (or in the structures of elemental and compound substances) involve the electrons. Ultimately, we would like to be able to use an understanding of the electronic structures of atoms to describe the structures and reactivities of molecules and ions.

A complete description of the electronic structure of an atom would include more than just the number and the spatial distribution of electrons within the atom. Nevertheless, most of the rest of what we would like to know about electronic structure is dictated by these two properties. Once the spatial distribution of the electrons is known, other important properties follow. For instance, the energies, ionization enthalpies, sizes, and magnetic properties of atoms all depend on the number and arrangement of the electrons within the atom.

Much of the experimental work on the electronic structures of atoms that was done prior to 1913 involved measuring those frequencies of electromagnetic radiation that were absorbed or emitted by atoms. It was found to be characteristic of atoms that they absorbed or emitted only certain sharply defined frequencies of electromagnetic radiation. The exact pattern of frequencies is characteristic of each particular substance, and the emission or absorption pattern is more complex for the heavier elements. Although the emission and absorption spectra for most of the elements were known precisely, a convincing explanation was not available for even the simplest case, the hydrogen atom.

It had been found that the atomic emission spectrum for hydrogen (Fig. 2-1) consisted of several series of **lines,** or spectroscopic emissions. Within each series, the lines become increasingly closely spaced until they converge at a limiting value. Rydberg recognized that the patterns created by these lines for

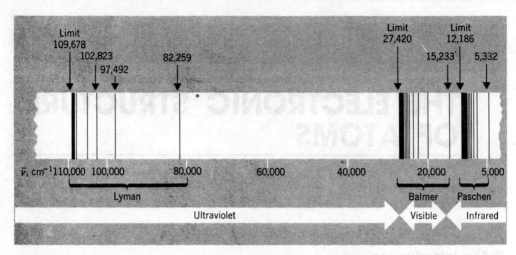

Figure 2-1   The emission spectrum of atomic hydrogen as recorded on a strip of film. Each line represents an emission frequency. Three series of lines are shown. Within each series, the lines converge to a limit. Two more well-defined series occur for hydrogen in the IR region, but are not shown here.

hydrogen conformed to the relationship shown in Eq. 2-1.1,

$$\bar{\nu} = \mathcal{R}\left(\frac{1}{m^2} - \frac{1}{n^2}\right) \qquad \begin{array}{l} m = 1, 2, 3, 4 \ldots \\ n = (m + 1), (m + 2), (m + 3), \ldots \end{array} \qquad (2\text{-}1.1)$$

where $\bar{\nu}$ represents the wave number of the line (ν/c), in units of reciprocal centimeters. The integer $m = 1$ gives rise to the Lyman series (Fig. 2-1) for which the convergence limit is 109,678 cm^{-1}. When $m = 2$, the Balmer series arises, and so on. Two more well-defined series of lines appear at lower energies (i.e., in the infrared portion of the spectrum), but are not shown in Fig. 2-1. In addition to deducing how the integers m and n could be used in Eq. 2-1.1 to generate the spectroscopic emission pattern for hydrogen, Rydberg also empirically determined that the constant $\mathcal{R} = 109,678$ cm^{-1}. Although it seems straightforward now, the accomplishment of Rydberg was remarkable. The existence of a quantitative description, Eq. 2-1.1, of the spectroscopic lines for hydrogen made it quite clear that the pattern of lines was significant. The pattern was clear, but the meaning was not.

The meaning was made clear in 1913 by the Danish physicist Niels Bohr, who realized that the Rydberg equation could not be explained in terms of the theories then in use. Bohr reasoned that if only discrete frequencies could be emitted or absorbed by an atom, then only discrete energies were possible for the electrons in the atom. Bohr broke with the tradition of classical physics and proposed that the electron could revolve indefinitely about the proton in orbits of fixed radii. According to classical physics, this should be impossible; the electron should spiral inward towards the nucleus, emitting a continuum of frequencies before crashing into the nucleus.

Bohr's theory for the electronic structure of the hydrogen atom was founded on the assumption that for each discrete orbit, the angular momentum of the electron must be quantized according to Eq. 2-1.2:

$$mvr = nh/2\pi \tag{2-1.2}$$

where n is an integer, m and v are the mass and velocity of the electron, respectively, r is the radius of the orbit, and h is Planck's constant. The electron traveling in an orbit with radius, r, would possess an angular momentum, mvr, which depended on the quantum number, n. These two proposals—stable orbits and the quantization of angular momentum (and hence of the radius and energy of the electron)—were in conflict with and utterly outside of the accepted physical theory of the time. However, by using these assumptions and by treating the rest of the problem in a perfectly traditional way, Bohr was able to show that *allowed* orbits were those with radii given by Eq. 2-1.3:

$$r = \frac{n^2 h^2 \epsilon_0}{\pi m Z e^2} \tag{2-1.3}$$

The requirement that mvr can take only those values that are multiples of $h/2\pi$ means that only certain values of r (those given by Eq. 2-1.3) are allowed. Electrons within orbits with discrete radii then have energies that are quantized according to Eq. 2-1.4:

$$E = -\frac{mZ^2 e^4}{8n^2 h^2 \epsilon_0^2} \tag{2-1.4}$$

The most exciting support for Bohr's theory was that the collection of constants other than the quantum number, n, in Eq. 2-1.4 is equal numerically to the value for $\mathscr{R}$, which Rydberg had determined empirically. In short, Bohr had obtained Eq. 2-1.5:

$$E = -\frac{R}{n^2} \tag{2-1.5}$$

The explanation for each series of spectroscopic lines in the spectrum for hydrogen was now at hand (see Fig. 2-2). An electron would have lowest (most negative) energy when in the orbit for which $n = 1$. The radius of this orbit ($a_0 = 0.529$ Å) can be calculated using Eq. 2-1.3. Each higher value of the quantum number yields a correspondingly larger and less stable orbit, that is, one with a less negative energy. If an electron is excited to an orbit with higher energy ($n \geq 2$) and returns to the ground state ($n = 1$), discrete energies equal to $\mathscr{R}[(1/1^2) - (1/n^2)]$ are emitted. In this case, the Lyman series of spectroscopic lines (Fig. 2-1) is observed. The other series arise when the electron drops from upper levels to those with $n = 2$ (Balmer series) and $n = 3$ (Paschen series), as shown in Fig. 2-2.

In all of these, Bohr made use of Planck's earlier postulate that also conflicted with classical physics, stating electromagnetic radiation is itself quan-

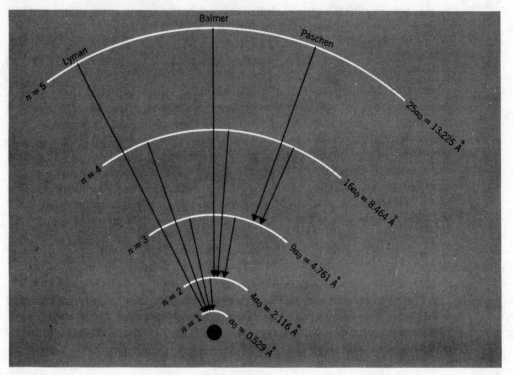

Figure 2-2   A diagram of the Bohr orbits and the corresponding energies for an electron in the hydrogen atom. Each arc represents a portion of an orbit. The transitions that give rise to the three series of spectroscopic lines of Fig. 2-1 are indicated.

tized. According to Planck, each quantum of electromagnetic radiation of frequency, ν, has the energy given by Eq. 2-1.6.

$$E = h\nu \tag{2-1.6}$$

The Bohr model was refined by Arnold Sommerfeld, who showed that finer features of the hydrogen spectrum, which were observed on application of a magnetic field, could be accounted for if elliptical, as well as circular orbits were used. This gave another quantum number that dictated the ellipticity of the orbits.

In spite of the success of the Bohr–Sommerfeld quantum theories for the hydrogen atom, the theories had to be abandoned for a number of reasons. For one thing, the approach could not be applied successfully to the interpretation of spectra for atoms more complex than hydrogen. Perhaps more important, later work showed that electrons cannot be regarded as discrete particles with precisely defined positions and velocities. It was not that the quantum approach was wrong, but that the electrons could not be described adequately by the simplistic notion that they are only particles. In fact, it became evident that electrons also possess the same wavelike properties that Planck had already ascribed (Eq. 2-1.6) to photons. We now know that this wave–particle duality (both wave and particle characteristics are necessary for a full description) is typical of all matter, not just photons and electrons.

2-2   Wave Mechanics

In 1924, the French physicist Louis Victor de Broglie suggested that all matter could exhibit wavelike properties. For particles such as electrons or nucleons that travel with velocity, v, de Broglie proposed the important matter–wave relationship shown in Eq. 2-2.1:

$$\lambda = h/mv \tag{2-2.1}$$

Matter with mass, m, and velocity, v (properties associated with particles) has a wavelength, λ (a property associated with waves). While all matter in motion would then have an associated waveform, the wavelength is only meaningful to spectroscopists when m is small. De Broglie's proposal was substantiated a few years later when the two Americans Clinton J. Davisson and L. H. Germer found experimental evidence that electrons do behave in a wavelike manner. They demonstrated that a beam of electrons is diffracted by a crystal in much the same way as a beam of X-rays. The wavelength that Davisson and Germer determined for the electrons was just that predicted by Eq. 2-2.1.

Concurrent with these developments was the proposal by the Viennese physicist, Erwin Schrödinger, that the electron be described in a way that would emphasize its wave nature. The Schrödinger **wave equation,** shown in its most general form in Eq. 2-2.2

$$H\Psi = E\Psi \tag{2-2.2}$$

represented a new method—**wave mechanics**—for describing the behavior of subatomic particles. Wave mechanics leads to the same energy levels of the electron in the hydrogen atom that Bohr obtained. In addition, it gives a better account of other properties of hydrogen, but most important, it can give a correct account of more complex atoms as well.

The method of wave mechanics as expressed in Eq. 2-2.2 is the method of operator algebra. The operator H, called the Hamiltonian operator, prescribes a series of mathematical operations that are to be performed on the wave function, Ψ. The wave function, Ψ, is a mathematical expression that describes or defines the electron in terms of its wave properties. If the electron is accurately described by the wave function, Ψ, then Ψ is said to be a proper wave function (an eigenfunction) for the Hamiltonian operator. According to the dictates of operator algebra, this will happen only when the mathematical manipulations prescribed by the Hamiltonian operator give the wave function back, unchanged, save for multiplication by the constant E. The constant, E, is the energy that the electron would have if it were to be described as, or behave according to, the wave function, Ψ. Although there is only one set of wave functions that can exactly satisfy the Schrödinger equation, and thus correspond exactly to those energies, E, actually possessed by the electron in the various states of the atom, the wave functions are not easy to determine. Instead, it is necessary to devise various trial wave functions and test them. A comparison of the energies observed spectroscopically (Fig. 2-1) with those calculated from a trial set of wave functions (each corresponding to an energy-level E) gives an indication of how closely the trial wave functions match the true wave properties of the electron.

For a system as simple as the hydrogen atom, the wave functions can be determined precisely. Some of these functions are given in abbreviated form in Table 2-1, where they are factored into their various components in the polar coordinates r, θ, and ϕ. The polar coordinates r, θ, and ϕ correspond to the Cartesian coordinates in the following ways: $x = r \sin\theta \cos\phi$, $y = r \sin\theta \sin\phi$, and $z = r \cos\theta$. The numbers a, b, and N_c take different values depending on the quantum numbers at hand.

The wave functions are three dimensional, and contain, as integers, the three quantum numbers n, ℓ and m_ℓ, and $m_s(\pm\frac{1}{2})$. It is the presence of different values of at least one of the four quantum numbers in each separate function that makes one function different and distinct from another. We shall have more to say about the quantum numbers in Section 2-3. First, it is important to understand the meaning of the wave functions themselves.

While it is difficult to assign a physical meaning to the wave function itself, its square gives us a measure of the electron density in the various regions about the nucleus. A three-dimensional plot of the values of Ψ^2 centered on the nucleus gives us an indication of those regions about the nucleus where the electron, if it were behaving as the waveform, Ψ, would be most densely distributed. According to this interpretation of Ψ^2, the electron is regarded as a smeared out distribution of negative charge whose density varies from place to place according to the magnitude of Ψ^2. We have a situation in which the electron is smeared about the nucleus in a way that varies with the distance, as governed by the radial portion of the wave function, $R(r)$, and in different angular patterns, as governed by the angular portion of the wave function, $\Theta(\theta)\Phi(\phi)$. If the electron is thought of as "being" the wave function, then the electron can be said to be distributed into an **orbital** (a term borrowed from the Bohr concept of orbits), which has a size dictated by the function $R(r)$, a shape dictated by the function, $\Theta(\theta)\Phi(\phi)$, and an energy, E, which can be calculated by using Eq. 2-2.2.

It is instructive to compare the Bohr result with that of wave mechanics. The exact (precisely defined) radius for the electron in the first Bohr orbit is $a_0 = 0.529$ Å. This is shown in Fig. 2-3 as a circle with radius a_0. The wave mechanical result is superimposed on this circle in Fig. 2-3, as a dot density pattern generated by the function $r^2R(r)^2$. This function represents the ad-

Table 2-1.   Some Hydrogenlike Wave Functions $\Psi = R(r)\Theta(\theta)\Phi(\phi)$ Factored Into Radial $[R(r)]$ and Angular $[\Theta(\theta)\Phi(\phi)]$ Components.
The factors a, b, *and* N_c *depend variously and in part on one or more of the quantum numbers* n, ℓ, *and* m_ℓ. *The value* a_0 *is the Bohr radius. The correspondence between spherical polar coordinates and the more familiar Cartesian coordinates* (x, y, *and* z) *is discussed in the text.*

Orbital	$R(r)$	$\Theta(\theta)\Phi(\phi)$
$1s$	$N_c\left(\dfrac{Z}{a_0}\right)^{3/2} e^{-br}$	$\left(\dfrac{1}{4\pi}\right)^{1/2}$
$2p_y$	$N_c\left(\dfrac{Z}{a_0}\right)^{3/2} (ar)e^{-br}$	$\left(\dfrac{3}{4\pi}\right)^{1/2} \sin\theta\,\sin\phi$
$3d_{xy}$	$N_c\left(\dfrac{Z}{a_0}\right)^{3/2} (ar)^2 e^{-br}$	$\left(\dfrac{15}{4\pi}\right)^{1/2} \sin\theta\,\cos\theta\,\sin\phi$

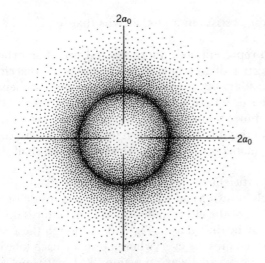

Figure 2-3 A comparison of the Bohr orbit (solid line—circle with radius a_0) and the quantum mechanical function $r^2R(r)^2$ (electron density pattern—maximum density at a distance a_0 from the nucleus).

ditional electron density that is encountered with each new spherical shell of thickness dr as the distance r from the nucleus increases. This function, $r^2R(r)^2$, has reached its maximum (most darkly shaded) at precisely the same 0.529 Å as for the Bohr model! The correspondence between the two theories in this respect is reassuring. The electron density in the same orbital is shown a different way in Fig. 2-4. Here $r^2R(r)^2$ is plotted as a function of distance from the nucleus. Because the angular portion of the wave function for this most stable orbital is a constant (see Table 2-1), the electron smear is the same at all angles, or spherically symmetric. What is shown, then, in Fig. 2-3 is actually a cross section of $r^2R(r)^2$ in the plane of the page. Any cross section that included the nucleus would be identical to Fig. 2-3. Any straight line starting at the

Figure 2-4 A comparison of the radial density distribution function, $r^2R(r)^2$, which has maximum value at $r = a_0$, and the Bohr radius, where $r = a_0$, exclusively.

nucleus could be used as the abscissa in a plot such as that for Fig. 2-4, with the same result.

Clearly, it is difficult to represent both the shape and size of an orbital on one graph. Where a cross section of an orbital is shown, one sees radial changes in electron density quite readily, but loses a sense of the three-dimensional "roundness" that orbitals have. Where shape is shown (look ahead to Fig. 2-6), one loses the ability to show attenuations in electron density as a function of $R(r)$. The best solution to this dilemma is shown in Fig. 2-5, where contour and shape are shown simultaneously for two orbitals that we shall discuss shortly.

In some cases it is not efficient to show the full contour diagram for an orbital. The orbital is simply drawn as an **enclosure surface,** inside of which a majority (arbitrarily, >95%) of the electron density is known to reside. Thus the shape of each orbital may be drawn as in Fig. 2-6. Although these shapes are constructed from Ψ^2 (which must be everywhere positive), each lobe of the orbital is given the sign of the original wave function, Ψ. What is not shown in the enclosure surfaces of Fig. 2-6 is the gradation in electron density that is contained in the function $R(r)$.

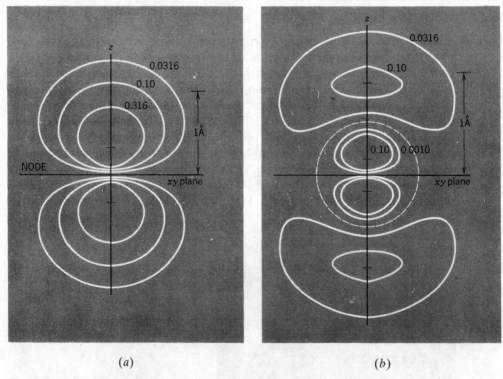

(a) $\qquad\qquad\qquad\qquad\qquad\qquad\qquad$ (b)

Figure 2-5 Contour maps of some orbitals, showing both shape and "internal" gradients in electron density. (*a*) The $2p$ orbital. (*b*) The $3p$ orbital. The contour lines are drawn at the points where some fraction (arbitrarily 0.0316, 0.10, and 0.316) of the maximum electron density has been reached. The maxima are indicated by the bars on the axes. From E. A. Ogryzlo and G. B. Porter, "Contour Surfaces for Atomic and Molecular Orbitals," *J. Chem. Educ.*, **1963**, *40*, 256–261. Used with permission.

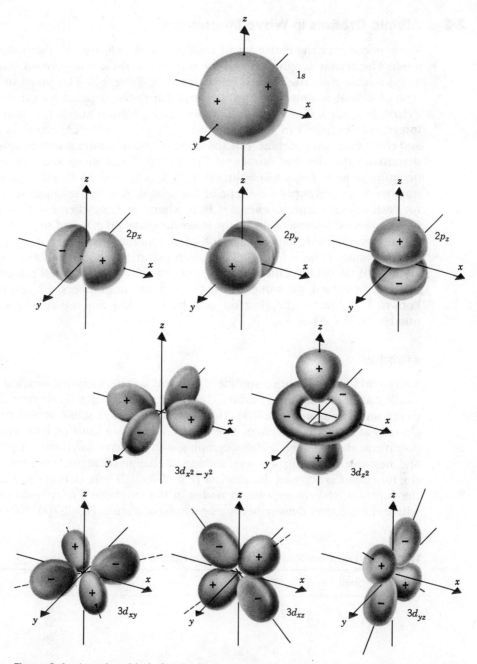

Figure 2-6 Atomic orbitals for the hydrogen atom, drawn as enclosure surfaces as described in the text. The lobes are derived from Ψ^2, and must be everywhere positive. They have been given the signs, however, of the original wave functions, Ψ, as this is information that becomes important when considering bonding via overlap of such orbitals.

2-3   Atomic Orbitals in Wave Mechanics

We now consider the entire set of orbitals for the electron in the hydrogen atom. The orbital designation and the unique set of the quantum numbers n, ℓ, and m_ℓ that gives rise to each one is listed in Table 2-2. The shape of each type of orbital is shown in Fig. 2-6, and the radial dependences, $R(r)$ and $r^2R(r)^2$, are graphed in Fig. 2-7. The principal quantum number, n, may take integral values from 1 to ∞, although values larger than 7 are spectroscopically and chemically unimportant. It is the value of this quantum number, n, which determines the size and energy of the orbital. For a given value of n, the quantum number ℓ may take values 0, 1, 2, 3, . . . , $(n - 1)$. It is this quantum number that determines the shape of the orbital. A letter designation is used for each orbital shape: s, when $\ell = 0$; p, when $\ell = 1$; d, when $\ell = 2$; f, when $\ell = 3$; followed alphabetically by the letter designations g, h, and so on. Finally, for any one orbital shape, the value of the quantum number m_ℓ may take integral values from $-\ell$ to $+\ell$. This latter quantum number governs the orientation of the orbital. Once the electron for the hydrogen atom is placed into one specific orbital, the values of the three quantum numbers n, ℓ, and m_ℓ are known. In addition, the electron may have a value for the spin quantum number (m_s) of $+\frac{1}{2}$ or $-\frac{1}{2}$.

s Orbitals

Every s orbital has quantum number $\ell = 0$ and is spherically symmetrical. The smallest such orbital, the 1s orbital, has its maximum electron density closest to the nucleus, as in Fig. 2-7(b). Hence this is the most stable orbital for the electron of the hydrogen atom. The sign of the 1s wave function is everywhere positive, as shown in Fig. 2-7(a). Beginning with the 2s orbital, there are positive and negative values for a wave function, a change occurring each time that the function $R(r)$ crosses the abscissa [Fig. 2-7(a)]. These changes in sign for the function $R(r)$ correspond to **nodes** in the functions $r^2R(r)^2$—values of r where the electron density becomes zero. Notice from Fig. 2-7(b) that as the

Table 2-2. Quantum Numbers and Atomic Orbital Designations

Shell	n	ℓ	m_ℓ	Orbital
K	1	0	0	1s
L	2	0	0	2s
	2	1	$-1, 0, +1$	2p
M	3	0	0	3s
	3	1	$-1, 0, +1$	3p
	3	2	$-2, -1, 0, +1, +2$	3d
N	4	0	0	4s
	4	1	$-1, 0, +1$	4p
	4	2	$-2, -1, 0, +1, +2$	4d
	4	3	$-3, -2, -1, 0, +1, +2, +3$	4f
O	5	0	0	5s
	—	—	—	—
	—	—	—	—

Figure 2-7 Plots for the hydrogenlike wave functions of (*a*) the radial function $R(r)$ versus r, the distance from the nucleus; and (*b*) the probability distribution functions $r^2R(r)^2$ versus r, the distance from the nucleus.

value of n increases, the maximum in the radial electron density shifts farther from the nucleus. Thus an orbital gets larger as the principal quantum number, n, increases. Correspondingly, the energy of the electron in such an orbital becomes less negative, meaning that the electron is less strongly bound.

p Orbitals

For each p orbital, the quantum number ℓ equals 1, and the shape is that shown in Fig. 2-6. Three values of the quantum number m_ℓ are possible $(-1, 0, +1)$, representing each of the three possible orientations in space. There is a node at the nucleus for each p orbital because the p-type wave function [Fig. 2-7(a)] has the value zero at the nucleus. The sign of the p orbital therefore changes at the nucleus. The $2p$ orbitals have no other nodes, but beginning with $3p$ there are additional radial nodes, as shown in Fig. 2-7. As was true for the s orbitals, the size of a p orbital depends on the principal quantum number in the order $2p$, $3p$, $4p$, and so on. This can be seen by comparing the positions of the largest maxima in the graphs of $r^2R(r)^2$ in Fig. 2-7(b).

d Orbitals

Each set of d orbitals consists of five members whose shapes are shown in Fig. 2-6. The five members arise because there are five possible values for the quantum number m_ℓ $(-2, -1, 0, +1, +2)$. Within each lobe of the d orbitals, the radial electron density changes as shown in Fig. 2-7. The following features are important. The d_{z^2} orbital is symmetrical about the z axis. The d_{xz}, d_{yz}, and d_{xy} orbitals are alike, except that they have their lobes in the xz, yz, and xy planes, respectively. The $d_{x^2-y^2}$ orbital has the same shape as the d_{xy}, but the former is rotated by 45° about the z axis so that its lobes lie on the x and y axes instead of between the x and y axes. The d orbitals appear only when the principal quantum number, n, has risen to the value three or greater.

f Orbitals

For each value of the principal quantum number $n \geq 4$, there is a set of seven f orbitals for which $\ell = 3$. Within this set of seven orbitals, the quantum number m_ℓ takes the seven values $-3, -2, -1, 0, +1, +2, +3$. The f orbitals play an important role in chemical behavior only for compounds of the lanthanides and actinides. The typical shapes of these orbitals are given in Fig. 2-8.

Energy Levels in the Hydrogen Atom

For the hydrogen atom, the order of increasing energy for the atomic orbitals is determined only by the principal quantum number, n. The energy of the electron is the same, regardless of whether it is in an s, p, d, or f orbital, as long as the principal quantum number, n, is the same. This is shown in Fig. 2-9, where for hydrogen (atomic number 1), the energies of the s, p, d, and f orbitals converge at a value that depends only on n. This is obviously not true for atoms with more than one electron. For these more complex atoms, the

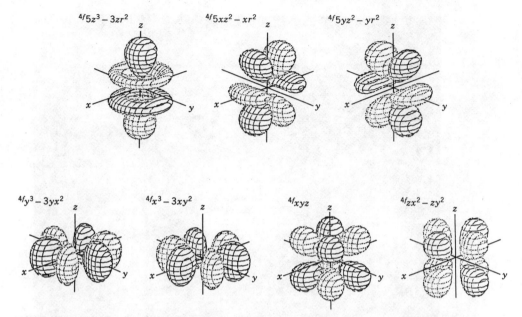

Figure 2-8 Shapes of the seven f orbitals. [Taken from Q. Kikuchi and K. Suzuki, *J. Chem. Educ.*, **1985**, *62*, 206–209, and used with permission.]

hydrogenlike atomic orbitals must be modified to reflect the pattern of energies shown in Fig. 2-9.

2-4 Structures of Atoms with Many Electrons

By using the data of Fig. 2-9, it is possible to arrange the atomic orbitals in the order needed in building up the electronic structures of atoms with atomic number greater than one. This ordering of atomic orbitals for multielectron atoms is shown in Fig. 2-10. Note that p orbitals retain their threefold degeneracy, d orbitals their fivefold degeneracy, and f orbitals their sevenfold degeneracy. The proper number of electrons is assigned to these orbitals starting at the bottom (lowest energy, most stable) and adding electrons in accordance with Hund's rule and the Pauli exclusion principle. Before writing the electron configurations for multielectron atoms, it is important to understand the ordering of the energy levels as shown in Fig. 2-10. Why, for a given value of the principal quantum number, n, are the atomic orbitals used in the order s, p, d, f, and so on? The answer to the question can be found in part by examining the relative amplitudes of the radial wave functions.

Radial Penetration of the Wave Functions

An electron in an atomic orbital that has appreciable electron density close to the nucleus is stabilized by close interaction with the positive charge of the nucleus, in the same way that the most stable Bohr orbit is the one with the smallest radius. One can evaluate the stability of an electron in various orbitals

Figure 2-9   The relative energies of the atomic orbitals as a function of atomic number.

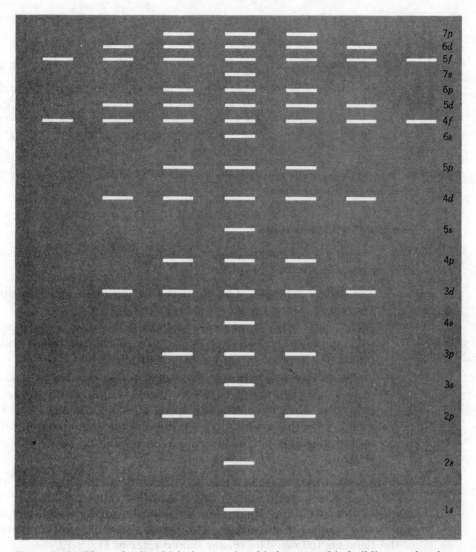

Figure 2-10 The order in which the atomic orbitals are used in building up the electron configurations of many-electron atoms. The orbitals are used in sequence, from the bottom, in accordance with the aufbau principle, Hund's rule, and the Pauli exclusion principle.

by comparing the radial electron density functions $r^2R(r)^2$, as is done in Fig. 2-11. For any given value of the principal quantum number, n, it is the s-type orbital, which most has appreciable electron density close to the nucleus, followed in order by p-, d-, and f-type orbitals. The relative order of stability for the various orbital types is, then, $s > p > d > f$, and so on, for any one value of n. This is the ordering the orbitals are given in Fig. 2-10. It should be noted, though, from Figs. 2-9 and 2-10 that at crucial points there is a crossing of the ns and $(n-1)d$ energy levels. This will become important in writing the electron configurations of the elements.

Figure 2-11 A comparison of the radial density distribution functions, $r^2R(r)^2$, showing the relative penetration of various orbitals.

Electron Configurations

The electrons are assigned to an atom by placing them into the various atomic orbitals according to three rules:

1. *The **aufbau principle.*** The electron configurations are built up from the bottom, using the lowest energy orbitals first.

2. ***Hund's rule.*** Where orbitals are available in degenerate sets, maximum spin multiplicity is preserved; that is, electrons are not paired until each orbital in a degenerate set has been half-filled.

3. *The **Pauli exclusion principle.*** No two electrons may have the same set of four quantum numbers. Where two electrons occupy the same orbital, they must have opposite spins: $m_s = +\frac{1}{2}$ for one electron and $m_s = -\frac{1}{2}$ for the second electron. Because the spin quantum number, m_s, can take only one of two values, an orbital can house at most two electrons.

If these rules, which we shall examine in more detail in Section 2-6, are followed, the electron configuration that is specified is the ground-state configuration. Other electron configurations are possible, but they respresent excited state configurations. A discussion of the ground-state electron configurations of the elements follows. The reader should refer to Fig. 2-12.

Elements of Period One

The following are electron configurations for the two elements of row one:

H $1s^1$

He $1s^2$

For both atoms, the principal quantum number, n, equals one. Row one of the periodic table is completed with the element He, because the only orbital ($1s$) in the first or **K shell** (where $n = 1$) becomes filled with two electrons. The electrons of subsequent atoms must begin using orbitals of the next shell, where $n = 2$.

Elements of Period Two

The eight elements of this row make use of the four orbitals with principal quantum number $n = 2$. The following are the ground-state electron config-

Figure 2-12 Periodic trends in electron configuration, showing the outermost or differentiating electrons for each element.

Group = IA(1), IIA(2), IIIA(3), IVA(4), VA(5), VIA(6), VIIA(7), VIII(8)(9)(10), IB(11), IIB(12), IIIB(13), IVB(14), VB(15), VIB(16), VIIB(17), VIIIB(18)

Closed Shell: K, L, M, N, O, P

s-Block Elements, *d*-Block Elements, *p*-Block Elements, *f*-Block Elements

s-block and p-block

Period	IA (1)	IIA (2)	IIIB (13)	IVB (14)	VB (15)	VIB (16)	VIIB (17)	VIIIB (18)	Closed Shell
1	1 H $1s^1$							2 He $1s^2$	K
2	3 Li $2s^1$	4 Be $2s^2$	5 B $2p^1$	6 C $2p^2$	7 N $2p^3$	8 O $2p^4$	9 F $2p^5$	10 Ne $2p^6$	L
3	11 Na $3s^1$	12 Mg $3s^2$	13 Al $3p^1$	14 Si $3p^2$	15 P $3p^3$	16 S $3p^4$	17 Cl $3p^5$	18 Ar $3p^6$	M
4	19 K $4s^1$	20 Ca $4s^2$	31 Ga $4p^1$	32 Ge $4p^2$	33 As $4p^3$	34 Se $4p^4$	35 Br $4p^5$	36 Kr $4p^6$	N
5	37 Rb $5s^1$	38 Sr $5s^2$	49 In $5p^1$	50 Sn $5p^2$	51 Sb $5p^3$	52 Te $5p^4$	53 I $5p^5$	54 Xe $5p^6$	O
6	55 Cs $6s^1$	56 Ba $6s^2$	81 Tl $6p^1$	82 Pb $6p^2$	83 Bi $6p^3$	84 Po $6p^4$	85 At $6p^5$	86 Rn $6p^6$	P
7	87 Fr $7s^1$	88 Ra $7s^2$							

d-Block Elements

Period	IIIA (3)	IVA (4)	VA (5)	VIA (6)	VIIA (7)	VIII (8)	VIII (9)	VIII (10)	IB (11)	IIB (12)
4	21 Sc $4s^2 3d^1$	22 Ti $4s^2 3d^2$	23 V $4s^2 3d^3$	24 Cr $4s^1 3d^5$	25 Mn $4s^2 3d^5$	26 Fe $4s^2 3d^6$	27 Co $4s^2 3d^7$	28 Ni $4s^2 3d^8$	29 Cu $4s^1 3d^{10}$	30 Zn $4s^2 3d^{10}$
5	39 Y $5s^2 4d^1$	40 Zr $5s^2 4d^2$	41 Nb $5s^1 4d^4$	42 Mo $5s^1 4d^5$	43 Tc $5s^2 4d^5$	44 Ru $5s^1 4d^7$	45 Rh $5s^1 4d^8$	46 Pd $5s^0 4d^{10}$	47 Ag $5s^1 4d^{10}$	48 Cd $5s^2 4d^{10}$
6	57 La $6s^2 5d^1$	72 Hf $6s^2 5d^2$	73 Ta $6s^2 5d^3$	74 W $6s^2 5d^4$	75 Re $6s^2 5d^5$	76 Os $6s^2 5d^6$	77 Ir $6s^2 5d^7$	78 Pt $6s^1 5d^9$	79 Au $6s^1 5d^{10}$	80 Hg $6s^2 5d^{10}$
7	89 Ac $7s^2 6d^1$	104	105	106	107	108	109			

f-Block Elements

Period														
6	58 Ce $6s^2$ $5d^0 4f^2$	59 Pr $6s^2$ $5d^0 4f^3$	60 Nd $6s^2$ $5d^0 4f^4$	61 Pm $6s^2$ $5d^0 4f^5$	62 Sm $6s^2$ $5d^0 4f^6$	63 Eu $6s^2$ $5d^0 4f^7$	64 Gd $6s^2$ $5d^1 4f^7$	65 Tb $6s^2$ $5d^0 4f^9$	66 Dy $6s^2$ $5d^0 4f^{10}$	67 Ho $6s^2$ $5d^0 4f^{11}$	68 Er $6s^2$ $5d^0 4f^{12}$	69 Tm $6s^2$ $5d^0 4f^{13}$	70 Yb $6s^2$ $5d^0 4f^{14}$	71 Lu $6s^2$ $5d^1 4f^{14}$
7	90 Th $7s^2$ $6d^2 5f^0$	91 Pa $7s^2$ $6d^1 5f^2$	92 U $7s^2$ $6d^1 5f^3$	93 Np $7s^2$ $6d^1 5f^4$	94 Pu $7s^2$ $6d^0 5f^6$	95 Am $7s^2$ $6d^0 5f^7$	96 Cm $7s^2$ $6d^1 5f^7$	97 Bk $7s^2$ $6d^0 5f^9$	98 Cf $7s^2$ $6d^0 5f^{10}$	99 Es $7s^2$ $6d^0 5f^{11}$	100 Fm $7s^2$ $6d^0 5f^{12}$	101 Md $7s^2$ $6d^0 5f^{13}$	102 No $7s^2$ $6d^0 5f^{14}$	103 Lw $7s^2$ $6d^1 5f^{14}$

urations for the elements:

Li $1s^2 2s^1$
Be $1s^2 2s^2$
B $1s^2 2s^2 2p^1$
C $1s^2 2s^2 2p^2$
N $1s^2 2s^2 2p^3$
O $1s^2 2s^2 2p^4$
F $1s^2 2s^2 2p^5$
Ne $1s^2 2s^2 2p^6$

Notice that with the element boron, the $2p$ orbitals begin to be used, eventually holding six electrons with the completion of the row at Ne. It is the **L shell** that becomes filled at Ne. It is upon this neon core [Ne] that the electron configurations for the elements of row three are built.

Elements of Period Three

Beginning with sodium, orbitals with principal quantum number $n = 3$ are used:

Na $[Ne]3s^1$
Mg $[Ne]3s^2$
Al $[Ne]3s^2 3p^1$
Si $[Ne]3s^2 3p^2$
P $[Ne]3s^2 3p^3$
S $[Ne]3s^2 3p^4$
Cl $[Ne]3s^2 3p^5$
Ar $[Ne]3s^2 3p^6$

The row is completed with Ar, where the three $3p$ orbitals are filled with two electrons each. In fact, it is characteristic of all elements in Group VIIIB(18) that they complete a row of the periodic table and have the filled outermost electron configuration np^6. Notice also that in row two it was the element boron where the appropriate np orbitals first were used. Here in row three, this is true of the element aluminum. Both elements are in Group IIIB(13) and have the outermost electronic configuration that is characteristic of all elements of Group IIIB(13): np^1. The $3d$ atomic orbitals were not used for the electron configurations of the elements of row three. Notice also from Fig. 2-10 that the $3d$ orbitals are not yet next in line to be used. The next orbital that is available is the $4s$ orbital, and it is the first to be used after the argon core [Ar] in writing the electron configurations for elements of row four. The shell that is completed with the third-row element Ar is the **M shell.**

Elements of Period Four

The fourth row of the periodic table begins with potassium, which has the characteristic outermost electron configuration of all elements in Group IA(1): ns^1.

K	$[Ar]4s^1$	Sc	$[Ar]4s^23d^1$	
Ca	$[Ar]4s^2$	Ti	$[Ar]4s^23d^2$	
		V	$[Ar]4s^23d^3$	
←	————————	Cr	$[Ar]4s^13d^5$	
Ga	$[Ar]4s^23d^{10}4p^1$	Mn	$[Ar]4s^23d^5$	
Ge	$[Ar]4s^23d^{10}4p^2$	Fe	$[Ar]4s^23d^6$	
As	$[Ar]4s^23d^{10}4p^3$	Co	$[Ar]4s^23d^7$	
Se	$[Ar]4s^23d^{10}4p^4$	Ni	$[Ar]4s^23d^8$	
Br	$[Ar]4s^23d^{10}4p^5$	Cu	$[Ar]4s^13d^{10}$	
Kr	$[Ar]4s^23d^{10}4p^6$	Zn	$[Ar]4s^23d^{10}$	

The $4s$ orbital becomes filled at the element calcium, which has the outermost configuration typical of all elements in Group IIA(2): ns^2. The two main groups of the periodic table are interrupted with the 10 elements Sc through Zn, where the previously unused $3d$ orbitals become available. The series of elements from Sc to Zn is 10 elements in length because the five d orbitals, holding 2 electrons each, require 10 electrons to be filled. After zinc, the row is completed with 6 elements having outermost electron configurations featuring successive use of the three $4p$ orbitals.

The orderly pattern of filling of the d orbitals seems to be interrupted at the elements Cr and Cu. In these cases a $4s$ electron is "borrowed" in order to obtain either a half-filled d orbital set (Cr) or a completely filled d orbital set (Cu). This leads in each case to a greater stability because of the half-filled or filled d orbital set. The same anomaly takes place for Mo [also of Group VIA(6)] and for the other elements of Group IB(11), Ag and Au.

Elements of Period Five

The elements of period five, beginning with Rb and ending with Xe follow the same pattern of electron configurations as that for the preceding period four. The valence orbitals in question are now, in order of use, the $5s$, $4d$, and $5p$ orbitals. The $5d$ and the $4f$ orbital sets are not used at this time. As was true for Cr and Cu in the first transition series, anomalies occur in the regular filling of the d orbitals at the elements Mo and Ag.

Elements of Period Six

Period six of the periodic table is composed of 32 elements from Cs(55) to Rn(86). The $6s$ orbital is filled at Ba. The $5d$ orbital set begins to be used with La, but the series is immediately interrupted by 14 elements. In this series of 14 elements, as well as in those immediately below them, the sevenfold degenerate f orbitals are used, two electrons eventually being distributed into each. Only then is the use of the d orbitals resumed at Hf. The row is ended with the usual p-block elements, in this case Tl through Rn.

There is an important reason why the ns orbital for any row, n, is used before the $(n - 1)d$ or the $(n - 2)f$ orbitals. The radial portion of the wave function for an s orbital is characteristically closer to the nucleus than d and f orbitals. Hence the $(n - 1)d$ orbital is higher in energy than the ns orbital for certain elements (see Fig. 2-9.) Consequently, the $3d$ orbitals are not used in row three, but in row four of the periodic table. Similarly, it is not until row six that the $4f$ and the $5d$ orbitals are used.

Elements of Period Seven

The elements of this period complete the periodic table. The short-lived elements 104–109 have now been detected. The $7s$-block elements Fr and Ra are followed by the second series of f-block elements, for which the $5f$ and $6d$ orbital energies are similar. It is not necessary to be concerned with the exact arrangement of electrons in these f and d orbitals because two or more different configurations differ so little in energy that the exact configuration in the ground state of the free atom has little to do with the chemical properties of the element in its compounds.

2-5   The Periodic Table

More than a century ago chemists began to search for a tabular arrangement of the elements that would group together those with similar chemical properties and also arrange them in some logical sequence. The sequence was generally the order of increasing atomic weights. As is well known, these efforts culminated in the type of periodic table devised by Mendeleev, in which the elements were arranged in horizontal rows with row lengths chosen so that like elements would form vertical columns.

It was Moseley who showed that the proper sequence criterion was not atomic weight but atomic number (although the two are only rarely out of register). It then followed that not only did the vertical columns contain chemically similar elements, but electronically similar atoms. We devote all of Chapter 8 to a discussion of the practical chemical aspects of the periodic table. Here, since we have just studied how the electron configurations of atoms are built up, it is appropriate to point out that these configurations lead logically to the same periodic arrangement as Mendeleev deduced from strictly chemical observations.

The vertical columns of the periodic tables on the inside of the front cover and elsewhere in this text are labeled in two fashions. First we give a traditional column (or group) designation using Roman numerals I–VIII, with letters A or B. Secondly, and parenthetically, we give the newest group designations adopted by the International Union of Pure and Applied Chemistry: Arabic numerals, 1–18.

To build up a periodic table based on similarities in electron configuration, a convenient point of departure is to require all atoms with outer ns^2np^6 configurations to fall in a column. It is convenient to place this column at the extreme right, and to include also He ($1s^2$). This column thus contains those elements called the **noble gases:** He, Ne, Ar, Kr, Xe, Rn.

If the elements that have a single electron in the ns orbitals are placed in the Group IA(1) column at the extreme left of the table, the remaining pattern of the table is established. The elements of Group IA(1) are called the **alkali metals.** The ionization enthalpies of the single s electrons in the valence shell of these elements is low, and the $+1$ cations of these elements are readily formed. The chemistry of these elements is mostly that of these $+1$ cations. Each of them is followed by one of the elements of Group IIA(2), which have the characteristic ns^2 configuration. These elements (Be, Mg, Ca, Sr, Ba, Ra) are called the **alkaline earth metals,** and characteristically form $+2$ cations.

If now we return to the noble gas column and begin to work back from right to left, it is clear that we shall get columns of elements with outer electron configurations ns^2np^5, ns^2np^4, . . . , ns^2np^1. The ns^2np^5 elements F, Cl, Br, I, and At are called the **halogens** (meaning salt formers). Those with the ns^2np^4 configurations are O, S, Se, Te, and Po; they are given the family name **chalcogens.** The other three columns, that is, ns^2np^3 (N, P, As, Sb, and Bi), ns^2np^2 (C, Si, Ge, Sn, and Pb), and ns^2np^1 (B, Al, Ga, In, and Tl), have no trivial group names.

Thus far we have developed a rational arrangement for nearly half of the elements. These elements, which involve outer shells consisting solely of s and p electrons are called the **main group elements.** In particular, they are either the **s-block elements** or the **p-block elements.** Most of the remaining ones are called **d-block elements.** They occupy the central region of the periodic table, between the two main blocks. Their occurrence at this position is due to the filling of the $(n - 1)d$ orbitals. Their electron configurations have already been discussed. With the exception of Group IIB(12) (Zn, Cd, and Hg), these elements are also called the **transition elements.** Their common characteristic is that either the neutral atom, or some important ion it forms, has an incomplete set of d electrons. The set of elements with incomplete $3d$ shells is called the **first transition series,** and those with partial $4d$ and $5d$ shells are called the **second** and **third transition series,** respectively.

The elements Zn, Cd, and Hg have unique properties. While they resemble the alkaline earths in giving no oxidation state higher than $+2$, they differ because the configuration immediately underlying their valence orbitals is a rather polarizable nd^{10} shell instead of a more tightly bound noble gas shell. Their chemistry will be taken up in a later chapter.

Finally, the 14 elements between La and Hf, in which the $4f$ orbitals are being filled, are placed at the bottom of the table, to avoid making it excessively wide. These elements are called the **lanthanides** because of their chemical resemblance to lanthanum. A somewhat similar set of elements, called the **actinides,** have partially filled $5f$ orbitals. They are placed beneath the corresponding lanthanides. These two series are collectively called the **f-block elements.**

2-6 Hund's Rule, Electron Configurations, and Effective Nuclear Charge

Thus far, for atoms in which there are partly filled p or d shells, the electron configurations have simply been written p^n or d^n. However, it is possible, and important, to specify them in greater detail. For instance, for the configuration p^2, there are 15 distinct ways of assigning quantum numbers to the two electrons in the three degenerate orbitals. All of the corresponding orientations of the two electrons are available to the atom, but only one assignment is most stable. The ground states for the p^n configurations are illustrated in Fig. 2-13.

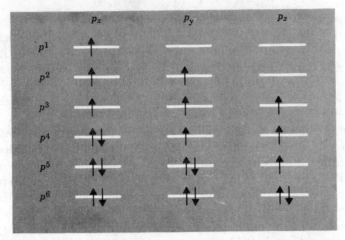

Figure 2-13   Application of the principle of maximum spin
multiplicity in the filling of the degenerate set of $2p$ orbitals
for the configurations $2p^1$–$2p^6$.

There are two important features of the pattern shown there:

1. Within a set of degenerate orbitals (in this case the p_x, p_y, and p_z), the
   electrons make use of different orbitals so long as it is possible.
2. Parallel spins (same value of m_s) are used until the Pauli exclusion principle requires pairing of spins.

The first of these features is partly a consequence of the charge of the electrons.
The electrons can minimize the repulsive forces among themselves by occupying different p orbitals. This is true because the p orbitals occupy regions
of space along different axes. Repulsive forces between the p electrons are
thus minimized when the electrons are distributed as far from one another as
possible. The second feature arises because pairing of electrons before it is
required by the Pauli exclusion principle leads to a less stable arrangement.
Consequently, we have Hund's rule: The most stable electronic state (among
several that are possible within a degenerate set of orbitals) is that state with
maximum spin multiplicity, namely, the one with the largest number of unpaired electron spins. This rule immediately implies the spreading out of
electrons into as much of the space surrounding the nucleus as is possible.
Hund's rule also implies that this spreading out of electron density leads to
extra stability not only for the individual electron at hand, but for the ensemble
of electrons that make up a multielectron atom. It is important to understand
how this stability arises. Part of the explanation involves the concept of **effective
nuclear charge.**

An electron will occupy that orbital, of all those yet unoccupied on an
atom, where the nucleus is most effective at offering positive charge to stabilize
the electron. It was J. C. Slater who realized that the effective nuclear charge,
Z^*, which is felt by an electron is not the actual charge, Z, of the nucleus of
the atom. Rather, the amount of nuclear charge actually felt by an electron
depends on the type of orbital in which the electron is housed, and on the

ability of other electrons in more penetrating orbitals to screen (or shield) the electron in question from the nucleus.

We have already pointed out that, among the orbitals having the same value of the principal quantum number, the s orbital is the most stable. Furthermore, any atomic orbital that places appreciable electron density between the nucleus and a second orbital is said to penetrate the region of space occupied by the second orbital. To the extent that this happens, the electron is more stable in the more penetrating orbital. The relative extent to which the various orbitals penetrate the electron clouds of other orbitals is $s > p > d > f >$ and so on. Thus for any given principal quantum number, n, an electron will experience the greatest effective nuclear charge when housed in an s orbital, then a p orbital, and so on. We have already cited this as the reason for the order of orbital filling among the elements. But what of the atoms of the p block of the periodic table where the last electron is placed in every case into an orbital of the same type? Consider the elements of row two, beginning with B and proceeding to Ne. Here, with each successive proton that is added in making the next element, there is added an electron into the $2p$ orbitals. Each new electron is added in accordance with Hund's rule. Also, each new electron experiences a new and different effective nuclear charge. At B the new electron is added into one of the p orbitals, say the p_x orbital. The new electron that is added for C must now go into another of the $2p$ orbitals, say the p_y. But the p_y orbital is perpendicular to the p_x orbital, and the p_y orbital is poorly screened by the p_x orbital from the nuclear charge. As a result, the effective nuclear charge for the last electron in carbon is higher than that for B. It is the geometry and the orientation of the p orbitals that makes them poor at shielding one another from the nucleus. Consider the next element, N. The third p electron that is added to make this element is poorly screened from the growing nuclear charge because the other two p electrons that are already there lie at 90° to this last one. Thus the effective nuclear charge for the differentiating electron of nitrogen is even higher. Where screening of an electron is poor, the effective nuclear charge is correspondingly high. Thus Hund's rule: Electrons spread out into a degenerate set of orbitals in order to experience this maximum effective nuclear charge.

This view is admittedly simplistic. There are other factors (such as the quantum mechanical exchange energy associated with a set of electrons with parallel spins), which influence the energies of the various electron configurations. These other issues need not detain us in the following limited discussion of shielding and effective nuclear charge.

Slater developed an empirical constant that represents the ability of an electron in one type of orbital to shield (screen) another electron in the same or a different type of orbital from the nuclear charge. This **screening constant**, σ, is used in Eq. 2-6.1:

$$Z^* = Z - \sigma \tag{2-6.1}$$

Here, Z is the actual number of protons (atomic number), and Z^* is that amount of nuclear charge that is effectively felt by any given electron. Where screening is small, the effective nuclear charge will be high. The values for σ in any configuration are calculated according to empirical rules developed by Slater. In order to calculate the screening constant, σ, for any one electron within a given electron configuration, we proceed as follows. All electrons in levels higher than that of the electron under consideration contribute zero to σ. Electrons in the same principal quantum level contribute 0.35 to σ. Electrons in the $(n - 1)$ shell each contribute 0.85 to σ. Electrons in deeper shells contribute 1.00 to σ. For d and f electrons we have the special rule that all inner shell electrons each contribute 1.0 to σ; that is, d and f electrons penetrate the core of the atom so little that we can say, approximately, that they don't penetrate at all.

To illustrate the application of these empirical rules, let us estimate the effective nuclear charge for one of the outer electrons (a $2p$ electron) of the fluorine atom, which has a configuration of $1s^2 2s^2 2p^5$. The inner shell, $1s^2$, contributes $2 \times 0.85 = 1.70$ to σ. Each of the electrons with $n = 2$ (other than the one under consideration) contributes 0.35. We have, therefore:

$$\sigma = 2 \times 0.85 + 6 \times 0.35$$
$$= 1.70 + 2.10 = 3.80$$

and

$$Z^* = 9 - 3.80 = 5.20$$

Values of Z^* for some other elements are listed in Table 2-3.

There are trends among the elements for the effective nuclear charge experienced by the last or **differentiating electron** of an element. We shall be able to illustrate this more completely by comparing other physical properties of the elements, as is done in the next section. Still, it is useful to pause long enough to compare the values of Z^* across a row. As is shown in Table 2-3, there is a steady increase (by 0.65 units) in Slater's Z^* across each row of the periodic table.

Other trends in Z^* are less meaningful. Also, values of Slater's Z^* become increasingly less reliable for the heavier elements, or in comparisons down a group of the periodic table. Modifications have been made, and more accurate effective nuclear charges have been estimated for all of the elements. Regard-

Table 2-3. Calculation of Effective Nuclear Charge, Z^*, According to Slater's Eq. 2-6.1, $Z^* = Z - \sigma$

	n	Z	σ	Z^*
1 (H)	1	0	1.00	
(He)	2	0.30	1.70	
2 (Li)	3	1.70	1.30	
(Be)	4	2.05	1.95	
(B)	5	2.40	2.60	
(C)	6	2.75	3.25	
(N)	7	3.10	3.90	
(O)	8	3.45	4.55	
(F)	9	3.80	5.20	
(Ne)	10	4.15	5.85	

less of the particular set of values for Z^* that one adopts, the important conclusion for our purposes is that the effective nuclear charge increases somewhat regularly from left to right across the rows of the periodic table, because of imperfect shielding.

2-7 Periodic Trends in the Properties of the Elements

There is an overall harmony among the properties of the elements and their electronic structures. In fact, the periodic trends that we shall discuss can be traced in part to differences in the orbitals in which the electrons are housed. The concepts that are to be used in establishing this harmony obey the following hierarchy:

1. The different interpenetrations of the atomic orbitals can be judged from an evaluation of the size of the orbitals, $R(r)^2$, and the orientations of the orbitals, $\Theta(\theta)^2\Phi(\phi)^2$.
2. Because of these different penetrations and orientations of the atomic orbitals, the orbitals are used in the sequence shown in Fig. 2-10.
3. Because of these different penetrations and orientations of the atomic orbitals, the valence electrons of the atoms experience different effective nuclear charges, as illustrated in Table 2-3.
4. Properties such as first ionization enthalpy also follow trends that reflect the different electron configurations in any period or group of the periodic table.

Ionization Enthalpy

The periodic trends in **first ionization enthalpies** (ΔH_{ion}) for the elements H to Rn are shown in Fig. 2-14. There are three major trends that merit comment. First, the maxima occur at the noble gases and the minima occur at the alkali metals. This is easily understandable, since the closed shell configurations of the noble gases are very stable and resist disruption, either to form chemical bonds or to become ionized. In the alkali metal atoms, there is an electron outside the preceding noble gas configuration. This electron is well shielded from the attraction of the nucleus; it is therefore relatively easy to remove. In terms of effective nuclear charges, the outermost ($2p$) electrons of Ne experience a Z^* of 5.85, whereas the outermost electron of the Na atom ($3s$) experiences an effective nuclear charge of only $11 - 10(0.85) = 2.50$. The ionization enthalpies, 2080 and 496 kJmol^{-1} are in accord with this.

Second, from each alkali metal (ns^1 configuration—minima in Fig. 2-14) across a row of the periodic table to the next noble gas (closed shell electron configuration—maxima in Fig. 2-14) there is an overall increase in ionization enthalpies. The increase is not perfectly regular, as will be discussed shortly. Nevertheless, the trend is obvious; across any row of the periodic table there occurs an increase, generally, in the first ionization enthalpies. This trend conforms to a similar pattern noted previously for effective nuclear charge. The effective nuclear charge grows across a row because of the cumulative effects of imperfect shielding by orbitals of the same principal quantum num-

Figure 2-14   Periodic trends in the first ionization enthalpies, ΔH_{ion}.

ber. As the effective nuclear charge increases, so does the energy necessary to ionize the atom.

Third, the increase just discussed is not smooth. Instead, there are two well-defined jogs that occur at corresponding positions in each series, that is, from Li to Ne, from Na to Ar and, with some differences due to intervention of the transition elements, in subsequent periods of the table. In each case, the ionization enthalpy drops from the s^2 to the s^2p configuration and again from the s^2p^3 to the s^2p^4 configuration. The explanation is most readily apparent if the facts are stated in a slightly different way, where the elements of the Li to Ne period are used as an example. The ionization enthalpies of B, C, and N increase regularly but they are all lower than values that would be extrapolated from Li and Be. This is because p electrons are less penetrating than s electrons. They are, therefore, more shielded and more easily removed than extrapolation from the behavior of s electrons would predict. Again, the ionization enthalpies of O, F, and Ne increase regularly, but all are lower than would be expected by extrapolation from B, C, and N. This is because the $2p$ shell is half-full at N and each of the additional $2p$ electrons enters an orbital already singly occupied. They are partly repelled by the electron already present in the same orbital and are thus less tightly bound.

Atomic Radii

It is necessary to distinguish among at least three different types of radii that might be listed for the elements. The **single-bond covalent radius,** r_{cov}, of an element represents the typical contribution by that element to the length of a predominantly covalent bond. Values for r_{cov} are estimated from the known lengths of covalent bonds involving any particular element, in the absence of multiple bonds. For instance, the covalent radius for fluorine is taken to be half the internuclear distance in the homonuclear diatomic F_2. Typical values for r_{cov} are listed in Fig. 2-15, along with two other important types of radii, r_{ion} and r_{vdw}. The values for the **ionic radii,** r_{ion}, represent radii assigned to the ions of the elements in predominantly ionic compounds. The values of the **van der Waals radii,** r_{vdw}, represent the normal van der Waals' (or nonbonded) distance of closest approach to an atom by another atom that is in contact with, but not covalently bound to it. Values of r_{vdw} are larger than those of r_{cov} because the contact or nonbonded distance between molecules in liquids or solids is greater than the distance between atoms that are covalently bound to one another within one molecule. Intermolecular forces are generally weaker than intramolecular bonds. Values of r_{cov} are greater than r_{ion} for cations because the cations are formed by removal of electron(s) from the atom. Conversely, anions are larger than their parent atoms, by reason of addition of electrons. We shall have more to say about these radii, their sources, and their uses. For now it is pertinent to consider the periodic trends in the values of these radii.

Two trends in the values tabulated in Fig. 2-15 need to be mentioned. First, down any particular group of the periodic table, the radii of the elements increase by large amounts due to the successive use (with each new row) of orbitals having principal quantum number, n, one higher than the last. For any group of the periodic table, the size of the elements increases as the quantum number, n, increases, or, as one descends the group. The size of the elements increases in spite of increasing effective nuclear charge because of the greater importance of placing electrons into higher level shells.

Secondly, across a row of the table, there is a progressive decrease in the size of the atoms within molecules (r_{cov}), as well as a decrease in the volume requirement of atoms between molecules (r_{vdw}). This decrease in size takes place in spite of the rather obvious fact that additional electrons become added with each new element! This demonstrates the importance of the imperfect shielding among the orbitals. As the effective nuclear charge grows across a row, the sizes of the atoms decrease.

Electron Attachment Enthalpies

The enthalpy change ΔH_{EA}, which accompanies addition of an electron(s) provides a measure of the willingness of an atom to form anions. Where these enthalpy changes are negative, formation of the anion is favorable (exo-thermic). For example, the electron configuration of the halogens allows addi-tion of an electron to form the uninegative ions:

$$X(g) + e^- \longrightarrow X^-(g) \tag{2-7.1}$$

Where positive values of ΔH_{EA} arise, an atom resists formation of the anion. In fact, for many elements, electron attachment enthalpies must be estimated because the normal chemistry of an element might be formation of cations rather than anions. The alkaline earth elements, for instance, have positive electron attachment enthalpies, reflecting the tendency of these elements to form +2 cations rather than anions. The electron attachment enthalpies of the noble gases are similarly positive, reflecting the stability of the closed shell configurations of these elements.

Radii (in pm), listed in the order:

r_{cov}
r_{vdw}
r_{ion}

(100 pm = 1 Å)

IA (1)	IIA (2)	IIIA (3)	IVA (4)	VA (5)	VIA (6)	VIIA (7)	VIII (8)	VIII (9)	VIII (10)	IB (11)	IIB (12)	IIIB (13)	IVB (14)	VB (15)	VIB (16)	VIIB (17)	VIIIB (18)
1 H 37/130/208(1−)																	2 He 54/140/—
3 Li 140/180/60(1+)	4 Be 120/—/31(2+)											5 B 83/—/41(3+)	6 C 77/170/—	7 N 73/155/—	8 O 70/140/140(2−)	9 F 68/135/119(1−)	10 Ne —/154/—
11 Na 154/230/96(1+)	12 Mg 148/170/65(2+)											13 Al 130/—/50(3+)	14 Si 117/210/—	15 P 110/185/212(3−)	16 S 103/185/190(2−)	17 Cl 99/180/170(1−)	18 Ar —/192/—
19 K 198/280/133(1+)	20 Ca 178/—/99(2+)	21 Sc 160/—/81(3+)	22 Ti —/—/68(4+)	23 V 131/—/—	24 Cr	25 Mn —/—/80(2+)	26 Fe 125/—/75(2+)	27 Co 125/—/72(2+)	28 Ni 125/—/69(2+)	29 Cu 128/140/91(1+)	30 Zn 120/140/74(2+)	31 Ga 130/190/62(3+)	32 Ge 122/—/—	33 As 121/—/—	34 Se 117/200/202(2−)	35 Br 114/190/187(1−)	36 Kr 110/200/—
37 Rb 220/—/148(1+)	38 Sr 192/—/113(1+)	39 Y 178/—/93(3+)	40 Zr 134/—/80(4+)	41 Nb	42 Mo	43 Tc	44 Ru 132/—/—	45 Rh 134/—/—	46 Pd —/160/—	47 Ag 144/170/108(1+)	48 Cd 149/160/97(2+)	49 In 148/190/81(3+)	50 Sn 140/220/71(4+)	51 Sb 141/—/92(3+)	52 Te 137/220/222(2−)	53 I 134/200/212(1−)	54 Xe 130/220/—
55 Cs 265/—/169(1+)	56 Ba 218/—/135(2+)	57 La —/—/113(3+)	72 Hf	73 Ta 143/—/—	74 W	75 Re	76 Os	77 Ir 136/—/—	78 Pt —/175/—	79 Au 144/170/—	80 Hg 150/150/110(2+)	81 Tl —/200/95(3+)	82 Pb 144/—/84(4+)	83 Bi 152/—/108(3+)	84 Po —/—/230	85 At	86 Rn
87 Fr	88 Ra —/—/140	89 Ac 187/—/111	104	105	106	107	108	109									

Figure 2-15 Periodic trends in atomic and ionic radii. For any element, the top value is an average single bond covalent radius, r_{cov}; the middle value is the average van der Waals' (nonbonded or contact) distance, r_{vdw}; the bottom value is a typical radius for a common ion of the element, taken from its most typical crystal lattice, r_{ion}. The values of r_{ion} are mostly those of Pauling, with the exception of Group VIIB (17), which are from Ladd. For more information concerning each type of radius listed here, see sections 3-3 and 3-4, as well as Chapter 4. A more thorough discussion is available in Chapter 1 of *Advanced Inorganic Chemistry, Fourth Edition,* by F. A. Cotton and G. Wilkinson, Wiley-Interscience, New York, 1980.

Where addition of a second electron is known to be common (i.e., the chalcogens, which form dinegative anions such as O^{2-}), the addition of the first electron is typically favorable. The addition of the second electron involves increasing electronic repulsions, making the overall process unfavorable from the standpoint of ΔH_{EA}. Still there is a rich chemistry of the stable oxides and sulfides, and so on, and more must be considered in assessing the stability of a particular anion. These complexities, coupled with the difficulties in measuring electron attachment enthalpies, make a discussion of periodic trends in electron attachment enthalpies less straightforward. Our interest in them is in their contribution to the next topic, electronegativities.

Electronegativities

Electronegativity, χ, is an empirical measure of the tendency of an atom in a molecule to attract electrons. (Chi, χ, is conventionally used for electronegativity as well as, later, for magnetic susceptibility.) It will, naturally, vary with the oxidation state of the atom, and for a number of reasons the numerical values that have been assigned should not be taken too literally. It is useful only as a semiquantitative notion.

It should be stressed that electronegativity is not the same as the enthalpy of electron attachment, ΔH_{EA}, although the two are related. R. S. Mulliken has shown that reasonable values of χ are roughly proportional to the average of the negative of the electron attachment enthalpy $(-\Delta H_{EA})$ and the ionization enthalpy (ΔH_{ion}). That is, electronegativities are determined in part by the tendency of an atom to gain additional electron density and by its tendency to retain the electron density it already has. A complete electronegativity scale cannot be established using this approach, however, because electron attachment enthalpies are not available for all of the elements.

Many other ways of computing electronegativities have been suggested. The first general method was proposed by Pauling. He suggested that if two atoms, A and B, had the same electronegativity, the strength of the A—B bond would be equal to the geometric mean of the A—A and B—B bond energies, since the electrons in the bond would be equally shared in purely covalent bonds in all three cases. He observed, however, that for the majority of A—B bonds the energy exceeds that geometric average because, in general, two different atoms have different electronegativities, and there is an ionic contribution to the bond in addition to the covalent one. He proposed that the "excess" A—B bond energies could be used as an empirical basis to determine electronegativity differences. For instance, the H—F bond energy is 566 kJ mol^{-1}, whereas the H—H and F—F bond energies are 436 and 158 kJ mol^{-1}, respectively. Their geometric mean is $(158 \times 436)^{1/2} = 262$ kJ mol^{-1}. The difference, Δ, is 304 kJ mol^{-1}. He then found that to get a consistent set of electronegativities, so that $\chi_A - \chi_B = (\chi_C - \chi_B) - (\chi_C - \chi_A)$, and so on, the electronegativity differences would have to obey the equation:

$$\chi_A - \chi_B = 0.102 \, \Delta^{1/2} \qquad (2\text{-}7.2)$$

Pauling originally assigned the most electronegative of the elements, fluorine,

Figure 2-16 Electronegativities of the elements. Values in bold type are calculated using the approach of A. L. Allred and E. G. Rochow, *J. Inorg. Nucl. Chem.*, **1958**, *5*, 264. Values in italics are estimated by Pauling's method (A. L. Allred, *J. Inorg. Nucl. Chem.*, **1961**, *17*, 215. Values in Roman type are obtained using Mulliken's method (H. O. Pritchard and H. A. Skinner, *Chem. Revs.*, **1955**, *55*, 745). Roman numerals at the top give the oxidation states used for the Pauling-type values.

Periodic table of electronegativities (element: bold = Allred–Rochow, italic = Pauling, roman = Mulliken):

I	II	III	IV	V	VI	VII	VIII	VIII	VIII	I	II	III	IV	V	VI	VII	0
H 2.20																	He
Li 0.97, *0.98*	Be 1.47, *1.57, 1.46*											B 2.01, *2.04, 2.01*	C 2.50, *2.55, 2.63*	N 3.07, *3.04, 2.33*	O 3.50, *3.44, 3.17*	F 4.10, *3.98, 3.91*	Ne
Na 1.01, *0.93, 0.93*	Mg 1.23, *1.31, 1.32*											Al 1.47, *1.61, 1.81*	Si 1.74, *1.90, 2.44*	P 2.06, *2.19, 1.81*	S 2.44, *2.58, 2.41*	Cl 2.83, *3.16, 3.00*	Ar
K 0.91, *0.82, 0.80*	Ca 1.04, *1.00*	Sc 1.20, *1.36*	Ti 1.32, *1.54*	V 1.45, *1.63*	Cr 1.56, *1.66*	Mn 1.60, *1.55*	Fe 1.64, *1.83*	Co 1.70, *1.88*	Ni 1.75, *1.91*	Cu 1.75, *1.90, 1.36*	Zn 1.66, *1.65, 1.49*	Ga 1.82, *1.81, 1.95*	Ge 2.02, *2.01*	As 2.20, *2.18, 1.75*	Se 2.48, *2.55, 2.23*	Br 2.74, *2.96, 2.76*	Kr
Rb 0.89, *0.82*	Sr 0.99, *0.95*	Y 1.11, *1.22*	Zr 1.22, *1.33*	Nb 1.23	Mo 1.30, *2.16*	Tc 1.36	Ru 1.42	Rh 1.45, *2.28*	Pd 1.35, *2.20*	Ag 1.42, *1.93, 1.36*	Cd 1.46, *1.69, 1.4*	In 1.49, *1.78, 1.80*	Sn 1.72, *1.96*	Sb 1.82, *2.05, 1.65*	Te 2.01, *2.10*	I 2.21, *2.66, 2.56*	Xe
Cs 0.86, *0.79*	Ba 0.97, *0.89*	La* 1.03, *1.10*	Hf 1.23	Ta 1.33	W 1.40, *2.36*	Re 1.46	Os 1.52	Ir 1.55, *2.20*	Pt 1.44, *2.28*	Au 1.42, *2.54*	Hg 1.44, *2.00*	Tl 1.44, *2.04*	Pb 1.55, *2.33*	Bi 1.67, *2.02*	Po 1.76	At 1.96	Rn
Fr 0.86	Ra 0.97	Ac** 1.00															

*Lanthanides:

La 1.03, *1.10*	Ce 1.06, *1.12*	Pr 1.07, *1.13*	Nd 1.07, *1.14*	Pm 1.07	Sm 1.07, *1.17*	Eu 1.01	Gd 1.11, *1.20*	Tb 1.10	Dy 1.10, *1.22*	Ho 1.10, *1.23*	Er 1.11, *1.24*	Tm 1.11, *1.25*	Yb 1.06	Lu 1.14, *1.27*

**Actinides:

Ac 1.00	Th 1.11	Pa 1.14	U 1.22, *1.38*	Np 1.22, *1.36*	Pu 1.22, *1.28*	Am	Cm	Bk	Cf	Es	Fm	Md

~1.2 (estimated)

62

χ = 4.00. From these data, we could calculate

$$\chi_H = 4.00 - 0.102(304)^{1/2} = 2.22 \tag{2-7.3}$$

A more recently proposed method of calculating electronegativities is that of Allred and Rochow. It has the advantage of being more easily applied to a larger number of the elements. The rationale is that an atom will attract electron density in a chemical bond according to Coulomb's law (Chapter 1), as shown in Eq. 2-7.4:

$$\text{Force} = \frac{(Z^*e)(e)}{4\pi\epsilon r^2} \tag{2-7.4}$$

where Z^* is the effective nuclear charge, e is the charge of the electron, and r is the mean radius of the electron, essentially r_{cov}. Equation 2-7.4 is the basis for the empirically adjusted electronegativities, which are given by Eq. 2-7.5:

$$\chi = 0.359 \frac{Z^*}{r^2} + 0.744 \tag{2-7.5}$$

The numerical constants are empirically derived to bring the values for electronegativity within a reasonable range.

Values for the three different electronegativities are listed in Fig. 2-16. The variation of these values with position in the periodic table is reasonable. The atoms with the highest electronegativities are those with the smallest radii and the highest effective nuclear charges (e.g., fluorine). The larger radii correspond to the lower electronegativities (e.g., cesium).

2-8 Magnetic Properties of Atoms and Ions

Any atom, ion, or molecule that has one or more unpaired electrons is *paramagnetic*, meaning, that it, or any material in which it is found, will be attracted into a magnetic field. In cases where paramagnetic atoms or ions are very close together they interact cooperatively and other more or less intense and more complicated forms of magnetism, ferromagnetism, and antiferromagnetism, in particular, are observed. We do not discuss these forms here as they have no direct chemical significance. Substances that contain no unpaired electrons (with certain exceptions that need not concern us here) are *diamagnetic*, meaning that they are repelled, weakly, by a magnetic field. Thus, the measurement of paramagnetism affords a powerful tool for detecting the presence and number of unpaired electrons in chemical elements and compounds.

The full power of magnetic measurements comes from the fact that the magnitude of the *magnetic susceptibility*, which is a measure of the force exerted by the magnetic field on a unit mass of the specimen, is related to the number of unpaired electrons present per unit weight—and, hence, per mole.

Actually, the paramagnetism of a substance containing unpaired electrons receives a contribution from the orbital motion of the unpaired electrons as well as from their spins. However, there are important cases where the spin contribution is so predominant that measured susceptibility values can be interpreted in terms of how many unpaired electrons are present. This correlation is best expressed by using a quantity called the *magnetic moment*, μ, which may be calculated from the measured susceptibility per mole, χ_M. It is best to use χ_M^{corr}, where a correction has been applied to the measured χ_M to allow for the diamagnetic effect which is always present, and which may be estimated from measurements on similar substances that lack the atom or ion that has the unpaired electrons.

Curie's Law

It was shown some 70 years ago by Pierre Curie that for most paramagnetic substances, the magnetic susceptibility varies inversely with absolute temperature. In other words the product $\chi_M^{corr} \times T$ is a constant, called the Curie constant for the substance. From the theory of electric and magnetic polarization it can be shown that, if the paramagnetic susceptibility is due to the presence of individual, independent paramagnetic atoms or ions within the substance, each with a magnetic dipole moment, μ, the following equation holds true:

$$\mu = 2.84\sqrt{\chi_M^{corr}T} \qquad (2\text{-}8.1)$$

It is seen that this expression incorporates Curie's law.

Now it can also be shown from the quantum theory for atoms (and ions) that the magnetic moment due entirely to the spins of n unpaired electrons on the atom or ion is given by

$$\mu = 2\sqrt{S(S + 1)} \qquad (2\text{-}8.2)$$

where S equals the sum of the spins of all the unpaired electrons, that is, $n \times \frac{1}{2}$. From Eq. 2-8.2, it can easily be calculated that for one to five unpaired electrons the magnetic moments should be those shown in Table 2-4. The unit for atomic magnetic moments is the Bohr magneton, BM.

To illustrate the application of these ideas, consider copper(II) sulfate, $CuSO_4 \cdot 5H_2O$. From the magnetic susceptibility the magnetic moment is found to be 1.95 BM. This value is only a little higher than the calculated value for

Table 2-4. Spin-Only Magnetic Moments, μ (in Bohr Magnetons)

Number of Unpaired Electrons (n)	S^a	μ(BM)
1	$\frac{1}{2}$	1.73
2	1	2.83
3	$\frac{3}{2}$	3.87
4	2	4.90
5	$\frac{5}{2}$	5.92

^{a}The total spin quantum number $S = n \times \frac{1}{2}$.

one unpaired electron, and the discrepancy can be attributed to the contribution made by orbital motion of the electron. Thus the magnetic properties of $CuSO_4 \cdot 5H_2O$ are in accord with the presence of a Cu^{2+} ion that should have a $[Ar]3d^9$ configuration with one unpaired electron. For comparison, $MnSO_4 \cdot 4H_2O$ has a magnetic moment of 5.86 BM, which is approximately the number expected for a Mn^{2+} ion with the electron configuration $[Ar]3d^5$.

STUDY GUIDE

Scope and Purpose

This chapter covers fundamental principles of atomic structure, wave mechanics for atoms, and the periodic table. These topics are important in subsequent discussions of structure, bonding, and reactivity. Additional help with these important topics is available in the works listed under **Supplementary Reading.** The student should master the material sufficiently to be able to give ready answers to the **Study Questions** listed under "A. Review." More demanding exercises are listed under "B. Additional Exercises."

Study Questions

A. Review

1. The emission lines of the hydrogen atom come in related sets. What is the form of the equations for these sets? An equation of this type is named for whom?

2. What were the two bold postulates made by Bohr that allowed him to derive an equation for the energies of the electron in a hydrogen atom?

3. Write and explain the meaning of the equation relating the energy and frequency of radiation. What is the constant in it called?

4. What does the term Bohr radius mean?

5. What is de Broglie's equation for the wavelength associated with a moving particle of mass (m) and velocity (v)? What physical effect first showed directly that the wave character of the electron really exists?

6. State the relationship between the Bohr orbit with $n = 1$ and the wave mechanical orbital with $n = 1$ for the hydrogen atom.

7. Specify the set of quantum numbers used to describe an orbital and state what values of each are possible.

8. State the quantum numbers for each of the following orbitals: $1s$, $2s$, $2p$, $4d$, $4f$.

9. Draw diagrams of each of the following orbitals: $1s$, $2p_x$, $2p_y$, $2p_z$, $3d_{z^2}$, $3d_{xy}$, $3d_{yz}$, $3d_{zx}$, $3d_{x^2-y^2}$.

10. State the exclusion principle in the form relevant to atomic structure. Show how it leads to the conclusion that in a given principal shell there can be only two s, six p, ten d, and fourteen f electrons.

11. What does the term penetration mean, and why is it important in understanding the relative energies of the s, p, d, and f electrons with the same principal quantum number?

12. Define each of the following: alkali metals; alkaline earth metals, halogens; noble gases; main group elements; d-block elements; f-block elements; lanthanides; transition elements.

13. What is Hund's first rule? Show how it is used to specify in detail the electron configurations of the elements from Li to Ne. ·

14. Why is the first ionization enthalpy of the oxygen atom lower than that of the nitrogen atom?

15. How is the magnetic moment of a substance containing an ion with unpaired electrons (e.g., $CuSO_4 \cdot 5H_2O$) related to its magnetic susceptibility at various temperatures if the substance follows Curie's law?

16. How is the magnetic moment, μ, related to the number of unpaired electrons if the magnetism is due solely to the electron spins? Calculate μ for an ion with three unpaired electrons.

17. R. S. Mulliken showed that electronegativity is related to both ΔH_{EA} and ΔH_{ion}. What is the relationship he gave?

B. Additional Exercises

1. The He^+ ion is a one-electron system similar to hydrogen, except that $Z = 2$. Calculate the wave numbers, in reciprocal centimeters, for the first and last lines in each of the three spectroscopic series corresponding to those discussed for the ·hydrogen atom.

2. The first ionization enthalpy for Li is 520 kJ mol^{-1}. This corresponds to complete removal of the electron from the nucleus, and is achieved when $n = \infty$. Calculate from this the effective charge felt by the $2s$ electron of Li. Why is this less than the actual charge of $+3$?

3. A consistent set of units that may be used in de Broglie's Eq. 2-2.1 is: λ in cm, mass in g, velocity in cm s^{-1}, and h (Planck's constant) in g cm^2 s^{-1} (or erg s). What is the wavelength in cm and in Å of (a) an electron traveling at 10^6 cm s^{-1}, a velocity typical in the electron microscope? (b) a baseball or cricket ball thrown at 10^3 cm s^{-1}? Assume that mass equals 2.00×10^2 grams.

4. Consider the ground-state electron configurations of the atoms with the following atomic numbers: 7, 20, 26, 32, 37, 41, 85, 96. Calculate the total spin quantum number, S, for each, as well as its magnetic moment in Bohr magnetons.

5. As noted for Fig. 2-1, there are two more series of lines in the emission spectrum for hydrogen. Calculate the position of the series limit for each.

6. Explain the trend in the ionization enthalpies illustrated in Figure 2-14 for the Noble gases.

7. If the wavelength of an electron is 6.0 Å, what is its velocity ($m = 9.1 \times 10^{-28}$ g)?

8. Prepare a graph of the effective nuclear charge Z^* versus Z using the data of Table 2-3. Explain any trends.

9. Use Eq. 2-7.5 and values for χ and r_{cov} found elsewhere in the chapter to estimate Z^* for elements 19, 20, 31, and 32. Explain the trends.

10. Explain the differences between the functions $R(r)$, $R(r)^2$, and $r^2 R(r)^2$, using for an example the $1s$ orbital for hydrogen.

11. Prepare dot density patterns similar to that of Fig. 2-3 for the following orbitals: $2p_x$, $3s$, and $3d_{xy}$. Both shape and the function $r^2 R(r)^2$ [Fig. 2-7(b)] must be considered.

SUPPLEMENTARY READING

Adamson, A. W., "Domain Representations of Orbitals," *J. Chem. Educ.,* **1965,** *42,* 141.

Atkins, P. W., *Molecular Quantum Mechanics,* Oxford University Press, New York, 1983.

Berry, R. S., "Atomic Orbitals," *J. Chem. Educ.,* **1966,** *43,* 283.

Cohen, I. and Bustard, T., "Atomic Orbitals: Limitations and Variations," *J. Chem. Educ.,* **1966,** *43,* 187.

Goodisman, J., *Contemporary Quantum Chemistry,* Plenum, New York, 1977.

Guillemin, V., *The Story of Quantum Mechanics,* Scribner, New York, 1968.

Johnson, R. C. and Rettew, R. R., "Shapes of Atoms," *J. Chem. Educ.,* **1965,** *42,* 145.

Karplus, M. and Porter, R. N., *Atoms and Molecules: An Introduction for Students of Physical Chemistry,* Benjamin, Menlo Park, CA, 1970.

Kikuchi, Q. and Suzuki, K., "Orbital Shape Representations," *J. Chem. Educ.,* **1985,** *62,* 206.

Ogryzlo, E. A. and Porter, G. B., "Contour Surfaces for Atomic and Molecular Orbitals," *J. Chem. Educ.,* **1963,** *40,* 256.

Perlmutter-Hayman, B., "The Graphical Representation of Hydrogen-Like Functions," *J. Chem. Educ.,* **1969,** *46,* 428.

Powell, R. E., "The Five Equivalent *d* Orbitals," *J. Chem. Educ.,* **1968,** *45,* 1.

Price, W. C., Chissick, S. S., and Ravensdale, T., Eds., *Wave Mechanics, The First 50 Years,* Butterworths, London, 1973.

Pritchard, H. O. and Skinner, H. A., "Electronegativity Scales," *Chem. Rev.,* **1955,** *55,* 745.

chapter 3

STRUCTURE AND BONDING IN MOLECULES

3-1 Introduction

Modern techniques such as X-ray crystallography and spectroscopy have made it possible for us to determine, with great accuracy, the structures of molecules and complex ions. As information about structure has increased, so has our understanding of bonding. The more powerful bonding theories have allowed us to make detailed predictions and comparisons regarding not only structure, but also spectroscopy, reactivity, and so on. The simpler bonding theories, although known to be incomplete and only partially accurate, have still been useful because of the lessons that they have provided about electronic structures in molecules. This is especially true of the localized bonding theories, which will be discussed shortly. Later in this chapter, we shall develop more sophisticated, delocalized bonding theories.

The material of the previous chapter is important here, because it is the electrons (and the orbitals in which they are housed) which are the focus of any discussion of bonding. We shall show how orbitals interact to provide new locations for the electrons within molecules, and we shall be concerned with how this leads to the bonding of atoms in molecules and complex ions. Once we have established the types of orbital interactions that generally take place within molecules and complex ions, we shall, then, have also gained insight into matters of structure, spectroscopy, and reactivity. To organize the subject, three main types of bonding are considered:

1. Covalent bonding between atom pairs (two-center bonds).
2. Delocalized (multicenter) covalent bonding.
3. Ionic Bonding.

The first two types are discussed in this chapter, while ionic bonding and related topics are considered in Chapter 4. In addition, a few special forms of bonding are discussed elsewhere, such as metallic bonding (Section 8-6), the hydrogen bond (Section 9-3), and ligand field theory (Chapter 23).

There is surely no bonding that is literally and completely *ionic* but, for practical purposes, a great many compounds can be treated to a reasonable approximation as if the attractive forces were just the electrostatic attractions

68

between ions of opposite charge. The treatment of these substances, for example, NaCl, MgO, NiBr$_2$, and the like, takes a different form from that used for covalent bonding, where electron sharing between atoms is considered the dominant factor. It is, therefore, appropriate to discuss the two subjects separately.

3-2   The Localized Bond Approach

The simplest view of the bonding in any molecule or complex ion is (1) the electrons that are involved in bonding remain localized between pairs of atoms, and (2) the bonding in the whole structure is the sum of the individual bonds between pairs of atoms. The approach is useful because of its simplicity and because it is easy to represent in molecular diagrams. In fact the Lewis concept of a localized electron pair bond is so much a part of the modern vernacular that it would be difficult to imagine doing without it. As we shall see, however, the idea that electrons always remain localized between atom pairs has important limitations.

Lewis Concepts

It was the American chemist, G. N. Lewis, who first recognized that bonding between atoms involves the sharing of electrons. According to the Lewis definition, one covalent bond between two atoms results from the sharing between the atoms of a pair of electrons. Such a pair of **bonding electrons** is considered to be localized or fixed between the two atoms, and the bond is represented by a line connecting the atoms. Electrons that are not shared between atoms are localized as **lone-pair** electrons on one or another atom(s) within a molecule. The electronic structure of the entire molecule is represented by the sum of all of the bonding pairs and the lone pairs of electrons. On the basis of these concepts, it is possible to represent the electronic structure of a molecule in diagramatic form. Such representations are called Lewis diagrams. Some chemical intuition is needed in drawing the **Lewis diagram** for a molecule or ion. The Lewis diagram for a molecule or ion represents an approximate arrangement of atoms and the location of all valence electrons within the structure. The familiar result can, with experience, be quickly written down for any of a number of classes of substances, and the utility of this approach is obvious.

Once the Lewis diagram has been correctly written for a substance, the approach of Lewis can be extended with the use of hybridization theory, and with the Valence Shell Electron Pair Repulsion (VSEPR) theory, to account for subtle aspects of geometry. These three concepts (i.e., the Lewis diagram, hybridization, and VSEPR theory) in unison become extraordinarily powerful as an approach to structure and bonding. Eventually the concepts fail, however, because of the limitations of viewing the electrons in a strictly localized way. Resonance can be added to the paradigm, but this represents only a temporary (although historically important) "fix." This localized approach to bonding is useful because of its simplicity.

Lewis Diagrams

When drawing a Lewis diagram for a molecule or complex ion, only the valence electrons of the atoms are used. The Lewis diagram is complete when the atoms have been connected properly and the valence electrons have been distributed within the structure as either bonding or lone electron pairs. It may be necessary to look up the actual structure or to make an educated guess about the placement of atoms within the molecule or complex ion. Some chemical intuition goes a long way here, and a little experience is required. Under most circumstances, a simple and symmetrical geometry is correct. Atoms that are present only once within a substance tend to reside at the center of the structure. Metals tend to be central atoms. Oxygen is commonly, and hydrogen nearly always, peripheral. Once the positions of the atoms have been set down, the distribution of electrons into the diagram is considered. In simple cases, the valence electrons are arranged so as to give an octet of electrons to each nonhydrogen atom, although exceptions are common, especially for atoms from rows three and below of the periodic table. Some examples follow.

For many substances the number of valence electrons is just sufficient to provide an octet for each nonhydrogen atom. These are **saturated** systems, and the Lewis diagrams can be written using single bonds exclusively. Examples are CH_4, NH_3, H_2O, and HF.

$$H-\overset{\overset{\displaystyle H}{|}}{\underset{\underset{\displaystyle H}{|}}{C}}-H \qquad \overset{..}{\underset{\underset{\displaystyle H}{|}}{N}}_{H \quad H} \qquad \overset{..}{\underset{H \qquad H}{O}} \qquad :\overset{..}{\underset{..}{F}}-H$$

Unsaturated substances are those where the number of valence electrons that are available within a molecule or complex ion is not sufficient to allow the Lewis diagram to be written using single bonds only. The use of **multiple bonds** between selected atoms is required, then, in order to complete the octet for each atom in the structure. As examples containing a double bond, consider NO_3^-, acetone, or SO_2

$$\left[\begin{array}{c} :\overset{..}{O} \\ \diagdown \\ N-\overset{..}{O}: \\ \diagup \\ :\overset{..}{O}: \end{array} \right]^- \qquad \begin{array}{c} \overset{..}{O} \\ \| \\ C \\ \diagup \quad \diagdown \\ H_3C \quad CH_3 \end{array} \qquad \overset{..}{\underset{..}{O}}\diagdown \overset{..}{\underset{}{S}} \diagup \overset{..}{\underset{}{O}} \cdot$$

A triple bond (or two double bonds) is necessary when there is extensive unsaturation, as in CO_2 or thiocyanate ion:

$$\overset{..}{O}=C=\overset{..}{O} \qquad \left[:\overset{..}{S}-C\equiv N: \right]^-$$

In each of these last examples, unsaturation requires the use of multiple bonds in order to maintain an octet of electrons for each atom, without using more than the number of valence electrons that are actually available.

For some **electron deficient** molecules, all of the available valence electrons are used before an **octet** is achieved for each nonhydrogen atom. The Lewis diagrams are written so as to reflect this electron deficiency, although more complete molecular orbital approaches give a better description of electron deficient molecules. The molecules that feature this electron deficiency almost always involve the elements boron, beryllium, or sometimes aluminum. An example is BeH_2

$$H—Be—H$$

Unsaturated systems are different from electron deficient ones. In the former, an octet is achieved through multiple bonding. In the latter case, the Lewis diagram is properly written with less than an octet of electrons for certain atoms.

For molecules or ions involving atoms beyond row two of the periodic table, the octet rule does not necessarily apply. These larger atoms may acquire more than an octet of electrons. This is called **valence shell expansion,** and it is made possible by the availability of valence-level d orbitals on these atoms. Examples include PCl_5, BrF_3, and XeF_2

The extra electrons in these electron rich molecules are always assigned to atoms of rows three and beyond. This is because these elements are larger and can accommodate the extra electrons by use of d orbitals.

In a preliminary fashion, we might also mention here the coordination compounds, which feature a central metal bonded to other groups. The groups that are bonded to the central metal are called ligands. Examples of coordination compounds are $Ni(CO)_4$, $[Co(NH_3)_6]^{3+}$, and $Pt(NH_3)_2Cl_2$. The Lewis diagrams for simple coordination compounds of the transition metals may be written without taking into consideration the presence of the $(n - 1)d$ electrons of the metal. The bonds are considered to be **coordinate covalent bonds** in which both electrons of the metal–ligand bond are supplied by the ligand. The ligands are considered to be simply **Lewis bases** (electron pair donors), and the metal centers are considered to be **Lewis acids** (electron pair acceptors). The octet rule does not apply. Instead, the ligands add enough electrons to those of the metal to bring the total for the metal to that of the next noble gas—18 valence electrons in all. Hence the octet rule is replaced by the **18-electron rule** because of the additional 10 electrons of the d orbitals in any transition series. Some examples of coordination compounds that obey the 18-

electron rule are $Ni(CO)_4$, $[Co(NH_3)_6]^{3+}$, and *cis*-$Pt(Cl)_2(NH_3)_2$

In each case the metal electrons are not listed in the Lewis diagram, but they are counted towards the 18 electron total. It should also be noted that many transition metal compounds have other than the closed shell, 18 electron total, and still they are perfectly stable. We shall have more to say about this in later chapters. For now it is interesting to note that the octet rule finds only limited application, being replaced by the 18-electron rule when considering the coordination compounds formed by metals.

Resonance

In many of the Lewis diagrams that were written previously, it would have been possible to have arranged the electrons about the fixed nuclei in different (but still perfectly proper) ways. In fact the Lewis description of the bonding in a molecule is not complete until all contributing possibilities have been written down. The overall result is delocalization of electrons within the structure through the recognition that other Lewis diagrams may be equally valid. This is **resonance,** and it is equivalent to the molecular orbital concept of delocalization. Contributing resonance forms for the molecules and ions that were discussed previously are given in Fig. 3-1.

Let us consider in detail the planar AB_3 systems such as BF_3, NO_3^-, and CO_3^{2-}. If we try to write a diagram for such a molecule or ion, in which each atom acquires an octet of electrons, we obtain structure 3-I:

3-I

This representation implies that there are two A—B single bonds and one A=B double bond, whereas, experimental data show conclusively that all A—B bonds and all B—A—B angles are equal. To bring theory and experiment into accord, the former is modified by the postulate that structure 3-I alone does not describe the actual molecule but is only one of three equivalent, hypothetical structures, 3-I to 3-III. The real molecule has an electron distribution corresponding to the average of these three contributing structures,

Figure 3-1 Resonance forms.

and is said to be a *resonance hybrid* of them. The double-headed arrow is used to indicate that the structures are mixing to give a resonance hybrid.

Care is required to avoid misinterpretation of the resonance concept. At no instant does the molecule actually have any one of the canonical structures. Each of these implies that one bond is stronger and thus presumably is shorter than the other two, whereas all three bonds are always entirely equivalent. The canonical structures have no real existence, in any way or sense, but their average corresponds to the actual structure.

The concept of resonance can be justified from an energy point of view. It can be shown that a resonance hybrid must have a lower energy, that is, be more stable, than any single contributing structure. This concept explains the fact that the molecule exists in the hybrid structure rather than any one of the contributing structures.

One particular type of resonance requires special mention, namely, *ionic–covalent resonance*. We pointed out in Section 2-7 that a bond between unlike atoms (A—B) is always more or less stronger than the average of the A—A and B—B bond strengths. This was used for calculating electronegativity differences, on the basis that an ionic or polar contribution to the bond made it stronger than the purely covalent bond alone. Actually, the situation is a little different, because it is resonance rather than simple additivity that Pauling invoked to account for the extra bond energy.

If A is more electronegative than B, the A—B bond can be represented by a resonance hybrid of structures 3-IVa and 3-IVb.

$$A—B \longleftrightarrow \; :\overset{\cdot\cdot}{\underset{\cdot\cdot}{A}}: \; ^-B^+$$

$$\text{3-IVa} \qquad \text{3-IVb}$$

As we explained, the actual A—B bond will then (1) combine the properties of both contributing structures, and (2) be more stable than either one alone. Thus, the actual A—B bond will be polar to an extent depending on how much structure 3-IVb contributes to the average structure. The increased strength of the bond, when it is compared with the strength expected for a purely covalent bond, will be proportional to the square of the electronegativity difference, since it is that difference which determines the importance of structure 3-IVb compared with structure 3-IVa.

When the Lewis diagram for a molecule or complex ion has been written correctly, one has accounted for all of the atoms and valence electrons of the structure. There is more, though, that needs to be known about the bonding in these structures. If an electron pair bond involves sharing of electrons between atoms, then how is this sharing accomplished? Which orbitals are involved on the two atoms, and which orbitals in the molecule? Why does the sharing of the electrons in a bond lead to stability? What geometry should one assign to the molecule overall, and what particular bond angles and lengths result? Obviously a wide variety of bond angles occur, not just the 90° angle at which the atomic p orbitals are disposed on any one atom. It quickly becomes apparent that atomic orbitals must be modified in such a way as to allow for the correct angles in molecules. Just as was true for atoms, orbitals must be provided for each electron, whether it is a member of a lone pair or a bonding pair. These orbitals (and the lone and bonding pairs that they house) must be arranged about each atom in the correct orientations, namely, those that are in agreement with geometry. An approach powerful enough to allow geometry to be predicted is what we seek.

In the localized bond approach, the answers to the questions just posed are obtained by employing the **hybridization** and **Valence Shell Electron Pair Repulsion** theories. It is assumed that bonding arises because of the overlap of orbitals (a concept that will be reinforced with molecular orbital theory), and that the proper set of orbitals for any atom in the structure can be deduced by knowing the number of groups (atoms plus lone pairs), which occupy the space around that particular atom. Let us begin the discussion with the simplest case, linear BeH_2.

Hybridization

In BeH_2, for example, it is perfectly satisfactory, for nearly any purpose, to consider that there is one electron pair localized between each adjacent pair of atoms. Thus, we have the simple, familiar representation, H:Be:H. An electron pair bond of the type indicated can be thought of as arising from the overlap of two orbitals, one from each of the atoms bonded, with the electrons concentrated in the region of overlap between the atoms. In the case of BeH_2, which is linear, this raises the question of how to account for the linearity. In answering that question, two new concepts, the valence state and hybridization, are introduced.

The beryllium atom has the electron configuration $1s^2 2s^2$. Thus its valence shell has only one occupied orbital and the electrons are paired. On the other hand, if it is to form two bonds, by sharing one electron with each of two other atoms, it must first be put into a state where each electron is in a different orbital, and each spin is uncoupled from the other and, thus, ready to be paired with the spin of an electron on the atom to which the bond is to be formed. When it is in this condition, the atom is said to be in a valence state.

For the particular case of BeH_2, the valence state of lowest energy is obtained by promoting one of the electrons from the $2s$ orbital to one of the $2p$ orbitals, and decoupling their spins. This requires the expenditure of about 323 kJ mol^{-1}.

Although the promotion of the Be atom to the valence state prepares it to form the two bonds to the H atoms, it does not provide an explanation or a reason why the molecule should be linear, rather than bent. The $2s$ orbital of Be has the same amplitude in all directions. Therefore, whichever of the $2p$ orbitals is used to form one Be—H bond, the other bond in which the $2s$ orbital is used could make any angle with it, insofar as overlap of the H $1s$ and Be $2s$ orbitals is concerned. However, the preference for a linear structure can be attributed to the fact that if a $2s$ and $2p$ orbital are mixed so as to form two *hybrid* (i.e., mixed) orbitals, better total overlap with the H $1s$ orbitals can be obtained. The results of mixing the $2s$ and $2p_z$ orbitals are shown in Fig. 3-2.

Each of the hybrid orbitals has a large positive lobe concentrated in a

Figure 3-2 The formation of two equivalent sp hybrid orbitals from linear combinations of a $2s$ and a $2p_z$ atomic orbital. The dots on the z axis represent the position of the atom on which the hybrid is constructed. The two orientations of the hybrids ($180°$ with respect to one another) result from the different sign used in the two linear combinations.

particular direction and is, therefore, able to overlap very strongly with an orbital on another atom located at an appropriate distance in that direction. Actual calculations show that the extent of overlap thus obtained is greater than that obtainable by using either a pure $2s$ or pure $2p_z$ orbital. This is not difficult to see without calculation, if we note that only half of the p_z orbital is found in the $+z$ direction and only half in the $-z$ direction. The $2s$ orbital is uniformly distributed in all directions. The hybrid orbitals, however, are each strongly concentrated in just one direction.

The linearity of the BeH_2 molecule suggests the use of the hybrid orbitals. It can be seen from Fig. 3-2 that the sp hybrids are oriented in the $+z$ and $-z$ directions because of the spatial properties of the s and p orbitals themselves. The best Be to H overlaps are then obtained by placing the H atoms along the $+z$ and $-z$ axes, as is shown in Fig. 3-3. The correctness of sp hybridization for Be is affirmed by the known linearity of the molecule; the best geometry is the one that disperses the two bonding pairs as far from one another as possible: 180°.

The hybrid orbitals just described are called sp hybrids, to indicate that they are formed from one s orbital and from one p orbital. There are also other ways of mixing s and p orbitals to obtain hybrid orbitals. The element boron forms many compounds, among which are the simple BX_3 substances that aptly illustrate the next important case of hybridization.

The boron atom has a ground-state electron configuration, $1s^2 2s^2 2p$. To form three bonds it must first be promoted to a valence state based on a configuration $2s 2p_x 2p_y$, in which the three valence electrons have decoupled their spins. The choice of $2p_x$ and $2p_y$ is arbitrary; any two $2p$ orbitals would be satisfactory. The ability of the central atom to form three bonds is now taken care of, but the question of securing maximum overlap must be dealt with. Again, it develops straightforwardly that by mixing the s and the two p orbitals equally, hybrid orbitals, called sp^2 hybrids can be formed, and they give superior overlap in certain definite directions, as is shown in Fig. 3-4. The three hybrid orbitals lie in the xy plane, and their maxima lie along the lines that are 120° apart. Thus, the BX_3 molecules have a planar, triangular structure.

Figure 3-3   The formation of covalent bonds in BeH_2 by overlap of sp hybrid orbitals on Be with $1s$ atomic orbitals on H.

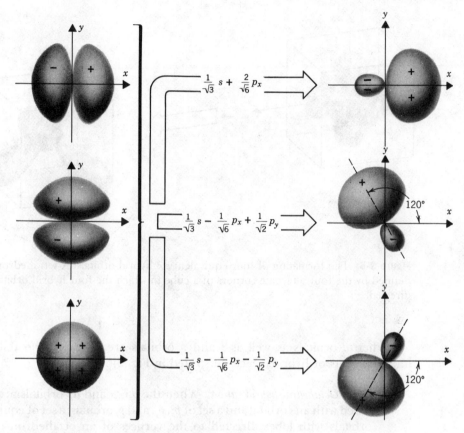

$$\frac{1}{\sqrt{3}} s + \frac{2}{\sqrt{6}} p_x$$

$$\frac{1}{\sqrt{3}} s - \frac{1}{\sqrt{6}} p_x + \frac{1}{\sqrt{2}} p_y$$

$$\frac{1}{\sqrt{3}} s - \frac{1}{\sqrt{6}} p_x - \frac{1}{\sqrt{2}} p_y$$

Figure 3-4 The formation of three equivalent sp^2 hybrid orbitals.

The next type of hybridization that we shall discuss is the last one in which only s and p orbitals are involved. Let us consider how the carbon atom combines with four hydrogen atoms to form methane. Again, promotion from a ground state ($1s^2 2s^2 2p^2$), which does not have a sufficient number of unpaired electrons, to the valence state ($2s2p_x2p_y2p_z$) is required first. Then the four orbitals of the valence state are mixed to give a set of four equivalent orbitals, each of which is called an sp^3 hybrid. This is shown in Fig. 3-5. The hybrid orbitals of the sp^3 set are directed towards the vertices of a tetrahedron. It should be realized that this geometry arises exclusively and directly from the algebra of hybridization. The geometry also happens to be that which most disperses the four C—H bonding pairs of electrons as far from one another as is possible.

In summary, an atom that has only s and p orbitals in its valence shell can form three types of hybrid orbitals, depending on the number of electrons available to form bonds:

sp hybrids give a linear molecule
sp^2 hybrids give a plane triangular molecule
sp^3 hybrids give a tetrahedral molecule

Figure 3-5   The formation of four equivalent sp^3 hybrid orbitals. A tetrahedron is defined by the four alternate corners of a cube to which the four hybrid orbitals are directed.

When d orbitals as well as s and p orbitals are available, the following important sets of hybrids, each illustrated in Fig. 3-6, can arise.

1. d^2sp^3, *Octahedral hybridization.* When the $d_{x^2-y^2}$ and d_{z^2} orbitals are combined with an s orbital and a set of p_x, p_y, and p_z orbitals, a set of equivalent orbitals with lobes directed to the vertices of an octahedron can be formed.

2. dsp^2, *Square-planar hybridization.* A $d_{x^2-y^2}$ orbital, an s orbital, and p_x and p_y orbitals can be combined to give a set of equivalent hybrid orbitals with lobes directed to the corners of a square in the xy plane.

3. sd^3, *Tetrahedral hybridization.* An s orbital and the set d_{xy}, d_{yz}, d_{zx} may be combined to give a tetrahedrally directed set of orbitals.

4. dsp^3, *Trigonal-bipyramidal hybridization.* The orbitals s, p_x, p_y, p_z, and d_{z^2} may be combined to give a nonequivalent set of five hybrid orbitals directed to the vertices of a trigonal bipyramid.

5. dsp^3, *Square-pyramidal hybridization.* The orbitals s, p_x, p_y, p_z, and $d_{x^2-y^2}$ may be combined to give a nonequivalent set of five hybrid orbitals directed to the vertices of a square pyramid.

The use of hybridized orbitals to explain bonding and correlate structures has become less common in recent years, giving way to the more general use of molecular orbital (MO) theory. The main reasons for this are that the MO approach lends itself more readily to quantitative calculations employing digital computers and because, with such calculations, it is possible to account for molecular spectra more easily. Nevertheless, the concept of hybrid orbitals retains certain advantages of simplicity and, in many instances, affords a very easy way to correlate and "explain" molecular structures.

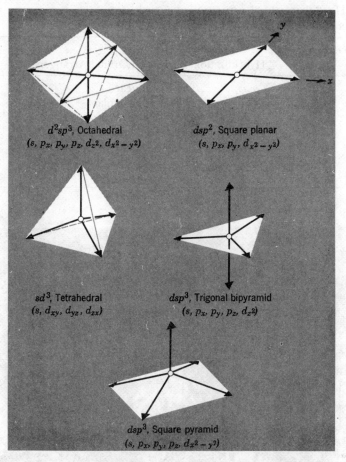

d^2sp^3, Octahedral
$(s, p_x, p_y, p_z, d_{z^2}, d_{x^2-y^2})$

dsp^2, Square planar
$(s, p_x, p_y, d_{x^2-y^2})$

sd^3, Tetrahedral
$(s, d_{xy}, d_{yz}, d_{zx})$

dsp^3, Trigonal bipyramid
$(s, p_x, p_y, p_z, d_{z^2})$

dsp^3, Square pyramid
$(s, p_x, p_y, p_z, d_{x^2-y^2})$

Figure 3-6 Five important hybridization schemes involving d orbitals. Arrows show the direction in which the hybrid orbitals point within each different set.

Valence Shell Electron Pair Repulsion (VSEPR) Theory

There is a very natural correlation between the hybridization that one chooses for an atom and the spatial requirements of the electrons (bonding pairs as well as lone pairs) that occupy the space surrounding that atom. Electron pairs, whether in bonds to other atoms or in lone-pair orbitals on the atom in question, will tend to stay as far apart from one another as possible, in order to minimize repulsions among the various pairs. The number of groups (bonded atoms or lone pairs), which must be accommodated about an atom determines the geometry (and hence, hybridization) at that atom, because the geometry is dictated by the need of each electron pair to have as great a distance as possible separating it and adjacent electron pairs. This broadly constitutes the approach of considering Valence Shell Electron Pair Repulsions (VSEPR), as developed principally by R. J. Gillespie. Once we know how many groups (atoms plus lone pairs) need to occupy the space around an atom, the best arrangement

Table 3-1   The Relationship between Occupancy $(x + y)$, Hybridization, and Geometry for the Structures AB_xE_y

Occupancy $(x + y)$	Hybridization	Hybrid Orbital Arrangement
Two	sp	Linear
Three	sp^2	Triangular
Four	sp^3, sd^3	Tetrahedral
	dsp^2	Square planar
Five	dsp^3	Square pyramidal
	dsp^3	Trigonal bipyramidal
Six	d^2sp^3	Octahedral

Figure 3-7   Idealized geometries for structures having the formulas AB_xE_y, where A is a central atom, B are peripheral atoms, and E are lone pairs residing on A.

of those groups can be deduced. Fine adjustments to structure can be explained by the greater repulsions associated with lone pairs. The lone pairs are considered to require more room at an atom (and are more repulsive towards other groups at that atom) because they are restricted by the charge of only one nucleus.

For purposes of accounting, it is convenient to define a quantity known as the occupancy for an atom. For structures AB_xE_y (where A is the central atom), x is the number of other atoms B bound to A, and y is the number of lone electron pairs, E, residing on atom A. The sum $(x + y)$ is what we shall call, for want of a better word, the **occupancy** of atom A. The space surrounding atom A is said to be *occupied* by $(x + y)$ other atoms or lone pairs. The occupancy of N in $:NH_3$ is four, for example. The occupancy for an atom is defined so that it is independent of the presence of multiple bonds; whether atoms B are singly or multiply bonded to atom A, each B still occupies only one position in the space surrounding atom A.

In Table 3-1 are listed the occupancies (atoms plus lone pairs) and the corresponding geometries that best minimize electron pair repulsions for each situation. Those hybridizations of the central atom that give a particular geometry are also listed. In Fig. 3-7 are shown the first-approximation shapes for the various molecules AB_xE_y. For the formulas AB_2, AB_3, AB_4, AB_5, and AB_6, in which there are no lone pairs, the molecular shapes are regular polyhedra: linear (AB_2), trigonal planar (AB_3), tetrahedral (AB_4), trigonal bipyramidal (AB_5), and octahedral (AB_6). Subgroups of these regular geometries are obtained for formulas with lone pairs, E, at the central atom. Although the positions of the lone pairs are specified, the geometry of the molecules is defined by the positions of the atoms A and B only. Thus for the formula AB_3E the four sp^3 hybrid orbitals of atom A are arranged roughly in the shape of a tetrahedron, but the molecule is said to be pyramidal. The following are specific examples of each structural type. The student should refer to Figs. 3-8 to 3-12.

Examples

AB_2

BeH$_2$. This molecule has been discussed previously. It only remains to point out that the unhybridized p orbitals on Be are perpendicular to the molecular axis as well as to one another.

CO$_2$. The central carbon is sp hybridized, as shown in Fig. 3-8, and the molecule is linear. The unhybridized p orbitals of carbon are involved in π-bonding with the atomic p orbitals of oxygen, as shown in Fig. 3-13. The two π bond systems are perpendicular to one another because the unhybridized atomic p orbitals of carbon are oriented 90° to one another. The π bonds each involve two regions of overlap (above and below the O—C—O bond axis). The σ bond system involves overlap of sp hybrids on carbon with sp^2 hybrids on oxygen. The σ bond system lies along the internuclear axis of the molecule, while the π bond system has a node along the internuclear axis. The azide anion N_3^- is completely analogous to CO_2.

AB₂

1. H—Be—H   ∠ HBeH = 180°

2. Ö=C=Ö   *sp* hybridized C
                       ∠ OCO = 180°

3. [N̈=N=N̈]⁻   *sp* hybridized central N
                       ∠ NNN = 180°

ABE

1. :C≡O: *sp* hybridized C and O

2. [:C≡N:]⁻

Figure 3-8 Examples of *sp* hybridization in structures AB$_x$E$_y$ where occupancy $(x + y) = 2$.

AB₃

$$\left[\begin{array}{c} \ddot{O} \quad \ddot{O} \\ C \\ :\ddot{O}: \end{array}\right]^{2-}$$

↕

$$\left[\begin{array}{c} \ddot{O} \quad \ddot{O} \\ C \\ :\ddot{O}: \end{array}\right]^{2-}$$ *sp²* hybridized C
                                    ∠ OCO = 120°

↕

$$\left[\begin{array}{c} \ddot{O} \quad \ddot{O} \\ C \\ :\ddot{O}: \end{array}\right]^{2-}$$

ABE₂

$$\begin{array}{c} H_3C \\ \quad \quad C=\ddot{O}: \\ H_3C \end{array}$$ *sp²* hybridized O

AB₂E

$$\left[\begin{array}{c} \ddot{N} \\ :\ddot{O} \quad \ddot{O}: \end{array}\right]^{-}$$

↕

$$\left[\begin{array}{c} \ddot{N} \\ :\ddot{O} \quad \ddot{O}: \end{array}\right]^{-}$$ *sp²* hybridized N
                                    ∠ ONO = 115°

Figure 3-9 Examples of *sp²* hybridization in structures AB$_x$E$_y$ where occupancy $(x + y) = 3$.

AB₄ sp^3 hybridized N
$\angle$ CNC = 109°

AB₃E sp^3 hybridized P
$\angle$ CPC = 99°

AB₂E₂ sp^3 hybridized O
$\angle$ HOH = 104°

ABE₃   [H₃C—Ö:]⁻ sp^3 hybridized O
(although see text)

Figure 3-10 Examples of sp^3 hybridization in structures AB_xE_y where occupancy $(x + y) = 4$.

ABE

CO. Carbon monoxide contains a triple bond: one σ and two mutually perpendicular π bonds. There is a lone pair of electrons on each atom, housed in an sp hybrid. The π bond system is illustrated in Fig. 3-13. It is sp hybridization that leaves two p atomic orbitals available on both C and O for the formation of these π bonds. Other examples that are **isostructural** (have the same structures) and **isoelectronic** (have the same electron configurations) are the ions CN⁻ and NO⁺.

AB₅ dsp^3 hybridized P
$\angle$ ClPCl = 120° in the equatorial plane

AB₄E   181°   103° dsp^3 hybridized S

AB₃E₂   87° dsp^3 hybridized Cl

AB₂E₃ dsp^3 hybridized I

Figure 3-11 Examples of dsp^3 hybridization in structures AB_xE_y where occupancy $(x + y) = 5$.

AB$_6$ d^2sp^3 hybridized S

AB$_5$E d^2sp^3 hybridized Br

AB$_4$E$_2$ d^2sp^3 hybridized I

AB$_3$E$_3$ d^2sp^3 hybridized Xe

AB$_2$E$_4$ d^2sp^3 hybridized Xe

Figure 3-12 Examples of d^2sp^3 hybridization in structures AB$_x$E$_y$ where occupancy $(x + y) = 6$.

For both systems described, namely, cases AB$_2$ and ABE, the atoms or lone pairs that occupy the space about an atom are disposed 180° from one another. This is because only two groups must be accommodated at the atom in question, that is, occupancy [the quantity $(x + y)$ in the cases AB$_x$E$_y$] is two. Linear geometry and sp hybridization always result under these circumstances. Other examples include alkynes (—C≡C—), nitriles (R—C≡N:), isonitriles (R—N≡C:), metal carbonyls (M—C≡O:), and cyanate (:N≡C—O⁻).

AB$_3$
CO$_3$$^{2-}$. The sp^2 hybridization of carbon in the carbonate ion allows for the use of one unhybridized p atomic orbital on carbon in the formation of one π bond. As shown for each resonance form in Fig. 3-9, π bonding can take place between the central carbon and any one of the three equivalent oxygen atoms, and three resonance forms are required to show this delocalization of the one π bond. For any one resonance form, the π bond is illustrated in Fig. 3-13. The ion has trigonal-planar geometry; the oxygen atoms are dispersed 120° with respect to one another in order to minimize repulsions among the electrons of the C—O bonds. This geometry is typical of other structures (e.g., BF$_3$ and SO$_3$) having occupancies of three for the central atoms. In the examples that follow, however, because of the presence of lone pairs, E, or nonequivalent substituents, B, the perfect 120° angles are not observed.

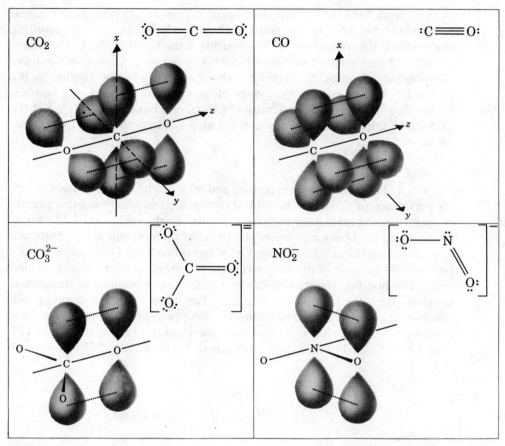

Figure 3-13 Examples of the formation of π bonds via overlap of unhybridized (atomic) p orbitals.

Carbonyls. For organic carbonyls such as $R_2C{=}O$, or for the acyls $R(X)C{=}O$ and the formyls $H_2C{=}O$, $X_2C{=}O$, and $M{-}C(H){=}O$ (a metal formyl), the carbon atom can be taken to be sp^2 hybridized, with occupancy equal to three. The groups that are bound to the central carbon are nonequivalent, and the idealized geometry of 120° is altered due to repulsions among the bonding electrons at carbon. Consider the formyls $H_2C{=}O$ and $X_2C{=}O$ shown in structures 3-V:

$$116° \qquad\qquad 111° \qquad\qquad 108°$$
$$\text{3-Va} \qquad\qquad \text{3-Vb} \qquad\qquad \text{3-Vc}$$

The electrons of the $C{=}O$ double bond require the greatest room in these structures. As a result, the HCH and XCX bond angles collapse from the normal 120° for sp^2 hybridization to those values listed in structures 3-V. Repulsions from the $C = O$ double-bond system become balanced by repulsions between the electrons of the two C—H or C—X bonds, and the resulting angles reflect the willingness of the electrons of the C—H or the C—X groups to approach one another in either $H_2C = O$ or $X_2C = O$. Obviously the more electronegative groups, X, allow for a closer approach to one another by the groups C—X. This occurs because the electron density in the C—X bonds is farther out towards the X extremities of the C—X bond (and collapse of the XCX bond angle is less troublesome) for atoms X with the higher electronegativities.

AB₂E

NO₂⁻. The nitrite anion is planar, and sp^2 hybridization is consistent with the occupancy of three for the central nitrogen atom. One π bond is present in each of the contributing resonance forms. As shown in Fig. 3-13, this π-bond system lies above and below the plane of the ion, and is perpendicular to it. Although the central nitrogen is sp^2 hybridized, the ONO angle is not a perfect 120° because of the larger volume requirement of the lone-pair electrons. The bonding electron pairs move closer to one another in response to repulsion from the lone pair of nitrogen. The larger lone-pair–bonding-pair repulsion is balanced by the less intense bonding-pair–bonding-pair interaction once the ONO angle has collapsed from the idealized 120° to the actual 115° found in the ion. This is shown in structure 3-VIa. Removal of one electron

| 115° | 132° | |
| 3-VIa | 3-VIb | 3-VIc |

from the nitrite anion gives the neutral radical NO_2, shown in structure 3-VIb. Here the ONO angle opens to the value 132° because only a lone electron, not a pair, is housed on the nitrogen. Now the most severe repulsion is between the electrons of the NO bonds, and the ONO angle can become larger without encountering restrictions from a full lone pair of electrons on nitrogen. For the cation, NO_2^+, the central nitrogen has occupancy equal to two, and as shown in structure 3-VIc, the geometry is linear.

ABE₂

Simple examples in this category include O_2 and NO^-. Otherwise, we must look to terminal atoms for more examples.

It is not necessary to specify a hybridization for terminal atoms. Whatever the bonding scheme, the geometry is linear by definition. The presence of lone pairs can be inferred from the Lewis diagrams, and the presence of single or multiple bonds can be inferred from the length of the bond. There are terminal atoms, though, where it is instructive to examine the hybridization, and such a case is the terminal oxygen of a carbonyl group in aldehydes or ketones. The occupancy formula for such an oxygen atom is ABE₂, and a double bond to C is typical. The hybridization of such an oxygen is said to be sp^2, and two of these hybrid orbitals are used to house the two lone pairs on oxygen. The other sp^2 hybrid forms a σ bond to carbon by overlap with an sp^2 hybrid from carbon. The σ bond to carbon and the two lone pairs of oxygen lie in a plane, and the π bond is perpendicular to this plane, above and below it. It is not necessary or proper to speak of the geometry at such a terminal atom, because it lies on the periphery of the molecule. It is helpful, though, to realize that the method of determining occupancy gives a hybridization that is consistent with the number of π bonds to the atom.

AB₄

In addition to the wide numbers of organic compounds having sp^3 hybridized carbon, there are important AB₄ examples among inorganic systems where the occupancy is also four. The best examples are the tetraoxides of the main group elements (general formula AO_4^{n-}) and the tetracoordinated compounds of the transition metals that contain a central metal and four ligands [e.g., $Ni(CO)_4$]. The geometry for main group atoms A is always tetrahedral. When A is a transition metal, the ligands can be arranged either in tetrahedral fashion (sp^3 hybridization) or in square-planar fashion (dsp^2 hybridization), as shown in Fig. 3-7 and in Table 3-1. It is the number of d electrons that determines which of these two geometries is preferred, although the d electrons are not considered in writing the Lewis diagram. More will be said about this in subsequent chapters. For now, we shall restrict our attention to the oxy anions AO_4^{n-} and the transition metal systems ML_4^{n+}.

AO_4^{n-}. The familiar ions phosphate (PO_4^{3-}), sulfate (SO_4^{2-}), and perchlorate (ClO_4^-) are isostructural and isoelectronic. The central atom is tetrahedrally surrounded by four oxygen atoms and an octet is achieved for all atoms in the ions when single bonds are used exclusively. As has already been shown for SO_4^{2-} in Fig. 3-1, there can be additional π bonding that increases the electron density at the central atom. This π bonding involves the use of empty d orbitals on the central atom, as shown in Fig. 3-14. Former lone pair electrons of oxygen are shared with the central atom through $d\pi$–$p\pi$ overlap. This requires a rehybridization of the terminal oxygens from sp^3 (A—O groups) to sp^2 (A=O groups). The terminal oxygen atoms are said to be π donors and the central atom A is said to be a π acceptor. The double-bond system is most

Figure 3-14 $d\pi$–$p\pi$ bonding. An empty d orbital on a central atom accepts electron density from a filled p orbital of another atom.

evident when the central atom has the highest electronegativity, e.g., ClO_4^-. $d\pi$–$p\pi$ bonding for elements of rows three and below of the periodic table is prominent because of the presence of valence-level d orbitals on these atoms. For rows one and two of the periodic table, the d orbitals are not in the valence levels, and are consequently too high in energy to be of use in bonding.

The availability of empty d orbitals also plays a role in the chemistries of third-row compounds, as illustrated by two examples with this same structure, AB_4. Both CCl_4 and the corresponding third-row compound of silicon, $SiCl_4$, are tetrahedral, with sp^3 hybridized central atoms. The carbon analog is stable towards attack by simple nucleophiles such as water, while the Si compound is not. The empty d orbitals in the valence shell of Si provide the needed site for nucleophilic attack, and the larger size of the central Si atom facilitates the hydrolysis shown in Eq. 3-2.1:

$$SiCl_4 + 4\ ROH \longrightarrow Si(OR)_4 + 4\ HCl \qquad (3\text{-}2.1)$$

One could add to the discussion of structures AB_4 the silicates, SiO_4^{4-}, and the tetrahedral XeO_4 that complete the isoelectronic series of tetraoxides of row three. It is more common, though, for silicate structures to occur in polymeric form (as discussed in Chapter 15) rather than as discrete anions. Xenon tetraoxide is an explosively unstable gas.

ML_4^{n+}. Transition metal compounds that are four coordinate may adopt either tetrahedral or square-planar geometry, depending on the number of d electrons that reside at the metal. Square-planar geometry is common for d^8 systems such as in structures 3-VIIa and 3-VIIb:

3-VIIa   3-VIIb

Tetrahedral geometry is found for d^{10} systems as in structures 3-VIIIa and 3-VIIIb:

3-VIIIa   3-VIIIb

AB₃E

Of the structures with occupancy four and one lone pair, the most familiar are the amines (:NR_3), the phosphines (:PR_3), the arsines (:AsR_3), and the stibines (:SbR_3). All are pyramidal, and can serve as Lewis bases by reason of the one lone pair on the central atom. In fact, these compounds serve as useful ligands for coordination to metals. The halides (e.g., :NX_3) should also be considered here.

As a class, the molecules may be taken to have sp^3 hybridized central atoms and roughly pyramidal molecular geometries. The lone pair of electrons causes deviations from the ideal 109.5° angles expected for perfect sp^3 hybrid sets. The HAH angle is smallest in the molecules :AH_3 where the central atom, A, is the largest:

| ∠ HNH = 107° | ∠ HPH = 94° | ∠ HAsH = 92° | ∠ HSbH = 91° |
| 3-IXa | 3-IXb | 3-IXc | 3-IXd |

The XAX angle is smallest in the molecules :AX_3 where the atoms X are most electronegative:

| ∠ ClNCl = 107° | ∠ FNF = 102° | ∠ ClPCl = 100° | ∠ FPF = 98° |
| 3-Xa | 3-Xb | 3-Xc | 3-Xd |

Presumably the A—X bonding electrons are polarized towards the electronegative atoms, X, so that collapse of the XAX angle is less troublesome where X is more electronegative.

The angles noted in structures 3-Xa to 3-Xd may indicate that the choice of sp^3 hybridization is inappropriate for some of the examples given. After all, angles close to 90° may indicate, if anything, a lack of hybridization for the central atoms Sb and As. The fully delocalized MO treatment, presented later in this chapter, offers a more satisfactory explanation of the bonding in such systems.

AB₂E₂

This familiar case includes the dihydrides of Group VIB(16) H_2O, H_2S, H_2Se, and H_2Te as shown in structures 3-XIa to 3-XId.

Ö	S̈	S̈e	T̈e
H⌣H	H⌣H	H⌣H	H⌣H
104°	92°	91°	90°
3-XIa	3-XIb	3-XIc	3-XId

The two lone pairs provide the most severe repulsions, and the ex that they require in order to minimize this repulsion is achieved by a decrease in the HAH angle. This is most readily accomplished for the larger central atoms Se and Te. In the later cases it is inappropriate to consider that the central atom is simply sp^3 hybridized. Other cases where this AB_2E_2 structure arises include the alcohols (ROH) and ethers (ROR).

ABE_3

It is unnecessary and inappropriate to assign a hybridization for a "central" atom such as A in the case ABE_3. It is not possible, nor is it necessary, to know the positions of the lone electron pairs. It is certain that the electron pairs are as far from one another as is possible, but it is a matter of theory, not fact, to speculate about the orbital arrangement for those electrons. (In contrast, it is possible to speak with authority about the positions of atoms.) Nevertheless, we have grown accustomed to speaking of the oxygen of alkoxides, RO^-, as being sp^3 hybridized, for instance, because this does provide maximum room for each of the three lone pairs of oxygen. It also correctly accounts for the single remaining bond to carbon in the octet of oxygen. One must examine the energy of the entire ion (including three electron pairs somewhat localized on the oxygen and a bonding pair somewhat localized between the carbon and the oxygen) before deciding if the best bond between oxygen and carbon is provided by overlap of two sp^3 hybrid orbitals. In short, a more delocalized bonding theory may prove better.

AB_5

This case begins the series in Fig. 3-11 in which the occupancy at a central atom is five. Where no lone-pair electrons reside at the central atom [PCl_5, $Fe(CO)_5$, or $CuCl_5^{3-}$], the geometry is a perfect trigonal bipyramid. As illustrated in structure 3-XII:

3-XII

the two axial positions in this polyhedron are not equivalent to the three equatorial ones. The **axial** groups are positioned above and below the triangular plane, while the three **equatorial** groups are positioned in the triangular plane. As shown in Figs. 3-6 and 3-7, it is one form of dsp^3 hybridization that gives this orbital arrangement.

An occupancy of five is also accommodated by square-pyramidal geometry and the other type of dsp^3 hybridization. In this case, however, it is the $d_{x^2-y^2}$ orbital that is required, as shown in Fig. 3-6. An interesting example of this geometrical difference is given by the compounds studied by R. R. Holmes and shown in structures 3-XIIIa and 3-XIIIb:

3-XIIIa

3-XIIIb

The Si atom of structure 3-XIIIa is at the center of a square pyramid, while that of structure 3-XIIIb is trigonal bipyramidal.

AB₄E

SF_4 has the structure given in Fig. 3-11. This structure is derived from that of the trigonal bipyramid, with the lone electron pair of S occupying an equatorial position. This structure is preferred because there is a close ~90° interaction between this lone pair and only two axial bonding pairs. The other bonding pairs are at a relatively distant 128°. Had the lone electron pair of S been put into an axial position, there would have been three close 90° interactions with bonding pairs in the equatorial positions. This would clearly be less stable.

AB₃E₂

ClF_3 has the distorted planar T-shape shown in Fig. 3-11. The axial FClF angle is not 180° because the two equatorial lone pairs push the two axial fluorines back from their formal positions.

AB₂E₃

The ICl_2^- ion is linear. Axial placement of the two chlorines allows the three lone pairs of I to be accommodated in the relatively "roomy" equatorial plane.

AB₆

Lastly, we consider the cases with occupancies of six and d^2sp^3 hybridization. The AB_6 system is represented by a host of transition metal compounds with octahedral or pseudooctahedral geometries, and further examples will be given in the following chapters. SF_6 is a good example of a main group nonmetal compound with octahedral geometry.

AB₅E

The lone pair on Br in BrF_5 gives the molecule a square-pyramidal geometry although the orbital arrangement is still roughly that of an octahedron. Unlike the trigonal bipyramid, all positions on the octahedron are equivalent, and placement of the lone pair is not an issue. This is not true of the next example, however.

AB₄E₂

The ion ICl_4^- is planar because two lone pairs on the central iodine are placed opposite (180°) one another. The other possibility is less stable because it would involve placement of lone pairs at 90° to one another.

AB₃E₃

The ion $[XeF_3]^+$ is T-shaped.

AB₂E₄

Xenon difluoride is a linear molecule with four equatorial lone pairs at the central Xe atom. The only other possible geometry for such a system with occupancy six would be to place the two fluorine atoms adjacent to one another on the octahedron, giving a bent molecule. This latter case is less favored because it results in one lone pair having three 90° interactions with other lone pairs. The existing structure is one in which each lone pair only suffers two such close (90°) interactions with other lone pairs.

3-3   Bond Lengths and Covalent Radii

If we consider a single bond between like atoms, say Cl—Cl, we can define the single-bond covalent radius of the atom as half of the bond length. Thus the Cl—Cl distance, 1.988 Å yields a covalent radius of 0.99 Å for the chlorine atom. In a similar way, radii for other atoms (e.g., 0.77 for carbon by taking one half the C—C bond length in diamond) are obtained. It is then gratifying to find that the lengths of heteronuclear bonds can often be predicted with useful accuracy. For example, from Table 3-2 we can predict the following bond lengths, in Angstroms, which agree pretty well with the measured values given in parentheses:

C—Si	1.94 (1.87)	P—Cl	2.09 (2.04)
C—Cl	1.76 (1.77)	Cl—Br	2.13 (2.14)

The agreement is not perfect, and that cannot be expected, since bond properties (including length) vary somewhat with the environment.

Multiple bonds are always shorter than corresponding single bonds. This is illustrated by bonds between nitrogen atoms:

$$N≡N \ (1.10 \ Å) \qquad N=N \ (1.25 \ Å) \qquad N—N \ (1.45 \ Å)$$

Consequently, double- and triple-bond radii can also be defined. For the elements C, N, and O, which form most of the multiple bonds, the double- and triple-bond radii are approximately 0.87 and 0.78 times the single-bond radii, respectively.

Table 3-2   Single-Bond Covalent Radii (in Angstroms)

H	0.28	C	0.77	N	0.70	O	0.66	F	0.64
		Si	1.17	P	1.10	S	1.04	Cl	0.99
		Ge	1.22	As	1.21	Se	1.17	Br	1.14
		Sn	1.40	Sb	1.41	Te	1.37	I	1.33

The hybridization of an atom affects its covalent radius; since s orbitals are more contracted than p orbitals, the radius decreases with increasing s character. For carbon we have the following single-bond radii:

$$C(sp^3), 0.77 \text{ Å} \qquad C(sp^2), 0.73 \text{ Å} \qquad C(sp), 0.70 \text{ Å}$$

When there is a great difference in the electronegativities (Section 2-7) of two atoms, the bond length is usually less than the sum of the covalent radii, sometimes by a considerable amount. Thus, from Table 3-2, the C—F and Si—F distances are calculated to be 1.44 and 1.81 Å, whereas the actual distances in CF_4 and SiF_4 are 1.32 and 1.54 Å. In the case of the C—F bond it is believed that the shortening can be attributed to ionic–covalent resonance, which strengthens and, hence, shortens (by 0.12 Å) the bond. For SiF_4 only part of the very pronounced shortening can be thus explained. Much of it is thought to be due to π bonding using filled fluorine $p\pi$ and empty silicon $d\pi$ orbitals.

3-4   Molecular Packing; van der Waals Radii

When molecules pack together in the liquid and solid states, their approach to one another is limited by short-range repulsive forces, which result from overlapping of the diffuse outer regions of the electron clouds around the atoms.

The actual distance apart at which any two molecules would come to rest is determined by the equalization of attractive and repulsive forces. There are also weak, short-range attractive forces between molecules which result from permanent dipoles, dipole–induced dipole, and so-called London forces. The latter arise from interaction between fluctuating dipoles whose time-average value in any one molecule is zero.

Collectively, all these attractive and repulsive forces that are neither ionic nor covalent are called *van der Waals forces*.

It develops that both the attractive and repulsive forces are of roughly constant magnitude over the vast majority of molecules and thus the distances between molecules in condensed phases do not vary a great deal. As a result it is possible to compile a list of van der Waals radii, which give the typical internuclear distances between nearest neighbor atoms in different molecules in condensed phases. van der Waals radii for some common atoms are listed in Table 3-3.

van der Waals radii are far greater than covalent radii and are roughly constant for isoelectronic species. Thus, in crystalline Br_2, the covalent radius of Br is 1.15 Å, whereas the van der Waals radius (half the shortest inter-

Table 3-3   van der Waals Radii of Nonmetallic Atoms (in Angstroms)

H	1.1–1.3						He	1.40
N	1.5	O	1.40	F	1.35		Ne	1.54
P	1.9	S	1.85	Cl	1.80		Ar	1.92
As	2.0	Se	2.00	Br	1.95		Kr	1.98
Sb	2.2	Te	2.20	I	2.15		Xe	2.18

Radius of a methyl group, 2.0 Å
Half-thickness of an aromatic ring, 1.85 Å

molecular Br $\cdots$ Br distance) is 1.95 Å. The latter differs little from the Kr $\cdots$ Kr packing distance of 1.98 Å in solid krypton, since Br when bonded to another atom is isoelectronic with the Kr atom.

3-5   The Delocalized Approach to Bonding. Molecular Orbital Theory

The description of the chemical bond from the standpoint of molecular orbital theory involves the simple and broadly applicable idea that a chemical bond can exist when outer orbitals on different atoms overlap so as to concentrate electron density between the atomic cores. As a qualitative guide to whether bonding will actually occur, the criterion of net positive overlap of atomic orbitals is of unparalleled usefulness. Consequently, the examination of these overlaps will be our first consideration.

Overlap of Orbitals

If two atoms approach each other closely enough for one orbital on each atom to have appreciable amplitude in a region of space common to both of them, the orbitals are said to overlap. The magnitude of the overlap may be positive, negative, or zero, according to the properties of the orbitals concerned. Examples of these three cases are illustrated in Fig. 3-15.

Overlap has a positive sign when the superimposed regions of the two orbitals have the same sign, both + or both −. Overlap has a negative sign when the superimposed regions of the two orbitals have opposite signs. Precisely zero overlap results when there are precisely equal regions of overlap with opposite signs.

The physical reason for the validity of the overlap criterion is straightforward. In a region where two orbitals, ϕ_1 and ϕ_2, have positive overlap, the electron density is higher than the mere sum of the electron densities of the two separate orbitals. That is, $(\phi_1 + \phi_2)^2$ is greater than $\phi_1^2 + \phi_2^2$, by $2\phi_1\phi_2$. More electron density is shared between the two atoms. The attraction of both nuclei for these electrons is greater than the mutual repulsion of the nuclei, and a net attractive force or bonding interaction therefore results.

This is shown in Fig. 3-16 for the H_2^+ ion. The full light lines (1) show the electron distributions in the $1s$ orbitals for each atom, ϕ_A^2 and ϕ_B^2. The light dash line (2) shows the simple sum of these, $\phi_A^2 + \phi_B^2$. If these two orbitals are brought together with the same sign, they give a positive overlap and the

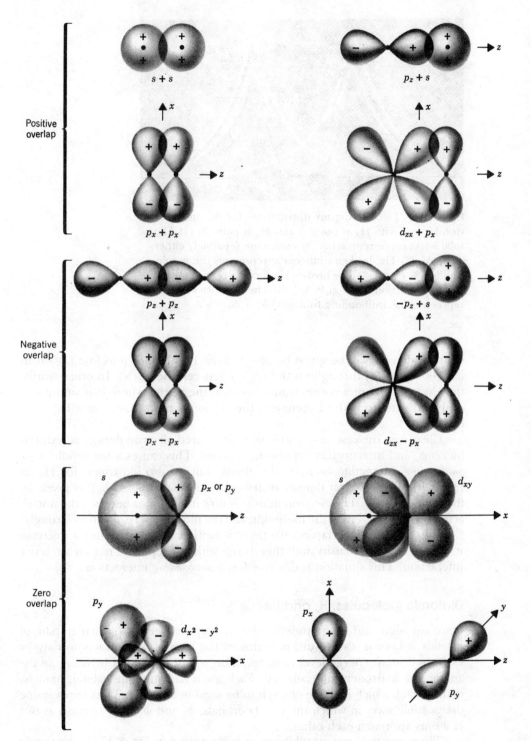

Figure 3-15 Some common types of orbital interaction leading to positive, negative, and zero overlap.

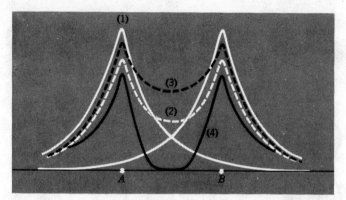

Figure 3-16 Electron density distributions for the one-electron H_2^+ ion, with H_A at point A and H_B at point B. (1) The solid white curve represents for each atom separately either ϕ_A^2 or ϕ_B^2. (2) The broken white curve represents the simple sum $(\phi_A^2 + \phi_B^2)/2$. (3) The broken black curve represents the bonding function $(\phi_A + \phi_B)^2/\sqrt{2}$. (4) The solid black curve represents the antibonding function $(\phi_A - \phi_B)^2/\sqrt{2}$.

electron density will be given by $(\phi_A + \phi_B)^2$. This is shown as line (3) which lies above line (2) throughout the region between the nuclei. In other words, the electron becomes concentrated between the nuclei where it is simultaneously attracted to both of them and the H_2^+ ion is more stable than $H^+ + H$ or $H + H^+$.

Clearly, in the case of negative overlap, shared electron density is reduced by $2\phi_1\phi_2$ and internuclear repulsion increases. This causes a net repulsive or *antibonding* interaction between the atoms. This is also illustrated for H_2^+ in Fig. 3-16. The electron density distribution given by $(\phi_A - \phi_B)^2$ is given by the solid curve (4). The electron density is now much lower between the nuclei, actually reaching zero at the midpoint, and the nuclei repel each other strongly.

When the net overlap is zero there is neither an increase nor a decrease in shared electron density and, therefore, neither a repulsive nor an attractive interaction. This situation is described as a *nonbonding* interaction.

Diatomic Molecules. H_2 and He_2

Once the sign and magnitude of the overlap between a particular pair of orbitals is known, the result, in terms of the energy of interaction, may be expressed in an energy-level diagram. This is best explained by using an example, the hydrogen molecule, H_2. Each atom has only one orbital, namely, its $1s$ orbital, which is stable enough to be used in bonding. Thus we examine the possible ways in which the two $1s$ orbitals, ϕ_1 and ϕ_2, may overlap as two H atoms approach each other.

There are only two possibilities, as is illustrated in Fig. 3-17. If the two $1s$ orbitals are combined with positive overlap, a bonding interaction results. The positively overlapping combination, $\phi_1 + \phi_2$, can be regarded as an orbital in itself, called a *molecular orbital* (MO), and denoted Ψ_b. The subscript b stands

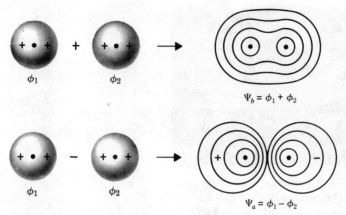

Figure 3-17 The $1s$ orbitals, ϕ_1 and ϕ_2, on two hydrogen or helium atoms may combine to form either a bonding MO, Ψ_b, or an antibonding MO, Ψ_a. The sign of Ψ_b is everywhere positive. The sign of Ψ_a changes between the nuclei; a nodal plane exists here because the value of Ψ_a is zero at the midpoint between the atoms.

for *bonding*. Similarly, the negatively overlapping combination, $\phi_1 - \phi_2$, also constitutes a molecular orbital, Ψ_a, where the subscript a stands for antibonding.

Let us now imagine that two hydrogen atoms approach each other so that the molecular orbital, Ψ_b, is formed. A MO, like an atomic orbital, is subject to the exclusion principle, which means that it may be occupied by no more than two electrons, and then only if these two electrons have opposite spins. Assuming that the two electrons present, one from each H atom, pair their spins and occupy Ψ_b a bond will be formed. The energy of the system will decrease as r, the internuclear distance, decreases following the curve labeled b in Fig. 3-18. At a certain value of the internuclear distance, r_e, the energy will reach a minimum and then begin to rise again, very steeply. At the minimum the attractive force due to the sharing of the electrons just balances the forces due to repulsions between particles of like charge. At shorter distances the repulsive forces increase very rapidly. It is this rapid increase in repulsive forces at short distances that causes the H_2 molecule (and all other molecules) to have a minimum energy at a particular internuclear distance and prevents the atoms from coalescing. This minimum energy, relative to the energy of the completely separated ($r = \infty$) atoms is called the bond energy and is denoted E_b in Fig. 3-18.

Now if the two H atoms approach each other so as to form the antibonding orbital, Ψ_a, with both electrons occupying that orbital, the energy of the system would vary as is shown in curve a. The energy would continuously increase, because at all values of r the interaction is repulsive.

We may now consider the possible formation of an He_2 molecule by using the same basic considerations, represented in Figs. 3-17 and 3-18, as for the H_2 molecule. Again, only the $1s$ orbitals are stable enough to be potentially useful in bonding. The He atom differs from the H atom in having two

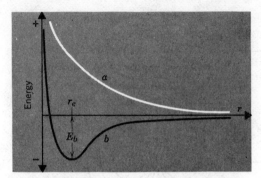

Figure 3-18 The variation of the energy associated with the antibonding orbital, Ψ_a (a-the solid white curve) and the bonding orbital, Ψ_b (b-the solid black curve) as a function of the distance r between the two atoms. The equilibrium internuclear distance r_e corresponds to the minimum in curve b. Here the stability associated with the bond is maximized.

electrons, and this is crucial because in the He_2 molecule there are then four electrons. This means that Ψ_b and Ψ_a must each be occupied by an electron pair. Therefore, whatever stabilization results from the occupation of Ψ_b, it is offset (actually outweighed), by the antibonding effect of the electrons in Ψ_a. The result is that no net, appreciable bonding occurs and the He atoms are more stable apart than together.

Homonuclear Diatomics in General

The foregoing explanation of why H_2 is a stable molecule and He_2 is not, when coupled with the previous results concerning orbital overlaps, provides all the essential features needed to discuss the bonding in all homonuclear

Figure 3-19 MO energy-level diagrams for the H_2 and He_2 molecules. The orbitals marked ϕ_1 and ϕ_2 are the contributing $1s$ atomic orbitals on either two H or two He atoms. The MO's marked Ψ_a and Ψ_b correspond to those diagramed in Fig. 3-17.

diatomic molecules. We shall consider explicitly the molecules that might be formed by the elements of the first short period, that is, Li_2, Be_2, . . . , F_2, Ne_2.

Before we do so, however, we introduce a different type of energy-level diagram from that in Fig. 3-18—one more suitable to molecules with many molecular orbitals. Instead of trying to represent the energy as a function of internuclear distance, we select one particular distance, namely, r_e (or the estimated value thereof). The energies of the molecular orbitals at that distance are then shown in the center of the diagram, and the energies of the atomic orbitals are shown for the separate atoms on each side of the diagram. The presence of electrons in the orbitals can then be represented by dots (or sometimes arrows). For H_2 and He_2 the appropriate diagrams are shown in Fig. 3-19.

Similar diagrams can be used when the two atomic orbitals are not of identical energy, in which case the appearance will be as is shown in Fig. 3-20. Two important features must be emphasized for this case. (1) The more the two atomic orbitals differ in energy to begin with, the less they interact and the smaller are the potential bonding energies. (2) While the molecular orbitals, Ψ_a and Ψ_b, in Fig. 3-19 contain equal contributions from ϕ_1 and ϕ_2, this is not true when ϕ_1 and ϕ_2 differ in energy. In that case, Ψ_b has more ϕ_2 character than ϕ_1 character while, conversely, Ψ_a has a preponderance of ϕ_1 character. When ϕ_1 and ϕ_2 differ very greatly in energy, the interaction becomes so small that Ψ_a is virtually identical in form and energy with ϕ_1 and Ψ_b with ϕ_2, as is shown in Fig. 3-20(b).

Diagrams of this type can be used to show the formation of bonding and antibonding molecular orbitals from any two atomic orbitals, or from two entire sets of atomic orbitals. We are interested here in the interactions of the entire set of $2s2p_x2p_y2p_z$ orbitals on one atom with the equivalent set on another.

(a)   (b)

Figure 3-20 MO energy-level diagrams for cases where the interacting atomic orbitals, ϕ_1 and ϕ_2, initially differ in energy. In (b) the energy difference between ϕ_1 and ϕ_2 is so great that, even were the symmetry correct, little overlap is possible. As a result, the molecular orbitals are only slightly different in either energy or shape from the initial atomic orbitals.

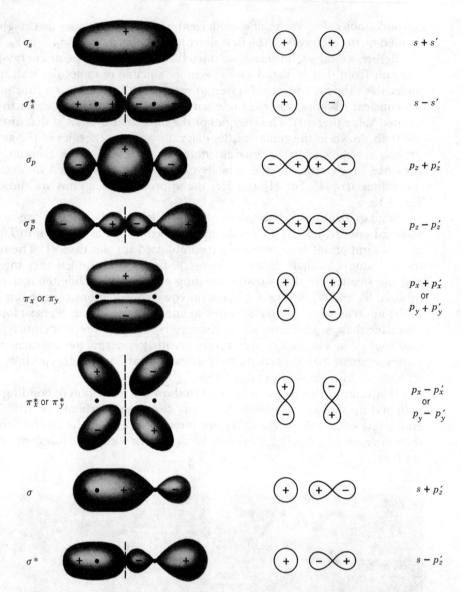

Figure 3-21 Diagrams showing each of the types of overlap that are important in a diatomic molecule. In the right-most column are given those algebraic combinations of orbitals on two adjacent atoms that lead to either bonding or antibonding molecular orbitals. Diagrams of these orbital combinations are given in the adjacent column. In each case, it is the z axis that is taken to be the internuclear axis, and by convention, the positive z direction for each atom is that which points towards the other atom. The sign for each lobe of an orbital is the sign of the original wave function, although the orbital is drawn from the square of the wave function. The algebraic sign for each combination in the right-hand column is chosen to give either a bonding or an antibonding interaction. The resulting molecular orbitals are given the designations listed in the left-most column, where the σ and π notation conforms to that explained in the text, and * indicates an antibonding MO. The approximate shapes of the molecular orbitals are given by the shaded figures. Each antibonding MO is characterized by a nodal plane perpendicular to the internuclear axis, as indicated by the dashed lines.

If we define the internuclear axis as the z axis, we first note that only certain overlaps can be nonzero, namely,

$$
\begin{array}{ccc}
2s & \text{with} & 2s' \\
2s & \text{with} & 2p_z' \\
2p_z & \text{with} & 2s' \\
2p_z & \text{with} & 2p_z' \\
2p_x & \text{with} & 2p_x' \\
2p_y & \text{with} & 2p_y'
\end{array}
$$

All the remaining 10 (e.g., $2s$ with $2p_x'$, $2p_x$ with $2p_y'$, etc.) are rigorously zero and need not be further considered.

Figure 3-21 shows the overlaps just mentioned in more detail, and indicates how the resulting molecular orbitals are symbolized. The first four types of overlap, whether positive (to give a bonding MO) or negative (to give an antibonding MO) give rise to molecular orbitals that are designated σ. The $p_x \pm p_x$ and $p_y \pm p_y$ overlaps give rise to orbitals designated π. The last two, $s \pm p_z'$, also give σ molecular orbitals. The basis for this notation will now be explained.

σ, π, and δ Notation

If we view a MO between two atoms along the direction of the bond, that is, we look at it end-on, the following possibilities must be considered, as shown in Fig. 3-22.

(a) We shall see a wave function that has the same sign, either $+$ or $-$, all the way around. In other words, as we trace a circle about the bond axis, no change in sign occurs throughout the entire circle. An MO of this kind is called a σ (sigma) MO. Such an MO can only be formed by overlap (either $+$ or $-$) of two atomic orbitals that also have the same property with respect to the axis in question. Thus these atomic orbitals can also be designated σ. Only the s and p_z orbitals in the sets we are using have this property. The symbol σ is used because σ is the letter s in the Greek alphabet, and a σ MO is analogous to an atomic s orbital, although it need not be formed from atomic s orbitals.

(b) We may see a wave function that is separated into two regions of opposite sign. With respect to the entire MO, there is a *nodal plane*. Precisely in this plane the wave function has an amplitude of zero, over the entire length of the bond. The symbol π, the Greek letter p, is used because this type of MO is analogous to an atomic p orbital. As is shown in Fig. 3-21, it can be formed by overlap of two suitably oriented p orbitals. In the simple case of a diatomic molecule, or any other linear molecule, π orbitals always come in pairs because there are always two similar p orbitals, p_x and p_y, on each atom. They are equivalent to each other and thus two equivalent π bonding molecular orbitals and two equivalent π antibonding molecular orbitals are formed.

(c) Although we shall not encounter this possibility until much later when we discuss certain transition metal compounds, there are molecular

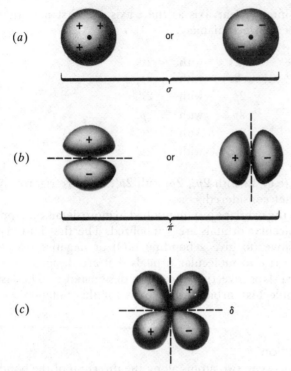

Figure 3-22 Characteristics of σ, π, and δ molecular orbitals as seen along (down) the internuclear axis, such that the first atom eclipses the second. As shown in the two examples of (*a*), σ molecular orbitals are not broken by any nodal planes that include the internuclear axis. Two examples of π molecular orbitals are shown in (*b*). These orbitals possess one plane that includes the internuclear axis. The δ-type MO of part (*c*) is formed by two *d*-type atomic orbitals placed face to face. These δ molecular orbitals possess two nodal planes that include the internuclear axis.

orbitals that have two nodal planes. These are called δ, the Greek letter d, orbitals. The δ molecular orbitals cannot be formed with *s* and *p* atomic orbitals, but the overlap of suitable atomic *d* orbitals, for example, two d_{xy} or two $d_{x^2-y^2}$ orbitals, will form a δ MO.

Antibonding orbitals shall be designated with an asterisk as follows: σ*, π*, and δ*.

The F₂ Molecule

We now consider energy-level diagrams for specific homonuclear diatomic molecules formed from the elements of row two in the periodic table. It is easiest to consider F_2 first, rather than Li_2, as will become apparent. Each fluorine atom has the electron configuration $1s^2 2s^2 2p^5$. The $1s$ electrons are so close to the nucleus and so much lower in energy than the valence shell that they play no significant role in bonding; this is almost always true of so-called inner shell electrons. Thus only the $2s$ and $2p$ orbitals and their electrons need be considered. (Recall, as well, that only valence electrons are considered in drawing a Lewis diagram.)

For a fluorine atom, the effective nuclear charge is high, and the energy difference between the $2s$ and $2p$ atomic orbitals is great. For this reason, in the F_2 molecule, the $2s$ orbital of one fluorine atom interacts only slightly with the $2p_z$ orbital on the other fluorine atom. The symmetry is proper for overlap, as shown in Fig. 3-21, but the energy difference between the two orbitals is so great that overlap is not effective. This is illustrated in Fig. 3-20(b). As a result, there is no contribution to bonding from interaction of these two orbitals. Thus only $2s–2s$, $2p_x–2p_x$, $2p_y–2p_y$, and $2p_z–2p_z$ interactions need to be considered, and the diagram of Fig. 3-23 is obtained. The internuclear axis is the z axis.

In Fig. 3-23 the π and π^* molecular orbitals are each doubly degenerate. They are formed by p_x to p_x and p_y to p_y overlap, so that the π molecular orbitals differ only in their orientation around the internuclear (z) axis. The overlap is positive for π_x ($2p_x + 2p_x$) and negative for π_x^* ($2p_x - 2p_x$), and similarly for π_y and π_y^*. The orbitals in Fig. 3-23 have the shapes designated in Fig. 3-21.

For F_2 there is a total of $(7 + 7) = 14$ valence electrons that must occupy these molecular orbitals in keeping with the *aufbau* principle, Hund's rule, and the Pauli exclusion principle. By adding electrons in this fashion, we get the occupation shown in Fig. 3-23. For all pairs of electrons except those of σ_p,

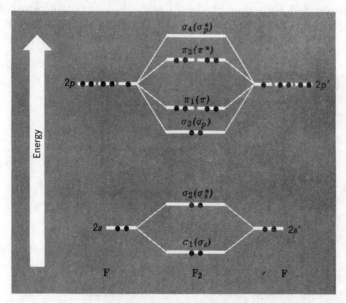

Figure 3-23 A MO diagram for the fluorine molecule, F_2. Atomic orbitals of each fluorine atom are listed on the left and the right. The molecular orbitals that result are listed in the center. The σ molecular orbitals are each singly degenerate, and are given the arbitrary designations $\sigma_1 \cdots \sigma_4$. The π_1 and π_2 levels are each doubly degenerate. The parenthetical MO designations correspond to those given in Fig. 3-21.

the stability gained for a bonding pair is offset by an antibonding pair of electrons. Hence, only the electron pair in σ_p gives a net bonding effect, and we conclude that the F_2 molecule has a single bond, in agreement with the Lewis diagram.

In general, **bond order** is defined in MO theory in just this way. If we take the number of electron pairs in bonding molecular orbitals (n_b) and subtract the number of pairs in antibonding molecular orbitals (n_a), we have the bond order, namely, $n_b - n_a$.

The Li₂ Molecule

For the Li_2 molecule the diagram is somewhat different because the $2s$ and $2p$ atomic orbital separation in the Li atom is smaller. Consequently the $2s$ orbital of one atom is close in energy to the $2p$ orbital of the second atom, and their overlap cannot be ignored. The diagram that shows this is Fig. 3-24, where the internuclear axis is again taken to be the z axis. As a result of s to p_z' and p_z to s' interactions, the molecular orbitals σ_2 and σ_3 have both p_z and s character, and there is an upward displacement of σ_3 so that it lies above π_x and π_y. Although this has practically no importance for the stability of Li_2, it will become important as we proceed to molecules with more electrons. For Li_2 the two valence electrons occupy σ_1, and the bond order is one. It is a weak bond because the overlap of such diffuse $2s$ atomic orbitals is poor. A computer-drawn electron density map for this bonding electron pair, represented as $[\sigma_1]^2$, is shown in Fig. 3-25. This quantitative representation of the overlap should be compared with that of the purely schematic depictions of Figs. 3-17 and 3-21.

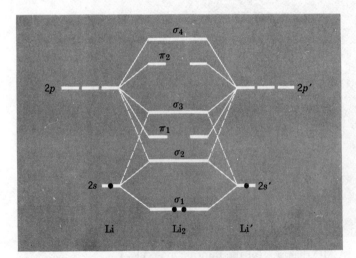

Figure 3-24 A MO diagram for the dilithium molecule, Li_2. As in F_2, the σ molecular orbitals are singly degenerate, and the π molecular orbitals are each doubly degenerate. Because of *s–p* mixing, however, as discussed in the text, the resulting molecular orbitals are not strictly those shown in Fig. 3-21.

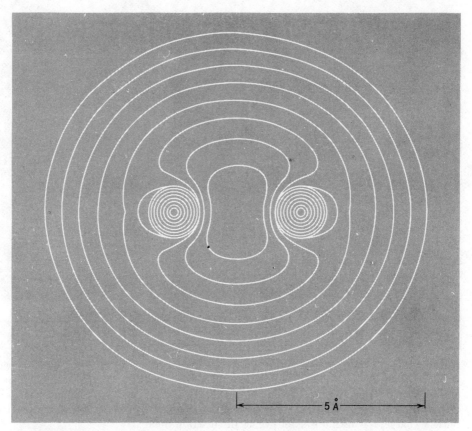

Figure 3-25 Electron density contours for the filled bonding MO σ_1, in Li_2. Each new contour line from the outside in represents an increase in electron density by a factor of two. The atoms are located at the positions of highest electron density.

The Complete Series

We can now consider the entire series of molecules from Li_2 to F_2. The progressive changes in orbital energies and electron populations from one extreme to the other are shown in Fig. 3-26, along with bond distances and energies. The dilithium molecule has the longest and weakest bond of all because it is only a single bond formed by overlap of two fairly diffuse $2s$ atomic orbitals. The Li atoms are large, and the effective nuclear charge is low.

The beryllium atom has the ground-state electron configuration $1s^2 2s^2$. Four valence electrons are to be considered for the Be_2 molecule, and these electrons are assigned as in Fig. 3-26. Because the bond order is zero, there is no stable Be_2 molecule.

For B_2 there are six electrons to occupy the molecular orbitals. The last two enter the doubly degenerate π_1 level according to Hund's rule. The B_2 molecule is, therefore, paramagnetic with two unpaired spins. The bond order is one because the σ_1 and σ_2 pairs cancel one another, leaving one net bond due to $[\pi_1]^2$. The bond distance is shorter and the bond energy is higher than in Li_2 because of the smaller size of the B atoms.

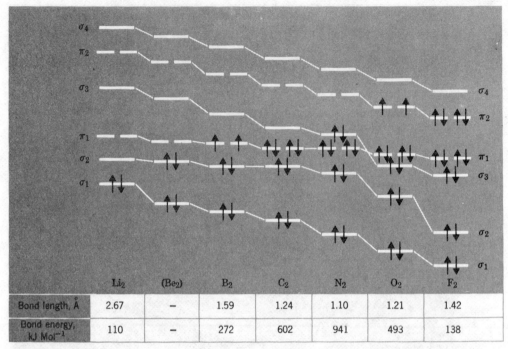

	Li$_2$	(Be$_2$)	B$_2$	C$_2$	N$_2$	O$_2$	F$_2$
Bond length, Å	2.67	–	1.59	1.24	1.10	1.21	1.42
Bond energy, kJ Mol^{-1}	110	–	272	602	941	493	138

Figure 3-26 MO energy-level diagrams for the diatomic molecules from Li$_2$ to F$_2$ showing the changes in MO energies, electron configurations, bond lengths, and bond energies. For molecules with high effective nuclear charge (e.g., F$_2$, O$_2$, and perhaps N$_2$), the molecular orbitals are essentially those of Fig. 3-21, as designated in Fig. 3-23. For molecules with low effective nuclear charge, *s–p* mixing is extensive, as discussed in the text.

For C$_2$ the π_1 orbitals are only slightly lower in energy than σ_3, but by enough to give the ground-state electron configuration $[\sigma_1]^2[\sigma_2]^2[\pi_1]^4$, as shown in Fig. 3-26. The C$_2$ molecule is diamagnetic and has a considerably shorter and stronger bond than does B$_2$. The excited state $[\sigma_1]^2[\sigma_2]^2[\pi_1]^3[\sigma_3]^1$ for C$_2$ lies only ~10 kJ mol^{-1} above the ground state.

The N$_2$ molecule has the highest bond order (three), the shortest bond, and the strongest bond of any molecule in the series. The bond order of three is in agreement with the Lewis diagram that has a triple bond, $:N\equiv N:$.

With the oxygen molecule, bond order and bond strength begin to decrease since, following N$_2$, only antibonding molecular orbitals remain to be occupied. For O$_2$, the two additional electrons enter the doubly degenerate π_2 level, which is antibonding. The bond order is two. The electrons in the π_2 level are unpaired, and this accords with the fact that the substance is paramagnetic with two unpaired electrons. The correct prediction of this by simple MO theory is in contrast with the difficulty of explaining it in Lewis terms. The Lewis approach correctly requires a double bond, but not the presence of two unpaired electrons.

The Ne$_2$ molecule is not stable, and the reason for this is clear. The bond order would be zero, because all molecular orbitals through σ_4 in Fig. 3-26 would be filled by the 16 valence electrons of two Ne atoms.

Heteronuclear Diatomic Molecules

The extension of the MO method for homonuclear diatomic molecules to include heteronuclear diatomic molecules such as CO and NO is not difficult. It depends on making allowance for the different effective nuclear charges of the two atoms. This is shown in Fig. 3-27 where the isoelectronic molecules

(a)

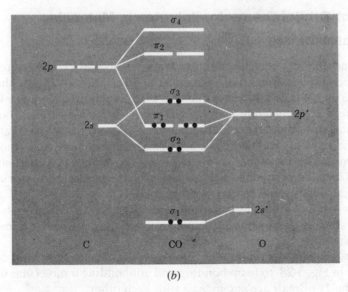

(b)

Figure 3-27 MO diagrams for (a) the dinitrogen molecule and (b) the carbon monoxide molecule. Both have the same number of electrons, but the MO diagrams are different because of the different starting energies for the atomic orbitals of C and O.

N_2 and CO are contrasted. There are two important features to be noted in this comparison. First, all orbitals of the oxygen atom lie at lower energies than the corresponding ones of the carbon atom, because oxygen has the higher effective nuclear charge. This is in keeping with Fig. 2-14, which indicates that the first ionization enthalpy of O is several hundred kilojoules per mole greater than that of C. Secondly, the $2s$–$2p$ energy separation is greater for O than for C. The resulting MO diagram for CO [Fig. 3-27(b)] emphasizes the overlap of the carbon $2s$ atomic orbital with that atomic orbital of O closest to it in energy, the oxygen $2p$ atomic orbital. This s–p mixing is not prominent in the MO diagram for N_2, Fig. 3-27(a).

For these reasons, the molecular orbitals for CO are significantly different from those for N_2. The highest filled MO for N_2 is σ_3 of Fig. 3-27(a). This is essentially σ_p of Fig. 3-21. Because it is an orbital of high bonding character, loss of an electron from this orbital (to form N_2^+) weakens the N—N bond. In CO, however, the highest filled MO [σ_3 of Fig. 3-27(b)] is slightly antibonding in character. Hence, the CO$^+$ ion has a slightly stronger bond than does CO.

Another important heteronuclear diatomic molecule is nitric oxide, NO. Since N and O differ by only one atomic number, the energy-level diagram for NO is rather similar to that of N_2. The additional electron of NO must occupy the antibonding π_2 orbital of Fig. 3-27(a). Because π_2 is antibonding, the last electron of NO is easily removed to form NO$^+$, which then has a stronger bond than does the neutral NO. The electronic structure of NO might, of course, equally well have been derived qualitatively by removing one electron from the configuration of the O_2 molecule.

3-6   Molecular Orbital Theory for Polyatomic Molecules

Linear Triatomics; BeH_2

The MO method can be generalized to larger molecules. To illustrate, let us consider the simplest linear triatomic molecule, BeH_2. Let us choose the z axis as the molecular axis. We first note that only σ molecular orbitals can be formed because the hydrogen atoms have only their $1s$ orbitals to use in bonding. These orbitals are themselves of σ character with respect to any axis that passes through the nucleus, and therefore they can contribute only to σ molecular orbitals. On the Be atom then, only the $2s$ and $2p_z$ orbitals can participate in bonding. The p_x and p_y orbitals, which have π character and zero overlap with any σ orbital, will play no role in bonding in BeH_2.

The $2s$ orbital of beryllium can combine with the two $1s$ orbitals of the hydrogen atoms to form bonding and antibonding molecular orbitals as is shown in Fig. 3-28.

The $2p_z$ orbital of beryllium also combines with the hydrogen $1s$ orbitals, as is shown in Fig. 3-28, to form bonding and antibonding σ molecular orbitals. In these, the $1s$ orbitals are *out of phase* with each other.

The important points to keep in mind about these four σ molecular orbitals are the following:

1. In each bonding MO, electron density is large and continuous between adjacent atoms, while in the antibonding molecular orbitals there is a node between each adjacent pair of nuclei.

Figure 3-28 The four σ molecular orbitals for the linear BeH_2. The dashed vertical lines are nodal planes perpendicular to the molecular axis. The notation for orbitals $\sigma_1 \cdots \sigma_4$ conforms to that used in Fig. 3-29. Those p atomic orbitals of Be that are perpendicular to the molecular axis have nonbonding interactions with the H $1s$ orbitals.

Figure 3-29 A MO energy-level diagram for BeH_2. The MO designations, σ_1–σ_4, correspond to those of Fig. 3-28. The two atomic p orbitals of Be that are unchanged in energy lie at right angles to the internuclear axis and have nonbonding interactions with the $1s$ atomic orbitals of the hydrogen atoms.

2. In each bonding MO, the wave function indicates that an electron pair occupying it is *spread out* over the whole molecule, and is shared by all of the atoms, not just a particular adjacent pair. In other words, in molecular orbitals electrons are *delocalized* over the whole extent of the MO.

The MO treatment of the bonding in BeH_2 can be expressed in terms of an energy-level diagram, as shown in Fig. 3-29. The main features here are that the hydrogen $1s$ orbitals lie at much lower energy (~ 400 kJ mol^{-1}) than the beryllium $2s$ orbital and that the p_x and p_y orbitals of Be carry over completely unchanged into the center column, because they do not overlap with any other orbitals. The four valence electrons, $2s^2$ from Be and $1s$ from each H, occupy σ_1 and σ_2. The total bond order of the Be—H bonds is two. Since each Be—H pair participates equally in the molecule, this is equivalent to saying that there are two equivalent B—H single bonds.

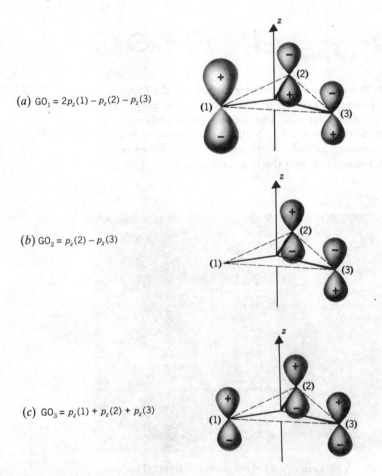

(*a*) $GO_1 = 2p_z(1) - p_z(2) - p_z(3)$

(*b*) $GO_2 = p_z(2) - p_z(3)$

(*c*) $GO_3 = p_z(1) + p_z(2) + p_z(3)$

Figure 3-30 Three combinations of p_z orbitals from the three outer B atoms of a planar AB_3 molecule. Each combination (called a group orbital, GO) is multicentered, and each is constructed to be used as a group in overlapping with the p_z atomic orbital of the central atom, A, as shown in Fig. 3-31.

Trigonal Planar Molecules; AB_3

A particularly important and more general application of MO theory in poly-atomic molecules deals with π bonding in planar systems. One important group is the symmetrical compounds of the general formula AB_3. Examples include BF_3, CO_3^{2-}, and NO_3^-. If these trigonal-planar systems are oriented so that the central atom is at the origin of the coordinate system and the molecular or ionic plane coincides with the xy plane, then the π bond system will be formed entirely by the p_z atomic orbitals of the four atoms. The π bond system must then have a node in the xy plane. It must also be equally dispersed over the three A — B bonds, in agreement with the resonance result discussed pre-viously. Uniquely, the MO approach involves overlap that encompasses the whole structure.

There are three linear combinations of p_z atomic orbitals from the separate peripheral B atoms of AB_3 which are important to the discussion. We shall not discuss the methods that are used to deduce these particular linear com-binations, except to point out that these three particular linear combinations have been chosen to provide the best total, positive overlap with the atomic p_z orbital of the central atom, A. These three linear combinations are termed **group orbitals,** as illustrated in Fig. 3-30. The linear combinations [group orbitals (GO)] represented in Fig. 3-30 arise from three distinct arrangements of the p_z atomic orbitals at the vertices of the AB_3 triangle. One group orbital of Fig. 3-30 overlaps with the p_z atomic orbital of the central atom, A, as shown

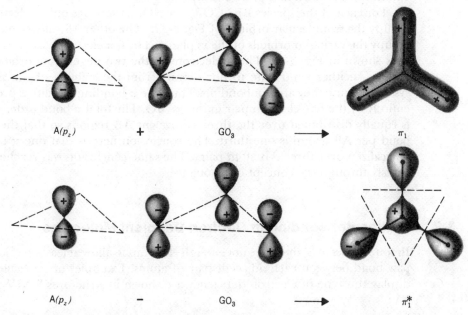

Figure 3-31 Diagrams showing how bonding (π_1) and antibonding (π_1^*) molecular orbitals are formed in an AB_3 molecule using the p_z orbital of the central atom, A, and a group orbital (GO_3 of Fig. 3-30) from the outer atoms, B. The molecular orbitals them-selves, at the right, are viewed from above. The molecular orbitals change sign in the molecular plane, as do the p_z atomic orbitals from which they are formed. In addition, π_1^* has three nodal planes perpendicular to the molecular plane.

Figure 3-32   The MO energy-level diagram for the π-bond system in a planar, symmetrical AB_3 molecule. The symbols π_1 and π_1^* correspond to those used in Fig. 3-31. The nonbonding orbitals π_{2a} and π_{2b} are essentially GO_1 and GO_2 of Fig. 3-30.

in Fig. 3-31. Two interactions are nonbonding, e.g., π_{2a} and π_{2b}, and the resulting molecular orbitals appear in the energy-level diagram of Fig. 3-32 with energies that are unchanged. One of the interactions shown in Fig. 3-31 is bonding, and this leads to the π_1 MO shown in Fig. 3-32. Its antibonding counterpart is listed in Fig. 3-32 as π_1^*.

For each of the species BF_3, CO_3^{2-}, or NO_3^-, there are only 6 electrons to occupy the π molecular orbitals of Fig. 3-32. (The other 18 valence electrons occupy the various σ orbitals of the xy plane.) The 6 π electrons are distributed as is shown in Fig. 3-32. The 4 electrons in the two degenerate orbitals, π_{2a} and π_{2b}, neither contribute to nor detract from the stability of the π-bond system because they are nonbonding. Thus, the π-bonding stability is provided entirely by the one electron pair in the π_1 MO. The total π bond order of one is equally distributed over the three equivalent AB regions so that the net π bond per AB group is one third. The conclusion here is that one π bond is delocalized over three AB atom pairs. The same conclusion was reached previously through the concept of resonance.

3-7   Multicenter Bonding in Electron Deficient Molecules

In some molecules, there are not enough electrons to allow at least one electron-pair bond between each adjacent pair of atoms. Examples of molecules that display this type of electron deficiency are shown in structures 3-XIV and 3-XV:

In structures 3-XIV and in the Al_2C_6 skeleton of structure 3-XV there are eight adjacent pairs of atoms, but there are only six pairs of electrons available for bonding. Eight bonds are required for the normal two-centered, two-electron distribution of bonds, and clearly this is not possible for structures 3-XIV and 3-XV. [Note that structures 3-XIV and 3-XV are the actual structures for molecules with empirical formulas BH_3 and $Al(CH_3)_3$.]

Both structures 3-XIV and 3-XV present the same problem for a bonding description. We shall concentrate on structure 3-XIV, since it is less cumbersome. We could try to account for structure 3-XIV by invoking a resonance description, namely, the canonical forms 3-XIVa and 3-XIVb:

$$
\begin{array}{cc}
\text{H}_2\text{B}\overset{\displaystyle\text{H}}{\diagdown}\underset{\displaystyle\text{H}}{\diagup}\text{BH}_2 & \text{H}_2\text{B}\underset{\displaystyle\text{H}}{\diagdown}\overset{\displaystyle\text{H}}{}\text{BH}_2 \\
\text{3-XIVa} & \text{3-XIVb}
\end{array}
$$

This would imply that, in each B----H----B bridge, one electron pair is shared between or distributed over two B----H bonds, giving each bridging BH group a bond order of one half. The electron deficiency is obvious, but the lack of formal bonds in each resonance form seems somewhat artificial. The remaining B—H bonds of the terminal BH groups are adequately described as normal two-centered, two-electron bonds. An analogous description could be used for the central Al—C bonds in structure 3-XV.

Another way to describe the bonding in structure 3-XIV is to use an MO treatment that encompasses only the bridging system. The terminal BH groups are handled separately as localized electron pair bonds, so that within each starting BH_2 unit there are ordinary B—H bonds formed using sp^3 hybrid orbitals on the B atoms. If these two BH_2 units are brought together as shown in Fig. 3-33(a), so as to make the H_2B----BH_2 sets of atoms coplanar, the remaining two sp^3 hybrid orbitals on each B atom point toward each other. Now, if the remaining two hydrogen atoms are placed in their proper bridging positions, then, as shown in Fig. 3-33(b), each of the $1s$ atomic orbitals of these hydrogen atoms overlaps with two of the sp^3 orbitals from the B atoms. In this way an orbital extending over each B----H----B unit is formed. There are two such orbitals. Each is three centered, has no nodes, and is, therefore, capable of bonding all three atoms together. Since each boron atom and each bridging hydrogen atom supplies one electron, there are four electrons to be distributed into the two three-centered orbitals. Thus one electron pair can be used for each three-centered orbital. In this way we establish a type of bond called a three-center, two-electron bond, abbreviated ($3c$–$2e$). Since one electron pair is shared between three atoms instead of two, ($3c$–$2e$) bonds have about one half the strength of the normal two-center, two-electron ($2c$–$2e$) bond. This is equivalent to the bond order of one half obtained in the resonance treatment.

To appreciate and utilize more fully the concept of ($3c$–$2e$) bonding, it is necessary to examine it in more detail. Suppose we consider only the sp^3 hybrid orbital on each B atom and the $1s$ orbital of the bridging H atom. These three atomic orbitals can be combined into three molecular orbitals as shown in Fig. 3-34. One of these, Ψ_b, is a bonding orbital; it is the same one already discussed. There is also an antibonding orbital, Ψ_a, which has a node between each

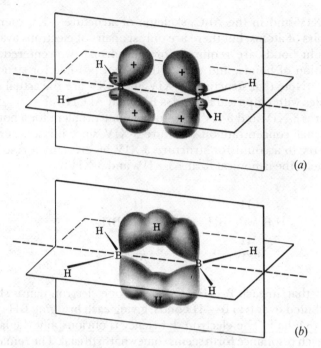

(a)

(b)

Figure 3-33   The formation of $3c–2e$ bonds in B_2H_6. The orientation of two coplanar BH_2 groups, with sp^3 hybrids on B atoms, is shown in-(a). When the bridging H atoms are placed as in (b), continuous overlap within each B—H—B arch results in two separate $3c–2e$ bonds.

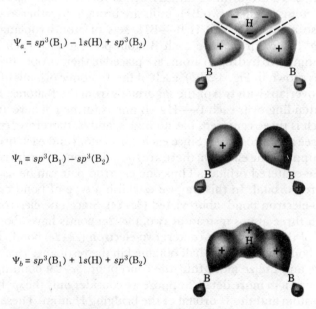

$\Psi_a = sp^3(B_1) - 1s(H) + sp^3(B_2)$

$\Psi_n = sp^3(B_1) - sp^3(B_2)$

$\Psi_b = sp^3(B_1) + 1s(H) + sp^3(B_2)$

Figure 3-34   The formation of three distinct three-center molecular orbitals in a B—H—B bridge system.

Figure 3-35 An energy-level diagram for the three molecular orbitals of Fig. 3-34 that are formed in a three-center B—H—B bridge bond of B_2H_6.

adjacent pair of atoms. The third orbital, Ψ_n, has the signs of the two sp^3 orbitals out of phase and cannot have any net overlap with the H $1s$ orbital. It is a *nonbonding* orbital.

We can now draw an energy-level diagram that expresses these results, as in Fig. 3-35. By placing an electron pair in Ψ_b, the bonding MO, we have a complete picture of the $(3c-2e)$ bonding situation.

In the case of $Al_2(CH_3)_6$, structure 3-XV, the $(3c-2e)$ bridge bonding can be described in a very similar fashion. Each Al atom provides sp^3 hybrid orbitals, as do the boron atoms in B_2H_6. Instead of the $1s$ orbital of the H atom, we now have the large positive lobe of a carbon sp^3 orbital at the center.

The energy-level diagram in Fig. 3-35 can be applied in other cases as well. It can be extended to cover some cases of $(3c-4e)$ bonding. In the FHF$^-$ ion, which is symmetrical (although most hydrogen bonds are weaker and unsymmetrical), each F atom supplies a σ orbital and an electron pair. Thus a set of orbitals essentially similar to that in the BHB system is used, and an energy-level diagram essentially like that in Fig. 3-35 is applicable. However, there are now two electron pairs. One pair occupies Ψ_b and the other Ψ_n. The pair in Ψ_n has no significant effect on the bonding because Ψ_n is a nonbonding orbital. The net result is that here, too, the bond orders are one half.

One other type of $(3c-4e)$ bonding must also be discussed since it is essential to the discussion of molecular shapes. Suppose we have a set of three atoms, B — A — B, most probably linear but possibly bent to some extent, such that the central atom uses a p orbital rather than an s orbital. The situation is shown in Fig. 3-36(a). Again, it is possible to form three multicenter orbitals as shown in Fig. 3-36(b). The result turns out to be very similar to that already seen where the central atom uses an s orbital, in that bonding, Ψ_b, nonbonding, Ψ_n, and antibonding, Ψ_a, orbitals are formed and the energy-level diagram is analogous, as is shown in Fig. 3-36(c).

The interesting result, in either Fig. 3-35 or 3-36, is that even if two electron pairs are available, the A — B bonds will have orders of only one half, because

Figure 3-36 The formation of three-center orbitals in a B—A—B system where the central atom A uses a *p* orbital. The orbitals that are used are shown in (*a*). The shapes of the molecular orbitals that are formed are shown in (*b*). An energy-level diagram showing the occupation of the orbitals for a 3*c*–4*e* bond is shown in (*c*).

one electron pair occupies the nonbonding orbital, Ψ_n. Here we are dealing with an orbitally deficient system rather than an electron deficient one. If the central atom in either case had an additional σ-type atomic orbital the system would be equivalent to that in BeH_2 and two bonds, each of order one, could be formed.

Multicenter bonding can occur in larger groups of atoms. There are, for example, compounds in which a single carbon monoxide ligand lies perpendicularly over the center of a triangular set of metal atoms, as in Fig. 3-37(*a*). In such cases, the best, simple way to describe the bonding is in terms of a (4*c*–2*e*) bond. If one orbital on each metal atom is directed toward the carbon lone-pair orbital of CO [σ₃ in Fig. 3-27(*b*)], there will be mutual overlap of all four orbitals, as is shown in Fig. 3-37(*b*), and the resulting four-center orbital will be occupied by the electron pair initially in σ₃ of the CO molecule.

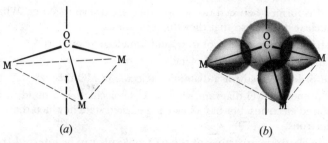

(a)   *(b)*

Figure 3-37 *(a)* The orientation of a CO group over three metal atoms as is found in some metal carbonyl compounds. *(b)* The overlap of three metal atom orbitals with themselves and with the σ_3 orbital [see Fig. 3-27(*b*)] of CO to form a four-center orbital. It is this orbital (and the electron pair that occupies it), which is responsible for binding of the CO group in this "capping" position over the three metal atoms. The electron pair originally filled σ_3 of the CO molecule.

STUDY GUIDE

Scope and Purpose

A brief and qualitative introduction to the twin subjects of structure and bonding has been given. These will be important topics in subsequent discussions of the reactions and properties of compounds. Bonding theory and molecular structure should not be taken as ends in themselves, but only as important tools in understanding the actual properties and reactivities of chemical compounds. Of the Study Questions, those marked "A. Review" should be used by the student as a self-study guide to mastery of the material in the text. More challenging exercises are listed under "B. Additional Exercises." Questions marked "C. Questions From the Literature of Inorganic Chemistry," require the use of specific journal articles.

Study Questions

A. Review

1. Why are the sign and magnitude of overlap between orbitals on adjacent atoms good indications of whether and how strongly the atoms are bonded?

2. Show with drawings how an *s* orbital, each of the three *p* orbitals, and each of the five *d* orbitals on one atom would overlap with the *s* orbital, one of the *p* orbitals, and any two of the *d* orbitals on another atom close to it. Characterize each overlap as positive, negative, or exactly zero.

3. Draw an energy-level diagram for the interaction of two atoms each with an *s* orbital. Show how the molecular orbitals would be occupied if the two atoms in question were H atoms and if they were He atoms. What conclusions are to be drawn about the formation of a bond in each case?

4. When a bond is formed between two atoms, they are drawn together. What limits their internuclear distance so that they do not coalesce?

5. State the defining characteristics of σ, π, and δ molecular orbitals.

6. What is meant by a node? A nodal plane?

7. How is bond order defined for a diatomic molecule in MO theory?

8. Show with an energy-level diagram why the C_2 molecule has a bond order of 2 and no unpaired electrons, but has a low-lying excited state in which there are two unpaired electrons.

9. Show how the electronic structure of the NO molecule can be inferred from that of O_2. Explain why NO^+ has a stronger bond than NO itself.

10. True or False: The set of valence shell orbitals ($2s$, $2p$) for N are of higher energy than those for C. Explain the reason for your answer.

11. Write the electron configurations for the ground states and the valence states of Be, B, C, and N atoms so that each one can form the maximum number of ($2c$–$2e$) (ordinary electron-pair) bonds.

12. What are the three important types of hybrid orbitals that can be formed by an atom with only s and p orbitals in its valence shell? Describe the molecular geometry that each of these produces.

13. State the geometric arrangement of bonds produced by each of the following sets of hybrid orbitals: dsp^2, d^2sp^3, dsp^3. For each one state explicitly which d and p orbitals are required for each geometric arrangement.

14. Explain in detail, using both the MO approach and the resonance theory why the NO bonds in NO_3^- have a bond order of $1\frac{1}{3}$.

15. Why is the use of hybrid orbitals preferable to the use of single atomic orbitals in forming bonds? Illustrate.

16. What does the term "electron deficient molecule" mean?

17. Why does B_2H_6 not have the same kind of structure as C_2H_6? Draw the structure that B_2H_6 does have and describe the nature of the two sorts of BH bonds therein.

18. Using the VSEPR model, predict the structures of the following ions and molecules BeF_2, CH_2, OF_2, PCl_4^+, SO_2, ClF_2^+, BrF_3, BrF_5, SbF_5, ICl_4^-.

19. Why are the $Kr \cdots Kr$ and intermolecular $Br \cdots Br$ distances in the solid forms of the two elements practically identical? How would you expect the $Br \cdots Br$ distances in solid CBr_4 to be related to the above distances?

B.   Additional Exercises

1. For the series of diatomics O_2^+, O_2, O_2^-, and O_2^{2-}, determine from an MO energy-level diagram how the bond lengths will vary and how many unpaired electrons each should have.

2. The ionization enthalpies for H and F are given in Fig. 2-14. Draw an MO energy-level diagram for the HF molecule. How is the polarity of the molecule indicated in this diagram?

3. Draw Lewis diagrams and predict the structures of $(CH_3)_2S$ (dimethyl sulfide) and $(CH_3)_2SO$ (dimethyl sulfoxide). How will the CSC bond angles differ?

4. Draw Lewis diagrams for each of the series OCO, NNO, ONO^+, NCO^-, NNN^-, and NCN^{2-}. What is the same in all of these systems?

5. Describe the bonding in Al_2Br_6.

6. Determine the hybridization for the central atom in $OPCl_3$, OSF_4, and OIF_5. Predict the fine points of geometry using VSEPR theory.

7. Predict the geometry of gaseous GeF_2, and explain your reasoning.

8. Choose a reasonable geometry for seven-coordinate iodine in IF_7.

9. Draw Lewis diagrams for O_3 and SO_2. For ozone, $\angle OOO = 117°$. For sulfur dioxide, $\angle OSO = 120°$. Explain.

10. CO_2, $HgCl_2$, and $(CN)_2$ are linear. Draw Lewis diagrams and assign hybridizations for each atom.

11. Consider the series CO_3^{2-}, NO_3^-, and SO_3. What geometry do you predict for each?

12. Construct an MO energy-level diagram for NO, NO^+, and NO^-. Determine the bond order and the number of unpaired electrons in each.

13. Describe the geometry and the hybridization in $[PtCl_6]^{2-}$.

14. Draw a qualitatively correct energy level diagram for the CO_2 molecule. Show that it accounts correctly for the presence of double bonds.

C. Questions from the Literature of Inorganic Chemistry

1. The structure of the pentafluorotellurate monoanion has been determined by X-ray techniques. (See S. H. Mastin, R. R. Ryan, and L. B. Asprey, *Inorg. Chem.*, **1970**, *9*, 2100–2103.) What is the oxidation state of Te in this anion? Draw the Lewis diagram for the anion. Determine the occupancy and the formula AB_xE_y for Te, and explain any deviations from ideal geometry using VSEPR theory.

2. Consider the compound $(CH_3)_3SnCl \cdot 2,6-(CH_3)_2C_5H_3NO$, whose structure has been determined by X-ray techniques. (See A. L. Rheingold, S. W. Ng, and J. J. Zuckerman, *Organometallics*, **1984**, *3*, 233–237.) Determine a hybridization for each atom in the structure. This compound can be considered to be an adduct of which Lewis acid and which Lewis base?

3. Sulfate becomes bound to four $Al(Me)_3$ fragments in the dianion $[Al_4Me_{12}SO_4]^{2-}$. (See R. D. Rogers and J. L. Atwood, *Organometallics*, **1984**, *3*, 271–274.) Using the bond angles and lengths as a guide, decide if the $AlMe_3$ groups alter the SO_4^{2-} group significantly upon formation of the $[Al_4Me_{12}SO_4]^{2-}$ product. Explain.

4. $SnCl_2$ can serve either as a Lewis acid (electron pair acceptor) or as a Lewis base (electron pair donor). In fact, it can do both, simultaneously. (See C. C. Hsu and R. A. Geanangel, *Inorg. Chem.*, **1980**, *19*, 110–119.) Draw a Lewis diagram for $SnCl_2$. Give an example where the Sn atom serves as (a) an electron pair donor, (b) an electron pair acceptor, and (c) both a donor and an acceptor. In each of these cases, list the occupancy and the hybridization at the Sn atom. Is there a change in either hybridization or geometry when $SnCl_2$ serves as a Lewis base or a Lewis acid?

SUPPLEMENTARY READING

Atkins, P. W., *Molecular Quantum Mechanics*, Oxford University Press, Oxford, 1983.

Ballhausen, C. J. and Gray, H. B., *Molecular Electronic Structures*, Benjamin–Cummings, Menlo Park, CA, 1980.

Ballhausen, C. J. and Gray, H. B., *Molecular Orbital Theory*, Benjamin, Menlo Park, CA, 1964.

Burdett, J. K., *Molecular Shapes. Theoretical Models of Inorganic Stereochemistry*, Wiley-Interscience, New York, 1980.

Cartmell, E. and Fowles, G. W. A., *Valency and Molecular Structure*, Butterworths, London, 1966.

Champion, A., *Chemical Bonding*, McGraw-Hill, New York, 1964.

Coulson, C. A., *Valence*, Oxford University Press, New York, 1964.

Coulson, C. A., *The Shape and Structure of Molecules*, 2nd ed., revised by R. McWeeny, Clarendon, Oxford, 1982.

DeKock, R. L. and Gray, H. B., *Chemical Structure and Bonding*, Benjamin–Cummings, Menlo Park, CA, 1980.

Ferguson, J. E., *Stereochemistry and Bonding in Inorganic Chemistry*, Prentice-Hall, Englewood Cliffs, NJ, 1974.

Gillespie, R. J., *Molecular Geometry*, Van Nostrand-Reinhold, London, 1972.

Goodisman, J., *Contemporary Quantum Chemistry*, Plenum, New York, 1977.

Karplus, M. and Porter, R. N., *Atoms and Molecules: An Introduction for Students of Physical Chemistry*, Benjamin, Menlo Park, CA, 1970.

Wade, K., *Electron Deficient Compounds*, Nelson, London, 1971.

Wahl, A. C., "Electron Density Maps," *Science,* **1966,** *151,* 961.

chapter 4

IONIC SOLIDS

4-1 Introduction

A great many inorganic solids, and even a few organic ones, can usefully be thought of as consisting of a three-dimensional array of ions. This ionic model can be developed in further detail in two main ways.

First, it is assumed that the energy of this array of ions can be treated as the sum of the following contributions:

1. Coulombic (electrostatic) attractive and repulsive energies.
2. Additional repulsive energy that results from repulsion between the overlapping outer electron density of adjacent ions.
3. A variety of minor energy terms, mainly van der Waals and zero point vibrational energy.

The important point to note here is that no explicit account is taken of covalent bonding. This is doubtless an oversimplification in *every* case, but evidently in many substances the pure ionic description leads to fairly accurate estimates of the enthalpies of formation of the compounds. There is probably a certain approximate compensation so that covalent bond energy, which may actually be present, arises at the expense of a nearly equal amount of coulomb energy. Thus, so long as the covalence is small, the error involved in assuming that one form of energy exactly offsets the other is an acceptable approximation.

Second, the main features of the structures of ionic solids can be understood by treating these substances as efficiently packed arrays of ions. To be efficient, the packing of ions in the structure of an ionic compound must maximize the number of contacts between oppositely charged ions while simultaneously keeping ions of the same sign as far apart as possible. A set of radii (r_{ion}, as defined in Chapter 2) for the different ions, together with a geometrical and electrostatic analysis can enable us to understand why, for example, NaCl, CsCl, and CuCl all have different structures.

4-2 The Lattice Energy of Sodium Chloride

We begin by considering how to calculate the enthalpy of forming a solid ionic compound from a dilute gaseous collection of the constituent ions. For definiteness, we shall first consider a specific example, NaCl. X-ray study shows that the atoms are arranged as in Fig. 4-1. If we assume that the atoms are in

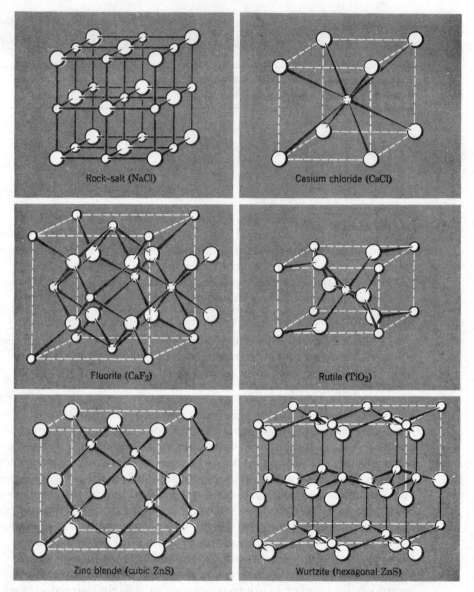

Figure 4-1 Six important ionic structures. Small circles denote metal cations, large circles denote anions.

fact the ions, Na^+ and Cl^-, the energy of the array can be calculated in the following way. The shortest Na^+—Cl^- distance is called r_0. The electrostatic energy between two neighboring ions is given by Eq. 4-2.1:

$$E \text{ (joules)} = \frac{e^2}{4\pi\epsilon_0 r_0} \qquad (\epsilon_0 = 8.854 \times 10^{-12} \text{ C}^2 \text{ m}^{-1} \text{ J}^{-1}) \qquad (4\text{-}2.1)$$

where e is the electron charge in coulombs, and ϵ_0 is the dielectric constant of a vacuum, as defined in Chapter 1.

Each Na^+ ion is surrounded by six Cl^- ions at the distance r_0 (in meters) giving an energy term $6e^2/4\pi\epsilon_0 r_0$. The next closest neighbors to a given Na^+ ion are 12 Na^+ ions which, by simple trigonometry, lie $\sqrt{2}r_0$ away. Thus, another energy term, with a minus sign because it is repulsive, is $-12e^2/\sqrt{2}r_0 4\pi\epsilon_0$. By repeating this sort of procedure, successive terms are found, leading to the expression:

$$E = \frac{1}{4\pi\epsilon_0}\left(\frac{6e^2}{r_0} - \frac{12e^2}{\sqrt{2}r_0} + \frac{8e^2}{\sqrt{3}r_0} - \frac{6e^2}{2r_0} + \cdots\right)$$

$$= \frac{e^2}{4\pi\epsilon_0 r_0}\left(6 - \frac{12}{\sqrt{2}} + \frac{8}{\sqrt{3}} - \frac{6}{2} + \frac{24}{\sqrt{5}} - \cdots\right) \tag{4-2.2}$$

The parenthetical expression in Eq. 4-2.2 is an infinite series. It eventually converges to a single value because the electrostatic interactions at great distances become unimportant.

It is possible to derive a general formula for the infinite series and to find the numerical value to which it converges. That value is characteristic of the structure and independent of what particular ions are present. It is called the *Madelung constant*, M_{NaCl}, for the NaCl structure. It is actually an irrational number, whose value can be given to as high a degree of accuracy as needed, for example, 1.747 . . . or 1.747558 . . . , or better. Madelung constants for many common ionic structures have been evaluated, and a few are given in Table 4-1 for illustrative purposes. The structures themselves, Fig. 4-1, will be discussed presently.

A unique Madelung constant is defined only for those structures in which all ratios of interatomic vectors are fixed by symmetry. In the case of the rutile structure there are two crystal dimensions that can vary independently. There is a different Madelung constant for each ratio of the two independent dimensions.

When a mole (N ions of each kind, where N is Avogadro's number) of sodium chloride is formed from the gaseous ions, the total electrostatic energy released is given by

$$E_e = NM_{NaCl}\left(\frac{e^2}{4\pi\epsilon_0 r_0}\right) \tag{4-2.3}$$

This is true because the expression for the electrostatic energy of one Cl^- ion would be the same as that for an Na^+ ion. If we were to add the electrostatic

Table 4-1 Madelung Constants for Several Structures

Structure Type	M
NaCl	1.74756
CsCl	1.76267
CaF_2	5.03878
Zinc blende	1.63805
Wurtzite	1.64132

energies for the two kinds of ions, the result would be twice the true electrostatic energy because each pairwise interaction would have been counted twice.

The electrostatic energy given by Eq. 4-2.3 is not the actual energy released in the process

$$Na^+(g) + Cl^-(g) = NaCl(s) \tag{4-2.4}$$

Real ions are not rigid spheres. The equilibrium separation of Na^+ and Cl^- in NaCl is fixed when the attractive forces are exactly balanced by repulsive forces. The attractive forces are coulombic and follow strictly a $1/r^2$ law. The repulsive forces are more subtle and follow an inverse r^n law where n is > 2 and varies with the nature of the particular ions. We can write, in a general way, that the total repulsive energy per mole at any value of r is

$$E_{rep} = \frac{NB}{r^n} \tag{4-2.5}$$

where B is a constant.

At the equilibrium distance, the net energy, U, for reaction 4-2.4 is determined by contributions from both repulsive (Eq. 4-2.5) and attractive (Eq. 4-2.3) forces. This is given by Eq. 4-2.6:

$$U = -NM_{NaCl}\left(\frac{e^2}{4\pi\epsilon_0 r}\right) + \frac{NB}{r^n} \tag{4-2.6}$$

where the algebraic signs are chosen in accord with the convention that the attractive forces produce an exothermic term, and the repulsive forces produce an endothermic term.

The constant B can now be eliminated if we recognize that at equilibrium (where $r = r_0$), the energy U is, by definition, at a minimum. Hence, the derivative of U with respect to r, evaluated at $r = r_0$, must equal zero. Differentiating Eq. 4-2.6 we get Eq. 4-2.7:

$$\left(\frac{dU}{dr}\right)_{r=r_0} = \frac{NM_{NaCl}e^2}{4\pi\epsilon_0 r_0^2} - \frac{nNB}{r_0^{n+1}} = 0 \tag{4-2.7}$$

which can be rearranged and solved for B

$$B = \frac{e^2 M_{NaCl}}{4\pi\epsilon_0 n} r_0^{n-1} \tag{4-2.8}$$

When the result of Eq. 4-2.8 is substituted into Eq. 4-2.6, we obtain Eq. 4-2.9:

$$U = -\frac{NM_{NaCl}e^2}{4\pi\epsilon_0 r_0}\left(1 - \frac{1}{n}\right) \tag{4-2.9}$$

The value of n can be estimated from the measured compressibility of NaCl to be 9.1.

In a form suitable for calculating numerical results, in kJ mol^{-1}, using r_0 in Angstroms, Eq. 4-2.9 becomes

$$U = -1389 \frac{M_{\text{NaCl}}}{r_0}\left(1 - \frac{1}{n}\right) \tag{4-2.10}$$

and inserting appropriate values of parameters we obtain Eq. 4-2.11.

$$U = -1389 \frac{1.747}{2.82}\left(1 - \frac{1}{9.1}\right)$$
$$U = -860 + 95 = -765 \text{ kJ mol}^{-1} \tag{4-2.11}$$

Notice that the repulsive energy (95 kJ mol^{-1}) equals only about 11% of the attractive (coulombic) energy (860 kJ mol^{-1}). The total is, therefore, not very sensitive to the value of n. A small error in the estimation of n from compressibility data is not highly significant. For instance, if a value of $n = 10$ had been used, an error of only 9 kJ mol^{-1} (or 1.2%) would have been made.

4-3 Generalization of the Lattice Energy Calculation

As mentioned in the previous section, the Madelung constant is determined solely by the geometry of the structure. For an ionic structure that is the same as that of NaCl, but where each ion has a charge of ± 2 (as in MgO), the Madelung constant for NaCl can still be used. It is only necessary to modify Eq. 4-2.9 to replace the quantity $-e^2$ with the appropriate charges. For MgO, this would be $(2e)(-2e)$. In general, Eq. 4-2.9 becomes Eq. 4-3.1:

$$U = -\frac{NM_{\text{NaCl}}Z^2 e^2}{4\pi\epsilon_0 r_0}\left(1 - \frac{1}{n}\right) \tag{4-3.1}$$

Equation 4-3.1 may be used for any structure whose Madelung constant is M_{NaCl}, and where the ions have the charges Z^+ and Z^-.

The value of n can be estimated for alkali halides by using the average of the following numbers:

He 5   Kr 10
Ne 7   Xe 12
Ar 9

where the noble gas symbol denotes the noble-gaslike electron configuration of the ion. Thus for LiF an average of the He and Ne values $(5 + 7)/2 = 6$ would be used.

4-4 The Born–Haber Cycle. Experimental Approaches to Lattice Energies

One test of whether an ionic model is a useful description of a substance is the ability of the model to produce an accurate value for the enthalpy of formation of the substance. It is not possible, though, to measure the enthalpy of reaction 4-2.4 or its reverse. It is not experimentally feasible to do so, because NaCl does not vaporize to give Na$^+$ and Cl$^-$. Rather it vaporizes to give NaCl(g) and, depending on temperature, a number of aggregates, (NaCl)$_x$(g), which dissociate at very high temperatures into atoms.

To circumvent this problem, the Born–Haber thermodynamic cycle is used. This is illustrated in Fig. 4-2. The cycle is useful because the formation of NaCl(s) from the elements according to Eq. 4-4.1:

$$Na(s) + \tfrac{1}{2} Cl_2(g) \longrightarrow NaCl(s) \tag{4-4.1}$$

can be broken down into a series of steps. If the enthalpies of these steps are added, algebraically, the result must equal the enthalpy for reaction 4-4.1, the enthalpy of formation (ΔH_f°) for NaCl(s):

$$\Delta H_f^\circ = \Delta H_{vap}^\circ + \tfrac{1}{2} \Delta H_{diss}^\circ + \Delta H_{EA}^\circ + \Delta H_{ion}^\circ + U \tag{4-4.2}$$

Each term in Eq. 4-4.2 corresponds to a step in the cycle shown in Fig. 4-2. The enthalpy terms correspond to the vaporization of sodium (ΔH_{vap}°), the dissociation of Cl_2 into gaseous atoms (ΔH_{diss}°), electron attachment to Cl(g) to give Cl(g)$^-$ (ΔH_{EA}°), the first ionization enthalpy of a gaseous sodium atom (ΔH_{ion}°), and the formation of NaCl(s) from gaseous ions (U).

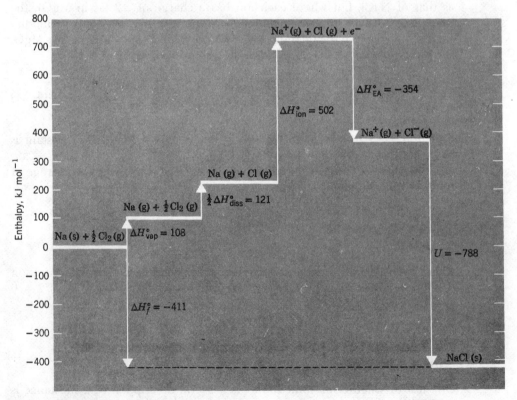

Figure 4-2   The Born–Haber cycle for NaCl.

Any one of the enthalpies in Eq. 4-4.2 can be calculated if the others are known. For NaCl all the enthalpies except U have been measured independently. The following summation can thus be made:

$$
\begin{array}{ll}
\Delta H_f^\circ & -411 \\
-\Delta H_{\text{vap}}^\circ & -108 \\
-\tfrac{1}{2}\,\Delta H_{\text{diss}}^\circ = & -121 \\
-\Delta H_{\text{EA}}^\circ & 354 \\
-\Delta H_{\text{ion}}^\circ & -502 \\
\hline
U \quad = & -788\,\text{kJ mol}^{-1}
\end{array}
\tag{4-4.3}
$$

The result is within 1% of the value of U obtained in very precise calculations. This good agreement supports (but does not prove) the idea that the ionic model for NaCl is a useful one.

4-5   Ionic Radii

In a manner similar in principle to that in which covalent radii were estimated, it is possible to assign radii to ions. The internuclear distance, d, between two ions in an ionic structure is assumed to be equal to the sum of the radii of the ions:

$$
d = r^+ + r^- \tag{4-5.1}
$$

By comparing distances in different compounds with an ion in common, it can be shown first that the radii of ions are substantially constant. For example, the difference in the radii of K^+ and Na^+ can be evaluated in four different halides:

$$
\begin{aligned}
r_{K^+} - r_{Na^+} &= d_{KF} - d_{NaF} = 0.35\ \text{Å} \\
&= d_{KCl} - d_{NaCl} = 0.33\ \text{Å} \\
&= d_{KBr} - d_{NaBr} = 0.32\ \text{Å} \\
&= d_{KI} - d_{NaI} = 0.30\ \text{Å}
\end{aligned}
$$

Actually, the apparent trend as the halide ion size increases is a real effect that can be understood in terms of packing considerations, but we shall not discuss that topic further. Suffice it to say that if $(r_{K^+} - r_{Na^+})$ is substantially constant, it is reasonable to assume that r_{K^+} and r_{Na^+} are themselves substantially constant.

It is easy to work out extensive sets of sums and differences of ionic radii. Then, provided that the actual radius of any one ion can be evaluated, the radii of all of the ions will be determined. This problem has no rigorous solution, but Pauling proposed a practical one, namely, that for two ions with

Table 4-2 Some Ionic Radii (in Angstroms)[a]

Main Group Elements

Li^+ 0.60	Be^{2+} 0.31	Al^{3+} 0.50			O^{2-} 1.40	H^- 2.08
Na^+ 0.96	Mg^{2+} 0.65	Ga^{3+} 0.62			S^{2-} 1.84	F^- 1.35
K^+ 1.33	Ca^{2+} 0.99	In^{3+} 0.81	Sn^{4+} 0.71		Se^{2-} 1.98	Cl^- 1.81
Rb^+ 1.48	Sr^{2+} 1.13	Tl^{3+} 0.95	Pb^{4+} 0.84	Pb^{2+} 1.21	Te^{2-} 2.21	Br^- 1.95
Cs^+ 1.69	Ba^{2+} 1.35					I^- 2.16

Transition Metal Ions

Ti^{4+} 0.68	Fe^{3+} 0.53	Mn^{2+} 0.80
Zr^{4+} 0.80	Cr^{3+} 0.55	Fe^{2+} 0.75
Ce^{4+} 1.01		Co^{2+} 0.72
		Ni^{2+} 0.69

Others

Zn^{2+} 0.74	Cd^{2+} 0.97	Hg^{2+} 1.10

[a]These are so-called Pauling radii, estimated using the essential assumption explained in the text but incorporating a number of additional small corrections.

the same noble gas configuration, say Na^+ and F^-, the ratio of the radii should be inversely proportional to the ratio of the nuclear charges felt by the outer electrons.

The nuclear charges that are felt by the outer electrons are the effective nuclear charges defined in Section 2-6. For Na^+ and F^-, the effective nuclear charge is given by $Z^* = Z - \sigma$. In each case, the value of the screening constant, σ, is 4.15. This is also the value for the isoelectronic Ne. The calculations develop as follows: $Z^*(Na^+) = 11.00 - 4.15 = 6.85$, while $Z^*(F^-) = 9.00 - 4.15 = 4.85$. Hence, according to Pauling's proposal, the ratio of the ionic radii should be given by Eq. 4-5.2:

$$\frac{r_{Na^+}}{r_{F^-}} = \frac{4.85}{6.85} = 0.71 \qquad (4\text{-}5.2)$$

Since the internuclear distance in NaF is 2.31 Å, we have Eq. 4-5.3:

$$r_{Na^+} + r_{F^-} = 2.31 \qquad (4\text{-}5.3)$$

Treating the ratio (Eq. 4-5.2) and the sum (Eq. 4-5.3) as a pair of simultaneous equations in two unknowns, we obtain the individual radii:

$$r_{F^-} = 1.35$$

$$r_{Na^+} = 0.96$$

The ionic radii in Table 4-2 were derived in this fashion. The values are of general utility, but should be corrected, as described in the next section, to account for differences among crystal lattices.

4-6 Geometries of Crystal Lattices

Figure 4-1 shows six of the most important structures formed by essentially ionic substances. The common qualitative feature of all these structures is that the ions are packed to maximize the contacts between those of opposite charge and to minimize repulsions between those of the same charge. In a three-dimensional sense, ions of opposite charge alternate. The nearest neighbors of one ion are ions of opposite charge. However, this qualitative idea alone does not account for all of the features that can be seen in Fig. 4-1. For AB-type compounds we see four structure types. Consider first those of NaCl and CsCl. The difference is that in the NaCl structure each cation has six nearest neighbor anions, whereas in the CsCl structure each cation has eight such neighbors. We say that the *coordination numbers* of the cations are six and eight, respectively. In both the zinc blende and wurzite structures the cation has a coordination number of only four. Again, for AB_2-type compounds there is a fluorite structure where the cation coordination number is four and a rutile structure where it is six. Why does a particular AB or AB_2 compound adopt one and not another of these structures?

The answer lies partly in a consideration of the relative sizes of the ions. Anions are almost always larger than cations, since the net excess of nuclear charge on cations draws their electron clouds in, while the excess of negative charge on anions causes the electron clouds to expand. The optimum arrangement should allow the maximum number of oppositely charged ions to be neighbors without unduly squeezing together ions of the same charge. Thus the greater the ratio of cation to anion size, the higher the coordination number of the cation can—and should—be. That is why the relatively large Cs^+ surrounds itself with eight Cl^- ions, but for the smaller Na^+ there are only six.

It is possible to treat this idea in a semiquantitative way, by finding, for each structure, that ratio, r^-/r^+, for which the anions just touch one another while making contact with the cation, a situation we shall call perfect packing. For the CsCl structure, the relevant geometric relations (Fig. 4-3) are as follows.

First, the anions just touch one another along the edge, a, of the cube. The radii of the two anions, therefore, combine to give the length of the cube edge, as in Eq. 4-6.1:

$$2r^- = a \tag{4-6.1}$$

Second, the cation touches each anion along the body diagonal of the cube, which has length $a\sqrt{3}$. The cation–anion distance is therefore half this distance, as in Eq. 4-6.2:

$$r^+ + r^- = \frac{\sqrt{3}}{2}\,a \tag{4-6.2}$$

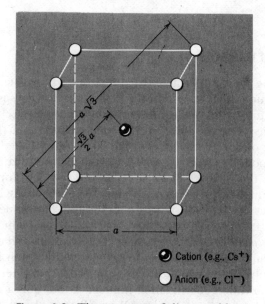

Cation (e.g., Cs^+)

Anion (e.g., Cl^-)

Figure 4-3 The geometry of the crystal lattice for CsCl.

Equations 4-6.1 and 4-6.2 define the geometric requirements for perfect packing of ions in the CsCl-type crystal lattice. Both equations are satisfied for values of r^+ and r^- such that $r^-/r^+ = 1.37$. Similar considerations suggest that perfect packing for octahedral coordination number six is achieved when $r^-/r^+ = 2.44$. Also, the tetrahedral coordination number four is preferred when $r^-/r^+ = 4.44$. This is summarized in Table 4-3.

It should be stressed, however, that the foregoing analysis based on ion sizes is only a part of the picture. It works best for compounds that are most truly ionic, namely, alkali and alkaline earth halides, oxides, and sulfides; but even some of these do not obey predictions based solely on the radius ratio. With compounds in which the ions are highly polarizable (e.g., copper(I) and zinc compounds) coordination numbers often are lower than expected.

In a case where the cation is very small relative to the anion ($r^-/r^+ \gg 4.44$), it will be impossible to achieve good cation–anion contact, even when anion–anion contacts are very close. Thus, ionic salts of this type are relatively unstable. Salts of the small cations Li^+, Be^{2+}, Al^{3+}, and Mg^{2+} with large polyatomic anions (e.g., ClO_4^-, CO_3^{2-}, NO_3^-, O_2^-) or even monatomic anions such as Cl^-, Br^-, and I^- are cases in point. The consequences of this are threefold.

1. In some cases, the anhydrous compounds are unstable relative to hydrates in which the cations surround themselves with water molecules. Thus $Mg(ClO_4)_2$ is a powerful absorbant for water, and lithium perchlorate forms a stable hydrate, $LiClO_4 \cdot 3H_2O$, whereas the other alkali metal perchlorates do not.

2. In other cases, the result of the bad packing is thermal instability such that the large polyatomic anion decomposes to leave behind a smaller one that can pack better with the small cation. Examples are

$$Li_2CO_3 \longrightarrow Li_2O + CO_2 \tag{4-6.3}$$

$$2NaO_2 \longrightarrow Na_2O + \tfrac{3}{2} O_2 \tag{4-6.4}$$

$$4Be(NO_3)_2 \longrightarrow Be_4O(NO_3)_6 + N_2O_4 + \tfrac{1}{2} O_2 \tag{4-6.5}$$

3. Related to point (1) are solubility relations. Thus $LiClO_4$ is about 10 times as soluble as $NaClO_4$ which, in turn, is about 10^3 times as soluble as $KClO_4$, $RbClO_4$, and $CsClO_4$. This trend is partly because the solvation enthalpies of the cations decrease as they increase in size, but it is enhanced by the fact that poor packing of the small Li^+ and Na^+ cations with the large ClO_4^- ions decreases the intrinsic stability of the crystals.

Table 4-3 The Radius Ratios r^-/r^+ That are Favored (Lead to Perfect Packing) in Several Crystal Structures

r^-/r^+	Structure Type	Coordination Number
1.37	CsCl	8
2.44	NaCl	6
4.44	ZnS	4

4-7   Structures with Close-Packed Anions

Many ionic compounds, particularly those in which the cations are small relative to the anions, have structures based on *close packing* of the spherical anions, with the cations occupying one or more sets of interstices. The NaCl structure is actually of this type, although it is not ordinarily useful to look at it that way.

Close packing of spheres in a single layer is shown in Fig. 4-4. The pattern produced is an array of contiguous equilateral triangles. Close packing in three dimensions is achieved by stacking such layers. Figure 4-5(*a*), in which the pattern is represented only by the centers of the spheres and connecting lines, shows how this is done so that the spheres of each layer nestle into depressions between spheres in the other layer.

The most important thing to note in Fig. 4-5(*a*) is that the spheres of layer (1) cover only *one half* the depressions in layer (2); thus, when layer (3) is added, there are two ways to do it. Spheres of layer (3) may be placed directly above those of layer (1), an arrangement that makes the first and third layers equivalent. The stacking pattern may therefore be called **ABA.** If this pattern is repeated, that is, spheres in the fourth layer are placed over those in the second, and so on, the long-range pattern is **ABABABA** . . . . This is called *hexagonal closest packing* (*hcp*), because the hexagonal symmetry of each layer is retained by the entire stack.

When the third layer is added, it may be placed as is shown in Fig. 4-5(*b*), that is, over those depressions in the first layer not covered by spheres in the second. This pattern may be described as **ABC.** If it is repeated indefinitely, **ABCABCABCA** . . . , we have *cubic closest packing* (*ccp*), so-called not because the hexagonal pattern is destroyed but because a cubic arrangement is produced. This can be recognized by standing a cube on one vertex with a body diagonal vertical. If now one sphere is placed at each vertex and one at the center of each face, it can be seen that portions of close-packed layers lie in horizontal planes, as is indicated in Fig. 4-6. Of course, random forms of close packing, **ABACBCACB** . . . , and so on, are possible, but occur only rarely.

It can be seen in Fig. 4-5(*a*) that between two layers of a close-packed structure there are two kinds of interstices: octahedral and tetrahedral. It is these that are occupied by cations in many close-packed halide and oxide structures. An example is the CdI_2 structure, Fig. 4-7, which is adopted by a

Figure 4-4   Close packing of spheres in a single plane.

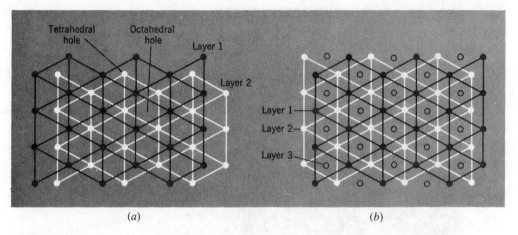

(a) (b)

Figure 4-5 (a) A diagram showing how two close-packed layers can be stacked to form both tetrahedral and octahedral holes between the layers. (b) A diagram showing three close-packed layers stacked so that no two are superimposed; this leads to the **ABC** or cubic close-packed (ccp) arrangement.

number of MX_2 compounds. The anions are hcp and the metal ions occupy octahedral holes but only in every other layer. $CdCl_2$ has a ccp array of anions with, again, every other layer of octahedral holes occupied. The NaCl structure is related to the $CdCl_2$ structure by filling the octahedral holes in every layer. In the BI_3 structure, adopted by many MX_3 compounds, every other layer of octahedral holes in a ccp array is two thirds occupied by cations.

Corundum, the α form of Al_2O_3, has an hcp array of oxide ions with two thirds of the octahedral holes occupied, but not in a layered fashion. This important structure is adopted by many other M_2O_3 compounds such as Fe_2O_3, V_2O_3, and Rh_2O_3.

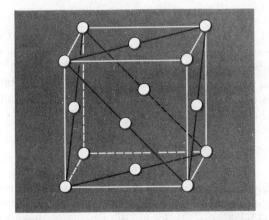

Figure 4-6 A view of a ccp array emphasizing its cubic symmetry.

Figure 4-7 A portion of the CdI_2 structure. Small spheres represent metal cations.

4-8   Mixed Metal Oxides

There is a large number of metal oxides, of great scientific and technical importance, which are essentially ionic substances. Many contain two or more different kinds of metal ions. They tend to adopt one of a few basic, general structures, the names of which are derived from the first compound—or an important one—found to have that structure.

The Spinel Structure

Spinel is a mineral, $MgAl_2O_4$. The structure is based on a ccp array of oxide ions, with Mg^{2+} ions in a set of tetrahedral holes and Al^{3+} ions in a set of octahedral holes. Many substances of the types $M^{2+}(M^{3+})_2O_4$, $M^{4+}(M^{2+})_2O_4$, and $M^{6+}(M^{+})_2O_4$ have this structure. More highly charged cations tend to prefer the octahedral holes so that in $M^{4+}(M^{2+})_2O_4$ compounds the octahedral holes are occupied by all the M^{4+} ions and one half of the M^{2+} ions.

The Ilmenite Structure

Ilmenite is the mineral $FeTiO_3$. Its structure is closely related to the corundum structure except that the cations are of two kinds. In ilmenite the cations are Fe^{2+} and Ti^{4+}, but many substances with the ilmenite structure have cations with charges of $(+1, +5)$ or $(+3, +3)$.

Small cation
Large cation
Oxide or halide ion

Figure 4-8   The perovskite structure.

The Perovskite Structure

Perovskite is the mineral $CaTiO_3$. Its structure, shown in Fig. 4-8, is based on a ccp array of oxide ions together with large cations, similar in size to the oxide ion. The smaller cations lie in octahedral holes formed entirely by oxide ions. Again, the individual cation charges are not important so long as their sum is $+6$. The structure is adopted by many fluorides with cations of disparate sizes, such as $KZnF_3$.

STUDY GUIDE

Scope and Purpose

The fundamental aspects of the bonding within ionic compounds have been discussed. In developing the model of ionic bonding, a complete lack of co-valency has been assumed. In addition, we have treated the simplest cases, those involving spherical ions. Where compounds are not perfectly ionic, or where complex, nonspherical ions are to be packed into a crystal lattice, the description of the bonding is not quite so straightforward. Still the principle of most efficient packing requires the same sorts of electrostatic and geometric considerations as have been presented here. The study questions marked "A. Review" require a straightforward understanding of the material presented in the chapter. Those study questions under "B. Additional Exercises" require application.

Study Questions

A. Review

1. What are the two main contributions to the cohesive energy of an ionic solid?

2. What is a Madelung constant? Why can the same Madelung constant be used for seemingly different substances?

3. What is n in the Born expression for the non-Coulomb repulsive energy? What are typical values for n?

4. Use Fig. 4-2 as a guide and write out balanced chemical equations for each step in the Born–Haber cycle for CrN, KF, and MgO.

5. What proposal did Pauling make to estimate the ratio of the radii of certain anion–cation pairs?

6. Define the coordination number of a cation in a crystal lattice. Why are we more concerned with the coordination number of the cation than the anion?

7. Describe a close-packed layer of spheres.

8. Show, with drawings, the two different ways to stack three close-packed layers of spheres.

9. Explain the difference between cubic and hexagonal closest packing.

10. How are the ilmenite and corundum structures related?

11. What is the name of the mineral whose formula is $MgAl_2O_4$? What other cation charges can exist in mixed oxides of this structure?

12. For the perovskite structure to occur, what must be true of the sizes of the cations?

B. Additional Exercises

1. Consider a line of alternating cations and anions. Evaluate the Madelung constant to within 1%.

2. Design a cycle of the Born–Haber type to evaluate the enthalpy of the reaction $NH_3(g) + H^+(g) \rightarrow NH_4^+(g)$.

3. For MgO, which has the NaCl structure, the unit cell edge is 4.21 Å. Use the approach of Pauling to evaluate the radii of Mg^{2+} and O^{2-}. Compare your results with those of Table 4-2.

4. What is the coordination number of each atom in the hexagonal close-packed structure?

5. Use a Born–Haber cycle to calculate the energy of electron attachment to O(g) to form $O^{2-}(g)$. You will need the information in Problem 4A, as well as the following: ΔH_f° of MgO(s) = -602 kJ mol^{-1}; ΔH_{vap} of Mg = 150.2 kJ mol^{-1}; ΔH_{diss} of O_2 = 497.4 kJ mol^{-1}; $\Delta H_{ion}(1) + \Delta H_{ion}(2)$ for Mg = 2188 kJ mol^{-1}.

6. In Table 4-3 are listed the ratios r^-/r^+ for *perfect* packing in structures having coordination numbers of four, six, and eight. In practice, a range of values for these ratios is observed within a series of compounds having the same structure. The typical ranges for the three coordination numbers are $(4.44 - 2.44)$ for coordination number four; $(2.44 - 1.37)$ for coordination number six; 1.37 and below for coordination number eight. With this in mind, predict coordination numbers of four, six, or eight for the compounds MgF, KBr, and LiCl.

7. Why do you think the value of n in the Born repulsion expression can be estimated from compressibility data, namely, the change in volume suffered by a substance for each unit change in pressure?

SUPPLEMENTARY READING

Adams, D. M., *Inorganic Solids*, Wiley, New York, 1974.

Dasent, W. E., *Inorganic Energetics*, 2nd ed., Cambridge University Press, London, 1982.

Galasso, F. S., *Structure and Properties of Inorganic Solids*, Pergamon Press, Elmsford, NY, 1970.

Greenwood, N. N., *Ionic Crystals, Lattice Defects and Non-Stoichiometry*, Butterworths, London, 1968.

Hannay, N. B., *Solid-State Chemistry*, Prentice-Hall, Englewood Cliffs, NJ, 1967.

Johnson, D. A., *Some Thermodynamic Aspects of Inorganic Chemistry*, 2nd ed., Cambridge University Press, London, 1982.

Krebs, H., *Fundamentals of Inorganic Crystal Chemistry*, McGraw-Hill, New York, 1968.

O'Keeffe, M. and Navrotsky, A., Eds., *Structure and Bonding in Crystals*, Vols. I and II, Academic, New York, 1981.

Wells, A. F., *Structural Inorganic Chemistry*, 5th ed., Oxford University Press, London, 1984.

chapter 5

THE CHEMISTRY OF SELECTED ANIONS

5-1 Introduction

We have thus far discussed covalent bonding and some of the characteristics of simple ionic compounds, that is, compounds consisting mainly of monatomic cations, such as Na^+ or Ca^{2+}, and monatomic anions, such as F^- or O^{2-}. However, much of inorganic chemistry deals with ionic compounds of more elaborate types. In these, either the cation, or the anion, or both of them are polyatomic species, within which there are bonds and stereochemical relationships quite analogous to those within the uncharged polyatomic species that we call molecules.

In the next two chapters, the properties of anions and cations are considered in more detail, with particular though not exclusive reference to the more complex, polyatomic members of each group. The chemistry of cations is generally called *coordination chemistry* and is discussed in the next chapter. Here, the general properties of anions, as well as the specific chemistry of some of the more important ones, are outlined.

One term that must be defined here, in a preliminary way, although the subject will be covered in detail in Chapter 6, is *ligands*. When an anion (or other group) is bonded to a metal ion, it is called a ligand.

We may classify anions as follows:

1. Simple anions, such as O^{2-}, F^-, or CN^-
2. Discrete oxo anions, such as NO_3^- or SO_4^{2-}.
3. Polymeric oxo anions, such as silicates, borates, or condensed phosphates.
4. Complex halide anions, for example, TaF_6^- and anionic complexes containing multibasic anions such as oxalate, for example, $[Co(C_2O_4)_3]^{3-}$.

Some of these, such as the oxide ion, O^{2-}, or most silicate anions, can exist only in the solid state. Others such as chloride ion, Cl^-, can exist also in aqueous solution. Further, some elements that form anions, notably the halogens, O, and S, may be bound to other elements by covalent bonds as in PCl_3, CS_2, or NO_2.

More complex anions such as dithiocarbamate ($R_2NCS_2^-$) or acetylacetonate ($CH_3COCHCOCH_3^-$), which occur mainly in coordination compounds are discussed in Chapter 6. Also described separately, since they constitute a quite different class of compounds, are those involving carbanions such as CH_3^-, $C_6H_5^-$, or $C_5H_5^-$ (Chapter 29). Hydride, H^-, and complex hydrido ions such as BH_4^- and AlH_4^- are also more conveniently treated separately (Chapters 9, 12, and 13). The most extensive, important, and varied classes of anions are those containing oxygen, and we discuss them first.

5-2   The Oxide, Hydroxide, and Alkoxide Ions

Oxides

The nature of several important oxide lattices has been discussed in Chapter 4. Discrete O^{2-} ions exist in many oxides but the ion cannot exist in aqueous solutions owing to the hydrolytic reaction

$$O^{2-}(s) + H_2O = 2\ OH^-(aq) \qquad K > 10^{22} \qquad (5\text{-}2.1)$$

As an example, consider Eq. 5-2.2:

$$CaO(s) + H_2O \longrightarrow Ca^{2+}(aq) + 2\ OH^- \qquad (5\text{-}2.2)$$

Thus only those ionic oxides that are insoluble in water are inert to it. When insoluble in water, they usually dissolve in dilute acids, as in Eq. 5-2.3:

$$MgO(s) + 2H^+(aq) \longrightarrow Mg^{2+}(aq) + H_2O \qquad (5\text{-}2.3)$$

Ionic oxides function as **basic anhydrides;** they react with water to produce aqueous metal hydroxides (Eq. 5-2.2) or with acids to produce water (Eq. 5-2.3).

In contrast, the covalent oxides of the nonmetals are usually acidic in water:

$$N_2O_5 + H_2O \longrightarrow 2H^+(aq) + 2NO_3^-(aq) \qquad (5\text{-}2.4)$$

When insoluble in water, as for some of the oxides of less electropositive metals, these **acidic anhydrides** still generally dissolve in base:

$$Sb_2O_5(s) + 2\ OH^- + 5H_2O \longrightarrow 2Sb(OH)_6^- \qquad (5\text{-}2.5)$$

Basic and acidic oxides will often combine directly, as in Eq. 5-2.6:

$$\underset{\text{Base}}{Na_2O} + \underset{\text{Acid}}{SiO_2} \xrightarrow{\text{Fusion}} Na_2SiO_3 \qquad (5\text{-}2.6)$$

Amphoteric oxides behave as bases towards strong acids and as acids toward strong bases. An example is ZnO, as in Eqs. 5-2.7 and 5-2.8:

$$ZnO + 2H^+(aq) \longrightarrow Zn^{2+} + H_2O \qquad (5\text{-}2.7)$$

$$ZnO + 2\ OH^- + H_2O \longrightarrow Zn(OH)_4^{2-} \qquad (5\text{-}2.8)$$

Some relatively inert oxides dissolve neither in acid nor in base. Examples are N_2O, CO, and MnO_2. When MnO_2 does react with concentrated hydrochloric acid, it is a redox reaction, not an acid–base reaction, which takes place because the Mn^{4+} ion is unstable and reacts with Cl^- as in reaction 5-2.9:

$$4H^+ + 2Cl^- + MnO_2 \longrightarrow Mn^{2+} + 2H_2O + Cl_2 \qquad (5\text{-}2.9)$$

Some elements form several oxides. For chromium, the most stable oxide is chromium(III) oxide, Cr_2O_3, which is formed when the metal or other oxides are heated in air. It is amphoteric, as described in the section below on hydrous oxides. The oxide with chromium in the highest oxidation state is chromium(VI) oxide, CrO_3, which is an acidic anhydride:

$$CrO_3 + H_2O \longrightarrow \underset{\text{Chromic acid}}{H_2CrO_4} \qquad (5\text{-}2.10)$$

In contrast, chromium(II) oxide, CrO, is a basic anhydride:

$$CrO + H_2O \longrightarrow \underset{\text{(unstable)}}{Cr(OH)_2} \qquad (5\text{-}2.11)$$

It is typical of all elements capable of forming several oxides that the oxide with the element in the highest formal oxidation state is most acidic, while that with the element in the lowest formal oxidation state is most basic.

Hydroxides

Discrete OH^- ions exist only in the hydroxides of the more electropositive elements such as Na or Ba. For such ionic materials, dissolution in water results in the formation of aquated metal ions and hydroxide ions, as in reaction 5-2.12

$$M^+OH^-(s) + nH_2O \longrightarrow M^+(aq) + OH^-(aq) \qquad (5\text{-}2.12)$$

and the substance is a strong base.

In the limit of an extremely covalent M—O bond, dissociation will occur to varying degrees according to Eq. 5-2.13

$$MOH + nH_2O \rightleftharpoons MO^-(aq) + H_3O^+(aq) \qquad (5\text{-}2.13)$$

and the substance must be considered an acid.

Amphoteric hydroxides are those in which there is the possibility of either kind of dissociation, the one of Eq. 5-2.14 being favored by a strong acid

$$M—O—H + H^+ = M^+ + H_2O \qquad (5\text{-}2.14)$$

whereas dissociation according to Eq. 5-2.15

$$M—O—H + OH^- = MO^- + H_2O \qquad (5\text{-}2.15)$$

is favored by a strong base, because the formation of water

$$H^+ + OH^- = H_2O \qquad K_{25°C} = 10^{14} \qquad (5\text{-}2.16)$$

is so highly favored. Similarly, the hydrolytic reactions of many metal ions, which are often written as in Eq. 5-2.17

$$M^{n+} + H_2O = (MOH)^{(n-1)+} + H^+ \qquad (5\text{-}2.17)$$

can be more realistically written as acid dissociations of the aquo ions, as in Eq. 5-2.18

$$M(H_2O)_x^{n+} = [M(H_2O)_{x-1}(OH)]^{(n-1)+} + H^+ \qquad (5\text{-}2.18)$$

The higher the positive charge on the metal, the more acidic are the hydrogen atoms of the coordinated water molecules.

The OH^- ion has the ability to form bridges between metal ions. Thus, there are various compounds of the transition metals containing hydroxo bridges between pairs of metal atoms, as in structure 5-I. Although bridges of the type 5-I are most common, there are also triply bridging hydroxo groups as in structure 5-II.

5-I   5-II

Hydrous Oxides

Many so-called metal hydroxides have no discrete hydroxide ions in the lattice of the crystalline compound. This is because the compounds are actually hydrous metal oxides, or oxides with varying degrees of hydration. Hydroxo bridges are involved in the early stages of the precipitation of hydrous metal oxides. In the case of Fe^{3+}, precipitation of $Fe_2O_3 \cdot nH_2O$—commonly, but incorrectly, written $Fe(OH)_3$—proceeds through the following stages on adding OH^-

$$\underset{pH < 0}{[Fe(H_2O)_6]^{3+}} \longrightarrow \underset{0 < pH < 2}{[Fe(H_2O)_5OH]^{2+}} \qquad (5\text{-}2.19)$$

$$\longrightarrow \underset{\sim 2 < pH < \sim 3}{[(H_2O)_4Fe(OH)_2Fe(H_2O)_4]^{4+}} \qquad (5\text{-}2.20)$$

$$\longrightarrow \underset{\sim 3 < pH < \sim 5}{\text{colloidal } Fe_2O_3 \cdot xH_2O} \qquad (5\text{-}2.21)$$

$$\longrightarrow \underset{pH \sim 5}{Fe_2O_3 \cdot nH_2O \text{ ppt}} \qquad (5\text{-}2.22)$$

Figure 5-1 An important type of tetrameric structure for $M(OR)_4$ alkoxides. The circles represent entire alkoxide groups.

Similar behavior is exhibited by chromium. The hydrous oxide, $Cr_2O_3 \cdot nH_2O$, is precipitated from chromium(III) solution by aqueous ammonia. The hydrous oxide is amphoteric, reacting not only with acid, as in Eq. 5-2.23,

$$Cr_2O_3 \cdot nH_2O + \text{acid} \longrightarrow [Cr(H_2O)_6]^{3+} \tag{5-2.23}$$

but also with bases to form polymeric chromite ions, $[CrO_2]_x{}^{n-} \cdot yH_2O$.

Alkoxides

Analogous to the hydroxide ion are the alkoxide ions, RO^-. These are stronger bases than OH^-, and are, therefore, immediately hydrolyzed, as in Eq. 5-2.24:

$$RO^- + H_2O = OH^- + ROH \tag{5-2.24}$$

Many alkoxides formally analogous to the hydroxides are known, for example, $Ti(OH)_4$ and $Ti(OR)_4$. The alkoxides are often polymeric owing to the existence of bridging RO^- groups similar to 5-I and 5-II. For example, the structure shown in Fig. 5-1 is a common one for $M(OR)_4$ compounds where the metal prefers a coordination number of six and the R group is not too large. Note that the structure of Fig. 5-1 contains all three types of RO^- groups: nonbridging (or terminal), doubly bridging, and triply bridging.

5-3   Oxo Anions

Oxo Anions of Carbon

Both carbonate ($CO_3{}^{2-}$) and bicarbonate ($HCO_3{}^-$) ions exist in crystalline ionic solids and in neutral or alkaline solutions. There are many naturally occurring carbonates, some of great importance, such as limestone, $CaCO_3$.

The ions (structures 5-III and 5-IV) are planar. In carbonate, because of delocalized π bonding (Section 3-6), the bond lengths are equal, and the bond angles are 120°. The carbonate ion constitutes an AB_3 system.

5-III   5-IV   5-V   5-VI

The soluble carbonates, such as those of the alkali metals, form solutions that are basic due to the hydrolysis shown in reaction 5-3.1:

$$CO_3^{2-} + H_2O = HCO_3^- + OH^- \qquad (5\text{-}3.1)$$

The majority of the carbonates are insoluble in water, the principal exceptions being salts of the alkali metals, or of Tl^+ or NH_4^+. When insoluble carbonates are precipitated from aqueous solution, the precipitates are frequently and variously contaminated with hydroxide. This is especially true for the transition metal ions, which have a great affinity for hydroxide.

Like the other oxoanions to be discussed here, carbonate can act as a ligand, for example, in $[Co(NH_3)_5CO_3]^+$, forming one bond to the metal, as in structure 5-V. It can also form two bonds to a metal (structure 5-VI), as in $[Co(NH_3)_4CO_3]^+$.

Oxalate, $C_2O_4^{2-}$, gives insoluble salts with +2 ions such as Cu^{2+}. It is frequently found as a ligand, usually forming two bonds to the same cation, as in $[Cr(C_2O_4)_3]^{3-}$, but it can act as a bridge also.

The *carboxylate* anions have several ways in which they can behave as ligands, as distinct from ionic behavior in say, sodium acetate. The main possibilities are structures 5-VII to 5-IX. The type of structure shown in structure 5-VIII is quite common and occurs in $Na[UO_2(RCO_2)_3]$. Symmetrical bridging (structure 5-IX) occurs in the binuclear carboxylates $M_2(CO_2R)_4$ of Cu^{II}, Cr^{II}, Mo^{II}, and Rh^{II} where four carboxylato bridges are formed.

5-VII   5-VIII   5-IX

Oxo Anions of Nitrogen

Nitrite, NO_2^-, occurs normally as an anion only in $NaNO_2$ or KNO_2. It can act as a ligand in several ways (structures 5-X, 5-XI, and 5-XII):

5-X　　　　　　5-XI　　　　　　5-XII

The occurrence of a particular form can often be deduced from infrared spectra. Finally, there are tautomers, *nitrito*, M—ONO, and *nitro*, M—NO$_2$. Such tautomers occur for organic compounds, and the first inorganic example was discovered by S. M. Jørgensen in 1894 when he isolated [Co(NH$_3$)$_5$ONO]Cl$_2$ and [Co(NH$_3$)$_5$NO$_2$]Cl$_2$. The nitro isomer is always the more stable one.

Nitrates are made by dissolving the metals, oxides, or hydroxides in HNO$_3$. The crystalline salts are frequently hydrated and soluble in water. Alkali metal nitrates give nitrites on strong heating; others decompose to the metal oxides, water, and nitrogen oxides.

Like nitrite, nitrate may bond in several ways in complexes, structures 5-XIII to 5-XVI. The symmetrical structure 5-XVI is quite common. Nitrate ion is a relatively weak ligand in aqueous solutions but cations of charge $+3$ or more are often complexed in solution as MNO$_3{}^{2+}$.

5-XIII　　　　　5-XIV　　　　　5-XV　　　　　5-XVI

Oxo Anions of Phosphorus

The most important oxo anions of phosphorus are those of P^V. They are derived from orthophosphoric acid, H$_3$PO$_4$, which is properly written O=P(OH)$_3$. Such orthophosphates have tetrahedral PO$_4$ groups, and are known in one form or the other (i.e., PO$_4{}^{3-}$, HPO$_4{}^{2-}$, or H$_2$PO$_4{}^-$) for most metal ions. Some are of practical importance, for example, ammonium phosphate fertilizers, and alkali metal phosphate buffers in analysis, and the like. Natural phosphorus minerals are all orthophosphates, a major one being *fluoroapatite*, Ca$_9$(PO$_4$)$_6$·CaF$_2$. Hydroxy apatites, partly carbonated, make up the mineral part of teeth.

The precipitation of insoluble phosphates from 3–6 M nitric acid is a characteristic of the $+4$ ions of Ce, Th, Zr, and U.

Phosphates also form complexes in aqueous solution with many of the metal ions.

Arsenates generally resemble phosphates and the salts are often isomorphous. However, *antimony* differs in giving crystalline antimonates of the type KSb(OH)$_6$.

Oxo Anions of Sulfur

The common oxo anions of sulfur are sulfite, SO_3^{2-} (pyramidal—structure 5-XVII); bisulfite, HSO_3^- (also pyramidal—structure 5-XVIII); sulfate, SO_4^{2-} (tetrahedral—structure 5-XIX); and bisulfate, HSO_4^- (tetrahedral—structure 5-XX).

The sulfate ion forms many complexes in which it may coordinate to the metal ion through one oxygen atom (structure 5-XXI), through two oxygen atoms (structure 5-XXII), or it may serve as a bridge between two metal atoms (structure 5-XXIII).

5-XVII   5-XVIII   5-XIX   5-XX

Selenates are generally similar to the salts of SO_4^{2-} or HSO_4^- and are often isomorphous with them. *Tellurates* are invariably octahedral as in Hg_3TeO_6, or $K[TeO(OH)_5]\cdot H_2O$, and the parent acid is best regarded as $Te(OH)_6$.

5-XXI   5-XXII   5-XXIII

Oxo Anions of the Halogens

Chlorates, bromates, and iodates are pyramidal ions, XO_3^-, known almost exclusively in alkali metal salts.

Iodates of $+4$ ions, Ce, Zr, Hf, Th, and so on, can be precipitated from $6\,M\,HNO_3$ and provide a useful separation of these elements.

The most important *perhalate ion* (XO_4^-) is the perchlorate ion (ClO_4^-). It forms soluble salts with virtually all metal ions except the larger alkali ions, K^+, Rb^+, and Cs^+. It is often used to precipitate salts of other large $+1$ cations, for example, $[Cr(en)_2Cl_2]^+$, but this is highly inadvisable for organometallic ions such as $(\eta^5\text{-}C_5H_5)_2Fe^+$, as these compounds are often treacherously explosive. It is safer to employ $CF_3SO_3^-$, BF_4^-, or PF_6^- ions. The perchlorate ion has only a small tendency to serve as a ligand and is often used to minimize complex formation. It does, however, have some ability to coordinate, and a few perchlorate complexes are known.

Perbromate ion is a laboratory curiosity. Periodates are of the two types: tetrahedral, IO_4^-, and the octahedral species, $IO_2(OH)_4^-$ and $IO_3(OH)_3^{2-}$. Both perbromates and periodates are chiefly important as oxidants.

Oxo Ions of the Transition Metals

Tetrahedral oxo anions, MO_4^{n-}, are formed by V^V, Cr^{VI}, Mo^{VI}, W^{VI}, Mn^{VI}, Mn^{VII}, Tc^{VII}, Re^{VII}, Fe^{VIII}, Ru^{VIII}, and Os^{VIII} and can exist in solutions and in crystalline salts. They are not of general utility as anions. The best known are the permanganate (MnO_4^-) and chromate (CrO_4^{2-}) ions that are widely used not as anions but as oxidants. We consider their chemistry elsewhere under the appropriate elements.

5-4   Polynuclear Oxo Anions

The oxo anions just discussed have 2, 3, or 4 oxygen atoms attached to a central atom to give a discrete anion. However, it is possible for one or more of these oxygen atoms to be shared between two atoms to give an ion with a bridge oxygen. One example of the simplest type is dichromate (structure 5-XXIV) formed from CrO_4^- on acidification. It is essentially two tetrahedra sharing one oxygen atom.

5-XXIV

Silicates and Borates

Silicates are built up on the basis of sharing oxygen atoms of tetrahedral SiO_4 units. *Borates,* which are rather similar, are built up from planar BO_3 or less commonly from tetrahedral BO_4 units. Linking of such units can produce small groups such as $O_3SiOSiO_3^{6-}$ or $O_2BOBO_2^{4-}$. However, cyclic (structure 5-XXV), infinite chain (structure 5-XXVI), and sheet structures can be formed also by appropriate oxygen sharing, and are of preeminent importance for silicates. The charges on the anions can be ascertained by regarding nonbridging oxygen atoms to be derived from an —OH group by loss of H^+.

Ring anion
$Si_3O_9^{6-}$
5-XXV

Infinite chain anion (pyroxene)
$(SiO_3^{2-})_n$
5-XXVI

An infinite sheet of SiO_4 units tetrahedrally linked in a two-dimensional network is shown in Fig. 5-2; the stoichiometry is $(Si_2O_5^{2-})_n$.

In silicate or borate structures, the specific nature of the cations or even

(a)   (b)

Figure 5-2 (a) The hexagonal arrangement of SiO_4 linked tetrahedra giving an infinite sheet of composition ($Si_2O_5^{2-}$). ● = Si.
○ = O. The Si atoms are coplanar, and each is substantially
eclipsed by a terminal (nonlinking) oxygen. (b) The tetrahedral arrangement for each Si atom in (a). The sheet is characterized by
three planes: one containing the capping (terminal) O atoms that
eclipse each Si in (a), a second plane containing each Si atom, and a
third plane formed by the network of bridging O atoms.

their charges are relatively unimportant so long as the total positive charge is
equivalent to the total negative charge. Thus, for the pyroxene structure, which
occurs in many minerals, we can have $MgSiO_3$, $CaMg(SiO_3)_2$, $LiAl(SiO_3)_2$, and
so on. The cations lie between the chains so that their specific identity is of
minor importance in the structure, so long as the required positive charge is
supplied. Similarly, for sheet anions, the cations lie *between* sheets. Such substances could be expected to cleave readily and this is found to be so in *micas*,
which are sheet silicates.

   The final extension to complete sharing of oxygens of each tetrahedron
leads, of course, to the structure of SiO_2, *silica*. However, if some of the formally
Si^{4+} "ions" are replaced by Al^{3+}, then the framework must have a negative
charge—and positive counter ions must be distributed through it. Such *framework minerals* are called *aluminosilicates*. They are among the most diverse, widespread, and useful natural silicate minerals. Many synthetic aluminosilicates
can be made, and several are manufactured industrially for use as ion exchan-
gers (when wet) and "molecular sieves" (when dry).

   Among the most important framework aluminosilicates are the *zeolites*.
Their chief characteristic is the openness of the $[(Al, Si)O_2]_n$ framework (Figs.

Figure 5-3 The arrangement of AlO$_4$ and SiO$_4$ tetrahedra that gives the cubooctahedral cavity in some zeolites and felspathoids. The ● represents Si or Al.

5-3 and 5-4). The composition is always of the type $M_{x/n}[(AlO_2)_x(SiO_2)_y] \cdot zH_2O$ where n is the charge of the metal cation, M^{n+}, which is usually Na^+, K^+, or Ca^{2+}, and the z is the number of moles of water of hydration, which is highly variable. The openness of these structures results in the formation of channels and cavities of different sizes ranging from 2 to 11 Å in diameter. Molecules of appropriate sizes may thus be trapped in the holes, and it is this property that makes possible their use as selective adsorbents. Such zeolites are called "molecular sieves." They are used also as supports for metals or metal complexes used in heterogeneous catalytic reactions. The zeolites used are mainly synthetic. For example, slow crystallization under precisely controlled conditions of a sodium aluminosilicate gel of proper composition gives the crystalline compound $Na_{12}[(AlO_2)_{12}(SiO_2)_{12}] \cdot 27H_2O$. This hydrated form can be used as a cation exchanger in basic solution.

In the hydrate all the cavities contain water molecules. In the anhydrous state obtained by heating in vacuum to ca. 350 °C, the same cavities may be occupied by other molecules brought into contact with the zeolite, providing such molecules are able to squeeze through the apertures connecting cavities. Molecules within the cavities then tend to be held there by attractive forces of electrostatic and van der Waals types. Thus the zeolite will be able to absorb and strongly retain molecules just small enough to enter the cavities. It will not absorb at all those too big to enter, and it will absorb weakly very small molecules or atoms that can enter but also leave easily. For example, straight-chain hydrocarbons but not branched-chain or aromatic ones may be absorbed.

Some *germanates* corresponding to silicates are known but Ge, Sn, and Pb more usually form octahedral anions, $[M(OH)_6]^{2-}$. *Borates* do not form frameworks and are ring or chain polymeric anions. The most common boron mineral, *borax*, $Na_2B_4O_7 \cdot 4H_2O$, contains an anion with the structure 5-XXVII.

5-XXVII

Polymeric or Condensed Phosphates

Orthophosphate anions can also be linked by oxygen bridges. Three types of building blocks occur (structures 5-XXVIII to 5-XXX). The resulting polymeric anions are called metaphosphates if they are cyclic (structure 5-XXXI) or polyphosphates if they are linear (structure 5-XXXII). Sodium salts of con-

$PO_{3.5}{}^{2-}$
End unit
5-XXVIII

$PO_3{}^-$
Middle unit
5-XXIX

$PO_{2.5}$
Branching unit
5-XXX

densed phosphates are widely used as water softeners as they form soluble complexes with calcium and other metals. Their use has led to some ecological problems, since phosphates also act as fertilizers and in lakes can lead to abnormally high growths of algae.

$P_3O_9{}^{3-}$
5-XXXI

$P_3O_{10}{}^{5-}$
5-XXXII

Figure 5-4 Model of a zeolite (edingtonite) showing the channels in the structure. The spheres represent oxygen atoms. The Si and Al atoms lie at the centers of O_4 tetrahedra and cannot be seen. Such a tetrahedron is most easily recognized at the lower right-hand corner of the model.

Condensed phosphates are usually prepared by dehydration of orthophosphates under various conditions of temperature (300–1200 °C) and also by appropriate dehydration of hydrated species as, for example,

$$(n - 2)NaH_2PO_4 + 2Na_2HPO_4 \xrightarrow{\text{Heat}}$$

$$\underset{\text{Polyphosphate}}{Na_{n+2}P_nO_{3n+1}} + (n - 1)H_2O \qquad (5\text{-}4.1)$$

$$nNaH_2PO_4 \xrightarrow{\text{Heat}} \underset{\text{Metaphosphate}}{(NaPO_3)_n} + nH_2O \qquad (5\text{-}4.2)$$

They can also be prepared by controlled addition of water to P_4O_{10}. The resulting complex mixtures of anions can be separated by ion exchange or chromatography.

The most important *cyclic* phosphate is *tetrametaphosphate*, which can be prepared by heating copper nitrate with slightly more than an equimolar amount

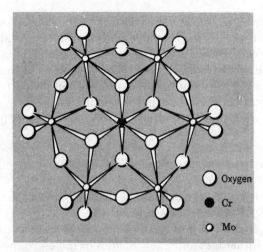

Figure 5-5 The structure of $[CrMo_6O_{21}H_6]^{3-}$. The hydrogen atoms are probably bound to oxygen atoms of the central octahedron.

of $H_3PO_4(75\%)$ slowly to 400 °C. The sodium salt can be obtained by treating a solution of the copper salt with Na_2S. Slow addition of P_4O_{10} to ice water gives ~75% of the P as tetrametaphosphate. Condensed arsenates exist only in the solid state, being rapidly hydrolyzed by water.

Polyanions of the Transition Metals

Next we look at the *transition metal polyanions*. Although we cannot discuss them in detail, the oxo anions of V^V, Nb^V, Ta^V, Mo^{VI}, and W^{VI} form extensive series of what are called *isopoly* and *heteropoly* anions. Both are built up by sharing oxygen atoms in MO_6 octahedra, where corners and edges, but not faces, may be shared. An example is shown in Fig. 5-5.

Isopoly anions, which contain only the element and oxygen, have stoichiometries such as $Nb_6O_{19}^{8-}$ and $Mo_7O_{24}^{6-}$. In heteropoly anions an additional metal or nonmetal atom is present. One example is $[Co_2^{II}W_{12}O_{42}]^{8-}$. The heteropoly salt ammonium phosphomolybdate, $(NH_4)_3[P^VMo_{12}O_{40}]$, is used in the determination of phosphorus while the large silicotungstate anion is sometimes used for precipitation of large $+1$ cations.

5-5 Halogen-Containing Anions

Ionic Halides

Most halides of metals in $+1$, $+2$, and $+3$ oxidation states are predominantly ionic in character. Of course, there is a uniform gradation from halides that are for all practical purposes purely ionic, through those of intermediate character, to those that are essentially covalent. Covalent halides and the preparation of halides are discussed in Chapter 20.

Many metals show their highest oxidation state in the fluorides. For very high oxidation states, which are formed notably with transition metals, for example, WF_6 or OsF_6, the compounds are generally gases, volatile liquids, or solids resembling closely the covalent fluorides of the nonmetals. The question as to whether a metal fluoride will be ionic or molecular cannot be reliably predicted, and the distinction between the types is not always sharp.

Fluorides in high oxidation states are often hydrolyzed by water, for example,

$$4RuF_5 + 10H_2O \longrightarrow 3RuO_2 + RuO_4 + 20HF \qquad (5\text{-}5.1)$$

The driving force for such reactions results from the high stability of the oxides and the low dissociation of HF in aqueous solution.

The halides of the alkali and alkaline earth elements (with the exception of Be) and of most of the lanthanides and a few halides of the *d*-group metals and actinides can be considered as mainly ionic materials. As the charge–radius ratio of the metal ions increases, however, covalence increases. Consider, for instance, the sequence KCl, $CaCl_2$, $ScCl_3$, $TiCl_4$. Potassium chloride is completely ionic, but $TiCl_4$ is an essentially covalent molecular compound. Similarly, for a metal with variable oxidation state, the lower halides will tend to be ionic, whereas the higher ones will tend to be covalent. As examples we can cite $PbCl_2$ and $PbCl_4$, and UF_4, which is an ionic solid, while UF_6 is a gas.

Most ionic halides dissolve in water to give hydrated metal ions and halide ions. However, the lanthanide and actinide elements in the $+3$ and $+4$ oxidation states form fluorides insoluble in water. Fluorides of Li, Ca, Sr, and Ba also are sparingly soluble. Lead gives a sparingly soluble salt, PbClF, which can be used for gravimetric determination of F^-. The chlorides, bromides, and iodides of Ag^I, Cu^I, Hg^I, and Pb^{II} are also insoluble. The solubility through a series of mainly ionic halides of a given element, $MF_n \rightarrow MI_n$ may vary in either order. In cases where all four halides are essentially ionic, the solubility order will be iodide > bromide > chloride > fluoride, since the governing factor will be the lattice energies, which increase as the ionic radii decrease. This order is found among the alkali, alkaline earth, and lanthanide halides. On the other hand, if covalence is fairly important, it can invert the trend, making the fluoride most and the iodide least soluble, as in the cases of Ag^+ and Hg_2^{2+} halides.

Halide Complex Anions

Complex halogeno anions, especially of fluoride and chloride, are of considerable importance. Halogeno anions may be formed by interaction of a metallic or nonmetallic halide acting as a Lewis acid toward the halide acting as a base:

$$AlCl_3 + Cl^- = AlCl_4^- \qquad (5\text{-}5.2)$$

$$FeCl_3 + Cl^- = FeCl_4^- \qquad (5\text{-}5.3)$$

$$BF_3 + F^- = BF_4^- \qquad (5\text{-}5.4)$$

$$PF_5 + F^- = PF_6^- \qquad (5\text{-}5.5)$$

Many such halogeno anions can be formed in aqueous solution. The relative affinities of F^-, Cl^-, Br^-, and I^- for a given metal ion is not fully understood. For crystalline materials, lattice energies are important. For BF_4^-, BCl_4^-, and BBr_4^-, the last two of which are known only in crystalline salts of large cations, lattice energies are governing. In considering the stability of the complex ions *in solution,* it is important to recognize that (a) the stability of the complex involves not only the bond strength of the M—X bond but also its stability relative to the stability of ion–solvent bonds, and (b) in general an entire series of complexes will exist, $M^{n+}(aq)$, $MX^{(n-1)+}(aq)$, $MX_2^{(n-2)+}(aq)$, . . . , $MX_x^{(n-x)+}(aq)$, where x is the maximum coordination number of the metal ion. These two points, of course, apply to all types of complexes in solution.

Generally the stability decreases in the series $F > Cl > Br > I$, but with some metal ions the order is the opposite, namely, $F < Cl < Br < I$. This is one of several problems involving acid–base interactions to be discussed in Chapter 7. It is to be emphasized that all complex fluoro "acids" such as HBF_4 and H_2SiF_6 are *necessarily strong*, since the proton can be bound *only* to a solvent molecule.

Halogeno anions are important in several ways. They are involved in many important reactions in which Lewis acids, particularly $AlCl_3$ and BF_3, take part; one example is the Friedel–Crafts reaction. For several elements, they are among the most accessible source materials; a good example is platinum as chloroplatinic acid, $(H_3O^+)_2PtCl_6$, or potassium chloroplatinite, K_2PtCl_4. Large or undeformable anions like BF_4^- or PF_6^- can be used to obtain sparingly soluble salts of appropriate cations. Finally, halide complex formation can be used for separations with anion-exchange resins. To take an extreme example, Co^{2+} and Ni^{2+}, can be separated by passing a strong HCl solution through an anion-exchange column. Co^{2+} readily forms $CoCl_3^-$ and $CoCl_4^{2-}$, whereas nickel does not give chloro complexes in aqueous solutions. Effective separation usually depends on properly exploiting the *difference* in complex formation between two cations *both* of which have some tendency to form anionic halide complexes.

Pseudohalides

Pseudohalides are substances containing two or more atoms that have halogenlike properties. Thus cyanogen, NC—CN, gives the *cyanide* ion, CN^-, and shows halogenlike behavior. Compare

$$Cu^{2+} + 2CN^- = CuCN + \tfrac{1}{2}(CN)_2 \qquad (5\text{-}5.6)$$

$$Cu^{2+} + 2\,I^- = CuI + \tfrac{1}{2}I_2 \qquad (5\text{-}5.7)$$

Other pseudohalide ions are *cyanate* (OCN^-) and *thiocyanate* (SCN^-). These are formed, respectively, from CN^- by oxidation, for example, by PbO, and by fusing, say, KCN with S_8. Their Ag^+ salts like those of the halides are insoluble in water.

The pseudohalide ions are very good ligands. For cyanate and thiocyanate there are two binding possibilities—through N or through O or S. For OCN, most nonmetals seem to be *N*-bonded in covalent compounds such as $P(NCO)_3$ while the corresponding thiocyanates are *S*-bonded.

Cyanate and the more numerous thiocyanate complexes usually have stoichiometries similar to the analogous halide complexes.

Cyanide is somewhat different in that the formation of cyanide *complexes* is restricted to transition metal *d*-block elements and Zn, Cd, and Hg. This suggests that π acceptor bonding is important in the binding of CN^- to the metal, which is almost invariably through carbon. The π acceptor character of CN^- is not nearly so high as for CO, RNC, or similar ligands (Chapter 28). This is clearly reasonable in view of its negative charge. Indeed, CN^- is a strong nucleophile, so that backbonding need not be invoked to explain the stability of its complexes with metals in $+2$ and $+3$ oxidation states. However, CN^- does have the ability to stabilize metal ions in low oxidation states as in, for example, $[Ni(CN)_4]^{4-}$. Here, some acceptance of electron density into π^* orbitals of CN^- is likely.

The majority of cyanide complexes are anionic, typical examples being $[Fe^{II}(CN)_6]^{4-}$, $[Ni(CN)_4]^{2-}$, and $[Mo(CN)_8]^{3-}$. By contrast with the similar halide complexes, the free acids of many cyano anions are known, for example, $H_4[Fe(CN)_6]$ and $H_3[Rh(CN)_6]$. The reason for this is that the proton can be located in hydrogen bonds between the cyano anions, that is, $M{-}CN \cdots H \cdots NC{-}M$.

5-6   The Sulfide and Hydrosulfide Anions

Only the alkalis and alkaline earths form sulfides that contain the S^{2-} ion. Only these sulfides dissolve in water. Although S^{2-} is not as extensively hydrolyzed as O^{2-}, nevertheless essentially only SH^- ions are present in aqueous solutions owing to the low second dissociation constant of H_2S. The S^{2-} ion is present in strongly alkaline solution, but it cannot be detected in solution less alkaline than 8 *M* NaOH owing to the reaction

$$S^{2-} + H_2O = SH^- + OH^- \qquad K \sim 1 \tag{5-6.1}$$

Polysulfide ions $S_n{}^{2-}$ are formed when solutions of alkali sulfides are boiled with sulfur. Salts can be crystallized. The ions contain kinked chains of sulfur atoms as illustrated by the $S_4{}^{2-}$, structure 5-XXXIII.

5-XXXIII

STUDY GUIDE

Scope and Purpose

The structures and chemistries of a number of important classes of anions have been presented. These anions are of particular interest to the discussion of coordination chemistry in Chapter 6, because the anions are important both as ligands and as counterions. Further details for each of the systems discussed here are available in later sections of this book. As usual, the study questions under "A. Review" are intended as a guide to the student.

Study Questions

A. Review

1. Why does the ion O^{2-} exist only in ionic lattices?
2. List the ways in which OH^- can act as a ligand.
3. List the elements that form oxoanions.
4. Many oxoanions can act as ligands in more than one way. Give the ways for
   (a) CO_3^{2-},   (b) SO_4^{2-},   (c) NO_3^-,   (d) $CH_3CO_2^-$,   (e) NO_2^-.
5. Draw the structures of $Cr_2O_7^{2-}$, $Si_2O_7^{6-}$, $B_2O_5^{4-}$.
6. How are two-dimensional silicate networks built up?
7. What is the composition of zeolites? What are molecular sieves?
8. How do the oxoanions of Ge, Sn, and Pb differ from silicates?
9. Draw structures for cyclic and linear condensed phosphates.
10. What is meant by the terms iso- and heteropoly anions?

B. Additional Exercises

1. Compare the properties of the oxides of Mg, B, Si, and Sb^V. What are their formulas, and which are acidic and/or basic?
2. Why is the oxide of an element most acidic in the highest oxidation state?
3. Titanium ethoxide is a tetramer, $[Ti(OEt)_4]_4$. Write a plausible structure for this molecule. Write a balanced equation for its reaction with water.
4. Compare the Lewis diagrams for the simpler oxoanions of S, Se, and Te.
5. What are the structures of the anions in $K_3B_3O_6$, CaB_2O_4, and $KB_5O_8 \cdot 4H_2O$?
6. Draw Lewis diagrams and discuss the nature of the multiple bonding in SO_4^{2-}, NO_3^-, and ClO_4^-. What orbitals are involved in the overlap that leads to π bonding in each case?
7. Draw an MO energy-level diagram for CN^-. What is the highest occupied MO? What is the lowest unoccupied MO? Draw the lowest unoccupied MO and show how it is involved in π bonding with a metal d-type orbital for metal cyanides.
8. Besides cyanide, what other pseudohalides might enter into π bonding with metals? Let the Lewis diagrams for these pseudohalides guide your thinking, and remember to consider d orbitals on atoms other than metals.
9. Draw Lewis diagrams for typical halate and perhalate anions, XO_3^- and XO_4^-, respectively, where X = halogen.
10. Predict the products of the reaction of the complexes $[Co(NH_3)_4CO_3]^+$ and $[Co(NH_3)_5CO_3]^+$ with acid.
11. Predict the product upon treating aqueous chromium(III) ion with ammonia.
12. The mineral chromite, $FeCr_2O_4$, can be formed by fusing which two simple, anhydrous oxides?

C. Questions from the Literature of Inorganic Chemistry

1. The following questions should be answered by consulting the paper by A. F. Reid and M. J. Sienko, *Inorg. Chem.*, **1967**, *6*, 521–524.

   (a) Write balanced chemical equations for the solid state reactions used to synthesize $ScTiO_3$ and $ScVO_3$ (two methods).

   (b) What is the oxidation state of Sc in Sc_2O_3 and in the mixed metal oxides, $ScVO_3$ and $ScTiO_3$? Based on magnetic susceptibility data available in the article, what oxidation state should be assigned to V in $ScVO_3$ and to Ti in $ScTiO_3$?

   (c) What is the electron configuration (d^n) for the V and Ti ions in $ScVO_3$ and $ScTiO_3$, respectively?

   (d) What is the likely crystal structure for $ScVO_3$ and $ScTiO_3$? How have the authors reached this conclusion?

SUPPLEMENTARY READING

Further details concerning individual anions and classes of anions can be found later in this book and in the following useful references.

Cotton, F. A. and Wilkinson, G., *Advanced Inorganic Chemistry*, 4th ed., Wiley-Interscience, New York, 1980.

Latimer, W. M. and Hildebrand, J. H., *Reference Book of Inorganic Chemistry*, 3rd ed., Macmillan, New York, 1951.

Purcell, K. F. and Kotz, J. C., *Inorganic Chemistry*, Saunders, Philadelphia, PA, 1977.

Wells, A. F., *Structural Inorganic Chemistry*, 5th ed., Clarendon, Oxford, 1984.

chapter 6

COORDINATION CHEMISTRY

6-1   Introduction

In all of their compounds, metals are surrounded by groups that are called ligands. The types of groups that may surround a metal atom or ion are greatly varied, but they may broadly be considered to be of two types: ligands that bond to metal atoms or ions through carbon atoms, and ligands that do not. The former are involved in organometallic compounds, and we postpone discussion of them until Chapters 28, 29, and 30. The branch of inorganic chemistry concerned with the remaining combined behavior of cations and their ligands is called coordination chemistry. There is, of course, no sharp dividing line between coordination chemistry and the chemistry of covalent molecules, including organometallic compounds. Nor is there a clear distinction between the chemistry of coordination compounds and that of ionic solids, in the other extreme. It is, however, traditional and convenient, in discussions of coordination compounds, to view the central metal as a cation, and to view the ligands as Lewis bases.

A few examples will help to illustrate the classification. We traditionally consider that methane and SF_6 are covalent substances, while treating BH_4^- and AlF_6^{3-} as if they were coordination compounds, formally derived from $B^{3+} + 4H^-$ and $Al^{3+} + 6F^-$, respectively. In terms of fundamental electronic properties, these distinctions would not be easy to defend. Similarly, metal–ligand bonding in $Na_3[AlF_6]$ and $AlF_3(s)$ cannot be qualitatively very different, even though we traditionally call the former a coordination compound (and AlF_6^{3-} a complex ion), and the latter an ionic compound.

The main justification for classifying many substances as coordination compounds is that their chemistry can conveniently be described in terms of a central cation M^{n+} about which a great variety of ligands L, L′, L″, and so on, may be placed in an essentially unlimited number of combinations. The overall charge on the resulting complex, $[M L_x L_y' L_z'' \ldots]$, is determined by the charge on M, and the sum of the charges on the ligands. For example, the Pt^{2+} ion forms a great many complexes, studies of which have provided much of our basic knowledge of coordination chemistry. Examples of its complexes, all of which can be interconverted by varying the concentrations of the different ligands are:

$$[Pt(NH_3)_4]^{2+} \quad [Pt(NH_3)_3Cl]^+ \quad [Pt(NH_3)_2Cl_2] \quad [Pt(NH_3)Cl_3]^- \quad [PtCl_4]^{2-}$$

For complexes of Pt^{2+} the four ligands lie at the vertices of a square with the Pt^{2+} ion at the center. Thus, structurally, four of the five complexes in this

157

series are, unambiguously:

$$
\begin{array}{cc}
\text{H}_3\text{N} \cdots \text{NH}_3 & \text{H}_3\text{N} \cdots \text{NH}_3 \\
\text{Pt} & \text{Pt} \\
\text{H}_3\text{N} \cdots \text{NH}_3 & \text{H}_3\text{N} \cdots \text{Cl} \\
\\
\text{H}_3\text{N} \cdots \text{Cl} & \text{Cl} \cdots \text{Cl} \\
\text{Pt} & \text{Pt} \\
\text{Cl} \cdots \text{Cl} & \text{Cl} \cdots \text{Cl}
\end{array}
$$

Notice that the structure of the middle member of the series, $[\text{Pt(NH}_3)_2\text{Cl}_2]$, is ambiguous from the formula. Two isomers, cis and trans, are possible and both are well known:

$$
\begin{array}{cc}
\text{Cl} \cdots \text{NH}_3 & \text{Cl} \cdots \text{NH}_3 \\
\text{Pt} & \text{Pt} \\
\text{Cl} \cdots \text{NH}_3 & \text{H}_3\text{N} \cdots \text{Cl} \\
\text{cis} & \text{trans}
\end{array}
$$

This is one of the simplest examples of the occurrence of isomers among coordination compounds. A number of other important cases will be discussed in Section 6-4.

The fundamental and classical investigations in coordination chemistry were carried out between about 1875 and 1915 by the Danish chemist S. M. Jørgensen (1837–1914) and the French–Swiss chemist Alfred Werner (1866–1919). When they began their studies the nature of coordination compounds was a huge puzzle, which the contemporary ideas of valence and structure could not accommodate. How, for example, could a stable metal salt such as MCl_n, combine with a group of stable, independently existing molecules, for example, $x\text{NH}_3$, to form a compound $\text{M(NH}_3)_x\text{Cl}_n$ with wholly new properties? How were bonds formed? What was the structure? Jørgensen and Werner prepared thousands of new compounds, seeking to find regularities and relationships that would suggest answers to these questions. Finally, Werner developed the concept of ligands surrounding a central metal ion—the concept of a coordination complex—and deduced the geometrical structures of many of them. His structure deductions were based on the study of isomers such as those just discussed. In this very instance, he reasoned that the arrangement had to be planar to give the two isomers; a tetrahedral structure could not account for their existence. Werner received the Nobel prize in Chemistry for his work in 1913.

6-2   Structures of Coordination Compounds

Coordination Numbers and Coordination Geometries

The term coordination number has already been introduced (Chapter 4) in discussing the packing of ions in crystal lattices. The term is also widely applied to the coordination compounds that are formed between a central metal (a cation or a zero-valent metal) and its ligands. Thus, whether one discusses an array of ions in a crystal lattice or a discrete complex ion (coordination compound), the **coordination number** is the number of groups that immediately surround the metal. In addition to the number of ligands surrounding a metal, it is important to know the arrangement of the ligands—the **coordination geometry.** There is a definite correspondence between coordination geometry and coordination number. The relationship is more complicated than that previously discussed (Chapter 3) between geometry and occupancy in compounds AB_xE_y, because for coordination compounds the number of d electrons can significantly influence geometry. We now discuss the most common coordination numbers, and under each, the most common coordination geometries.

Coordination Number Two

This is relatively rare, occurring mainly with the $+1$ cations of Cu, Ag and Au, and with Hg^{2+}. The coordination geometry is linear. Examples include the ions $[H_3N—Ag—NH_3]^+$, $[NC—Ag—CN]^-$, and $[Cl—Au—Cl]^-$. Such complexes are typically unstable towards the addition of further ligands, as in Eq. 6-2.1:

$$[Cu(CN)_2]^- + 2CN^- \longrightarrow [Cu(CN)_4]^{3-} \qquad (6\text{-}2.1)$$

Coordination Number Three

The most important geometries for complexes with coordination number three are the trigonal plane and the trigonal pyramid. Examples are the planar HgI_3^- and $[Cu(CN)_3]^{2-}$ and the pyramidal $SnCl_3^-$. The latter can be considered to be derived from the Lewis acid $SnCl_2$ and the Lewis base (ligand) Cl^-, as in Eq. 6-2.2:

$$SnCl_2 + Cl^- \longrightarrow Cl \diagup \overset{\displaystyle \overset{..}{Sn}}{\underset{\displaystyle Cl}{\big|}} \diagdown Cl^- \qquad (6\text{-}2.2)$$

In some cases where the empirical formula might suggest three coordination (for example, $AlCl_3$, $FeCl_3$, and $PtCl_2PR_3$), there exist, instead, dinuclear structures in which two ligands are shared so as to give each metal center an effective coordination number of four. Two such examples are shown in structures 6-I and 6-II:

6-I   6-II

Coordination Number Four

This is one of the most important coordination numbers, giving either tetrahedral or square-planar coordination geometries. Tetrahedral complexes predominate, being formed almost exclusively by nontransition metals and by transition metals other than those near the right of the d block. The variety of compounds that adopt the tetrahedral geometry is striking. Examples include $Li(H_2O)_4^+$, BeF_4^{2-}, BH_4^-, $AlCl_4^-$, $CoBr_4^{2-}$, ReO_4^-, and $Ni(CO)_4$. Tetrahedral geometry is preferred for valence electron configurations d^0 or d^{10}, as well as for d^n configurations where square-planar geometry (or coordination number expansion to an octahedron) is not favored by the number of d electrons. It is the d^8 electron configuration that characteristically leads to square-planar geometry. Thus, it is common for complexes of the ions Ni^{2+}, Pd^{2+}, Pt^{2+}, Rh^+, Ir^+, and Au^{3+}. It is also a common geometry for complexes of the d^9 ion, Cu^{2+}. The special preference of the d^8 metal ions for the square-planar geometry occurs because this requires only one d orbital to be used in forming the four metal–ligand σ bonds, namely, the $d_{x^2-y^2}$ orbital, which has lobes pointing towards the ligands. It is then possible for the four electron pairs of the metal ion to occupy the remaining four d orbitals without being repelled by the electron pairs that form the metal–ligand bonds. For the d^9 case, only one electron has to be placed in the high energy $d_{x^2-y^2}$ orbital.

Coordination Number Five

This coordination number is less common than four or six, but is still very important. The two most symmetrical coordination geometries are the trigonal bipyramid (structure 6-III) and the square pyramid (structure 6-IV):

6-III   6-IV

These two geometries (previously discussed in Chapter 3) usually differ little in energy, and one may become converted into the other by small changes in bond angles. Consequently, many five-coordinate complexes do not have either structure precisely, but a structure that is intermediate between the two. Moreover, even those that do have one or the other structure in the crystal may become stereochemically nonrigid in solution, the ligands interchanging positions rapidly, as explained in Section 6-6. An interesting further illustration of the similar stabilities of the two geometries for coordination number five is afforded by the $[Ni(CN)_5]^{3-}$ ion, which forms one crystalline salt in which both geometries are found.

Coordination Number Six

This is enormously important, since nearly all cations form six-coordinate complexes. Practically all of these have one geometrical form, the octahedron, structure 6-V. It is essential to recognize that the octahedron is an extremely symmetrical figure, even though some of the stylized ways of drawing it might not show this clearly. All six ligands, and all six M—L bonds are equivalent in a regular octahedral ML_6 complex.

6-V   6-VI

As with other prototype geometries, we continue to describe complexes as "octahedral" even when different kinds of ligands are present and, hence, the full symmetry of the true octahedron cannot be retained. Even in cases where all ligands are chemically the same, octahedra are often distorted, either by electronic effects inherent in the metal ion or by forces in the surroundings. A compression or elongation of one L—M—L axis relative to the other two is called a *tetragonal* distortion, structure 6-VI, whereas a complete breakdown of the equality of the axes gives a *rhombic* distortion, structure 6-VII. If the octahedron is compressed or elongated on an axis connecting the centers of two opposite triangular faces, the distortion is called *trigonal,* structure 6-VIII.

6-VII   6-VIII

There are a very few cases in which six ligands lie at the vertices of a trigonal prism, structure 6-IX. The prism is related to the octahedron in a simple way: If one triangular face of an octahedron is rotated 60° relative to the one opposite to it, a prism is formed. The superior stability of the octahedron compared with the prism has, at least, two causes. The most evident is steric: The octahedron allows the ligands to stay further away from each other, on the average, than does the prism for any given M—L distance. It is also likely that in most cases the metal ion can form stronger bonds to an octahedral set of ligands. The cases where a trigonal prism is found mostly involve either a set of six sulfur atoms, which may interact directly with each other to stabilize the prism, or some sort of rigid cage ligand, which forces the prismatic arrangement.

6-IX

Higher Coordination Numbers

Coordination numbers of seven, eight, and nine are not infrequently found for some of the larger cations. In each of these cases there are several geometries that generally do not differ much in stability. Thus complexes with high coordination numbers are characteristically stereochemically nonrigid (Section 6-6).

For seven coordination there are three fairly regular geometries: (1) the pentagonal bipyramid (structure 6-X), (2) an arrangement derived from the octahedron by spreading one face to make room for the seventh ligand (structure 6-XIa), and (3) an arrangement similarly derived from a trigonal prism (structure 6-XIb).

6-X   6-XIa   6-XIb

Coordination number eight also has three important geometries, all of which are shown in Fig. 6-1. The cube itself is rare, since by distorting to either the antiprism or the triangular dodecahedron, interligand repulsions can be diminished while still maintaining close M—L contacts.

For the nine coordination the only symmetrical arrangement is that shown in Fig. 6-2. This is observed in many lanthanide compounds in the solid state.

Types of Ligands

The majority of ligands are anions or neutral molecules that can be thought of as electron-pair donors. Common ones are F^-, Cl^-, Br^-, CN^-, NH_3, H_2O, CH_3OH, and OH^-. Ligands such as these, when they donate one electron pair to one metal atom, are called *monodentate* (literally, one-toothed) ligands. The

Figure 6-1 Important geometries for eight-coordinate complexes: The cube and its two principal distortions (a) to produce a square antiprism, and (b) to produce a dodecahedron.

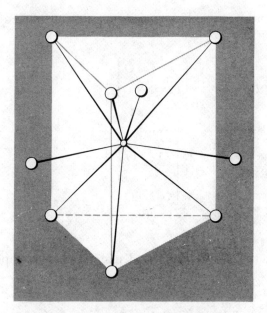

Figure 6-2 The structure of many nine-coordinate complexes. Six ligands (three each, top and bottom) define the trigonal prism that is capped above each rectangular face by one of three "equatorial" ligands.

five complexes of Pt^{2+} mentioned in the introduction contain only monodentate ligands, Cl^- and NH_3.

Ligands that contain two or more atoms, each of which can simultaneously form a two-electron donor bond to the same metal ion, are called *polydentate* ligands. They are also called *chelate* (from the Greek for claw) ligands since they appear to grasp the cation between the two or more donor atoms.

Bidentate Ligands

These are the most common of the polydentate ligands. Neutral ones include diamines, diphosphines, and diethers that form stable five-membered rings with the metal:

$$H_2\ddot{N}CH_2CH_2\ddot{N}H_2 \qquad \text{Ethylenediamine, en}$$

$$(C_6H_5)_2\ddot{P}CH_2CH_2\ddot{P}(C_6H_5)_2 \qquad \text{Diphos}$$

$$CH_3\ddot{O}CH_2CH_2\ddot{O}CH_3 \qquad \text{Glyme}$$

Some important bidentate ligands form six-membered rings with the metal, for example, bipyridyl and acetylacetonate:

Bipyridyl, bipy   Acetylacetonate, acac

A number of common anions serve as chelates, forming four-membered rings with the metal:

Carboxylates   Nitrate

Dithiocarbamates   Sulfate

Polydentate Ligands

These include tri-, quadri-, penta-, and hexadentate ligands. Examples of tridentate ligands are

Diethylene triamine, dien   Terpyridyl, terpy

Quadridentate ligands may be of the open chain type, such as the following Schiff base derived from acetylacetone, but more important are the many

acacen

macrocyclic ligands, such as porphyrin (structure 6-XII) and its derivatives, phthalocyanine (structure 6-XIII), and a host of similar molecules that can be synthesized readily, for example, structure 6-XIV.

6-XII   6-XIII   6-XIV

There are also the tripod ligands that favor the formation of trigonal-bipyramidal complexes, as shown in structure 6-XVa. An example is the molecule $N[CH_2CH_2P(C_6H_5)_2]_3$, which coordinates as in structure 6-XVb:

$(Ph = C_6H_5)$

6-XVa   6-XVb

Isomerism in Coordination Compounds

Geometrical Isomerism

One of the reasons coordination chemistry can become quite complicated is that there are many ways in which isomers can arise. We have already observed that square complexes of the type ML_2X_2 can exist as cis and trans isomers. Other important forms of geometrical isomerism are illustrated in structures 6-XVI to 6-XIX. Isomers of octahedral complexes that are of particular importance are the trans, structure 6-XVI, and cis, structure 6-XVII, isomers of the ML_4X_2 species and the facial (structure 6-XVIII) and meridional (structure 6-XIX) isomers of ML_3X_3 species.

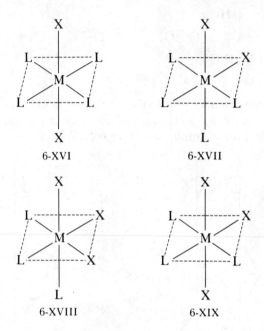

6-XVI   6-XVII

6-XVIII   6-XIX

Optical Isomerism

Optical isomers are molecules that are mirror images of each other that cannot be superimposed. Since they cannot be superimposed, they are not identical, even though all their internal distances and angles are identical. They also react identically unless the reactant is also one of a pair of optical isomers. Their most characteristic difference, which gives rise to the term *optical,* is that each one causes the plane of polarization of plane-polarized light to be rotated, but in opposite directions.

Two molecules that are optical isomers in this sense are called enantiomorphs. Their existence was first recognized among organic compounds when a tetrahedral carbon atom was bonded to four different groups, as in lactic acid:

It was one of Werner's accomplishments to recognize that for certain types of octahedral complexes, enantiomorphs should also exist. He prepared and resolved these compounds and used this result to support his hypothesis that the coordination geometry was indeed octahedral. Among the most important

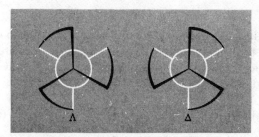

Figure 6-3 Diagrams of tris-chelate complexes showing how the absolute configurations are defined according to twist. The two optical isomers are oriented to show their mirror image relationship. The view for each is along the axis of three-fold symmetry.

enantiomorphous octahedral complexes are those that contain two or three bidentate ligands. The enantiomorphs of a $M(L—L)_2X_2$ complex are shown as structures 6-XX and 6-XXI. Those of the $M(L—L)_3$ type are structures 6-XXII and 6-XXIII.

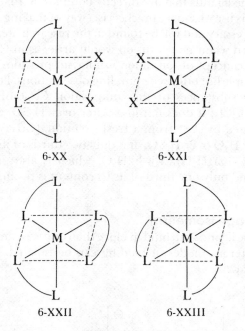

For the latter, which are called tris-chelate complexes, another useful way to regard them is shown in Fig. 6-3, where the view is perpendicular to one pair of opposite triangular faces of the octahedron. Viewed in this way, the molecules have the appearance of helices, like a ship's propellor, with the twist of the helix being opposite in the two cases. Figure 6-3 also defines a notation for the absolute configurations: Λ (Greek capital lambda) for laevo or left; Δ (Greek capital delta) for dextro or right.

Ionization Isomerism

Compounds may have the same empirical formula and still differ in which anions are coordinated to the metal and which are present as counterions within the crystal lattice. Such isomers yield different ions when dissolved, as illustrated by Eqs. 6-2.3 and 6-2.4:

$$[Co(NH_3)_4Cl_2]NO_2 \longrightarrow [Co(NH_3)_4Cl_2]^+ + NO_2^- \qquad (6\text{-}2.3)$$

$$[Co(NH_3)_4Cl(NO_2)]Cl \longrightarrow [Co(NH_3)_4Cl(NO_2)]^+ + Cl^- \qquad (6\text{-}2.4)$$

The two reactants in these equations, $[Co(NH_3)_4Cl_2]NO_2$ and $[Co(NH_3)_4Cl(NO_2)]Cl$, are ionization isomers. Consider also the three ionization isomers shown in Eqs. 6-2.5 to 6-2.7:

$$[Co(en)_2(NO_2)Cl]SCN \longrightarrow [Co(en)_2(NO_2)Cl]^+ + SCN^- \qquad (6\text{-}2.5)$$

$$[Co(en)_2(NO_2)SCN]Cl \longrightarrow [Co(en)_2(NO_2)SCN]^+ + Cl^- \qquad (6\text{-}2.6)$$

$$[Co(en)_2(SCN)Cl]NO_2 \longrightarrow [Co(en)_2(SCN)Cl]^+ + NO_2^- \qquad (6\text{-}2.7)$$

In these illustrations the square brackets are used to enclose the metal atom and all the ligands that are directly bound to it, that is, are in the coordination shell. This use of square brackets is a way of making this distinction in formulas when necessary and will be found in the research literature. They can, however, be omitted when no confusion would arise, as in $Co(NH_3)_3Cl_3$.

The concept of ionization isomerism provides the key to understanding many simple but otherwise puzzling observations. For example, there are three different substances of the composition $CrCl_3 \cdot 6H_2O$. One is violet and is $[Cr(H_2O)_6]Cl_3$; it does not lose water over H_2SO_4 and all Cl^- is immediately precipitated by Ag^+ from a fresh solution. $[Cr(H_2O)_5Cl]Cl_2 \cdot H_2O$ is green; it loses one H_2O over H_2SO_4 and only two thirds of its Cl content is precipitated promptly. $[Cr(H_2O)_4Cl_2]Cl \cdot 2H_2O$, which is also green, loses two H_2O over H_2SO_4 and only one third of its Cl content is promptly precipitated.

Linkage Isomerism

Some ligands can bind in more than one way, and often isomeric complexes with different modes of binding can be isolated. The oldest example is the isomeric pair:

Nitro   Nitrito

Other ligands prone to give linkage isomers, or at least to bind in different ways in different compounds, are SCN^-, which may use either S or N as the donor atom and sulfoxides, $R_2S{=}O$, which may use either S or O as the donor. A ligand that can bond in two ways is called an ambidentate ligand.

Coordination Isomerism

In compounds where both cation and anion are complex, the distribution of ligands can vary, giving rise to isomers. The following are examples:

$$[Co(NH_3)_6][Cr(CN)_6] \quad \text{and} \quad [Cr(NH_3)_6][Co(CN)_6]$$
$$[Cr(NH_3)_6][Cr(SCN)_6] \quad \text{and} \quad [Cr(NH_3)_4(SCN)_2][Cr(NH_3)_2(SCN)_4]$$
$$[Pt^{II}(NH_3)_4][Pt^{IV}Cl_6] \quad \text{and} \quad [Pt^{IV}(NH_3)_4Cl_2][Pt^{II}Cl_4]$$

6-3 Nomenclature for Coordination Compounds

The naming of coordination compounds follows the rules established by the International Union of Pure and Applied Chemistry (IUPAC). The most important rules, which find frequent use, will be presented here.

Designations for Ligands

When they form part of the name of a coordination compound, some ligands have special names:

NH_3	ammine
H_2O	aqua
NO	nitrosyl
CO	carbonyl

Anionic ligands have their usual names but they are modified to end in *o*; for example:

$CH_3CO_2^-$	acetato
CN^-	cyano
F^-	fluoro
O^{2-}	oxo
O_2^{2-}	peroxo
OH^-	hydroxo
H^-	hydrido

Other types of anions having names ending in *ate* are given ligand names ending in *ato*, e.g. SO_4^{2-}, sulfato.

Organic radicals, even if treated as anions when figuring the formal oxidation number of the metal, are given their usual names as radicals, for example:

CH_3	methyl
C_6H_5	phenyl

Most other ligands receive their ordinary names, but with spaces omitted:

$(CH_3)_2SO$	dimethylsulfoxide
$(NH_2)_2CO$	urea
C_5H_5N	pyridine
$(C_6H_5)_3P$	triphenylphosphine

The ligands N_2 and O_2 are called *dinitrogen* and *dioxygen*.

Order of Listing

The ligands are listed first, the metal last. Ligands are usually listed in alphabetical order, ignoring prefixes that designate the number of each type of ligand that occurs more than once in the coordination sphere. Coordination spheres that bear an overall positive charge (i.e., are cations) are named before their counteranions. Coordination compounds that bear an overall negative charge (i.e., are anions) are named after their countercations.

Metal Ions and Oxidation Numbers

For neutral and cationic complexes, the usual name of the metal is used, followed by a Roman numeral in parentheses giving its formal oxidation number. When the complex is an anion, the metal is designated by a word ending in *ate* and sometimes by using a Latin form, for example, ferrate, cuprate, with the formal oxidation number in parentheses.

Numerical Prefixes

The occurrence of two or more ligands, or metal atoms, is indicated with the following prefixes.

2	di (bis)	8	octa
3	tri (tris)	9	nona (ennea)
4	tetra (tetrakis)	10	deca
5	penta (pentakis)	11	undeca
6	hexa (hexakis)	12	dodeca
7	hepta		and so on

The prefixes in parentheses are used when the name of the ligand already contains a prefix from this list, for example, ethylenediamine or triphenylphosphine.

At this point, we illustrate with some examples. Note that in formulas the metal atom is mentioned first, followed by the ligands.

$[Co(NH_3)_5CO_3]Cl$	Pentaamminecarbonato-cobalt(III) chloride
$[Cr(H_2O)_4Cl_2]Cl$	Tetraaquadichloro-chromium(III) chloride
$K_2[OsCl_5N]$	Potassium pentachloro-nitridoosmate(VI)
$[(C_6H_5)_4As][PtCl_2(H)CH_3]$	Tetraphenylarsonium-dichlorohydridomethyl-platinate(II)
$Mo[(C_6H_5)_2PCH_2CH_2P(C_6H_5)_2]_2(N_2)_2$	Bis(1,2-diphenylphosphino-ethane)bis(dinitrogen)-molybdenum(0)

Indicating Isomers

When a particular isomer is to be specified, an italic prefix followed by a hyphen is used. Important ones are *cis-*, *trans-*, *fac-*, and *mer-*. These last two are used for octahedral complexes of the types found in structures 6-XVIII and 6-XIX, respectively, and are abbreviations for *fac*ial and *mer*idional. Thus, if in structure 6-XIX, the L ligands were $(C_2H_5)_3P$, the X ligands H, and the metal ruthenium, we would have

$$mer\text{-}[Ru\{(C_2H_5)_3P\}_3H_3]$$

mer-Tris(triethylphosphine)trihydridoruthenium(III)

As we can observe in this and other illustrations, parentheses and curly brackets are sometimes necessary to avoid confusion. Common sense is usually the best guide in using them.

Bridging Ligands

A bridging ligand is designated by the prefix μ-. When there are two bridging groups of the same kind, di-μ- is used. The bridging ligand(s) is listed in order with the other ligands, set off between hyphens, unless the molecule is symmetrical so that a more compact name results from placing it first. The following examples illustrate this fact.

$$[(NH_3)_5Co\text{—}NH_2\text{—}Co(NH_3)_4(H_2O)]Cl_5$$

Pentaamminecobalt(III)-μ-amidotetraammineaquacobalt(III) chloride

$$\left[(NH_3)_4Co \underset{\underset{H_2}{N}}{\overset{O_2}{\diagup\diagdown}} Co(NH_3)_4 \right]^{4+}$$

Tetraamminecobalt(III)-μ-amido-μ-superoxotetraamminecobalt(III)

The bridging —O_2— group in the above example is named for the superoxide anion, O_2^-, because physical data suggest the −1 charge.

$$[(NH_3)_5Cr\text{—}OH\text{—}Cr(NH_3)_5]Br_5$$

μ-Hydroxobis[pentaamminechromium(III)] bromide

$$\left[(NH_3)_2Pt \underset{Cl}{\overset{Cl}{\diagup\diagdown}} Pt(NH_3)_2 \right] Cl_2$$

Di-μ-chlorobis[diammineplatinum(II)] chloride

6-4   The Stability of Coordination Compounds

Equilibrium Constants for the Formation of Complexes in Solution

The formation of complexes in aqueous solution is a matter of great importance not only in inorganic chemistry but also in biochemistry, analytical chemistry, and in a variety of applications. The extent to which an aquo cation combines with ligands to form complex ions is a thermodynamic problem and can be treated in terms of appropriate expressions for equilibrium constants.

Suppose we put a metal ion, M, and some monodentate ligand, L, together in solution. Assuming that no insoluble products are formed, nor any species containing more than one metal ion, equilibrium expressions of the following sort will describe the system:

$$M + L = ML \qquad K_1 = \frac{[ML]}{[M][L]}$$

$$ML + L = ML_2 \qquad K_2 = \frac{[ML_2]}{[ML][L]}$$

$$ML_2 + L = ML_3 \qquad K_3 = \frac{[ML_3]}{[ML_2][L]}$$

$$\vdots \qquad \vdots \qquad \vdots \qquad \vdots$$

$$ML_{N-1} + L = ML_N \qquad K_N = \frac{[ML_N]}{[ML_{N-1}][L]} \qquad (6\text{-}4.1)$$

There will be N such equilibria, where N represents the maximum coordination number of the metal ion, M, for the ligand L. N may vary from one ligand to another. For instance, Al^{3+} forms $AlCl_4^-$ and AlF_6^{3-}, and Co^{2+} forms $CoCl_4^{2-}$ and $Co(NH_3)_6^{2+}$, as the highest complexes with the ligands indicated.

Another way of expressing the equilibrium relations is the following:

$$M + L = ML \qquad \beta_1 = \frac{[ML]}{[M][L]}$$

$$M + 2L = ML_2 \qquad \beta_2 = \frac{[ML_2]}{[M][L]^2}$$

$$M + 3L = ML_3 \qquad \beta_3 = \frac{[ML_3]}{[M][L]^3}$$

$$\vdots \qquad \vdots \qquad \vdots \qquad \vdots$$

$$M + NL = ML_N \qquad \beta_N = \frac{[ML_N]}{[M][L]^N} \qquad (6\text{-}4.2)$$

Since there can be only N independent equilibria in such a system, it is clear that the K_i's and the β_i's must be related. The relationship is indeed, rather obvious. Consider, for example, the expression for β_3. Let us multiply both numerator and denominator by $[ML][ML_2]$ and then rearrange slightly:

$$\beta_3 = \frac{[ML_3]}{[M][L]^3} \cdot \frac{[ML][ML_2]}{[ML][ML_2]}$$

$$= \frac{[ML]}{[M][L]} \cdot \frac{[ML_2]}{[ML][L]} \cdot \frac{[ML_3]}{[ML_2][L]}$$

$$= K_1 K_2 K_3 \qquad (6\text{-}4.3)$$

It is not difficult to see that this kind of relationship is perfectly general, namely:

$$\beta_k = K_1 K_2 K_3 \ldots K_k = \prod_{i=1}^{i=k} K_i \qquad (6\text{-}4.4)$$

The K_i's are called the *stepwise formation constants* (or stepwise stability constants), and the β_i's are called the *overall formation constants* (or overall stability constants); each type has its special convenience.

The set of stepwise formation constants, K_i's, provide particular insight into the species present as a function of concentrations. With only a few exceptions, there is generally a slowly descending progression in the values of the K_i's in any particular system. This is illustrated by the data for the Cd^{2+}—NH_3 system where the ligands are uncharged and by the Cd^{2+}—CN^- system where the ligands are charged.

$$Cd^{2+} + NH_3 = [Cd(NH_3)]^{2+} \qquad K = 10^{2.65}$$

$$[Cd(NH_3)]^{2+} + NH_3 = [Cd(NH_3)_2]^{2+} \qquad K = 10^{2.10}$$

$$[Cd(NH_3)_2]^{2+} + NH_3 = [Cd(NH_3)_3]^{2+} \qquad K = 10^{1.44}$$

$$[Cd(NH_3)_3]^{2+} + NH_3 = [Cd(NH_3)_4]^{2+} \qquad K = 10^{0.93} \ (\beta_4 = 10^{7.12}) \qquad (6\text{-}4.5)$$

$$Cd^{2+} + CN^- = [Cd(CN)]^+ \qquad K = 10^{5.48}$$

$$[Cd(CN)]^+ + CN^- = [Cd(CN)_2] \qquad K = 10^{5.12}$$

$$[Cd(CN)_2] + CN^- = [Cd(CN)_3]^- \qquad K = 10^{4.63}$$

$$[Cd(CN)_3]^- + CN^- = [Cd(CN)_4]^{2-} \qquad K = 10^{3.55} \ (\beta_4 = 10^{18.8}) \qquad (6\text{-}4.6)$$

Thus, typically, as ligand is added to the solution of metal ion, ML first forms more predominantly than any other complex in the series. As addition of ligands is continued, the ML_2 concentration rises rapidly, while the ML concentration drops, then ML_3 becomes dominant, ML and ML_2 becoming unimportant, and so on, until the highest complex, ML_N, is formed to the nearly complete exclusion of all others at very high ligand concentrations.

A steady decrease in K_i as i increases is almost always observed, although occasional exceptions occur because of unusual steric or electronic affects. The principal reason for the decrease is statistical. At any given step, say from ML_n to ML_{n+1}, there is a certain probability for the complexes ML_n to gain another ligand, and a different probability for ML_{n+1} to lose a ligand. As n increases, there are more ligands to be lost and fewer places $(N - n)$ in the coordination shell to accept additional ligands. For a series of steps ML to ML_2, $\ldots$, ML_5 to ML_6, the magnitude of log K_i tends to decrease by about 0.5 at each step for statistical reasons alone.

Many methods of chemical analysis and separation are based on the formation of complexes in solution, and accurate values for formation constants are helpful. For example, different transition metal ions can be selectively determined by complexation with the hexadentate chelate, $EDTA^{4-}$, shown in Fig. 6-4. By adjusting the concentration of $EDTA^{4-}$ and the pH, one ion can be complexed while another ion (which is simultaneously in solution) is not

$[Co(EDTA)]^-$

$EDTA^{4-}$

Figure 6-4   The chelation of a metal by the hexadentate ligand $EDTA^{4-}$.

complexed. This is the basis for the determination of Th^{4+} in the presence of divalent cations. The analysis is made possible by the large difference in formation constants for the $EDTA^{4-}$ complexes of the $4+$ and $2+$ cations. $EDTA^{4-}$ is less selective among ions of like charge, but the addition of CN^- allows the determination of the alkaline earth cations in the presence of the cations of Zn, Cd, Cu, Co, and Ni, because the latter form more stable complexes with CN^- than with $EDTA^{4-}$.

The Chelate Effect

As a general rule, a complex containing one (or more) five- or six-membered chelate rings is more stable (has a higher formation constant) than a complex that is as similar as possible but lacks some or all of the chelate rings. A typical illustration is

$$Ni^{2+}(aq) + 6NH_3(aq) =$$

$\beta_6 = 10^{8.6}$

$$Ni^{2+}(aq) + 3H_2NCH_2CH_2NH_2(aq) = \left[\begin{array}{c} \\ \end{array} \right]^{2+}_{(aq)} \qquad \beta_3 = 10^{18.3}$$

The complex with three chelate rings is about 10^{10} times more stable. Why should this be true? As with all questions concerning thermodynamic stability, we are dealing with free energy changes, $\Delta G°$, and we first look at the contributions of enthalpy and entropy, to see if one or the other is the main cause of the difference.

We can more directly compare these two reactions by combining them in the equation:

$$Ni(NH_3)_6^{2+}(aq) + 3(en)(aq) = Ni(en)_3^{2+}(aq) + 6NH_3(aq) \qquad (6\text{-}4.7)$$
$$(en = ethylenediamine)$$

for which

$$K = 10^{9.7}$$
$$\Delta G° = -RT \ln K = -67 \text{ kJ mol}^{-1} = \Delta H° - T \Delta S°$$
$$\Delta H° = -12 \text{ kJ mol}^{-1}$$
$$-T \Delta S° = -55 \text{ kJ mol}^{-1}$$

It is evident that both enthalpy and entropy favor the chelate complex, but the entropy contribution is far more important. Data for a large number of these reactions, with many different metal ions and ligands, show that enthalpy contributions to the chelate effect are sometimes favorable, sometimes unfavorable, but always relatively small. The general conclusion is that *the chelate effect is essentially an entropy effect*. The reason for this is as follows.

The nickel ion is coordinated by six H_2O molecules. In each of the first two reactions, these six H_2O molecules are liberated when the nitrogen ligands become coordinated. On that score, the two processes are equivalent. However, in one case *six* NH_3 molecules *lose* their freedom at the same time, and there is no net change in the number of particles. In the other case, only *three* en molecules lose their freedom, and thus there is a net increase of 3 mol of individual molecules. The reaction with three en causes a much greater increase in disorder than does that with six NH_3 molecules and, therefore, $\Delta S°$ is more positive (more favorable) in the former case than in the latter. It is easy to see that this reasoning is general for all such comparisons of a chelate with a nonchelate process.

Another way to state the matter is to visualize a chelate ligand with one donor atom attached to a metal ion. The other donor atom cannot then get very far away, and the probability of it, too, becoming attached is greater than if it were in an entirely independent molecule, with access to the entire volume of solution. Thus the chelate effect weakens as ring size increases. The effect is greatest for five- and six-membered rings, becomes marginal for seven-membered rings, and is unimportant thereafter. When the ring to be formed is large, the probability of the second donor atom attaching itself promptly to the same metal atom is no longer large as compared with its encountering a different metal atom, or as compared with the dissociation of the first donor atom before the second one makes contact.

6-5   Reactivity of Coordination Compounds

Virtually all of transition metal chemistry and a great deal of the rest of inorganic chemistry could be included under this title, taken in its broadest sense. Only three aspects will be covered in this and the following sections: substitution reactions, electron transfer reactions, and isomerization reactions. Additional aspects of reactivity will be discussed in Chapters 28–30, under organometallic compounds. A detailed correlation of structure, bonding, and reactivity will have to be postponed until Chapter 23 and later, when a discussion of bonding in coordination compounds can be developed.

Substitution Reactions of Octahedral Complexes

The ability of a complex to engage in reactions that result in replacing one or more ligands in its coordination sphere (by other ligands in solution, for instance) is called its lability. Those complexes for which such substitution reactions are rapid are called **labile,** whereas those for which such substitution reactions proceed slowly (or not at all), are called **inert.** We note that these terms are kinetic terms, because they reflect rates of reaction. They should not be confused with the thermodynamic terms **stable** and **unstable,** which refer to the tendency of species to exist (as governed by the equilibrium constants K or β) under equilibrium conditions. A simple example of this distinction is provided by the $[Co(NH_3)_6]^{3+}$ ion, which will persist for months in an acid medium because of its kinetic inertness (slow reactivity) despite the fact that it is thermodynamically unstable, as shown by the large equilibrium constant ($K \sim 10^{25}$) for reaction 6-5.1:

$$[Co(NH_3)_6]^{3+} + 6H_3O^+ \longrightarrow [Co(H_2O)_6]^{3+} + 6NH_4^+ \qquad (6\text{-}5.1)$$

In contrast, the overall formation constant ($\beta_4 = 10^{22}$) for reaction 6-5.2 indicates that the thermodynamic stability of $[Ni(CN)_4]^{2-}$ is high.

$$Ni^{2+} + 4CN^- \longrightarrow [Ni(CN)_4]^{2-} \qquad (6\text{-}5.2)$$

Nevertheless, the rate of exchange of CN^- ligands with excess CN^- in solution is immeasurably fast by ordinary techniques. The complex $[Ni(CN)_4]^{2-}$ is both thermodynamically stable and kinetically labile; the terms are not contradictory. It is not required, in other words, that there be any relationship between thermodynamic stability and kinetic lability. Of course this lack of any necessary relation between thermodynamics and kinetics is to be found generally in chemistry, but its appreciation here is especially important.

A practical definition of the terms labile and inert can be given. Inert complexes are those whose substitution reactions have half-lives longer than a minute. Such reactions are slow enough to be studied by classical techniques where the reagents are mixed and changes in absorbance, pH, gas evolution, and so on, are followed directly by the observer. Data can be taken conveniently for such reactions. Labile complexes are those that have half-lives for a reaction under a minute. Special techniques are required for collecting data during such reactions, as they may appear to be finished within the time of mixing.

In the first transition series, virtually all octahedral complexes save those of Cr^{III} and Co^{III}, and sometimes Fe^{II}, are normally labile; that is, ordinary complexes come to equilibrium with additional ligands (including water) so rapidly that the reactions appear instantaneous by ordinary techniques of kinetic measurement. Complexes of Co^{III} and Cr^{III} ordinarily undergo substitution reactions with half-lives of hours, days, or even weeks at 25 °C.

Two extreme mechanistic possibilities may be considered for any ligand substitution process or for any single step in a series of substitution reactions. First, there is the dissociative (D) mechanism in which the ligand to be replaced dissociates from the metal center, the vacancy in the coordination sphere then being taken by the new ligand. This mechanism is shown in Eq. 6-5.3:

$$[L_5MX] \xrightarrow{\text{Slow}} X + \underset{\substack{\text{Five-coordinated}\\\text{intermediate}}}{[L_5M]} \xrightarrow[\text{Fast}]{+Y} [L_5MY] \qquad (6\text{-}5.3)$$

where L represents a nonlabile ligand, X is the leaving ligand, and Y is the entering ligand. The important feature of such a mechanism is that the first step (dissociation of the leaving group) is rate determining. Once formed by cleavage of the bond to the leaving group, X, the five-coordinate intermediate will react with the new ligand, Y, almost immediately. This mechanism for ligand substitution is comparable to the S_N1 mechanism in organic systems, because the formation of the intermediate with reduced coordination number is unimolecular, as well as rate determining.

The other extreme possibility for ligand substitution is the addition–elimination mechanism, or the associative (A) mechanism. In this case the new ligand, Y, attacks the original complex directly to form a seven-coordinate intermediate in the rate-determining step, as shown in Eq. 6-5.4:

$$[L_5MX] + Y \xrightarrow{\text{Slow}} \left[L_5M \underset{Y}{\overset{X}{<}} \right] \xrightarrow{\text{Fast}} [L_5MY] + X \qquad (6\text{-}5.4)$$

After rate-determining association between the entering ligand, Y, and the metal complex, the leaving group, X, is lost in a fast step. The rate-determining step is bimolecular for the mechanism shown by Eq. 6-5.4.

Unfortunately, these two extreme mechanisms are just that—extremes—

and observed mechanisms are seldom so simple. Instead of a five- or seven-coordinate intermediate, a transition state may be reached in which some degree of bond breaking accompanies a given degree of bond making. The interchange of the ligands X and Y would be accomplished mostly by breaking the bond to the leaving group (interchange–dissociative, I_d) or by making the bond to the entering group (interchange–associative, I_a), but in each case both ligands are bound to the metal to one extent or another. In Fig. 6-5 are presented reaction profiles for each of the four mechanistic cases just mentioned.

To complicate matters further, the rate law that is determined for a reaction from kinetic data cannot be used to identify the mechanism for that reaction. This happens because additional steps in the overall substitution may take place, obscuring the simple first- and second-order rate laws that are expected for unimolecular and bimolecular processes, respectively. The three most important cases that illustrate this sort of complication are (1) solvent intervention, (2) ion-pair formation, and (3) conjugate-base formation.

1. Solvent Intervention. Many reactions of complexes have been studied in solvents that are themselves ligands. Water, for instance, is a respectable ligand, and is present in aqueous solution in high and effectively constant concentration ($\sim 55.5\ M$). The substitution of X by Y might take place by the sequence of reactions 6-5.5 and 6-5.6:

$$[L_5MX] + H_2O \longrightarrow [L_5MH_2O] + X \qquad \text{(Slow)} \qquad (6\text{-}5.5)$$

$$[L_5MH_2O] + Y \longrightarrow [L_5MY] + H_2O \qquad \text{(Fast)} \qquad (6\text{-}5.6)$$

A simple first-order rate law would be observed, and yet either reaction 6-5.5 or 6-5.6 could proceed by an A (or I_a) or a D (or I_d) mechanism.

Intervention of the solvent in reaction 6-5.5 obscures the molecularity of the rate-determining step; the reaction will necessarily be observed to be first order because of the high and constant concentration of the entering ligand, H_2O.

'2. Ion-pair Formation. When the reacting complex and the entering ligand are both ions, especially when both have high charges, ion pairs (or outer-sphere complexes, as they are sometimes called) will form, as in Eq. 6-5.7:

$$[L_5MX]^{n+} + Y^{m-} = \{[L_5MX]Y\}^{n-m} \qquad (6\text{-}5.7)$$

In the product of reaction 6-5.7, the entering ligand Y has been stabilized at the outer edge of the coordination sphere of the complex $[L_5MX]^{n+}$ primarily by electrostatics. In cases where charges on ions are not involved, an entering group, Y, may be bound at the periphery of the metal complex through, for instance, hydrogen bonding. Outer-sphere or ion-pair equilibrium constants K_{os} are generally in the range 0.05–40, depending on the charges on the ions and on their effective radii. Where ion pairs (or neutral outer-sphere complexes) are featured as intermediates in the reaction path that leads to ligand substitution, then observed rate laws will be second order, whether or not the

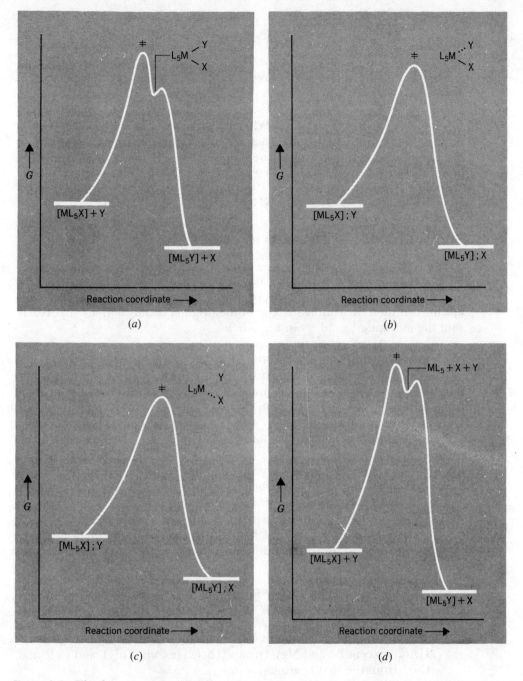

Figure 6-5 The four general mechanisms for ligand substitution in the complexes [ML_5X]. L are nonlabile ligands, X is the leaving ligand, and Y is the entering ligand. (*a*) The associative or A mechanism in which an intermediate of expanded coordination number is formed first through rate-determining entry of the ligand, Y. (*b*) The interchange-associative mechanism (I_a), in which the transition state is reached mostly through formation of the bond ($M\cdots Y$) to the entering ligand. The notations [ML_5X];Y and [ML_5Y];X for the reactants and products, respectively, represent outer-sphere complexes (or ion pairs) as formed in reaction 6-5.7. (*c*) The interchange–dissociative mechanism (I_d), in which the transition state is reached mostly through breaking the bond ($M\cdots X$) to the leaving ligand. Again, the reactants and products are outer-sphere complexes (or ion pairs) as featured in reaction 6-5.7. (*d*) The dissociative or D mechanism in which an intermediate of reduced coordination number is formed first through rate-determining cleavage of the bond to the leaving group.

mechanism at the rate-determining step involves associative or dissociative activation.

3. *Conjugate-Base Formation.* When experimental rate laws contain [OH⁻], there is the question whether OH⁻ actually attacks the metal in a true associative fashion, or whether it appears in the rate law through operation of the mechanism shown in Eqs. 6-5.8 and 6-5.9:

$$[Co(NH_3)_5Cl]^{2+} + OH^- = [Co(NH_3)_4(NH_2)Cl]^+ + H_2O \qquad (Fast) \qquad (6\text{-}5.8)$$

$$[Co(NH_3)_4(NH_2)Cl]^+ \xrightarrow[\text{then } H^+]{+Y^-} [Co(NH_3)_5Y]^{2+} + Cl^- \qquad (Slow) \qquad (6\text{-}5.9)$$

In this conjugate-base (CB) mechanism, the hydroxide first deprotonates a ligand (usually NH_3) forming the conjugate base, here leading to the NH_2^- ligand. It is then the conjugate base of the original metal complex that reacts with the incoming ligand, as in Eq. 6-5.9.

Water Exchange in Aqua Ions

Since many reactions in which complexes are formed occur in aqueous solution, one of the most fundamental reactions to be studied and understood is that in which the water ligands in the aqua ion, $[M(H_2O)_n]^{m+}$, are displaced from the first coordination shell by other ligands. Included here is the simple case in which the new ligand is another water molecule, the water-exchange reaction.

A partial survey of results is given in Fig. 6-6. Not shown here are systems where the water exchange is characteristically slow: Cr^{3+}, Co^{3+}, Rh^{3+}, Ir^{3+}, and Pt^{2+}. These five typically inert aqua ions have exchange rate constants in the range 10^{-3}–10^{-6} s⁻¹. Those ions included in Fig. 6-6 are broadly considered to be labile, but a range of 10^{10} in lability is covered. It is convenient to divide the ions into four classes, depending on these rate constants for water exchange:

Class I. Rate constants for water exchange exceed 10^8 s⁻¹ for ions that fall into this class. The exchange process is as fast here as is allowed by diffusion within the solvent, that is, these are diffusion-controlled reactions. Ions that fall into this class include those of Group IA(1), Group IIA(2) (except Be and Mg), Group IIB(12) (except Zn^{2+}), and Cr^{2+} and Cu^{2+} from the first transition series.

Class II. Ions that fall into this class have water-exchange rate constants in the range 10^4–10^8 s⁻¹. These include many of the 2+ ions of the first transition series (excepting V^{2+}, which is slower and Cr^{2+} and Cu^{2+}, which are in Class I), and the 3+ ions of the lanthanides.

Class III. Water exchange rate constants cover the range 1–10^4 for ions in this class: Be^{2+}, Al^{3+}, Ga^{3+}, V^{2+}, and some others.

Class IV. These are the ions mentioned previously that are inert, having rate constants for water exchange in the range 10^{-3}–10^{-6}.

There are a number of important trends that should be noted in the data

Figure 6-6 Characteristic rate constants (s^{-1}) for substitution of inner-sphere water ligands in various aqua ions. [Adapted from Eigen, M., *Pure and Applied Chemistry*, **1963**, *6*, 105, with revised data kindly provided by M. Eigen. See also H. P. Bennetto, and E. F. Caldin, *J. Chem. Soc. A*, **1971**, 2198.]

of Fig. 6-6. First consider either of the series of ions in Groups IA(1), IIA(2), IIB(12), or IIIB(13), where partially filled d orbitals are not featured. In each of these series, the exchange rate constant decreases as the size of the ion decreases, that is, exchange rates are lower for the smaller ions. We expect that the leaving ligands will be more tightly bound by ions of smaller size because the smaller ions (of those with a given charge) are the ones with the higher charge densities. The data of Fig. 6-6 indicate, then, that a dissociative process (D or I_d) operates in water exchange; dissociation of the leaving group is slower (smaller rate constants) where the leaving group is bound more tightly (to a smaller ion).

Such simple correlations of rate and size do not work for ions of the transition series, where the number of d electrons can influence reactivity. Compare, for instance, Cr^{2+}, Ni^{2+}, and Cu^{2+}, which have similar radii, but different reactivities. Also, the inertness of Co^{3+} is completely out of line with ionic size. More will be said later about these ions. For now, it is useful to note that transition metal ions that are typically inert include those with d^6 electron configurations (Co^{3+}, Rh^{3+}, and Ir^{3+}) and those with d^3 electron configurations (Cr^{3+}). The characteristically labile ions include the d^4 (Cr^{2+}) and d^9 (Cu^{2+}) systems.

Anation Reactions

An important reaction of the aqua ions is the addition of an anion, as in Eq. 6-5.10:

$$[M(H_2O)_6]^{n+} + X^- \longrightarrow [M(H_2O)_5X]^{(n-1)+} + H_2O \qquad (6\text{-}5.10)$$

Such reactions are especially germane to the synthesis of new complexes starting with the simple aqua ions. Anation reactions may also be considered to include reactions in which coordinated water in the substituted complexes $[ML_5H_2O]^{n+}$ is replaced by an incoming anion. In either case, two remarkably general observations have been made concerning the rates at which water ligands are replaced by anions:

1. For a given aqua ion and a series of entering monoanions, X^- (or a separate series of dianions), the rate constants for anation show little or no dependence (less than a factor of 10) on the identity of the entering ligand.

2. Rate constants for anation of a given aqua ion are practically the same (perhaps ~ 10 times slower) as the rate constant for water exchange for that aqua ion.

The most reasonable explanation for these observations is that the overall process involves the following three steps:

$$[M(H_2O)_6]^{n+} + X^- \overset{K_{os}}{=} \{[M(H_2O)_6]X\}^{(n-1)+} \qquad (6\text{-}5.11)$$

$$\{[M(H_2O)_6]X\}^{(n-1)+} \overset{k_0}{\longrightarrow} \{[M(H_2O)_5]X\}^{(n-1)+} + H_2O \qquad (6\text{-}5.12)$$

$$\{[M(H_2O)_5]X\}^{(n-1)+} \overset{\text{Very}}{\underset{\text{fast}}{\longrightarrow}} [M(H_2O)_5X]^{(n-1)+} \qquad (6\text{-}5.13)$$

In the first step an outer-sphere complex (here an ion pair) is formed with an equilibrium constant K_{os}, Eq. 6-5.11. A coordinated water molecule is then lost (Eq. 6-5.12) with rate constant k_0, a rate constant that should be close to that for water exchange in the parent aqua ion. In the third step, which is fast, and may not be distinct from the second step, the entering ligand X^- slips into the coordination spot vacated by the water ligand. The most appropriate rate law for the overall sequence from reactions 6-5.11 to 6-5.13 is given by Eq. 6-5.14:

$$\text{rate} = k_{obs}[M(H_2O)_6^{n+}][X^-] \qquad (6\text{-}5.14)$$

Experimentally, one expects to observe second-order kinetics where such a mechanism operates, and the observed second-order rate constant k_{obs} should be equal to the product $K_{os}k_0$. Values for K_{os} can be estimated and divided into the experimentally determined k_{obs}, yielding k_0. When this is done, for any of a number of anation reactions, the values for k_0 closely resemble those for the simple water exchange in $[M(H_2O)_6]^{n+}$. This is taken to be evidence that the mechanism for anation also involves dissociative activation. When coupled with a lack of dependence on the identity of the entering ligand (as long as ions of like charge are compared), this is a convincing argument.

Aquation Reactions

Complexes that are present in aqueous solution are susceptible to aquation or hydrolysis reactions in which a ligand is replaced by water. Even where other entering ligands, Y, are part of an overall reaction, it appears that there are few reactions in which the leaving ligand, X, is not first replaced by water. Thus solvent intervention is a key feature in substitutions of X by Y, and aquation of the ligand X in $[ML_5X]$ is a reaction of fundamental importance.

Our discussion will emphasize aquation of the ligand X in amine complexes of Co^{III}, as in Eq. 6-5.15, where A represents an amine-type ligand such as NH_3

$$[CoA_5X]^{n+} + H_2O \longrightarrow [CoA_5OH_2]^{(n+1)+} + X^- \qquad (6\text{-}5.15)$$

The rate law observed for such aquation reactions is a two-term rate law, shown in Eq. 6-5.16:

$$\text{rate} = k_a[CoA_5X^{n+}] + k_b[CoA_5X^{n+}][OH^-] \qquad (6\text{-}5.16)$$

The first term, involving the acid hydrolysis rate constant k_a, predominates at low pH, where $[OH^-]$ is low. The second term, involving the base hydrolysis rate constant k_b, predominates at high pH. The two-term rate law is an indication that two paths for aquation are possible, an acid hydrolysis and a base hydrolysis reaction path. At intermediate values of pH, both paths will be available. In general, k_b is $\sim 10^4$ times k_a, and it is often true that complexes that are inert under acidic conditions become labile in the presence of bases. The ammines of Co^{III}, for instance, are so labile towards substitution in aqueous base that they generally decompose in that medium through rapid, successive substitutions leading to hydroxides and hydrous metal oxides.

Acid Hydrolysis. The general equation for acid hydrolysis is reaction 6-5.15. The ligand undergoing substitution is replaced in the first coordination sphere by the entering ligand, water. Since the entering ligand is present in high and effectively constant concentration, the rate law does not contain $[H_2O]$, and tells us nothing about the order of the reaction with respect to water. The rate law is, in fact, simply a first-order rate law, as shown in Eq. 6-5.17:

$$\text{rate} = k_a[CoA_5X^{n+}] \qquad (6\text{-}5.17)$$

and the observed rate constant is always a simple, first-order rate constant, k_a. For these reasons, the rate law itself does not provide the means for deciding whether the reactions proceed by D or A mechanisms. The means for determining mechanism must be sought elsewhere. Hundreds of specific reactions have been studied, and, although numerous exceptions exist, most acid hydrolysis reactions of octahedral complexes appear to proceed through dissociative processes (D or I_d). Some of the evidence that supports this conclusion comes from the study of (1) leaving group effects, (2) steric effects, and (3) charge effects.

The effect of the leaving ligand on the acid hydrolysis rate constant k_a can be seen in the data of Table 6-1. C. H. Langford (and later A. Haim) has pointed out that the dependence is linear. This is shown in Fig. 6-7, and is called a linear free energy relationship. The rate constant, k_a, for reaction 6-5.15 is seen to be linearly dependent on the equilibrium constant, K_a, for reaction 6-5.18:

$$[CoA_5OH_2]^{3+} + X^- = CoA_5X^{2+} + H_2O \qquad K_a \qquad (6\text{-}5.18)$$

Where the equilibrium constant K_a is largest, the anion X^- (here NCS^- or F^-) is most tightly bound to cobalt in the complex CoA_5X^{2+}. As can be seen in the data of Table 6-1, these are also the systems that are least labile (have the smallest k_a). The most labile complexes (large k_a) have the least tightly bound anions X^- (small K_a). One concludes that the strength of the bond to the leaving group is important in controlling the rate of the reaction. Furthermore, that the slope in Fig. 6-1 is exactly 1.0, as pointed out by Langford, indicates that the nature of X^- in the transition state is the same as its nature in the products of the reaction: a solvated anion. In other words, one must completely cleave the bond to the leaving group in order to reach the transition state for the reaction. A dissociative mechanism is suggested, and I_d is the most reasonable proposal since no five-coordinate intermediate has been detected.

Linear free energy relationships have been observed for other reactions. A plot similar to that of Fig. 6-7 can be constructed from the data for reaction 6-5.19:

$$[IrA_5X]^{2+} + H_2O = [IrA_5OH_2]^{3+} + X^- \qquad (6\text{-}5.19)$$

The slope for such a plot is 0.9, and the rate constants k_a follow the trend $NO_3^- > I^- > Br^- > Cl^-$. The smaller slope indicates a less complete requirement for breaking the bond to the leaving group before the transition state is reached.

Table 6-1 Rate Constants k_a for the Reactions

$$[CoA_5X]^{2+} + H_2O \longrightarrow [CoA_5OH_2]^{3+} + X^-$$

and Equilibrium Constants K_a for the Reactions

$$[CoA_5OH_2]^{3+} + X^- = [CoA_5X]^{2+} + H_2O$$

X	$k_a\ (s^{-1})$	$K_a\ (M^{-1})$
NCS^-	5.0×10^{-10}	470
F^-	8.6×10^{-8}	20
$H_2PO_4^-$	2.6×10^{-7}	7.4
Cl^-	1.7×10^{-6}	1.25
Br^-	6.3×10^{-6}	0.37
I^-	8.3×10^{-6}	0.16
NO_3^-	2.7×10^{-5}	0.077

$$CoA_5X^{2+} + H_2O \xrightarrow{k_a} CoA_5H_2O^{3+} + X^-$$

$$CoA_5OH_2^{3+} + X^- \underset{}{\overset{K_a}{\rightleftharpoons}} CoA_5X^{2+} + H_2O$$

Figure 6-7 A plot of log k_a (the acid hydrolysis rate constant for reaction 6-5.15) versus $-\log K_a$ (the equilibrium constant for reaction 6-5.18). The slope of the plot is 1.0, indicating that factors controlling the strength of the Co—X bond (as measured by K_a) also influence the lability of the Co—X bond (as measured by k_a).

The dissociative nature of the acid hydrolysis mechanisms for octahedral complexes is also indicated by studies of steric effects. The data obtained by R. G. Pearson for reaction 6-5.20 are typical.

$$[Co(A—A)_2Cl_2]^+ + H_2O \longrightarrow [Co(A—A)_2Cl(OH_2)]^{2+} + Cl^- \quad (6\text{-}5.20)$$

The ligands A—A in reaction 6-5.20 are bidentate diamines that have been substituted in the carbon chains to provide increased crowding in the coordination sphere of the cobalt reactant. The data in Table 6-2 are typical of those for reactions that exhibit steric acceleration; the complexes having the larger ligands, A—A, react more quickly. Dissociative activation is indicated. No five-coordinate intermediate has been detected, so an I_d mechanism is assigned.

Charge effects also indicate dissociative activation for substitution reactions of octahedral complexes of cobalt. Compare, for instance,

$$Co(NH_3)_5Cl^{2+} \quad (k_a = 6.7 \times 10^{-6}\ s^{-1})$$

with

$$trans\text{-}[Co(NH_3)_4Cl_2]^+ \quad (k_a = 1.8 \times 10^{-3}\ s^{-1})$$

Table 6-2   Acid Hydrolysis Rate Constants for Aquation of the First Chloride Ligand in the Complexes *trans*-$[Co(A—A)_2Cl_2]^+$, Where A—A Represents a Bidentate Diamine Ligand with Increasing Substitution in the Carbon Chain[a]

A—A	k_a (s^{-1})
H_2N NH_2	3.2×10^{-5}
(with CH_3) H_2N NH_2	6.2×10^{-5}
H_3C CH_3 / H_2N NH_2	4.2×10^{-3}
H_3C CH_3 / H_3C— —CH_3 / H_2N NH_2	3.3×10^{-2}

[a]From the work of R. G. Pearson, C. R. Boston, and F. Basolo, *J. Am. Chem. Soc.*, **1953**, *75*, 3089.

Where the charge on the cobalt reactant is highest, the rate of separation of the anion Cl^- is slowest.

There are exceptions, but the majority of octahedral complexes appear to undergo substitution through mechanisms that involve dissociation of the leaving group as a predominant step. However the extreme D mechanism should be assigned only to those rare systems where a five-coordinate intermediate can be detected.

Base Hydrolysis.   Aquation reactions of octahedral complexes of Co^{III} that take place in basic solution display the rate law shown in Eq. 6-5.21:

$$\text{rate} = k_b[CoA_5X^{n+}][OH^-] \tag{6-5.21}$$

This is simply the second-order term in the general rate law, Eq. 6-5.16. The second-order rate term in Eq. 6-5.16 predominates in basic solution, so that one observes simple second-order kinetics (Eq. 6-5.21).

The interpretation of a term of the type $k_b[CoA_5X^{n+}][OH^-]$ in a rate law for base hydrolysis has long been disputed. It could, of course, be interpreted as representing a genuine associative (A) process, OH^- being a nucleophile. However, the possibility of a conjugate base (CB) mechanism (Eqs. 6-5.8 and 6-5.9) must be considered. There are arguments on both sides, and it is possible that the mechanism for base hydrolysis may vary for different complexes. Studies of base hydrolysis of Co^{III} complexes suggest that, for these complexes, the CB mechanism is the reasonable one.

As has already been mentioned, base hydrolysis of Co^{III} complexes is generally much faster than acid hydrolysis because $k_a > k_b$ in Eq. 6-5.16. This, in itself, provides evidence against a simple A mechanism, and, therefore, in favor of the CB mechanism, because there is no reason to expect OH^- to be uniquely capable of attack on the metal. In the reactions of square complexes, OH^- turns out to be a distinctly inferior nucleophile toward Pt^{II}.

The CB mechanism, of course, requires that the reacting complex have, at least, one protonic hydrogen atom on a nonleaving ligand, and that the rate of reaction of this hydrogen be fast compared with the rate of ligand displacement. It has been found that the rates of proton exchange in many complexes subject to rapid base hydrolysis are, in fact, some 10^5 times faster than the hydrolysis itself {e.g., in $[Co(NH_3)_5Cl]^{2+}$ and $[Co(en)_2NH_3Cl]^{2+}$}. Such observations are in keeping with the CB mechanism but afford no positive proof of it.

If the CB mechanism is indeed correct, there is the question of why the conjugate base so readily dissociates to release the ligand X. In view of the very low acidity of coordinated amines, the concentration of the conjugate base is a very small fraction of the total concentration of the complex. Thus, its reactivity is enormously greater, by a factor far in excess of the mere ratio of k_b/k_a. It can be estimated that the ratio of the rates of aquation of $[Co(NH_3)_4NH_2Cl]^+$ and $[Co(NH_3)_5Cl]^{2+}$ must be greater than 10^6. Two features of the conjugate base have been considered in efforts to account for this reactivity. First, there is the obvious charge effect. The conjugate base has a charge that is one unit less positive than the complex from which it is derived. Although it is difficult to construct a rigorous argument, it seems entirely unlikely that the charge effect, in itself, can account for the enormous rate difference involved. It has been proposed that the amide ligand could labilize the leaving group, X, by a combination of electron repulsion in the ground state and a π-bonding contribution to the stability of the five-coordinate intermediate, as is suggested in Fig. 6-8.

(a)   *(b)*

Figure 6-8 A diagram showing how an amide group can promote the dissociation of the trans ligand X through (a) electronic repulsion in the ground state and (b) stabilization of the five-coordinate intermediate via π bonding.

Attack on Ligands. There are some reactions where ligand exchange does not involve the breaking of metal–ligand bonds, but instead, bonds within the ligands themselves are broken and reformed. One well-known case is the aquation of the carbonato complexes according to Eq. 6-5.22:

$$[Co(NH_3)_5OCO_2]^+ + 2H_3{*}O^+ \longrightarrow$$
$$[Co(NH_3)_5(H_2O)]^{3+} + 2H_2{*}O + CO_2 \qquad (6\text{-}5.22)$$

When isotopically labeled water, H_2*O, is used, it is found that no $*O$ gets into the coordination sphere of the cobalt during aquation.

The most likely path for this aquation involves proton attack on the oxygen atom bonded to cobalt (structure 6-XXIV). This is followed by elimination of CO_2 and protonation of the hydroxo complex, as in reaction 6-5.23:

$$
\left\{
\begin{array}{c}
Co(NH_3)_5-O\cdots C\!\!\begin{array}{c}O\\ \diagdown\\ O\end{array}\\[4pt]
H^+\\
\vdots\\
O\\
H\diagup\ \diagdown H\\
\text{Transition state}
\end{array}
\right\}
\longrightarrow
\left[\begin{array}{c}Co(NH_3)_5-O\\ \mid\\ H\end{array}\right]^{2+}
\qquad (6\text{-}5.23)
$$

6-XXIV $\qquad$ $+H^+\downarrow$

$\qquad\qquad\qquad\qquad [Co(NH_3)_5(H_2O)]^{3+}$

As another example, consider the reaction of nitrite with the pentaammineaquacobalt(III) ion, as in Eq. 6-5.24:

$$[CoA_5(*OH_2)]^{3+} + NO_2^- \longrightarrow [CoA_5(N*OO)]^{2+} + H_2O \qquad (6\text{-}5.24)$$

Isotopic labeling studies show that the oxygen of the aqua ligand is one of the oxygen atoms that is in the nitro ligand. This remarkable result can be explained by the sequence of reactions 6-5.25 to 6-5.27:

$$2NO_2^- + 2H^+ = N_2O_3 + H_2O \qquad (6\text{-}5.25)$$

$$[Co(NH_3)_5*OH]^{2+} + N_2O_3 \underset{\text{Fast}}{\longrightarrow} \left\{\begin{array}{c}(NH_3)_5CO-*O\cdots H\\ \vdots\qquad\quad\vdots\\ ON\cdots ONO\end{array}\right\} \qquad (6\text{-}5.26)$$

$$\text{Transition state}$$

$$HNO_2 + [Co(NH_3)_5*ONO]^{2+} \xrightarrow{\text{Slow}} [Co(NH_3)_5(NO*O)]^{2+} \qquad (6\text{-}5.27)$$

In the transition state, it is an O—H bond that is broken, not a Co—O bond. The oxygen of the aqua ligand is, therefore, retained in the nitro ligand.

Substitution Reactions in Square Complexes

For square complexes, the mechanistic problem is more straightforward and better understood. One might expect that four-coordinate complexes would be more likely than octahedral complexes to react by associative pathways because the coordination sphere is less congested to start with. Extensive studies of Pt^{II} complexes have shown that this is true.

For reactions in aqueous solution, of the type shown in Eq. 6-5.28,

$$PtL_3X + Y \longrightarrow PtL_3Y + X \qquad (6\text{-}5.28)$$

Figure 6-9 The two reaction paths for ligand substitution in square complexes, as indicated by the two-term rate law, Eq. 6-5.29. The k_1 path involves rate-determining formation of the aquated intermediate $[PtL_3(OH_2)]^{n+}$ and subsequent, rapid substitution of the aqua ligand by Y. Both of these steps in the k_1 path appear to involve associative activation. The k_2 path involves direct replacement of X by Y, also via associative activation.

L represents nonlabile ligands, X is the leaving ligand, and Y is the entering ligand. Reactions of the type shown in Eq. 6-5.28 are found to have the rate law shown in Eq. 6-5.29:

$$\text{rate} = k_1[PtL_3X] + k_2[PtL_3X][Y] \qquad (6\text{-}5.29)$$

Such a two-term rate law indicates that two paths are available for reaction, a first-order path characterized by the rate constant k_1, and a second-order path characterized by the rate constant k_2. It is believed that the second path (k_2) proceeds through a genuine associative (A) mechanism in which Y is added to the Pt center to form a five-coordinate intermediate. The first path (k_1) represents a two-step process in which X is first replaced by solvent (water) in the rate-determining step. (This k_1 path involves, then, solvent intervention, and must, for the same reasons previously discussed for aquation reactions of octahedral complexes, obey first-order kinetics.) The k_1 path is completed when the intervening water ligand is, in turn, replaced by X. The two paths indicated by the rate law (Eq. 6-5.29) are shown in Fig. 6-9. Both paths appear to involve associative activation, and A or I_a mechanisms for each step of either the k_1 or the k_2 paths are assigned. Some of the evidence for this follows.

Charge Effects

Consider the series of Pt^{II} complexes with charges varying from $+1$ to -2:

$$[Pt(NH_3)_3Cl]^+ \qquad [Pt(NH_3)_2Cl_2] \qquad [Pt(NH_3)Cl_3]^- \qquad [PtCl_4]^{2-}$$

The observed rate constants, k_1 (for aquation in water solvent) vary only by a factor of two. This is a remarkably small variation, given the large differences in charge among the complexes. Pt—Cl bond breaking should be more difficult in the complexes with the higher positive charge. Also, complexes with the higher positive charge should favor approach of the nucleophile. Since neither of these trends is observed, an associative process is indicated in which both Pt—Cl bond breaking and Pt—OH$_2$ bond making are of comparable importance.

Steric Effects

Steric acceleration is observed for substitution reactions of octahedral complexes, and this was taken to be evidence for a dissociative nature in such reactions. For square complexes, substitution reactions are retarded by steric crowding at the metal center, and this is taken to be evidence that the entering ligand Y must approach the metal center in order to reach the transition state. This result is consistent with either an associative (A) or an interchange (I$_a$) mechanism.

Entering Ligand Effects

The second-order rate constant, k_2, in Eq. 6-5.29 is strongly dependent on the nature of the entering ligand. A reactivity series can be established in which the entering ligands, Y, are placed in order depending on the value of k_2:

$$F^- \sim H_2O \sim OH^- < Cl^- < Br^- \sim NH_3 \sim \text{olefins} < C_6H_5NH_2 < C_5H_5N$$
$$< NO_2^- < N_3^- < I^- \sim SCN^- \sim R_3P$$

This is essentially the order of nucleophilicity towards Pt^{II} that is expected for these ligands, and an associative mechanism is indicated.

Stereochemistry

A general representation of the stereochemical course of substitution reactions of square complexes is given in Fig. 6-10. It should be carefully noted that this process is entirely stereospecific: cis and trans starting materials lead, respectively, to cis and trans products. Whether any of the three intermediate configurations possess enough stability to be regarded as actual intermediates rather than merely phases of the activated complex remains uncertain.

Nonlabile Ligands. The trans Effect

A particular feature of substitution at square complexes is the important role played by nonlabile ligands that are trans to the leaving ligand. Consider reaction 6-5.30:

$$[PtLX_3] + Y \longrightarrow [PtLX_2Y] + X \qquad (6\text{-}5.30)$$

Any one of three labile ligands, X, can be replaced by the entering ligand, Y. Furthermore, the ligand X that is replaced can be either cis or trans to L, leading to cis or trans orientation of Y with respect to L in the product. It has

Figure 6-10 The steric course of ligand substitution in square complexes, and the structure (trigonal bipyramidal) of the five-coordinate intermediate. The ligands C_1 and C_2 that occupy axial positions in the intermediate trigonal bipyramid are the ligands that are cis to the leaving group, X, in the reactant. The ligand, T, in the reactant is the strongest trans director, as it lies trans to the leaving ligand, X. The entering ligand, Y, the leaving ligand, X, and the trans ligand, T, share the equatorial positions of the trigonal-bipyramidal intermediate. The new ligand, Y, in the product occupies the coordination position that was vacated by the leaving ligand, X.

been found that the relative proportions of cis and trans products varies appreciably with the nature of the ligand, L. Ligands, L, that strongly favor substitution to give trans products in reactions such as Eq. 6-5.30 are said to be strong trans directors. A fairly extensive series of ligands, L, may be arranged in order with respect to their tendency to be strong trans directors:

$$H_2O, OH^-, NH_3, py (NC_5H_5) < Cl^-, Br^- < SCN^-, I^-, NO_2^-,$$
$$C_6H_5^- < SC(NH_2)_2, CH_3^- < H^-, PR_3 < C_2H_4, CN^-, CO$$

This is also known as the *trans-effect* series. It is to be emphasized that the trans effect is here defined solely as a kinetic phenomenon. It is the effect of the ligand L on the rate of substitution in the position trans to itself. A strong trans director (a ligand high in the trans effect series) promotes more rapid substitution of the ligand trans to itself than it does of the ligand cis to itself.

The trans effect has proved very useful in rationalizing known synthetic procedures and in devising new ones. As an example, we consider the synthesis of the cis and trans isomers of $[Pt(NH_3)_2Cl_2]$. The synthesis of the cis isomer is accomplished by treatment of the $[PtCl_4]^{2-}$ ion with ammonia, as in Eq. 6-5.31:

$$(6\text{-}5.31)$$

Since Cl^- has a greater *trans* directing influence than does NH_3, substitution of NH_3 into $[Pt(NH_3)Cl_3]^-$ is least likely to occur in the position *trans* to the NH_3 already present and, thus, the *cis* isomer is favored. The trans isomer is synthesized by treating $[Pt(NH_3)_4]^{2+}$ with Cl^-, as in Eq. 6-5.32:

$$
\begin{array}{ccc}
\begin{array}{cc}
H_3N & NH_3 \\
& Pt \\
H_3N & NH_3
\end{array}
& \xrightarrow{Cl^-} &
\begin{array}{cc}
H_3N & NH_3 \\
& Pt \\
H_3N & Cl
\end{array}
& \xrightarrow{Cl^-} &
\begin{array}{cc}
Cl & NH_3 \\
& Pt \\
H_3N & Cl
\end{array}
\end{array}
\qquad (6\text{-}5.32)
$$

In this case the intermediate is disposed to give the trans isomer because of the greater trans effect of Cl^-. The first Cl^- directs the second Cl^- to the trans position.

All theorizing about the trans effect must recognize the fact that since it is a kinetic phenomenon, depending on activation energies, the stabilities of *both* the ground state and the activated complex are relevant. The activation energy can be affected by changes in one or the other of these energies or by changes in both.

The earliest attempt to explain the trans effect was the so-called polarization theory of Grinberg, which is primarily concerned with effects in the ground state. This theory deals with a postulated charge distribution as is shown in Fig. 6-11. The primary charge on the metal ion induces a dipole in the ligand, L, which in turn induces a dipole in the metal. The orientation of this dipole on the metal is such as to repel negative charge in the trans ligand, X. Hence, X is less attracted by the metal atom because of the presence of L. This theory would lead to the expectation that the magnitude of the trans effect of L and its polarizability should be monotonically related, and for some ligands in the trans effect series, for example, H^-, $I^- > Cl^-$, such a correlation is observed. In effect, this theory says that the trans effect is attributable to a ground-state weakening of the bond to the ligand that is to be displaced.

An alternative theory of the trans effect was developed with special reference to the activity of ligands such as phosphines, CO, and olefins, which are known to be strong π acids (see Chapter 28 for further details). This model attributes their effectiveness primarily to their ability to stabilize a five-coor-

Figure 6-11 The arrangement of dipoles along the trans L–M–X axis according to the polarization theory of the trans effect.

Figure 6-12 The postulated activated complex (a five-coordinate trigonal bipyramid) for reaction of Y with trans-MA_2LX to displace X.

dinate transition state or intermediate. This model is, of course, only relevant if the reactions are bimolecular; there is good evidence that this is true in the vast majority of, if not all, cases. Figure 6-12 shows how the ability of a ligand to withdraw metal $d\pi$ electron density into its own empty π or π^* orbitals could enhance the stability of a species in which both the incoming ligand, Y, and the outgoing ligand, X, are simultaneously bound to the metal atom.

Very recently, evidence has been presented to show that even in cases where stabilization of a five-coordinate activated complex may be important, there is still a ground-state effect—a weakening and polarization of the trans bond. In the anion $[C_2H_4PtCl_3]^-$ the Pt—Cl bond trans to ethylene is slightly longer than the cis ones, the Pt—*trans*-Cl stretching frequency is lower than the average of the two Pt—*cis*-Cl frequencies, and there is evidence that the *trans*-Cl atom is more ionically bonded.

The present consensus among workers in the field appears to be that, in each case, over the entire series of ligands whose trans effect has been studied, both the ground-state bond weakening and the activated-state stabilizing roles may be involved to some extent. For a hydride ion or a methyl group it is probable that we have the extreme of pure, ground-state bond weakening. With the olefins the ground-state effect may play a secondary role compared with activated-state stabilization, although the relative importance of the two effects in such instances remains a subject for speculation, and further studies are needed.

Electron Transfer Reactions

These are oxidation–reduction (redox) reactions in which an electron passes from one complex to another. Electron transfer reactions may involve substitution of one or more ligands in the first or inner coordination spheres of either reactants or products, but this is not necessary. An example of an electron transfer reaction is given by Eq. 6-5.33

$$Fe^{2+}(aq) + Ce^{4+}(aq) \longrightarrow Fe^{3+}(aq) + Ce^{3+}(aq) \qquad (6\text{-}5.33)$$

in which the aqua ion of Ce^{IV} is reduced by the aqua ion of Fe^{II}.

Figure 6-13 Free energy versus reaction coordinate for a self-exhange reaction. The profile is symmetrical because the reactants and products are identical. For other electron transfer reactions known as cross reactions, the products are at a lower energy than reactants, in proportion to the electrochemical potential ($\Delta G = -nFE$) for the reaction.

An electron transfer reaction may take place so that there is actually no net chemical change, as in Eq. 6-5.34:

$$[*Fe(CN)_6]^{2-} + [Fe(CN)_6]^{3-} = [*Fe(CN)_6]^{3-} + [Fe(CN)_6]^{2-} \quad (6\text{-}5.34)$$

Reactions such as Eq. 6-5.34 are called **self-exchange** reactions. Self-exchange reactions can only be followed by using isotopic tracers or certain magnetic resonance techniques. They are of interest because there is no change in free energy as a consequence of reaction, and the free energy profile (Fig. 6-13) is symmetrical.

There are two well-established general mechanisms for electron transfer reactions. In the first, called an **outer-sphere** electron transfer mechanism, only the outer, or solvent, coordination spheres of the two metal complexes are displaced during the reaction. No substitution of the ligands in the inner coordination spheres of either reactant is needed in order for electron transfer to take place. (There are required changes in metal–ligand bond lengths, however.) In the second mechanism, called **inner-sphere** electron transfer, the inner coordination sphere of one reactant must first undergo substitution to accept a new ligand. The new ligand must serve, once substitution has taken place, to bridge the two metal centers together. This bridging ligand is common to the inner coordination spheres of both metal centers.

The Outer-Sphere Mechanism

This mechanism is certain to be the correct one when both complexes participating in the reaction undergo ligand substitution reactions more slowly than they participate in electron transfer reactions. An example is the reaction shown in Eq. 6-5.35:

$$[Fe^{II}(CN)_6]^{4-} + [Ir^{IV}Cl_6]^{2-} \rightleftharpoons [Fe^{III}(CN)_6]^{3-} + [Ir^{III}Cl_6]^{3-} \quad (6\text{-}5.35)$$

where both reactants are "inert" towards substitution ($t_{1/2} > 1$ ms), but the redox reaction is fast ($k = 10^5 \, \text{L mol}^{-1}\text{s}^{-1}$). Clearly the electron transfer process is not constrained to wait for substitution to take place or it would be itself as slow as substitution. The outer-sphere mechanism is also the correct one when no ligand is capable of serving as a bridging ligand.

The two steps of a general outer-sphere mechanism can be illustrated using reaction 6-5.35. There is a preequilibrium, characterized by the constant K_{os}, in which an outer-sphere complex (or ion pair) is formed, as in Eq. 6-5.36.

$$[Fe(CN)_6]^{4-} + [IrCl_6]^{2-} = [Fe(CN)_6]^{4-}/[IrCl_6]^{2-} \qquad K_{os} \qquad (6\text{-}5.36)$$

$$[Fe(CN)_6]^{4-}/[IrCl_6]^{2-} \longrightarrow [Fe(CN)_6]^{3-} + [IrCl_6]^{3-} \qquad k_{et} \qquad (6\text{-}5.37)$$

This encounter (outer-sphere complex or ion pair) between the reactants brings them to within the internuclear separation required for electron transfer. The electron transfer step (Eq. 6-5.37) takes place within this outer-sphere complex, only after metal–ligand bond lengths have been altered enough to allow the electron transfer to take place adiabatically—without further change in energy. R. Marcus has recognized that the electron transfer should be adiabatic, because electron motion should be faster than nuclear motion. In other words, the electron transfer takes place quickly, once internuclear distances have become appropriately adjusted. For the complex that is being oxidized, metal–ligand distances in the activated complex must generally become shorter, because of the higher positive charge that is to exist on the metal upon oxidation. The complex being reduced must achieve longer metal–ligand bond distances in the activated complex, in anticipation of the lower positive charge that develops at the metal upon reduction.

Self-Exchange. Some self-exchange reactions that are believed to proceed by outer-sphere mechanisms are listed in Table 6-3. (The second-order rate laws that one usually observes for such reactions do not in themselves indicate

Table 6-3 Rate Constants for Some Self-Exchange Reactions that Proceed via Outer-Sphere Mechanisms

Reactants	Rate Constants ($\text{L mol}^{-1}\text{s}^{-1}$)
$[Fe(bipy)_3]^{2+}$, $[Fe(bipy)_3]^{3+}$ $[Mn(CN)_6]^{3-}$, $[Mn(CN)_6]^{4-}$ $[Mo(CN)_8]^{3-}$, $[Mo(CN)_8]^{4-}$ $[W(CN)_8]^{3-}$, $[W(CN)_8]^{4-}$ $[IrCl_6]^{2-}$, $[IrCl_6]^{3-}$ $[Os(bipy)_3]^{2+}$, $[Os(bipy)_3]^{3+}$	10^4–10^6
$[Fe(CN)_6]^{3-}$, $[Fe(CN)_6]^{4-}$	7.4×10^2
$[MnO_4]^-$, $[MnO_4]^{2-}$	3×10^3
$[Co(en)_3]^{2+}$, $[Co(en)_3]^{3+}$ $[Co(NH_3)_6]^{2+}$, $[Co(NH_3)_6]^{3+}$ $[Co(C_2O_4)_3]^{3-}$, $[Co(C_2O_4)_3]^{4-}$	$\sim 10^{-4}$

an outer-sphere mechanism; one also observes second-order kinetics for most inner-sphere electron transfer processes.)

The range covered by these rate constants is very large, extending from 10^{-4} up to, perhaps, the very high rate constants typical of processes that are slowed only by the ability of the reactants to diffuse through the solvent ($\sim 10^9$). It is possible to account qualitatively for the observed variation in rate constants in terms of the different amounts of energy required to change the metal–ligand bond distances from their initial values to those needed in the transition state. For the case of self-exchange reactions, the transition state must be symmetrical; the two halves of the activated complex must be identical. The lengthening of metal–ligand bonds that is required of the complex undergoing reduction is equal to the shortening of the metal–ligand bonds that is required of the complex undergoing oxidation. After all, self-exchange simply transforms one reactant into the other, with no net chemical change (Fig. 6-13). Furthermore, it can be shown that an unsymmetrical transition state would correspond to a higher activation energy and, therefore, would not lie along the preferred reaction path.

In the seven fastest reactions of Table 6-3 there is very little difference in the metal–ligand bond lengths in the two reacting complexes, and thus very little energy of bond stretching and bond compressing is needed to achieve the symmetrical transition state. For the MnO_4^-/MnO_4^{2-} pair the bond length difference is somewhat greater, and for the last three reactions there is a considerable difference between the two reactants in metal–ligand bond distance.

Cross Reactions. Electron transfer reactions between dissimilar complexes (e.g., reactions 6-5.33 and 6-5.35) are called **cross reactions.** For cross reactions there is a net decrease in free energy, and the free energy profile is not symmetrical. A linear free energy relationship exists for such reactions, and the faster reactions tend to be those for which the free energy change is most favorable. Marcus and Hush have derived the relationship shown in Eq. 6-5.38:

$$k_{12} = [k_{11}k_{22}K_{12}f]^{1/2} \tag{6-5.38}$$

This equation allows the calculation of the rate constant for a cross reaction (k_{12}) from the two appropriate self-exchange rate constants (k_{11} and k_{22}) and the equilibrium constant for the overall cross reaction (K_{12}). The constant f in Eq. 6-5.38 is a statistical and steric factor that is usually ~ 1. The linear free energy relationship arises because the rate of reaction (as measured by k_{12}) depends on the net free energy change of the reaction (as measured by K_{12}). In fact, it is a general result that the faster cross reactions are those with the larger equilibrium constants. Thus rate constants for cross reactions are generally higher than those for the comparable self-exchanges.

As a specific example consider the cross reaction shown in Eq. 6-5.39:

$$[Fe(CN)_6]^{4-} + [Mo(CN)_8]^{3-} \longrightarrow [Fe(CN)_6]^{3-} + [Mo(CN)_8]^{4-} \tag{6-5.39}$$

for which k_{12} is sought. The equilibrium constant, K_{12}, for reaction 6-5.39 is 1.0×10^2, and the electrochemical potential is $E = 0.12$ V. The self-exchange reactions that apply are given in Eqs. 6-5.40 and 6-5.41:

$$[Fe(CN)_6]^{4-} + [Fe(CN)_6]^{3-} \longrightarrow$$
$$[Fe(CN)_6]^{3-} + [Fe(CN)_6]^{4-} \qquad k_{11} \quad (6\text{-}5.40)$$

$$[Mo(CN)_8]^{3-} + [Mo(CN)_8]^{4-} \longrightarrow$$
$$[Mo(CN)_8]^{4-} + [Mo(CN)_8]^{3-} \qquad k_{22} \quad (6\text{-}5.41)$$

Values for the self-exchange rate constants are $k_{11} = 7.4 \times 10^2$ L mol^{-1} s^{-1} and $k_{22} = 3.0 \times 10^4$ L mol^{-1} s^{-1}. Substitution of these values into Eq. 6-5.38, and using a value for f of 0.85 yields the prediction that k_{12} should be $\sim 4 \times 10^4$ L mol^{-1} s^{-1}. The value that is obtained experimentally is 3×10^4 L mol^{-1} s^{-1}.

The Inner-Sphere (or Ligand-Bridged) Mechanism

Ligand-bridged transition states have been shown to occur in a number of reactions, mainly through the elegant experiments devised by H. Taube and his students. He has demonstrated that the following general reaction occurs:

$$[Co(NH_3)_5X]^{2+} + Cr^{2+}(aq) + 5H^+$$
$$= [Cr(H_2O)_5X]^{2+} + Co^{2+}(aq) + 5NH_4^+ \quad (6\text{-}5.42)$$

(X = F$^-$, Cl$^-$, Br$^-$, I$^-$, SO$_4^{2-}$, NCS$^-$, N$_3^-$, PO$_4^{3-}$, P$_2$O$_7^{4-}$,

CH$_3$CO$_2^-$, CH$_3$C$_7$CO$_2^-$, crotonate, succinate, oxalate, maleate)

The significance and success of these experiments rest on the following facts. The Co^{III} complex is not labile while the Cr^{II} aquo ion is, whereas, in the products, the [Cr(H$_2$O)$_5$X]$^{2+}$ ion is not labile while the Co^{II} aquo ion is. It is found that the transfer of X from [Co(NH$_3$)$_5$X]$^{2+}$ to [Cr(H$_2$O)$_5$X]$^{2+}$ is quantitative. The most reasonable explanation for these facts is a mechanism such as that illustrated in Eq. 6-5.43.

$$Cr^{II}(H_2O)_6^{2+} + Co^{III}(NH_3)_5Cl^{2+} \longrightarrow [(H_2O)_5Cr^{II}ClCo^{III}(NH_3)_5]^{4+}$$

$$\Updownarrow \text{Electron transfer}$$

$$Cr(H_2O)_5Cl^{2+} + Co(NH_3)_5(H_2O)^{2+} \longleftarrow [(H_2O)_5Cr^{III}ClCo^{II}(NH_3)_5]^{4+} \quad (6\text{-}5.43)$$

$$\Big\downarrow H^+, H_2O$$

$$Co(H_2O)_6^{2+} + 5NH_4^+$$

Since all Cr^{III} species, including [Cr(H$_2$O)$_6$]$^{3+}$ and Cr(H$_2$O)$_5$Cl^{2+}, are substitution inert, the quantitative production of Cr(H$_2$O)$_5$Cl^{2+} must imply that electron transfer, $Cr^{II} \rightarrow Co^{III}$, and Cl^- transfer from Co to Cr are mutually interdependent acts, neither possible without the other. Postulation of the binuclear, chloro-bridged intermediate appears to be the only chemically credible way to explain this. As implied by Eq. 6-5.42, many ligands can serve as ligand bridges in inner-sphere reactions.

In reactions between Cr^{2+} and CrX^{2+} and between Cr^{2+} and $Co(NH_3)_5X^{2+}$, which are inner sphere, the rates decrease as X is varied in the order $I^- > Br^- > Cl^- > F^-$. This seems reasonable if ability to "conduct" the transferred electron is associated with polarizability of the bridging group, and it appeared that this order might even be considered diagnostic of the mechanism. However, the opposite order is found for the $Fe^{2+}/Co(NH_3)_5X^{2+}$ and for the $Eu^{2+}/Co(NH_3)_5X^{2+}$ reactions. Moreover, the $Eu^{2+}/Cr(H_2O)_5X^{2+}$ reactions give the order first mentioned, thus showing that the order is not simply a function of the reducing ion used. The order must, of course, be determined by the relative stabilities of transition states with different X, and the variation in reactivity order has been rationalized on this basis.

There are now a number of cases, for example, those of $Co(NH_3)_5X^{2+}$ with $[Co(CN)_5]^{3-}$, where X = F^-, CN^-, NO_3^-, and NO_2^-, and that of Cr^{2+} with $[IrCl_6]^{2-}$, in which the electron transfer is known to take place by both inner- and outer-sphere pathways.

6-6   Stereochemical Nonrigidity

No molecule is strictly rigid in the sense that all the interatomic distances and bond angles are fixed at one precise set of values. On the contrary, all molecules, even at the absolute zero, constantly execute a set of vibrations, such that all of the atoms oscillate with amplitudes of a few tenths of an angstrom, about their average positions. In this sense, no molecule is rigid, but there are many molecules that undergo rapid deformational rearrangements of a much greater amplitude, in which atoms actually change places with each other. Such rearrangements are found among an enormous variety of compounds, including inorganic molecules such as PF_5, metal carbonyls, organometallic compounds, and organic molecules. Molecules that behave in this way are called stereochemically nonrigid. The recognition of stereochemical nonrigidity and its study is only possible by nuclear magnetic resonance (nmr) spectroscopy. Let us consider one of the earliest inorganic examples, PF_5.

Five-Coordinate Complexes. PF_5

This molecule is known to have a trigonal-bipyramidal structure. It would be expected that the fluorine (^{19}F) nmr spectrum would show a complex multiplet of relative intensity two for the axial fluorine atoms and another of intensity three for the equatorial ones. The multiplets would result from coupling of each type of fluorine to those of the other type, and from coupling of both types to the phosphorus atom which has a spin of one-half. In fact, only a sharp doublet is seen, indicating that, as far as nmr can tell, all five fluorine atoms are equivalent; the doublet structure results from their coupling to the phosphorus atom.

This result is due to the axial and equatorial fluorine atoms changing places with one another so rapidly (>10,000 times/s) that the nmr spectrometer cannot sense the two different environments and records all five of them at a single frequency, which is the weighted average of those frequencies that each separate environment would have. The fact that the splitting of the fluorine resonance into a doublet by the phosphorus atom is not lost shows that the exchange of places occurs without breaking the P—F bonds.

The generally accepted explanation for the rapid exchange of axial and equatorial fluorine atoms in PF_5 was suggested by R. S. Berry and is shown in Fig. 6-14. This rearrangement pathway has two main stages. First, there is a concerted motion of the two axial F atoms and two of the equatorial ones so that these four atoms come into the same plane and define a square. All of these four are now equivalent to each other, and the entire set of five defines a square pyramid. Second, a trigonal-bipyramidal arrangement is now recovered. There are two equally probable ways for this to happen. In one, the same F atoms that were initially axial can return to axial positions. This would do nothing to cause exchange. However, if the other diagonally opposite pair of F atoms that were initially equatorial move to axial positions (while the other two, which were initially axial necessarily become equatorial), an exchange of positions involving all but one of the F atoms is accomplished. The same process can now be repeated in such a way that the equatorial F atom that did not exchange the first time becomes exchanged. If this process is repeated indefinitely, all F atoms will constantly pass back and forth between axial and equatorial positions.

It is to be noted that the molecules that exist immediately before and after the rearrangement steps (or after any number of steps) are chemically identical. They differ only in the interchange of indistinguishable nuclei; the process causes no net chemical change and has $\Delta H° = \Delta S° = \Delta G° = 0$. Molecules of this type are by far the commonest and most important stereochemically nonrigid molecules and are called *fluxional molecules.*

An important fact to note about the process occurring in PF_5 is that it consists of a rearrangement of one of the more symmetrical forms of five-coordination, the trigonal bipyramid (tbp), into the other, the square pyramid (sp), and then back to an equivalent version of the first in which some ligands have changed places. This type of process has been called polytopal rearrangement, because the two different arrangements of the ligand set are polytopes.

For coordination number five, the tbp and sp arrangements seldom differ

Figure 6-14 A simple mechanism that interchanges axial and equatorial ligands of a trigonal bipyramid by passage through a square pyramidal intermediate.

greatly in energy, so that whichever one is the preferred arrangement in a given substance, the other one can provide a low energy pathway for averaging the ligand environments. Thus, as a general rule, five-coordinate species are fluxional, even at very low temperatures.

Polytopal rearrangements are generally facile for complexes with coordination numbers higher than six as well. This is because while one symmetrical structure may be somewhat more stable than any other, other arrangements are only a few kilojoules less stable, and with ordinary thermal energies available they provide accessible intermediates for rearrangement. As an example, consider an eight-coordinate complex with dodecahedral structure. The eight ligands are not all equivalent but fall into two sets, the A's and the B's as shown in Fig. 6-1. It is easy to see how the dodecahedron could be converted by relatively slight changes in interatomic distances into either a cubic or a square antiprismatic intermediate from which a new dodecahedron with the A's and B's interchanged would be recovered.

Six-Coordinate Complexes. Racemization of tris-Chelate Complexes

Octahedral complexes are generally not fluxional. That is, even when isomers such as cis and trans isomers of MX_4Y_2 complexes interconvert, they do so by ligand dissociation and recombination rather than by any intramolecular rearrangement. It has been shown in a few cases that intramolecular rearrangement by way of a twist does occur. These are mostly tris-chelate species where the process studied is racemization.

As we stated previously, these exist in enantiomeric configurations, Λ and Δ (Fig. 6-3). At various rates, depending on the metal ion involved and the experimental conditions, these can interconvert, and a sample consisting entirely of one enantiomer will eventually racemize, that is, become a mixture of both in equal quantities. Possible pathways for racemization fall into two broad classes: (1) those without breaking of metal–ligand bonds, and (2) those with bond rupture.

Two possible pathways without bond rupture that have long been recognized are the trigonal (or Bailar) twist and the rhombic (Ray–Dutt) twist, shown as (*a*) and (*b*) in Fig. 6-15. Many dissociative (bond-rupture) type pathways may be imagined; one is shown as (*c*) in Fig. 6-15. It appears that racemization most often occurs via some pathway with bond rupture, although in a few cases there is evidence for the trigonal twist.

Notice in Fig. 6-3 that if the top part of the Λ isomer is twisted relative to the bottom half by 120°, the molecule will pass through a trigonal-prismatic intermediate structure and then become the Δ isomer. This sort of process, shown in Fig. 6-15(*a*), is in general not facile and is rapid only in cases where the chelate ligands have a relatively short distance between their donor atoms (a small "bite"). Since the distance to be spanned is shorter in the eclipsed trigonal-prismatic intermediate than in the octahedral structure, such ligands cause the two structures to be closer in stability so that the prism becomes a thermally accessible intermediate or transition state.

Fluxional behavior will be mentioned again later in discussing metal carbonyls (Chapter 28) and organometallic compounds (Chapter 29).

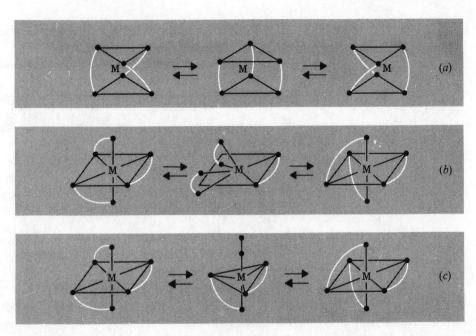

Figure 6-15 Three possible paths for racemization of a tris-chelate complex. (*a*) The trigonal twist. (*b*) The rhombic twist. (*c*) One of many paths involving metal–ligand bond rupture.

STUDY GUIDE

Scope and Purpose

An overview has been presented of the structures, nomenclature, reactivities, stabilities, and so on, of coordination compounds. We shall return to these topics in later chapters where theories of bonding will be added to the discussion. For now, we have confined the discussion to compounds that are traditionally considered to be coordination compounds; organometallic compounds will be covered in Chapters 28–30. The extensive material on mechanisms of reactions may be considered by the instructor to be optional, without much loss in continuity when moving on into later chapters. The general aspects of substitution reactions may, however, be useful, and we encourage some treatment of the differences between associative and dissociative processes.

Study Questions

A. Review

1. For each coordination number from two to nine, mention the principal geometrical arrangement (or arrangements).
2. What does each of the following abbreviations stand for: tbp, sp, *fac, mer*?

3. What is meant by tetragonal, rhombic, and trigonal distortion of an octahedron?

4. What do the terms *chelate* and *polydentate* mean?

5. What are the structures of the following ligands: acetylacetonate, ethylenediamine, diethylenetriamine, $EDTA^{4-}$?

6. Show with drawings the enantiomorphs of $M(L—L)_2X_2$ and $M(L—L)_3$ type complexes.

7. Give one example of each of the following types of isomers: ionization isomers, linkage isomers, coordination isomers.

8. Write the names of each of the following: $[Co(NH_3)_4(en)]Cl_3$, $[Cr(en)Cl_4]^-$, $[Pt(acac)NH_3Cl]$, $[Ru(NH_3)_5N_2](NO_3)_2$, $KFeCl_4$.

9. What are the two principal sets of equilibrium constants (K_i's and β_i's) for expressing the formation of a series of complexes, ML, ML_2, ML_3, and so on? How are they related?

10. Except in rare cases how do the magnitudes of the constants, K_i, vary with increasing i? What is the underlying reason for this, regardless of the charges?

11. What is meant by the *chelate effect*? Give an example.

12. For what ring sizes is it most important? How do you explain it?

13. Explain the difference between kinetic inertness (or lability) and thermodynamic stability (or instability).

14. What are the two limiting mechanisms for ligand exchange?

15. Explain how solvent intervention, ion-pair formation, and conjugate-base formation can affect the observed rate law.

16. Why does the rate law tell us nothing as to the true order of an aquation (acid hydrolysis) reaction carried out in aqueous solution?

17. True or false: the high rate of basic hydrolysis of $[Co(NH_3)_5Cl]^{2+}$ is attributable to the exceptional ability of OH^- to attack the cobalt ion nucleophilically. If false, give an alternative explanation of the high rate.

18. Why do many square complexes have two-term rate laws for ligand replacement reactions?

19. What is meant by the term *trans effect*?

20. Discuss the two general mechanisms for electron transfer reactions.

21. Describe the type of reaction and the reasoning used by Taube to prove that certain electron transfer reactions must occur by way of a bridged intermediate.

22. What is meant by a fluxional molecule? What is the experimental evidence that proves PF_5 to be one?

B. Additional Exercises

1. Show with drawings how axial–equatorial exchange in a square-pyramidal complex, AB_5, could occur via a tbp intermediate.

2. Draw all the isomers of an octahedral complex having four different monodentate ligands. Indicate optical isomers.

3. Show how the experimental determination of the number of isomers of $[Co(NH_3)_4Cl_2]^+$ would enable you to show that the coordination geometry is octahedral, not trigonal prismatic.

4. Why do you think most species, such as $AlCl_3$, $[CuCl_3]^-$, $Pt(NH_3)_2Cl^+$, are not actually such three-coordinate monomers but, instead, dimerize?

5. Suppose you prepared $[Co(en)_2Cl_2]^+$. Ignoring possible ring conformation effects, how many isomers, geometric and optical, could be formed?

6. Write the proper names for the complexes
   (a) $K_3[Co(C_2O_4)_3]$ (b) $Fe(CO)_5$
   (c) $[Co(NH_3)_5Cl]Cl_2$ (d) $[Co(en)_3]_2(SO_4)_3$
   (e) $Na_2[PtCl_4]$ (f) $[Ru(NH_3)_5(N_2)]Cl_2$
   (g) $Na[Fe(CO)_4H]$ (h) $K_2[Fe(CN)_5NO] \cdot 2H_2O$
   (i) $[(NH_3)_5Co-NC-Co(CN)_5]$

7. Draw all the possible isomers of the dinuclear complex $L_2X_2M(\mu\text{-}X)_2ML_2X_2$, where L is a ligand that cannot be a bridge.

8. Assign an inner-sphere or an outer-sphere mechanism for the following reactions, and draw out the details of the reaction sequence:

   (a) $\left[Co(NH_3)_5N \bigcirc\!\!-\!\!\bigcirc N \right]^{3+}$ + $[Fe(CN)_5OH_2]^{3-}$

   The Co^{III} reactant is substitution inert, while the Fe^{II} reactant is substitution labile. The products are $Co^{2+}(aq)$, which is substitution labile and

   $\left[Fe(CN)_5N \bigcirc\!\!-\!\!\bigcirc N \right]^{2-}$,

   which is substitution inert.
   (b) $[Co(NH_3)_6]^{3+}$ + $[Fe(CN)_5OH_2]^{3-}$
   The hexaammine of cobalt is substitution inert and the Fe^{II} reactant is substitution labile. The products are $Co^{2+}(aq)$ and $[Fe(CN)_5OH_2]^{2-}$.

9. For $[PtX_4]^{2-}$ complexes both ligand exchange rates and thermodynamic stability increase in the order X = Cl < Br < I < CN. Explain why these observations are not inconsistent.

10. Using the trans effect sequence given in the text, devise rational procedures for selectively synthesizing each of the three isomers of $[Pt(py)NH_3NO_2Cl]$.

11. If application of the Marcus equation were to be made in order to predict the electron transfer rate constants k_{12} for the following cross reactions, then list the self-exchange reactions for which self-exchange rate constants k_{11} and k_{22} would be needed.
    (a) $[Fe(CN)_6]^{4-}$ + $[Co(en)_3]^{3+}$
    (b) $Fe^{3+}(aq)$ + $[Cr(phen)_3]^{2+}$
    (c) $[Rh(phen)_3]^{3+}$ + $[Ru(phen)_3]^{2+}$

12. Predict the value for the second-order rate constants k_{12} for the following cross reactions, assuming in each case that f in the Marcus equation equals 0.8.
    (a) $[Fe(CN)_6]^{4-}$ + $[MnO_4]^-$ where $K_{12} = 2.5 \times 10^3$.
    (b) $[Mo(CN)_8]^{4-}$ + $[IrCl_6]^{2-}$ where $K_{12} = 1.5 \times 10^2$,
        $k_{11} = 3.0 \times 10^4 \text{ L mol}^{-1}\text{s}^{-1}$ and $k_{22} = 2.3 \times 10^5 \text{ L mol}^{-1}\text{s}^{-1}$.

C. Questions from the Literature of Inorganic Chemistry

1. Consider the paper by L. R. Carey, W. E. Jones, and T. W. Swaddle, *Inorg. Chem.*, **1971**, *8*, 1566–1570, dealing with the mechanisms of aquation reactions of $[Cr(H_2O)_5X]^{2+}$ complexes.

(a) What evidences do the authors cite for discounting the D mechanism?

(b) For which reactions is an I_a mechanism suspected? An I_d mechanism?

(c) List the principal evidences that the authors cite for these mechanistic assignments.

(d) How do these mechanistic results differ from those for the cobalt(III) ammines?

2. Consider the papers by C. Shea and A. Haim, *J. Am. Chem. Soc.*, **1971**, *93*, 3055–3056, and *Inorg. Chem.*, **1973**, *12*, 3013–3015.

(a) Draw the structures (including oxidation states of the metals and overall charge on the complexes) of the reactants, intermediates, and products of the redox reactions reported in these papers. Include the intermediates for both adjacent and remote attack. Realize that the compounds that are abbreviated $CrNCS^{2+}$, $CrSCN^{2+}$, and Cr^{2+} are probably six-coordinate complexes.

(b) How were the yields of $CrSCN^{2+}$ and $CrNCS^{2+}$ determined? Is there likely to be any uncatalyzed isomerization of these forms of linkage of the SCN^- ligands in these products?

(c) What is the reaction that the authors call the "Cr^{2+}-catalyzed isomerization of $CrSCN^{2+}$ to $CrNCS^{2+}$"? How does this isomerization take place, and what must be true of the labilities of the Cr^{2+} and Cr^{3+} complexes?

(d) How do the reductants Cr^{2+} and $[Co(CN)_5]^{3-}$ differ in reactions with $[(NH_3)_5Co—NCS]^{2+}$ and in reactions with $[(NH_3)_5Co—SCN]^{2+}$?

(e) Why is the isomer $[(NH_3)_5Co—NCS]^{2+}$ susceptible only to remote attack by the reductant?

3. Consider the paper: A. J. Miralles, A. P. Szecsy, and A. Haim, *Inorg. Chem.*, **1982**, *21*, 697–699.

(a) To what fundamental steps in the reaction sequence do the authors ascribe each of the spectroscopic changes that take place upon mixing reactants?

(b) What two consecutive redox reactions take place in these systems? What are their mechanisms? What are their relative rates? Why was an ion pair observable only for the first?

(c) How have the authors decided upon the orientation of the reactants within the ion pairs that precede the first outer-sphere electron transfer process?

4. Consider the paper by J. L. Burmeister, *Inorg. Chem.*, **1964**, *3*, 919–920. Propose a mechanism for the synthesis [reaction (1)] of $[Co(CN)_5—SCN]^{3-}$.

SUPPLEMENTARY READING

Atwood, J. D., "Inorganic and Organometallic Reaction Mechanisms," Brooks/Cole, Monterey, CA, 1985.

Basolo, F. and Johnson, R. C., *Coordination Chemistry*, Benjamin, Menlo Park, CA, 1964.

Basolo, F. and Pearson, R. G., *Mechanisms of Inorganic Reactions*, 2nd ed., Wiley, New York, 1967.

Benson, D., *Mechanisms of Inorganic Reactions in Solution*, McGraw-Hill, New York, 1968.

Cannon, R. D., *Electron Transfer Reactions*, Butterworths, London, 1980.

Edwards, J. O., "Inorganic Reaction Mechanisms," Parts I and II, Vols. 13 and 17, *Progress in Inorganic Chemistry*, Wiley-Interscience, New York, 1970 and 1972.

Edwards, J. O., *Inorganic Reaction Mechanisms*, Benjamin, Menlo Park, CA, 1964.

Langford, C. H. and Gray, H. B., *Ligand Substitution Processes*, Benjamin, Menlo Park, CA, 1984.

Lippard, S. J., *Progress in Inorganic Chemistry. An Appreciation of Henry Taube*, Vol. 30, Wiley-Interscience, New York, 1983.

Martell, A. E., Ed., *Coordination Chemistry*, Vols. 1 and 2, Van Nostrand–Reinhold, New York, 1971 and 1978.

Sykes, A. G., *Kinetics of Inorganic Reactions*, Pergamon Press, Elmsford, NY, 1966.

Taube, H., *Electron Transfer Reactions of Complex Ions in Solution*, Academic, New York, 1970.

Twigg, M. V., Ed., *Mechanisms of Inorganic and Organometallic Reactions*, Vols. 1 and 2, Plenum, New York, 1982 and 1984.

Wilkins, R. G., *The Study of Kinetics and Mechanism of Reactions of Transition Metal Complexes*, Allyn and Bacon, Boston, 1974.

chapter 7

SOLVENTS, SOLUTIONS, ACIDS, AND BASES

The majority of chemical reactions and many measurements of properties are carried out in a solvent. The properties of the solvent are crucial to the success or failure of the study. For the inorganic chemist, water has been the most important solvent, and it will continue to be, but many other solvents have been tried and found useful. A few of them, and the concepts that influence the choice of a solvent, are discussed here. Closely connected with the properties of solvents is the behavior of acids and bases. In this chapter some fundamental concepts concerning acids and bases are also presented.

7-1 Solvent Properties

Properties that chiefly determine the utility of a solvent are

1. The temperature range over which it is a liquid.
2. Its dielectric constant.
3. Its donor and acceptor (Lewis acid–base) properties.
4. Its protonic acidity or basicity.
5. The nature and extent of autodissociation.

The first two are of rather obvious import and need not detain us long. The others will merit discussion in subsequent sections.

Liquid Range

Solvents that are liquid at room temperature and 1-atm pressure are most useful because they are easily handled, but it is also desirable that measurements or reactions be feasible at temperatures well above and below room temperature. As Table 7-1 shows, N,N-dimethylformamide (DMF), propane-1,2-diol carbonate, and acetonitrile are especially good in this respect.

Dielectric Constant

The ability of a liquid to dissolve ionic solids depends strongly although not exclusively on its *dielectric constant*, ϵ. The force, F, of attraction between cations

Table 7-1 Properties of Some Useful Solvents[a]

Name	Abbreviation	Formula	Liquid Range °C	ϵ/ϵ_0
Water	—	H_2O	0 to 100	82
Acetonitrile	—	CH_3CN	−45 to 82	38
N,N-Dimethylformamide	DMF	$HC(O)N(CH_3)_2$	−61 to 153	38
Dimethyl sulfoxide	DMSO	$(CH_3)_2SO$	18 to 189	47
Nitromethane	—	CH_3NO_2	−29 to 101	36
Sulfolane	—	(ring) SO_2	28 to 285	44
Propane-1,2-diol carbonate	—	(ring) $C=O$	−49 to 242	64
Hexamethylphosphoramide	HMP	$OP[N(CH_3)_2]_3$		30
Glycol dimethyl ether	Glyme	$CH_3OCH_2CH_2OCH_3$	−58 to 83	3.5
Tetrahydrofuran	THF	(ring) O	−65 to 66	7.6
Dichloromethane	—	CH_2Cl_2	−97 to 40	9
Ammonia	—	NH_3	−78 to −33	23 (−50 °C)
Sulfuric acid	—	H_2SO_4	10 to 338	100
Hydrogen fluoride	—	HF	−83 to 20	84 (0 °C)
Hydrogen cyanide	—	HCN	−14 to 26	107

[a] Instead of the absolute value of ϵ, we give here the ratio of ϵ to ϵ_0, the latter being the value for a vacuum. In subsequent sections the term "dielectric constant" refers to this ratio.

and anions immersed in a medium of dielectric constant ϵ, is inversely proportional to ϵ, as in Eq. 7-1.1:

$$F = \frac{q^+ q^-}{4\pi\epsilon r^2} \tag{7-1.1}$$

Thus, water ($\epsilon = 82\epsilon_0$ at 25 °C, where ϵ_0 is for a vacuum) reduces the attractive force nearly to 1% of its value in the absence of a solvent. Solvents with lower dielectric constants are less able to reduce the attractive forces (F in Eq. 7-1.1) between dissolved cations and anions. Such solvents are, therefore, less able to dissolve ionic substances.

7-2 Donor and Acceptor Properties; Solvent Polarity

The ability of a solvent to keep a given solute in solution depends considerably on its ability to solvate the dissolved particles, that is, to interact with them in a quasichemical way. For ionic solutes, there are both cations and anions to be solvated. Commonly, the cations are smaller [e.g., $Ca(NO_3)_2$, $FeCl_3$] and the solvation of the cations is of prime importance. The solvation of simple cations is essentially the process of forming complexes in which the ligands are solvent molecules. The order of coordinating ability toward typical cations for some common solvents is

$$DMSO > DMF \approx H_2O > acetone \approx (CH_3CHCH_2)O_2CO \approx CH_3CN$$
$$> (CH_2)_4SO_2 > CH_3NO_2 > C_6H_5NO_2 \gg CH_2Cl_2$$

Acceptor properties are usually manifested less specifically. The positive ends of the solvent molecule dipoles will orient themselves toward the anions.

It is noteworthy that in general the dielectric constant and the ability to solvate ions are related properties, tending to increase simultaneously, but there is no quantitative correlation. The more polar the molecules of a solvent the higher its dielectric constant tends to be (although the extent of hydrogen bonding plays a very important role also); at the same time, the more polar a molecule the better able it is to use its negative and positive regions to solvate cations and anions, respectively.

7-3   Protic Solvents

These contain ionizable protons and are more or less acidic. Examples are H_2O, HCl, HF, H_2SO_4, and HCN. Even ammonia, which is usually considered a base, is a protic solvent and can supply H^+ to stronger bases. Protic solvents characteristically undergo autodissociation.

Autodissociation of Protic Solvents

For some of the examples just mentioned, the autodissociation reactions can be written in the simplest way as follows:

$$2H_2O = H_3O^+ + OH^- \tag{7-3.1}$$

$$2HCl = H_2Cl^+ + Cl^- \tag{7-3.2}$$

$$2HF = H_2F^+ + F^- \tag{7-3.3}$$

$$2H_2SO_4 = H_3SO_4^+ + HSO_4^- \tag{7-3.4}$$

$$2NH_3 = NH_4^+ + NH_2^- \tag{7-3.5}$$

In each of reactions 7-3.1 to 7-3.5, autodissociation involves proton transfer between two solvent molecules to give the protonated solvent cation and the deprotonated solvent anion.

The significance of autodissociation is that solutes encounter not only the molecules of the solvent but the cations and anions that form in the autodissociation process. The autodissociations of several of the acid solvents are discussed in detail in Section 7-11. Here, we give a closer examination of the processes in water and ammonia. These simple equations do not consider in detail the further solvation of the primary products of autodissociation, and this is of importance.

Water

A more general equation for the autodissociation of water is

$$(n + m + 1)H_2O = [H(H_2O)_n]^+ + [HO(H_2O)_m]^-$$ (7-3.6)

For the hydrogen ion, $[H(H_2O)_n]^+$, there is strong association of H^+ with one water molecule to give H_3O^+, a pyramidal ion (structure 7-I) isoelectronic with NH_3. This ion is observed in a number of crystalline compounds. In water it is further solvated. Another species actually observed in crystals is the $H_5O_2^+$ ion (structure 7-II). Probably the $H_9O_4^+$ ion (structure 7-III) is the largest well-

$$\left[H \overset{O-H}{\underset{\sim118°}{\diagup}} H \right]^+ \qquad \left[\overset{H}{\underset{H}{\diagdown}} O \cdots H \cdots O - H \atop H \right]^+$$

7-I   7-II

$$\left[H_2O \cdots \underset{H}{\diagdown} O - H \overset{OH_2}{\underset{OH_2}{\diagup}} \right]^+$$

7-III

defined species. The extent of autodissociation (Eq. 7-3.6) is slight, as shown by the small value for the equilibrium constant, Eq. 7-3.7:

$$K'_{25\,°C} = \frac{[H^+][OH^-]}{[H_2O]} = (1.0 \times 10^{-14})/55.56$$ (7-3.7)

In practice, the essentially constant 55.56 M concentration of H_2O molecules is omitted (because it *is* constant), and the constant $K_{25\,°C} = [H^+][OH^-] = 1.0 \times 10^{-14}$ is used.

Liquid Ammonia

Liquid ammonia is a colorless liquid that is useful as a solvent over the temperature range -78 to -33 °C. Its autodissociation (Eq. 7-3.5) is less than that of water:

$$K_{-50\,°C} = [NH_4^+][NH_2^-] = 10^{-30}$$ (7-3.8)

Here too, autodissociation involves proton transfer between two solvent molecules to form the conjugate base of ammonia (NH_2^-) and the conjugate acid of ammonia (NH_4^+).

7-4   Aprotic Solvents

There are three broad classes of aprotic solvents:

1. *Nonpolar, or very weakly polar, nondissociated liquids, which do not solvate strongly.* Examples are CCl_4 and hydrocarbons. Because of low polarity, low dielectric constants, and poor donor power, these are not powerful solvents except for other nonpolar substances. Their main value, when they can be used, is that they play a minimal role in the chemistry of reactions carried out therein.

2. *Nonionized but strongly solvating (generally polar) solvents.* Examples of this type are CH_3CN, *N,N*-dimethylformamide (DMF), dimethyl sulfoxide (DMSO), tetrahydrofuran (THF), and SO_2. These have in common the facts that they are aprotic, that no autodissociation equilibria are known to occur, and that they strongly solvate ions. In other respects they differ. Some are high boiling (DMSO), others are low boiling (SO_2); some have high dielectric constants (DMSO, 45) while others are of low polarity (THF, 7.6). For the most part, they solvate cations best by using negatively charged oxygen atoms, but sulfur dioxide has pronounced acceptor ability, and solvates anions and other Lewis bases effectively. For example, the molecular adduct $(CH_3)_3N \rightarrow SO_2$ can be isolated.

3. *Highly polar, autoionizing solvents.* Some of these are interhalogen compounds such as BrF_3 and IF_5 whose structures were discussed in Chapter 3. Examples of their autoionizations are given in Eqs. 7-4.1 and 7-4.2:

$$2BrF_3 = BrF_2^+ + BrF_4^- \tag{7-4.1}$$

$$2\ IF_5 = IF_4^+ + IF_6^- \tag{7-4.2}$$

Another example is trichlorophosphine oxide:

$$2Cl_3PO = Cl_2PO^+ + Cl_4PO^- \tag{7-4.3}$$

which undergoes autoionization through Cl^- transfer.

7-5   Molten Salts

These represent a kind of extreme of aprotic, autoionizing solvents. In them ions predominate over neutral molecules which, in some cases, are of negligible concentration. The alkali metal halides and nitrates are among the "totally" ionic molten salts, whereas others such as molten halides of zinc, tin, and mercury contain many molecules, as well as ions.

Low melting points are often achieved with either mixtures or by using halides of alkylammonium ions. Thus an appropriate mixture of $LiNO_3$, $NaNO_3$, and KNO_3 has a melting point as low as 160 °C and $(C_2H_5)_2H_2NCl$ has a melting point of 215 °C.

Examples of important reactions carried out in molten salts are the following preparations of low-valent metal salts:

$$CdCl_2 + Cd \xrightarrow{\text{Liquid AlCl}_3} Cd_2[AlCl_4]_2 \qquad (7\text{-}5.1)$$

$$Re_3Cl_9 \xrightarrow{\text{Liquid (C}_2\text{H}_5)_2\text{H}_2\text{NCl}} [(C_2H_5)_2H_2N]_2[Re_2Cl_8] \qquad (7\text{-}5.2)$$

The industrial production of aluminum is carried out by electrolysis of a solution of Al_2O_3 in molten Na_3AlF_6.

7-6 Solvents for Electrochemical Reactions

A good solvent for electrochemical reactions must meet several criteria. Generally, electrochemical reactions involve ionic substances, so that a dielectric constant of 10 or better is desirable. Second, the solvent must have a wide range of voltage over which it is not oxidized or reduced so its own electrode reactions will not take precedence over those of interest.

Water is a widely useful solvent for electrochemistry. Because of its high dielectric constant and solvating ability, it dissolves many electrolytes. Its intrinsic conductance is suitably low. Its range of redox stability is fairly wide, as shown by the following potentials, although its reduction is often a limitation:

$$O_2 + 4H^+(10^{-7}M) + 4e^- = 2H_2O \qquad E° = +0.82 \text{ V} \qquad (7\text{-}6.1)$$

$$H^+(10^{-7}M) + e^- = \tfrac{1}{2}H_2 \qquad E° = -0.41 \text{ V} \qquad (7\text{-}6.2)$$

Acetonitrile, CH_3CN, is widely used for solutes such as organometallic compounds or salts containing large alkylammonium ions, which are insufficiently soluble in water. It is stable over a wide range of voltages.

N,N-dimethylformamide, $HC(O)N(CH_3)_2$, is similar to CH_3CN but more easily reduced. Dichloromethane is sometimes used for organic solutes as is nitromethane. Molten salts are also useful.

7-7 Purity of Solvents

Although it is obvious that a solvent should be pure if reproducible and interpretable results are to be obtained, it is not always obvious what subtle forms of contamination can occur. Of particular importance are water and oxygen. Oxygen is slightly soluble in virtually all solvents, and saturated solutions are formed on brief exposure to air, for example, when pouring. Oxygen can be partially removed by bubbling nitrogen through the liquid, but only by repeatedly freezing and pumping on a vacuum line can it be completely removed. Certain organic solvents, especially ethers, react with oxygen on long exposure to air, forming peroxides. The solvents can best be purified of these by distillation from reductants (e.g., hydrides) or by passage through "molecular sieves," Section 5-4.

Water also dissolves readily in solvents exposed to the air or to glass vessels that have not been baked dry. It is important to recognize that even small quantities of H_2O on a weight percentage basis can be important. For example, acetonitrile, which contains only 0.1% by weight of water, is about 0.04 M in H_2O, so that the properties of 0.1 M solutions can be seriously influenced by the *trace* of water.

7-8   Definitions of Acids and Bases

The concepts of acidity and basicity are so pervasive in chemistry that acids and bases have been defined many times and in various ways. One definition, probably the oldest, is so narrow as to pertain only to water as solvent. According to this, acids and bases are sources of H^+ and OH^-, respectively. A somewhat broader, but closely allied definition that is applicable to all protonic solvents is that of Brønsted and Lowry.

Brønsted–Lowry Definition

An acid is a substance that supplies protons and a base is a proton acceptor. Thus, in water, any substance that increases the concentration of hydrated protons (H_3O^+) above that due to the autodissociation of the water is an acid, and any substance that lowers it is a base. Any solute that supplies hydroxide ions is a base, since these combine with protons to reduce the H_3O^+ concentration. However, other substances such as sulfides, oxides, or anions of weak acids (e.g., F^-, CN^-) are also bases.

Solvent System Definition

This can be applied in all cases where the solvent has a significant autoionization reaction, whether protons are involved or not. Some examples are

$$2H_2O = H_3O^+ + OH^- \qquad (7\text{-}8.1)^*$$

$$2NH_3 = NH_4^+ + NH_2^- \qquad (7\text{-}8.2)$$

$$2H_2SO_4 = H_3SO_4^+ + HSO_4^- \qquad (7\text{-}8.3)$$

$$2\,OPCl_3 = OPCl_2^+ + OPCl_4^- \qquad (7\text{-}8.4)$$

$$2BrF_3 = BrF_2^+ + BrF_4^- \qquad (7\text{-}8.5)$$

A solute that increases the cationic species natural to the solvent is an acid; one that increases the anionic species is a base. Thus, for the BrF_3 solvent, a compound such as BrF_2AsF_6, which dissolves to give BrF_2^+ and AsF_6^- ions, is an acid, while $KBrF_4$ is a base. If solutions of acid and base are mixed, a neutralization reaction, producing a salt and solvent molecules, takes place:

$$\underbrace{BrF_2^+ + AsF_6^-}_{\text{Acid}} + \underbrace{K^+ + BrF_4^-}_{\text{Base}} = \underbrace{K^+ + AsF_6^-}_{\text{Salt}} + \underbrace{2BrF_3}_{\text{Solvent}} \qquad (7\text{-}8.6)$$

Even for protonic solvents this is a broader and more useful definition, because it explains why acid or base character is not an absolute property of the solute. Rather, the acid or base character of a substance can only be specified in relation to the solvent used. For example, in water, CH_3CO_2H (acetic acid) is an acid:

$$CH_3CO_2H + H_2O = H_3O^+ + CH_3CO_2^- \tag{7-8.7}$$

In the sulfuric acid solvent system, CH_3CO_2H is a base:

$$H_2SO_4 + CH_3CO_2H = CH_3CO_2H_2^+ + HSO_4^- \tag{7-8.8}$$

As another example, urea, $H_2NC(O)NH_2$, which is essentially neutral in water, is an acid in liquid ammonia:

$$NH_3 + H_2NC(O)NH_2 = NH_4^+ + H_2NC(O)NH^- \tag{7-8.9}$$

The Lux–Flood Definition

Consider reaction 7-8.10:

$$CaO + H_2O \longrightarrow Ca(OH)_2 \tag{7-8.10}$$

in which CaO serves as a basic anhydride, and consider reaction 7-8.11:

$$CO_2 + H_2O \longrightarrow H_2CO_3 \tag{7-8.11}$$

in which CO_2 serves as an acidic anhydride. In these two cases, CaO and CO_2 are first allowed to react with water, and the hydration products are readily recognized as a base, $Ca(OH)_2$, and an acid, H_2CO_3. Furthermore, reaction 7-8.12

$$Ca(OH)_2 + H_2CO_3 \longrightarrow CaCO_3 + H_2O \tag{7-8.12}$$

is readily recognized as a neutralization reaction in which a salt (plus solvent) is formed. The salt, $CaCO_3$, may be prepared directly, without intervention of solvent, as in Eq. 7-8.13:

$$CaO + CO_2 \longrightarrow CaCO_3 \tag{7-8.13}$$

It is natural to continue to regard Eq. 7-8.13 as an acid–base reaction. Some other examples of direct reactions between acidic and basic oxides are given in Eqs. 7-8.14 and 7-8.15:

$$CaO + SiO_2 \longrightarrow CaSiO_3 \tag{7-8.14}$$

$$3Na_2O + P_2O_5 \longrightarrow 2Na_3PO_4 \tag{7-8.15}$$

The general principle involved in such processes was recognized by Lux and Flood, who proposed that an acid be defined as an oxide ion acceptor and a base as an oxide ion donor. Thus, in reactions 7-8.13 to 7-8.15, the bases CaO and Na_2O donate oxide ions to the acids CO_2, SiO_2, and P_2O_5, to form the ions CO_3^{2-}, SiO_3^{2-}, and PO_4^{3-}.

The Lux–Flood concept of acids and bases is very useful in dealing with high temperature, anhydrous systems such as those encountered in the oxide chemistries of ceramics and metallurgy. Furthermore, the Lux–Flood definition has a direct relation to the aqueous chemistry of acids and bases because the bases are oxides (basic anhydrides) that react with water as in Eq. 7-8.16:

$$Na_2O + H_2O \longrightarrow 2Na^+ + 2\,OH^- \qquad (7\text{-}8.16)$$

and the acids are oxides (acidic anhydrides) that react with water as in Eq. 7-8.17:

$$P_2O_5 + 3H_2O \longrightarrow 2H_3PO_4 \qquad (7\text{-}8.17)$$

The Lewis Definition

One of the most general—and useful—of all definitions was proposed by G. N. Lewis, who defined an acid as an electron-pair acceptor and a base as an electron-pair donor. This definition includes the Brønsted–Lowry definition as a special case, since the proton can be regarded as an electron-pair acceptor and the base, be it OH^-, NH_2^-, HSO_4^-, and so on, as an electron-pair donor. Consider Eq. 7-8.18, for example.

$$H^+ + :OH^- = H:OH \qquad (7\text{-}8.18)$$

The Lewis definition covers a great many systems where protons are not involved at all, however. The reaction between ammonia and BF_3, for example, is an acid–base reaction:

$$\underset{\substack{\text{Lewis} \\ \text{base}}}{H_3N:} + \underset{\substack{\text{Lewis} \\ \text{acid}}}{BF_3} \longrightarrow H_3N:BF_3 \qquad (7\text{-}8.19)$$

In the Lewis sense, all of the usual ligands can be regarded as bases and all metal ions can be regarded as acids. The degree of affinity of a metal ion for ligands can be termed its Lewis acidity, and the tendency of a ligand to become bound to a metal ion can be regarded as a measure of its Lewis basicity.

Base and acid strengths in the Lewis sense are not fixed, inherent properties of the species concerned, but vary somewhat with the nature of the partner. That is, the order of base strength of a series of Lewis bases may change when the type of acid with which they are allowed to combine changes. We discuss this in the next section.

Observe that, for a given donor or acceptor atom, basicity or acidity can be influenced greatly by the nature of the substituents. Substituent influence can be either electronic or steric in origin.

Electronic Effects

The electronegativity of substituents exercises an obvious effect. Thus base strength and acid strength are affected oppositely, as the following examples show.

$$\text{Base strength} \quad (CH_3)_3N > H_3N > F_3N$$

$$\text{Acid strength} \quad (CH_3)_3B < H_3B < F_3B$$

The more electron withdrawing (electronegative) the substituent the more it enhances Lewis acidity and diminishes Lewis basicity.

However, more subtle electronic effects can also be important. On simple electronegativity grounds the following order of acid strengths would be predicted: $BF_3 > BCl_3 > BBr_3$. Experimentally, just the opposite is found. This can be understood when the existence of π interactions in the planar molecules is taken into account, and when it is noted that, after the Lewis acid has combined with a base, the BX_3 group becomes pyramidal and the boron atom no longer interacts with the π electrons of the X atoms. Simple calculations indicate that the B—X π interactions will decrease in strength in the order $F \geqslant Cl > Br$. Therefore, BF_3 is a weaker Lewis acid than BCl_3 because the planar BF_3 molecule is stabilized to a greater extent than BCl_3 by B—X π bonding. Borate esters, $B(OR)_3$, are also surprisingly weak Lewis acids for the same reason.

Steric Effects

These may be of several kinds. For the following three bases (structures 7-IV to 7-VI) base strength toward the proton increases slightly from structure

7-IV to 7-V and is virtually the same for structures 7-V and 7-VI, as is expected from the ordinary inductive effect of a methyl group. However, with respect to $B(CH_3)_3$, the order of basicity is

$$\text{structure 7-IV} \approx \text{structure 7-VI} \geqslant \text{structure 7-V}$$

This results from the steric hindrance between the ortho methyl group of the base and the methyl groups of $B(CH_3)_3$. For the same reason quinuclidine, (structure 7-VII) is a far stronger base toward $B(CH_3)_3$ than is triethylamine, (structure 7-VIII):

7-VII   7-VIII

A different sort of steric effect results as the bulk on the boron atom in a BR_3 acid is increased. Since, as we stated previously, the BR_3 molecule goes from planar to pyramidal when it interacts with the base, the R groups must be squeezed into considerably less space. As the R groups increase in size, this effect strongly opposes the formation of the $A:BR_3$ compound, thus effectively decreasing the acidity of BR_3.

7-9   "Hard" and "Soft" Acids and Bases and HSAB Concepts

It has been known for a long time that metal ions can be sorted into two groups according to their preference for various ligands. Let us consider the ligands formed by the elements of Groups VB(15), VIB(16), and VIIB(17). For Group VB(15) we might take a homologous series such as R_3N, R_3P, R_3As, R_3Sb, and for Group VIIB(17) we take the anions themselves, F^-, Cl^-, Br^-, and I^-. For type (a) metals, complexes are most stable with the lightest ligands and less stable as each group is descended. For the type (b) elements the trend is just the opposite. This is summarized as follows:

Complexes of type (a) metal	Ligands			Complexes of type (b) metal
Strongest	R_3N	R_2O	F^-	Weakest
↑	R_3P	R_2S	Cl^-	↓
	R_3As	R_2Se	Br^-	
Weakest	R_3Sb	R_2Te	I^-	Strongest

Type (a) metal ions include principally:

1. Alkali metal ions.
2. Alkaline earth ions.
3. Lighter and more highly charged ions, for example,

$$Ti^{4+}, Fe^{3+}, Co^{3+}, Al^{3+}$$

Type (b) metal ions include principally:

1. Heavier transition metal ions, such as

$$Hg_2^{2+}, Hg^{2+}, Pt^{2+}, Pt^{4+}, Ag^+, Cu^+$$

2. Low-valent metal ions such as the formally zero-valent metals in metal carbonyls.

This empirical ordering proved very useful in classifying and to some extent predicting relative stabilities of complexes. Later, Pearson observed that it might be possible to generalize the correlation to include a broader range of acid–base interactions. He noted that the type (a) metal ions (acids) were small, compact, and not very polarizable and that they preferred ligands (bases) that were also small and less polarizable. He called these acids and bases "hard." Conversely, the type (b) metal ions, and the ligands they prefer, tend to be larger and more polarizable; he described these acids and bases as "soft." The empirical relationship could then be expressed, qualitatively, by the statement that *hard acids prefer hard bases and soft acids prefer soft bases*. Although the point of departure for the "hard and soft" terminology was the concept of polarizability, other factors undoubtedly enter into the problem. There is no unanimity among chemists as to the detailed nature of "hardness" and "softness," but clearly coulombic attraction will be of importance for hard–hard interactions while covalence will be quite significant for soft–soft interactions. The participation of both electrostatic and covalent forces in acid–base interactions will be considered in the next section.

7-10 Covalent and Ionic Components of Lewis Acid–Base Interactions

In an attempt to account quantitatively for the enthalpies, ΔH_{AB}, of combining a Lewis acid, A, with a Lewis base, B, the following type of equation has been proposed.

$$-\Delta H_{AB} = E_A E_B + C_A C_B \qquad (7\text{-}10.1)$$

The form of this equation is based on the notion that for each acid–base interaction there will be both electrostatic and covalent components. It is then further *postulated* that the tendency of an individual acid or base to contribute to electrostatic and covalent interaction with *any* partner is a fixed characteristic that is measured by E_A or E_B for the electrostatic part and C_A or C_B for the covalent part. Thus the electrostatic contribution to the total enthalpy change is given by $E_A E_B$ and the covalent contribution is given by $C_A C_B$. The acid–base interaction will be favorable where ΔH_{AB} in Eq. 7-10.1 is a large negative number. This will occur when either term $E_A E_B$ or $C_A C_B$ is large. This is tantamount to requiring that A and B be properly matched; either A and B should both form adducts principally through electrostatic interaction (have large E) or they should both form adducts principally through covalence (have large C).

It is necessary to assign arbitrarily one each of the E_A, E_B, C_A, and C_B parameters before a unique set can be developed purely by data-fitting procedures.

This scheme, which has been advocated by R. S. Drago and his students, has some advantage over the simple HSAB concept, simply because it (a) has more parameters, and (b) at least attempts to be quantitative. However, the HSAB picture can also be extended by adding the concepts of strong and weak to those of hard and soft. In other words, every acid and base can be classified by its position in the hard–soft scale *and* by its strength. Thus we might find ourselves describing some base as "moderately weak and fairly soft," "very hard but weak," and so on.

7-11 Some Common Protic Acids

Sulfuric Acid, H_2SO_4

This acid is of enormous industrial importance and is manufactured in larger quantities than any other. The preparation requires first the burning of sulfur to SO_2. Oxidation of SO_2 to SO_3 must then be catalyzed either homogeneously by oxides of nitrogen (lead chamber process) or heterogeneously by platinum (contact process). Sulfuric acid is ordinarily sold as a 98% mixture with water (18 M). The pure substance is obtained as a colorless liquid by addition of sufficient SO_3 to react with the remaining H_2O. The solid and liquid are built of SO_4 tetrahedra linked by hydrogen bonds.

Addition of further SO_3 to 100% H_2SO_4 gives *fuming sulfuric acid or oleum,* which contains polysulfuric acids such as pyrosulfuric acid, $H_2S_2O_7$ and, with more SO_3, $H_2S_3O_{10}$, and $H_2S_4O_{13}$.

Sulfuric acid is not a very strong oxidizing agent, but it is a powerful dehydrating agent for carbohydrates and other organic substances, often degrading the former to elemental carbon:

$$C_nH_{2n}O_n \xrightarrow{H_2SO_4} nC + H_2SO_4 \cdot nH_2O \qquad (7\text{-}11.1)$$

The equilibria in pure H_2SO_4 are complex. Besides self-ionization

$$2H_2SO_4 = H_3SO_4^+ + HSO_4^- \qquad K_{10\,°C} = 1.7 \times 10^{-4} \text{ mol}^2 \text{ kg}^2 \qquad (7\text{-}11.2)$$

there are hydration–dehydration equilibria, such as:

$$2H_2SO_4 = H_3O^+ + HS_2O_7^- \qquad (7\text{-}11.3)$$

$$2H_2SO_4 = H_2O + H_2S_2O_7 \qquad (7\text{-}11.4)$$

$$H_2SO_4 + H_2S_2O_7 = H_3SO_4^+ + HS_2O_7^- \qquad \text{and so on} \qquad (7\text{-}11.5)$$

Nitric Acid

The normally available, concentrated acid is about 70% by weight HNO_3 in water. It is colorless when pure but is often yellow as a result of photochemical decomposition, which gives NO_2:

$$2 \text{ HNO}_3 \xrightarrow{h\nu} 2 \text{ NO}_2 + H_2O + \tfrac{1}{2} O_2 \qquad (7\text{-}11.6)$$

Red, "fuming" nitric acid is essentially 100% HNO_3, which contains additional NO_2.

The pure acid is a colorless liquid or solid that must be stored below 0 °C to avoid thermal decomposition according to the same equation as Eq. 7-11.6 for photochemical decomposition. In the pure liquid the following equilibria occur:

$$2HNO_3 = H_2NO_3^+ + NO_3^- \qquad (7\text{-}11.7)$$

$$H_2NO_3^+ = NO_2^+ + H_2O \qquad (7\text{-}11.8)$$

While aqueous nitric acid below 2 M concentration is not strongly oxidizing, the concentrated acid is a very powerful oxidizing agent. It will attack nearly all metals except for Au, Pt, Rh, and Ir and a few others that quickly become passivated (covered with a resistant oxide film) such as Al, Fe, and Cu.

Aqua Regia

A mixture of about three volumes of HCl to one volume of HNO_3, prepared from the concentrated aqueous acids, is known as aqua regia. It contains free Cl_2 and ClNO, and is, therefore, a powerful oxidizing agent. It readily dissolves even Au and Pt, owing to the ability of Cl^- to stabilize the Au^{3+} and Pt^{2+} cations by forming the complexes $AuCl_4^-$ and $PtCl_6^{2-}$. Aqua regia may also be used to dissolve certain difficulty soluble salts because of its combined oxidizing and coordinating abilities. HgS, for example, dissolves in aqua regia both because the sulfide is oxidized to sulfur, and because the mercury(II) ion is stabilized by formation of the complex ion, $HgCl_4^{2-}$.

Perchloric Acid, $HClO_4$*

This is normally available in concentrations 70–72% by weight. The pure substance, which can be obtained by vacuum distillation in presence of the dehydrating agent $Mg(ClO_4)_2$, is stable at 25 °C for only a few days, decomposing to give off Cl_2O_7. Both the pure and the concentrated aqueous acid react explosively with organic matter. The ClO_4^- ion is a very weak ligand, and perchloric acid and alkali perchlorates are, therefore, of use in preparing solutions in which complexing of cations is to be minimized.

The Hydrohalic Acids HCl, HBr, and HI

These three acids are similar but differ markedly from hydrofluoric acid, which we describe in this section. The pure compounds are pungent gases at 25 °C but are highly soluble in water to give strongly acidic solutions. One molar solutions are virtually 100% dissociated. For aqueous HBr and especially HI, their reactivity as simple acids is complicated by the reducing character of the Br^- and I^- ions.

Only HCl (bp -85 °C) has been much studied as a pure liquid. Its autoionization according to Eq. 7-11.9 is small,

$$3HCl = H_2Cl^+ + HCl_2^- \tag{7-11.9}$$

but many organic and some inorganic compounds dissolve to give conducting solutions. A number of compounds containing the $[Cl—H—Cl]^-$ and $[Br—H—Br]^-$ ions have been isolated.

Hydrofluoric Acid, HF

In aqueous solution HF is a weak acid,

$$HF + H_2O = H_3O^+ + F^- \qquad K_{25°C} = 7.2 \times 10^{-5} \tag{7-11.10}$$

This is due mainly to the great strength of the H—F bond. The aqueous acid readily attacks glass and silica because the stable SiF_6^{2-} ion can be formed;

$$6HF(aq) + SiO_2 = 2H_3O^+ + SiF_6^{2-} \qquad (7\text{-}11.11)$$

and it is used commercially to etch glass.

In contrast to the aqueous solution, liquid HF (bp 19.5 °C) is one of the strongest acids known. The principal self-ionization equilibria are

$$2HF = H_2F^+ + F^- \qquad (7\text{-}11.12)$$

$$F^- + nHF = HF_2^- + H_2F_3^- + H_3F_4^- \qquad \text{and so on} \qquad (7\text{-}11.13)$$

There are a few substances that act as solvent–system acids towards liquid HF, namely, as fluoride ion acceptors. Through F^- transfer, they serve to increase the concentration of the solvent cation, H_2F^+. An example is SbF_5, which operates as in Eq. 7-11.14:

$$2HF + SbF_5 = H_2F^+ + SbF_6^- \qquad (7\text{-}11.14)$$

Liquid HF has a dielectric constant (84 at 0 °C) comparable to that of water, and it is an excellent solvent for a wide range of inorganic and organic compounds.

7-12   Some Rules Concerning the Strengths of Oxy Acids

Acids consisting of a central atom surrounded by O atoms and OH groups, $XO_n(OH)_m$ are very common, including H_2SO_4, H_3PO_4, HNO_3, and so on. For these acids there are two important generalizations:

1. The ratio of successive dissociation constants, K_n/K_{n-1} is 10^{-4} to 10^{-5}, (which is equivalent to $pK_{n-1} - pK_n = 4.5 \pm 0.5$, where $pK = -\log K$).

2. The magnitude of K_1 depends on n, the number of additional oxygen atoms besides those in OH groups. The more of these, the greater the acid strength, according to:

n	K_1	Acid Strength
3	Very, very large	Very strong
2	$\sim 10^2$	Strong
1	$10^{-2} - 10^{-3}$	Medium
0	$10^{-7.5} - 10^{-9.5}$	Weak

The basis for these rules, and their general validity lies in the delocalization of the charge of the anions. For a given initial dissociation,

$$XO_n(OH)_m = [XO_{n+1}(OH)_{m-1}]^- + H^+ \qquad (7\text{-}12.1)$$

the greater the number $(n + 1)$ of oxygen atoms in the conjugate base $[XO_{n+1}(OH)_{m-1}]^-$, the more the negative charge of the anion can be spread out, and thus the more stable is the anion. For instance, the negative charge in nitrate is dispersed uniformly, as in structure 7-IX, in the same way that the π-bond in an AB_3 system is delocalized *via* resonance. For cases where there

$$-1/3 O \cdots \cdots O^{-1/3}$$
$$N$$
$$O^{-1/3}$$

7-IX

are many oxygen atoms and only a single proton, for example $HClO_4$, delocalization of the negative charge in the conjugate base is very effective, and the dissociation of a proton from the parent acid is very favorable. In contrast, when $n = 0$, there is practically no delocalization of negative charge in the anion, and dissociation of a proton from the parent "acid" is not favorable. An example is $Te(OH)_6$, which is not appreciably acidic, because there is little charge delocalization in $Te(OH)_5O^-$.

The steady decrease in the values of K_1, K_2, K_3, and so on, occurs because after each dissociation, there is an increased negative charge that lessens the tendency of the next proton to depart.

Apparent exceptions to rule (2) turn out not to have simple $XO_n(OH)_m$ type structures. For example, phosphorous acid, H_3PO_3 would have $K_1 \approx 10^{-8}$ if it were $P(OH)_3$. In fact, the value of K_1 is about 10^{-2}, which should mean that it has $n = 1$. It actually does belong in that group since its structure is $HPO(OH)_2$, with one hydrogen atom directly attached to P. Similarly, hypophosphorous acid, H_3PO_2 has $K_1 \approx 10^{-2}$ and its actual structure is $H_2PO(OH)$.

Carbonic acid also deviates from expectation, but for a different reason. For $CO(OH)_2$ we expect $K_1 \approx 10^{-2}$, whereas the measured value is $\sim 10^{-6}$. This occurs because much of the solute in a solution of *carbonic acid* is present as loosely hydrated CO_2 and not as $CO(OH)_2$. When a correction is made for this, the true dissociation constant of $CO(OH)_2$ is found to be $10^{-3.6}$, which is close to the expected range.

7-13 Superacids

There are a number of liquids that are considerably more acidic, by as much as 10^6–10^{10} times, than concentrated aqueous solutions of so-called very strong acids such as nitric and sulfuric acids. These are called superacids, and in recent years a great deal of new chemistry has been found to occur in these media. Superacid systems are necessarily nonaqueous, since the acidity of any aqueous system is limited by the fact that the strongest acid that can exist in the presence of water is H_3O^+. Any stronger acid simply transfers its protons to H_2O to form H_3O^+.

To measure superacidity it is necessary to define a scale that goes beyond the normal pH scale and that is defined in terms of an experimental measurement. The usual one is the Hammett acidity function, H_0, defined as follows:

$$H_0 = pK_{BH^+} - \log \frac{[BH^+]}{[B]} \qquad (7\text{-}13.1)$$

B is an indicator base, and BH^+ is its protonated form. pK_{BH^+} is $-\log K$ for dissociation of BH^+. The ratio $[BH^+]/[B]$ can be measured spectrophotometrically. By employing bases with very low basicities (very negative pK values), the H_0 scale may be extended to the very negative values appropriate to the superacids. The H_0 scale becomes identical to the pH scale in dilute aqueous solution. Crudely, H_0 values can be thought of as pH values extending below pH = 0.

The first superacid systems to be studied quantitatively were very concentrated solutions of H_2SO_4. Pure H_2SO_4 has $H_0 = -12$; it is thus about 10^{12} times more acidic that 1 M aqueous H_2SO_4. When SO_3 is added, to produce oleum, H_0 can reach about -15.

Hydrofluoric acid has H_0 of about -11, and the acidity is increased to *ca* -12 on the addition of fluoride ion acceptors such as SbF_5.

Superacid media that have found wide application are obtained on addition of AsF_5 or SbF_5 to fluorosulfonic acid, HSO_3F. Pure fluorosulfonic acid has $H_0 = -15$ and is useful because of its wide liquid range, from -89 to $+164\ °C$, its ease of purification, and the fact that it does not attack glass provided it is free of HF. The self-ionization of HSO_3F is

$$2HSO_3F = H_2SO_3F^+ + SO_3F^- \qquad (7\text{-}13.2)$$

and any additive that increases the concentration of $H_2SO_3F^+$ increases the acidity. The addition of about 10 mol % of SbF_5 to HSO_3F increases $-H_0$ to about 19. A 1:1 molar mixture of HSO_3F and SbF_5 is colloquially known as "magic acid," although the additional SbF_5 beyond about 10% does little to increase the acidity.

The ability of SbF_5 to increase the acidity of HSO_3F is due mainly to the equilibrium

$$2HSO_3F + SbF_5 = H_2SO_3F^+ + SbF_5(SO_3F)^- \qquad (7\text{-}13.3)$$

through which the concentration of the solvent cation $H_2SO_3F^+$ is increased.

Superacid media have been used in many ways. The most obvious is to protonate molecules not normally thought of as bases, for instance, aromatic hydrocarbons. Thus, fluorobenzene in HF/SbF_5 or HSO_3F/SbF_5 produces the ion (structure 7-X)

7-X

Many other cationic species that would be immediately destroyed by even the weakest of bases can be prepared in and isolated from superacid media. These include carbonium ions as in Eq. 7-13.4:

$$(CH_3)_3COH \xrightarrow{\text{Superacid}} (CH_3)_3C^+ + H_3O^+ \qquad (7\text{-}13.4)$$

and halogen cations as in Eq. 7-13.5:

$$I_2 \xrightarrow{\text{Superacid}} I_2^+ \text{ and/or } I_3^+ \qquad (7\text{-}13.5)$$

It is also possible to prepare some remarkable polynuclear cations of sulfur, selenium, and tellurium, such as S_4^{2+}, S_8^{2+}, Se_4^{2+}, and Te_4^{2+}.

STUDY GUIDE

Scope and Purpose

We have presented an overview of the properties of solvents and of acids and bases that are important to the material in subsequent chapters. It is also intended that the various definitions of acids and bases that are set down in the chapter will find appropriate use in describing reactions. It is a principal goal that the student learn to recognize the various types and descriptions of acids and bases, and that the student develop a ready appreciation for which definition or description most suits a particular reaction. The relative strengths of acids and bases and the relative extents of autoionization, and so on, are also important concepts and trends that have been discussed.

Study Questions

A. Review

1. Name some properties that determine the utility of a solvent.
2. What is the principal effect of dielectric constant?
3. What is the relationship between donor and/or acceptor ability of a solvent and its ability to function as a solvent?
4. Name four protic solvents besides water.
5. Discuss the autodissociation of water and the forms of the hydrated proton.
6. In liquid NH_3 what are the species characteristic of acids? And bases?
7. Describe the three classes of aprotic solvents, mentioning examples of each.
8. Name an important industrial process that employs a molten salt as a solvent.
9. What two properties are generally important in a solvent for electrochemical reactions?
10. Name two common impurities in solvents and indicate how they can be removed.
11. State the Brønsted–Lowry definition of acids and bases.
12. Discuss the solvent system definition and show how it includes the Brønsted–Lowry definition as a special case.
13. Why is acetic acid not an acid in H_2SO_4?

14. To what sort of systems does the Lux–Flood concept apply? Give a representative equation.

15. State the Lewis definition of acids and bases and write three equations that illustrate it, including one that involves a protonic acid.

16. Why is F_3N a much weaker base than H_3N?

17. Why is BBr_3 a stronger acid than BF_3?

18. Describe the origin of the concept of hard and soft acids and bases.

19. Write the type of equation used to account for the combined effect of both electrostatic and covalent forces in acid–base interactions.

20. What are the main properties of each of the following common acids? H_2SO_4, HNO_3, $HClO_4$, HF.

21. Rank the following acids in order of their strengths $HClO_2$, $HClO_3$, $HClO_4$, H_2SeO_3, H_3AsO_4, $HMnO_4$, H_2SeO_4. Explain your reasoning.

22. What is the definition of the Hammett acidity function, H_0?

23. Why does the addition of SbF_5 to HSO_3F cause H_0 to become more negative?

B. Additional Exercises

1. Consider acetic acid as a solvent. Its dielectric constant is ~ 10. What is its mode of self-ionization likely to be? Name some substances that will be acids and some that will be bases in acetic acid. Will it be a better or poorer solvent than H_2O for ionic compounds?

2. State whether each of the following would act as an acid or a base in liquid HF.

$$BF_3,\ SbF_5,\ H_2O,\ CH_3CO_2H,\ C_6H_6$$

In each case write an equation, or equations, to show the basis for your answer.

3. Dimethyl sulfoxide is a very good solvent for polar and ionic materials. Why?

4. Why are only superacids good solvents for species such as $I_2{}^+$, $Se_4{}^{2+}$, $S_8{}^{2+}$, and so on? How would they react with less acidic solvents, such as H_2O or HNO_3?

5. Why do you think phosphines (R_3P) and phosphine oxides (R_3PO) differ considerably in their base properties?

6. Which member of each pair would you expect to be the more stable? (1) $PtCl_4{}^{2-}$ or $PtF_4{}^{2-}$. (2) $Fe(H_2O)_6{}^{3+}$ or $Fe(PH_3)_6{}^{3+}$. (3) $F_3B:THF$ or $Cl_3B:THF$. (4) $(CH_3)_3B:PCl_3$ or $(CH_3)_3B:P(CH_3)_3$. (5) $(CH_3)_3Al:pyridine$ or $(CH_3)_3Ga:pyridine$. (6) $Cl_3B:NCCH_3$ or $(CH_3)_3B:NCCH_3$.

7. In terms of the hard and soft acid and base concept, which end of the SCN^- ion would you expect to coordinate to Cr^{3+}, Pt^{2+}?

8. Estimate pK_1 values for H_2CrO_4, $HBrO_4$, $HClO$, H_5IO_6, and HSO_3F.

9. Write equations for the probable main self-ionization equilibria in liquid HCN.

10. AlF_3 is insoluble in HF, but dissolves when NaF is present. When BF_3 is passed into the solution, AlF_3 is precipitated. Account for these observations using equations.

11. What change in hybridization is necessary when the following serve as Lewis acids: BF_3, $AlCl_3$, and $SnCl_2$?

12. Balance the equation for the oxidation of Au by aqua regia.

13. Draw the Lewis diagram and predict the structure for $SiF_6{}^{2-}$.

14. Write equations representing the autoionization of the following solvents, and classify the process as hydrogen ion or halide ion transfer: (a) HCl, (b) HNO_3, (c) $OPCl_3$, (d) HF. Identify which species in these systems are the solvent's conjugate acid and the solvent's conjugate base.

15. Draw the Lewis diagrams for all species involved in Eq. 7-13.2. Discuss this equilibrium (a) in terms of the solvent system definition of acids and bases and (b) in terms of the Lewis definition of acids and bases.

16. Boric acid, $B(OH)_3$, acts as an acid in water, but does not do so via ionization of a proton. Rather, it serves as a Lewis acid towards OH^-. Explain with the use of a balanced equation.

17. K_1 is about 10^{-2} for the three acids H_3PO_4 (orthophosphoric acid), H_3PO_3 (phosphorus acid), and H_3PO_2 (hypophosphorus acid). Use this information to draw the Lewis diagram for each.

SUPPLEMENTARY READING

Barton, A. F. M., *Handbook of Solubility Parameters and Other Cohesive Parameters*, CRC Press, Cleveland, OH, 1983.

Bell, R. P., *The Proton in Chemistry*, 2nd ed., Chapman Hall, London, 1973.

Burger, K., *Ionic Solvation and Complex Formation Reactions in Non-Aqueous Solvents*, Elsevier, New York, 1983.

Drago, R. S., "A Modern Approach to Acid–Base Chemistry," *J. Chem. Educ.*, **1974**, *51*, 300.

Gillespie, R. J., "The Chemistry of Superacid Systems," *Endeavour*, **1973**, *32*, 541.

Gillespie, R. J., "Fluorosulfonic Acid and Related Superacid Media," *Acc. Chem. Res.*, **1968**, *1*, 202–209.

Gutmann, V., *The Donor–Acceptor Approach to Molecular Interactions*, Plenum, New York, 1978.

Ho, Tse-Lok, *Hard and Soft Acid and Base Principles in Organic Chemistry*, Academic, New York, 1977.

Jensen, W. B., *The Lewis Acid–Base Concepts. An Overview*, Wiley, New York, 1980.

Lagowski, J. J., Ed., *The Chemistry of Non-Aqueous Solvents*, Vols. 1 and 2, Academic, New York, 1966 and 1967.

Luder, W. F. and Zuffanti, S., *The Electronic Theory of Acids and Bases*, 2nd ed., Dover, New York, 1961.

Olah, G. A., Surya Prakash, G. K., and Sommer, J., *Superacids*, Wiley-Interscience, New York, 1985.

Pearson, R. G., Ed., *Hard and Soft Acids and Bases*, Dowden, Hutchinson, and Ross, Stroudsburg, 1973.

Seaborg, G. T., "The Research Style of G. N. Lewis," *J. Chem. Educ.*, **1984**, *61*, 93.

chapter 8

THE PERIODIC TABLE AND THE CHEMISTRY OF THE ELEMENTS

8-1 Introduction

Inorganic chemistry has often been said to comprise a vast collection of unrelatable facts in contrast to organic chemistry, where there appears to be a much greater measure of systematization and order. This is in part true, since the subject matter of inorganic chemistry is far more diverse and complicated and the rules for chemical behavior are often less well established. The subject matter is complicated because even among elements of similar electronic structure, such as Li, Na, K, Rb, and Cs, Group IA(1), differences arise because of differences in the size of atoms, ionization potentials, hydration, solvation energies, or the like. Some of these differences may be quite subtle—for example, those that enable the human cell and other living systems to discriminate between Li, Na, and K. In short, every element behaves in a different way.

Organic chemistry deals with many compounds that are formed by a *few* elements, namely, carbon in sp, sp^2, or sp^3 hybridization states, along with H, O, N, S and the halogens, and less commonly B, Si, Se, P, Hg, and so on. The chemistry is mainly one of molecular compounds that are liquids or solids commonly soluble in nonpolar solvents, distillable, or crystallizable and normally stable to, though combustible in, air or oxygen.

Inorganic chemistry by contrast deals with many compounds formed by *many* elements. It involves the study of the chemistry of more than 100 elements that can form compounds as gases, liquids, or solids whose reactions may be— or may have to be—studied at very low or very high temperatures. The compounds may form ionic, extended-covalent, or molecular crystals and their solubility may range from essentially zero in all solvents to high solubility in alkanes; they may react spontaneously and vigorously with water or air. Furthermore, while compounds in organic chemistry almost invariably follow the octet rule with a maximum coordination number and a maximum valence of 4 for all elements, inorganic compounds may have coordination numbers up to 14 with those of 4, 5, 6, and 8 being especially common, and valence numbers from -2 to $+8$. Finally, there are types of bonding in inorganic compounds that have no parallel in organic chemistry where σ and $p\pi$—$p\pi$ multiple bonding normally prevail.

Although various concepts help to bring order and systematics into inorganic chemistry, the oldest and still the most meaningful concept of order is the periodic table of the elements. As we pointed out in Chapter 2, the order in the periodic table depends on the electronic structures of the gaseous atoms. By successively adding electrons to the available energy levels, we can build up the pattern of the electronic structures of the elements from the lightest to the heaviest one currently known, element 109. Moreover, on the basis of the electron configurations, the elements can be arranged in the conventional long form of the periodic table.

However, the periodic table can also be constructed solely on the basis of the chemical properties of the elements, and one of its chief uses is to provide a compact mnemonic device for correlating chemical facts. In this chapter, the periodic table is discussed from the chemical, instead of the theoretical, aspect. In effect, the kinds of chemical observations that originally stimulated chemists such as Mendeleev to devise the periodic table are examined here. Now, in addition, we are able to correlate such facts, and to interpret them, in terms of the electronic structures of the atoms.

Recently Discovered Elements

Elements with atomic numbers 104–109 have been discovered recently. There is not yet agreement on symbols or names for these synthetically prepared elements, and there is not expected to be any important chemistry associated with them. The detection in Germany, for instance, of element 109 is based on the observation of a single decay event after 3 weeks of bombarding a bismuth target with ^{58}Fe. The half-life of isotope-226, of the element 109, is about 5 ms. Element 108 is claimed on the basis of three decay events from long-term bombardment of a lead target with ^{58}Fe. The half-life of the 265-isotope of element 108 is about 3 ms. The Soviets claim detection of element 106, and this has been confirmed in the United States. The Soviets singly claim the detection of element 107.

PART A
THE NATURE AND TYPES OF THE ELEMENTS

8-2   Monatomic Elements: He, Ne, Ar, Kr, Xe, and Rn

The noble gases, with their closed shell electronic structures, are necessarily monatomic. In the vapor, mercury ($5d^{10}6s^2$) is also monatomic. However, liquid mercury, despite its relatively high vapor pressure and solubility in water and other solvents, has appreciable electrical conductivity and is bright and metallic in appearance. This is because the $6p$ orbitals are available to participate in metallic bonding.

8-3   Diatomic Molecules: H_2, N_2, O_2, F_2, Cl_2, Br_2, and I_2

For the halogens, the formation of a single electron-pair bond in a diatomic molecule completes the octet. For nitrogen and oxygen, multiple bonding allows for a simple diatomic molecule. P_2 and S_2 are stable at elevated temperatures, but not at 25 °C. In hydrogen, formation of a single bond completes the $1s$ shell for each atom.

8-4   Discrete Polyatomic Molecules: P_4, S_n, and Se_8

For the second-row and heavier elements, $p\pi$–$p\pi$ bonding of the type found in N_2 and O_2 is less effective. The formation by phosphorus and sulfur of the normal number of single electron-pair bonds as expected from their electronic structures, namely, three and two, respectively, leads either to discrete molecules or to chain structures, which are more stable than the diatomics.

White phosphorus has tetrahedral P_4 molecules (structure 8-I) with the P—P distance 2.21 Å, and the P—P—P angles are, of course, 60°. The small angle implies that the molecule might be strained. Strain in this sense would mean that the total energy of the six P—P bonds in the P_4 molecule is less than the total energy of six P—P bonds formed by P atoms having normal bond angles (90°–100°). Current theoretical work indicates that such strain energy is not very large, although sufficient to make white phosphorus less stable than black phosphorus, where all P—P—P bond angles are normal. White phosphorus is also much more reactive than the black allotrope. As_4 and Sb_4 molecules are also formed on condensation from vapor but for them the tetrahedral structure is still less stable, readily transforming to the black phosphorus type of structure.

8-I

Sulfur has a profusion of allotropes; these contain multiatom sulfur rings. The largest ring thus far known is S_{20}. The allotropes are referred to as cyclohexasulfur, cyclooctasulfur, and the like. Chains occur in *catenasulfur*, S_x. The thermodynamically most stable form is orthorhombic sulfur, Fig. 8-1, which contains S_8 rings.

8-5   Elements with Extended Structures

In some elements, atoms form 2, 3, or 4 single covalent bonds to each other to give chains, planes, or three-dimensional networks, namely, extended structures. The most important elements that do this are

C	P^a	S^a
Si	As	Se^a
Ge	Sb	Te
Sn^b	Bi	

(*a*) Also molecular   (*b*) Also metallic

S − S = 2.059 Å
∠S − S − S = 107° 54′
Dihedral angle = 98.9°

(a)

(b)

Figure 8-1 The structure of orthorhombic sulfur. (*a*) The cyclic S_8 molecule. (*b*) Stacking of S_8 molecules in the solid.

Some of these have allotropes of either molecular or metallic types. Those with metallic allotropes are discussed here, as are the ones that form extended, three-dimensional, covalent networks. First we discuss boron, which forms limited networks based on variously linked 12-atom units.

Elemental boron has several allotropes, all based on B_{12} icosahedra, structure 8-II (next page). In the α-rhombohedral allotrope, the B_{12} units are packed as "spheres" in roughly cubic closest packing. The icosahedral units are linked weakly together. The β-rhombohedral form of boron also has icosahedral units linked in a complicated way. A tetragonal form of the element has B_{12} units arranged in layers that are linked through B—B bonds. The latter, obtained

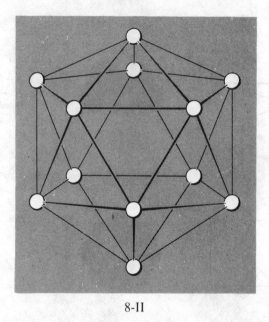

8-II

by crystallization of liquid boron, is the thermodynamically stable form of the element. Its structure accounts for the high melting point (2250 ± 50 °C) and for the chemical inertness of boron. The element is properly considered to be a metalloid, and its weakly linked B_{12} structure gives it properties intermediate between those of the molecular and the metallic substances.

The Group IVB(14) elements all have the diamond structure shown in Fig. 8-2. This has a cubic unit cell, but it can, for some purposes, be viewed

(a)   (b)

Figure 8-2   The diamond structure seen from two points of view. (*a*) The conventional unit cell. (*b*) A view showing how layers are stacked; these layers run perpendicular to the body diagonals of the cube. Remember, however, that this is not a layer structure; its properties are the same in all directions.

as a stacking of puckered, infinite layers. All atoms in the diamond structure are equivalent, each being surrounded by a perfect tetrahedron of four other atoms. Each atom forms a localized two-electron bond to each of its neighbors. The extended, three-dimensional, covalent network structure clearly accounts for the extreme hardness of diamond.

Silicon and *Germanium* normally have the diamond structure. *Tin* has the diamond structure also, but in addition displays the equilibrium shown in Eq. 8-5.1:

$$
\begin{array}{ccc}
\alpha\text{-Sn} & \overset{18\ °C}{\rightleftharpoons} & \beta\text{-Sn} \\
\text{"Grey"} & & \text{"White"} \\
\text{diamond} & & \text{distorted cp} \\
d^{20} = 5.75 & & d^{20} = 7.31
\end{array}
\qquad (8\text{-}5.1)
$$

The white allotrope has a more efficient, near-ideal, closest-packing (cp) structure, and this accounts for the higher density of the white (β-Sn) allotrope, compared to the α-Sn allotrope, which has the diamond structure. (d^{20} in Eq. 8-5.1 represents density, in grams per cubic centimeter, at 20 °C.)

Carbon also exists as *graphite*, which has the layer structure shown in Fig. 8-3. The separation of the layers, 3.35 Å, is about the sum of the van der Waals radii for C and indicates that the forces between the layers should be weak. This accounts for the softness and lubricity of graphite, since the layers can easily slip over one another. Each C atom is surrounded by only three neighbors; after forming one σ bond with each neighbor, each C atom still has one electron and these electrons are paired up into a system of π bonds as in structure 8-III. Resonance leads to essential equivalence so that the C—C bond distances are all 1.415 Å.

8-III

This is a little longer than the C—C distance in benzene where the bond order is 1.5 and corresponds to a C—C bond order in graphite of ~1.33. Since $p\pi$–$p\pi$ multiple bonding is clearly involved, the other Group IVB(14) elements cannot form this type of structure. The continuous π system in each layer makes possible good electrical conductance, especially in directions parallel to the layers. The conductance in these directions is 10^4 times greater than it is in the direction perpendicular to the layers. In diamond the conductance is only 10^{-18} of that in the graphite layers. For the elements Si, Ge and Sn in

Figure 8-3   The normal structure of graphite.

their diamond type structures the conductances steadily increase until at tin it is comparable to that within the graphite layers. This is an excellent illustration of increasing metallic character as a group is descended.

In Group VB(15), *phosphorus* has numerous polymorphs. The common red form, which may be a mixture of forms, has not been structurally characterized. Black phosphorus, obtained by heating white phosphorus under pressure, has the structure shown in Fig. 8-4. Each phosphorus atom is bound to three neighbors by single bonds, 2.17–2.20 Å long. The double layers thus formed are stacked with an interlayer distance of 3.87 Å. As is true for graphite, the layer structure of black P leads to flakiness of the crystals. It also accounts for the lack of reactivity, for example, to air, compared to P_4.

Arsenic, Sb, and *Bi* all form crystals whose structures are similar to that of black phosphorus. However, they are bright and metallic in appearance and have resistivities which are comparable to those of metals such as Ti or Mn. Clearly, structure alone does not fix the properties of a substance. In As, Sb,

Figure 8-4   The arrangement of atoms in the double layers found in crystalline black phosphorus.

and Bi, the larger atomic orbitals lead to the formation of energy bands rather than purely localized bonds. This gives rise to increasing metallic character.

The chain form of *sulfur, catenasulfur,* is the main component of the so-called plastic sulfur obtained when molten sulfur is poured into water. It can be drawn into long fibers that contain helical chains of sulfur atoms. It slowly transforms to orthorhombic S_8.

The stable form of *selenium,* grey, metal-like crystals obtained from melts, contains infinite spiral chains. There is evidently weak interaction of a metallic nature between neighboring atoms of different chains, but in the dark the electrical conductivity of selenium is not comparable to that of true metals (resistivity 2×10^{11} $\mu\Omega$ cm). However, it is notably photoconductive and is hence used in photoelectric devices, and is essential to the process of xerography.

Tellurium is isomorphous with grey Se, although it is silvery white and semimetallic (resistivity 2×10^5 $\mu\Omega$ cm). The resistivity of S, Se, and Te has a negative temperature coefficient, usually considered a characteristic of non-metals.

8-6   Metals

The majority of the elements are metals. These have many physical properties different from those of other solids, notably: (1) high reflectivity; (2) high electrical conductance, decreasing with increasing temperature; (3) high thermal conductance; and (4) mechanical properties such as strength and ductility. There are three basic metal structures: *cubic* and *hexagonal close packed* (illustrated in Section 4-7) and *body-centered cubic, bcc* (Fig. 8-5). In *bcc* packing each atom has only 8 instead of 12 nearest neighbors, although there are 6 next nearest neighbors that are only about 15% further away. It is only 92% as dense an arrangement as the *hcp* and *ccp* structures. The distribution of these three structure types, *hcp, ccp,* and *bcc,* in the periodic table is shown in Fig. 8-6. The majority of the metals deviate slightly from the ideal structures, especially those with *hcp* structures. For the *hcp* structure the ideal value of c/a, where c and a are the hexagonal unit-cell edges, is 1.633. All metals having this structure have a smaller c/a ratio (usually $1.57 - 1.62$) except zinc and cadmium.

The characteristic physical properties of metals as well as the high coor-

Figure 8-5 A body-centered cubic (bcc) structure.

Figure 8-6 The occurrence of hexagonal close-packed (hcp), cubic close-packed (ccp), and body-centered cubic (bcc) structures among the elements. Where two or more symbols are used, the largest represents the stable form at 25°C. The symbol labeled hcp/ccp signifies a mixed . . . *ABCABABCAB* . . . type of close packing, with overall hexagonal symmetry. [Adapted with permission from H. Krebs, *Grundzuge der Anorganishen Kristallchemie, F. Enke Verlag, 1968.*]

dination numbers (either 12 or 8 nearest neighbors plus 6 more that are not too remote) suggest that the *bonding in metals* is different from that in other substances. There is no ionic contribution, and it is also impossible to have two-electron covalent bonds between all adjacent pairs of atoms, since there are neither sufficient electrons nor sufficient orbitals. An explanation of the characteristic properties of metals is given by the so-called band theory. This is very mathematical but the principle can be illustrated.

Imagine an array of atoms so far apart that their atomic orbitals do not interact. Now suppose this array contracts. The orbitals of neighboring atoms begin to overlap and interact with each other. So many atoms are involved that at the actual distances in metals, the interaction forms essentially continuous energy bands that spread through the metal (Fig. 8-7). The electrons in these bands are *completely delocalized*. Observe also that some bands may overlap. In Fig. 8-7 where Na is used as an illustration, the 3*s* and 3*p* bands overlap.

The energy bands can also be depicted as in Fig. 8-8. Here energy is plotted horizontally, and the envelope indicates on the vertical the number of electrons that can be accommodated at each value of the energy. Shading is used to indicate filling of the bands.

Completely filled or completely empty bands, as shown in Fig. 8-8(*a*), do not permit net electron flow and the substance is an *insulator*. Covalent solids can be discussed from this point of view (though it is unnecessary to do so) by saying that all electrons occupy low-lying bands (equivalent to the bonding

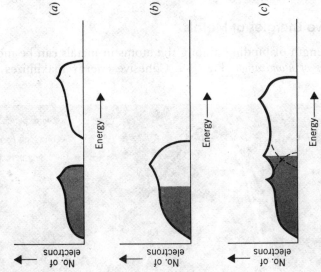

Figure 8-8 Envelopes of energy bands, with shading to indicate filling. (*a*) an insulator, (*b*) a metallic conductor, (*c*) overlapping conduction bands as in Na.

Figure 8-7 Energy bands of sodium as a function of internuclear distance. The actual equilibrium distance is represented by r_0. [Reproduced by permission from J. C. Slater, *Introduction to Chemical Physics*, McGraw-Hill, New York, 1939.]

orbitals) while the high-lying bands (equivalent to antibonding orbitals) are entirely empty. Metallic conductance occurs when there is a partially filled band, as in Fig. 8-8(*b*); the transition metals, with their incomplete sets of *d* electrons, have partially filled *d* bands and this accounts for their high conductances. Overlapping bands, as in Na, are illustrated in Fig. 8-8(*c*).

Cohesive Energies of Metals

The strength of binding among the atoms in metals can be measured by the *enthalpies of atomization*, Fig. 8-9. Cohesive energy maximizes with elements

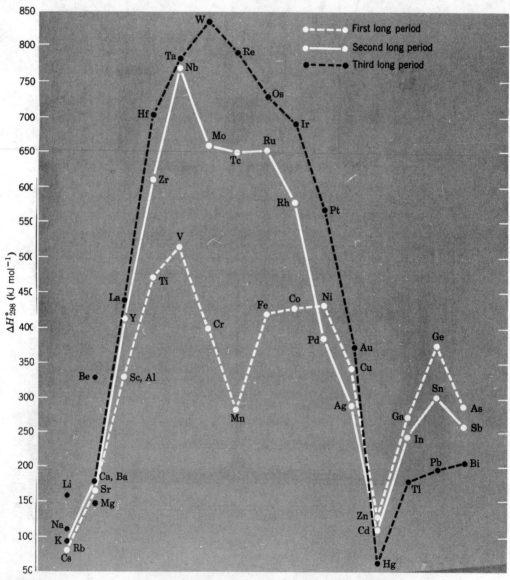

Figure 8-9 Heats of atomization of metals, ΔH°_{298} for M(s) $\rightarrow$ M(g). [Reproduced by permission from W. E. Dasent, *Inorganic Energetics,* Second Edition, Cambridge University Press, New York, 1982.]

having partially filled d shells, that is, with the transition metals. However, it is particularly with the elements near the middle of the second and third transition séries, especially Nb—Ru and Hf—Ir, that the energies are largest, reaching 837 kJ mol⁻¹ for tungsten. It is noteworthy that these large cohesive energies are principally due to the structure of the metals where high coordination numbers are involved. For a *hcp* or *ccp* structure, there are 6 bonds per metal atom (since each of the 12 nearest neighbors has a half-share in each of the 12 bonds). Each bond, even when cohesive energy is 800 kJ mol⁻¹, has an energy of only 133 kJ mol⁻¹, roughly half the C—C bond energy in diamond where each carbon atom has only four neighbors, but there are three times as many of them.

PART B
THE CHEMISTRY OF THE ELEMENTS IN RELATION TO THEIR POSITION IN THE PERIODIC TABLE

We can now proceed to a more detailed commentary on the chemical reactivity and types of compounds formed by the elements. The periodic table forms the basis for the discussion, starting with the simplest chemistry, namely, that of hydrogen, and proceeding to the heaviest elements.

8-7   Hydrogen, 1s¹

The chemistry of hydrogen depends on three electronic processes:

1. *Loss of the 1s valence electron.* This forms merely the proton, H^+. Its small size, $r \sim 1.5 \times 10^{-13}$ cm, relative to atomic sizes $r \sim 10^{-8}$ cm, and its small charge result in a unique ability to distort the electron clouds surrounding other atoms. The proton *never* exists as such except in gaseous ion beams. It is invariably associated with other atoms or molecules. Although the hydrogen ion in water is commonly written as H^+, it is actually H_3O^+ or $H(H_2O)_n^+$.

2. *Acquisition of an electron.* The H atom can acquire an electron forming the *hydride ion*, H^- with the He $1s^2$ structure. This ion exists only in crystalline hydrides of the most electropositive metals, for example, NaH, CaH₂.

3. *Formation of an electron pair bond.* Nonmetals and even many metals can form covalent bonds to hydrogen.

The chemistry of hydrogen-containing substances depends greatly on the nature of the other elements and groups in the compound. The extent to which the compounds dissociate in polar solvents, acting as acids in the general way shown in Eq. 8-7.1:

$$HX \rightleftharpoons H^+ + X^-$$ (8-7.1)

is particularly dependent on the nature of X.

Also important is the electronic structure and coordination number of the whole molecule. Consider BH_3, CH_4, NH_3, OH_2, and FH. The first acts as a Lewis acid, and dimerizes instantly to B_2H_6; CH_4 is unreactive and neutral; NH_3 has a lone pair and is a base; H_2O with two lone pairs can act as a base or as a very weak acid; HF, a gas, is a much stronger though still weak acid in aqueous solution.

All H—X bonds necessarily have some polar character with the dipole oriented $\overset{\delta+}{H}$—$\overset{\delta-}{X}$ or $\overset{\delta-}{H}$—$\overset{\delta+}{X}$. The term "hydride" is usually given to those compounds in which the negative end of the dipole is on hydrogen, for example, in SiH_4, $\overset{\delta+}{Si}$—$\overset{\delta-}{H}$. However, although HCl as $\overset{\delta+}{H}$—$\overset{\delta-}{Cl}$ is a strong acid in aqueous solution, nevertheless, it is a gas and is properly termed a covalent hydride.

8-8   Helium, $1s^2$, and the Noble Gases, ns^2np^6

The second element *helium*, He, $Z = 2$ has the closed $1s$ shell; its very small size leads to some physical properties that are unique to liquid helium. The physical properties of the other noble gases vary systematically with size. Although the first ionization energies are high, consistent with their chemical inertness, the values fall steadily as the size of the atom increases. The ability to enter into chemical combination with other atoms should increase with decreasing ionization potential and decreasing energy of promotion to states with unpaired electrons—that is, $ns^2np^6 \rightarrow ns^2np^5(n + 1)s$. The threshold of chemical activity is reached at Kr, but few compounds have been isolated. The reactivity of Xe is much greater, and many compounds of Xe with O and F are known (Chapter 21). The reactivity of Rn is presumably greater still than that of the other noble gases, but since the longest-lived isotope (^{222}Rn) has a half-life of only 3.825 days, only limited tracer studies can be made.

8-9   Elements of the First Short Period

The third element *lithium*, Li, $Z = 3$ has the structure $1s^22s$. With increasing Z, electrons enter the $2s$ and $2p$ levels until the closed shell configuration, $1s^22s^22p^6$, is reached at neon. The seven elements Li–F constitute the first members of the *groups* of elements.

Although these elements have many properties in common with the heavier elements of their respective groups—which is to be expected in view of the similarity in the outer electronic structures of the *gaseous* atoms—they nevertheless show highly individual behavior in many important respects. We have already seen that O_2 and N_2 form diatomic molecules, whereas their congeners, S and P, form polyatomic molecules or chains. Indeed, the differences between the chemistries of B, C, N and O, and Al, Si, P and S, and the heavier members of these groups are sufficiently striking that in many ways it is not useful to regard the elements of the first short period as prototypes for their congeners. The closest analogies between the elements of the first short period and the heavier elements of particular groups occur for Li and F, followed by Be.

Figure 8-10 First ionization enthalpies of the elements Li–Ne. See also Fig. 2-14.

The increase in nuclear charge and consequent changes in the extranuclear structure result in extremes of physical and chemical properties. In Fig. 8-10 are given the first ionization enthalpies. The low ionization enthalpy for *lithium* is in accord with facile loss of an electron to form the Li^+ ion, which occurs both in solids and in solution. It accords also with the high reactivity of lithium to oxygen, nitrogen, water, and many other elements.

For *beryllium*, Be, the first (899 kJ mol^{-1}) and especially the second (1757 kJ mol^{-1}) ionization enthalpies are sufficiently high that total loss of both electrons to give Be^{2+} does not occur even with the most electronegative elements: Even in BeF_2 the Be—F bonds have appreciable covalent character. The ion in aqueous solution, $[Be(H_2O)_4]^{2+}$, is very strongly aquated and undergoes hydrolysis quite readily to give species with Be(OH) bonds.

For the succeeding elements, the absence of any simple cations under any conditions is to be expected from the high ionization enthalpies. Note that the values (Fig. 8-10) for B, C, and N increase regularly but that they are lower than the values that would be predicted by extrapolation from Li and Be. This arises because p electrons are less penetrating than s electrons—they are, therefore, shielded by the s electrons and are removed more easily. Another discontinuity occurs between N and O. This occurs because the $2p$ shell is half-full, that is, $p_x p_y p_z$ at N. The p electrons added in O, F, and Ne thus enter p orbitals that are already singly occupied. Hence, they are partly repelled by the p electron already present in the same orbital and are thus less tightly bound.

The electron attachment enthalpies (Section 1-2) become increasingly more negative from Li to F, and the electronegativities (Sections 1-2 and 2-7) of the elements increase from Li to F.

Boron, $2s^2 2p^1$, has no simple ion chemistry associated with cations of the type B^{n+}. Rather, it is bound covalently in all of its compounds, as in oxoanions, organoboron compounds, or hydrides.

Anion formation first appears for carbon, which forms C_2^{2-} and some other polyatomic ions, although the existence of C^{4-} is uncertain. N^{3-} ions are stable in nitrides of highly electropositive elements. Oxide (O^{2-}) and fluoride (F^-)

are common in solids but observe that O^{2-} ions cannot exist in aqueous solutions. Compare

$$O^{2-} + H_2O = 2\,OH^- \qquad K > 10^{22} \qquad (8\text{-}9.1)$$

$$F^- + H_2O = HF + OH^- \qquad K = 10^{-7} \qquad (8\text{-}9.2)$$

Carbon is a true nonmetal and its chemistry is dominated by single, double, and triple bonds to itself or to nitrogen, oxygen, and a few other elements. What distinguishes carbon from other elements is its unique ability to form chains of carbon–carbon bonds (called catenation) in compounds—as distinct from the element itself.

Nitrogen as nitrogen gas, N_2, is relatively unreactive because of the great strength of the $N\equiv N$ bond and its electronic structure. Nitrogen compounds are covalent, usually involving three single bonds, although multiple bonds such as $C\equiv N$ or $Os\equiv N$ can exist. With electropositive elements, ionic nitrides containing N^{3-} may be formed.

The diatomic molecule *oxygen* has two unpaired electrons and consequently is very reactive. There is an extensive chemistry with covalent bonds as in $(CH_3)_2C{=}O$, $(C_2H_5)_2O$, CO, SO_3, and the like. However, well-defined oxide ions O^{2-}, O_2^-, and O_2^{2-} exist in crystalline solids. Hydroxide ions, OH^-, exist both in solids and in solutions, although in hydroxylic solvents the OH^- ion is doubtlessly hydrated via hydrogen bonds.

Fluorine is extremely reactive due largely to the low bond energy in F_2. This is a result, in part, of repulsions between nonbonding electrons. Ionic compounds containing F^- ions and covalent compounds containing $X{-}F$ bonds are well established. Owing to the high electronegativity of fluorine, such covalent bonds are generally quite polar in the sense $X^+{-}F^-$.

Covalent Bonds

A few points may be mentioned here.

1. Note that Be, B, and C have fewer electrons in their ground states than the number of electron pair bonds they normally form. This has been explained previously in terms of promotion to valence states.

2. The elements of the first short period obey the octet rule. Since they have only four orbitals ($2s$, $2p_x$, $2p_y$, $2p_z$) in their valence shells, there are never more than eight electrons in their valence shells. This means that the maximum number of electron-pair bonds is four. The octet rule breaks down for elements from the second short period.

For example, phosphorus, $3s^2 3p^3 3d^0$ can be excited to a valence state $3s^1 3p^3 3d^1$ with an expenditure of energy so modest that the heat of formation of the two additional bonds will more than compensate for it. On the other hand, promotion of N, $2s^2 2p^3$ to any state with five unpaired electrons, such as $2s^1 2p^3 3d^1$, would require more promotional energy than could be recovered by the extra bond formation energy.

For C, promotion from $2s^2 2p^2$ to $2s 2p^3$ gives the valence of four. For N ($2s^2 2p^3$) only three of the five electrons can possibly be unpaired, in O only two, and in F only one. Hence, these elements are limited to valences of two, three, and one. On the other side of C, that is, in Li, Be, and B, the valences are less than four because of lack of electrons to occupy the orbitals, so that by electron sharing these can show valences of only one, two, and three, respectively.

3. Where there are fewer electrons than are required to fill the energetically useful orbitals, as in trivalent boron compounds such as BCl_3, BF_3, and $B(CH_3)_3$, there is a strong tendency to utilize these orbitals by combining with compounds that have an excess of electrons. Such compounds are those of trivalent nitrogen such as NH_3, $N(CH_3)_3$, and so on, or oxygen, such as H_2O, $(C_2H_5)_2O$, and so on, that have unshared electron pairs. The former are thus acceptors of electrons (Lewis acids) and the latter are donors of electrons (Lewis bases). The formation of a dative bond is shown in Fig. 8-11.

Notice that while nitrogen compounds have only one unshared pair, $:NR_3$, oxygen compounds have two $:\overset{..}{O}R_2$; normally only one of the electron pairs is used and only in a very few cases does oxygen form four bonds. Beryllium compounds with two empty orbitals usually fill these by forming compounds with two donor molecules, BeX_2L_2.

Note that such donor–acceptor behavior is not confined to elements of the first short period, but is quite general. Adducts may be formed between compounds whenever one compound has empty orbitals and the other has unshared electron pairs.

Compounds of many elements may act as acceptors, but donors are commonly compounds of trivalent N, P, and As and compounds of divalent O and S. However, a very important class of donors are the halide and pseudohalide ions and ions such as hydride, H^-, and carbanions such as CH_3^- or $C_6H_5^-$. Some representative examples are

$$BF_3 + F^- = BF_4^- \tag{8-9.3}$$

$$PF_5 + F^- = PF_6^- \tag{8-9.4}$$

$$AlCl_3 + Cl^- = AlCl_4^- \tag{8-9.5}$$

$$PtCl_4 + 2Cl^- = PtCl_6^{2-} \tag{8-9.6}$$

$$Ni(CN)_2 + 2CN^- = Ni(CN)_4^{2-} \tag{8-9.7}$$

$$Co(NCS)_2 + 2SCN^- = Co(NCS)_4^{2-} \tag{8-9.8}$$

$$BH_3 + H^- = BH_4^- \tag{8-9.9}$$

$$Al(CH_3)_3 + CH_3^- = Al(CH_3)_4^- \tag{8-9.10}$$

Lewis-base behavior is also shown by some transition metal compounds, as we discuss later. One example is the compound $(\eta^5\text{-}C_5H_5)_2ReH$, which is as strong a base to protons as NH_3. The reason why some atoms succeed in increasing their coordination numbers from three to four but seldom from two to four can be understood if we consider the polar nature of the dative bond. The donor and acceptor molecules are both electrically neutral. When the bond is

Figure 8-11 The formation of a dative bond between boron in a BX_3 acceptor and nitrogen in an NY_3 donor.

formed, the donor atom has, in effect, lost negative charge rendering it positive. It has only half-ownership of an electron pair that formerly belonged to it entirely. Conversely, the acceptor atom now has extra negative charge. This would be true for complete sharing of the electron pair (structure 8-IV). Lesser polarity is introduced if the electron pair remains more the property of the donor atom than the acceptor (structure 8-V), in which case we indicate only charges $\delta +$ and $\delta -$ on the atoms.

$$\overset{-e \;\; +e}{B:N} \qquad \overset{\delta - \qquad\quad \delta +}{B\ldots\ldots:N} \qquad \overset{\delta + \;\; \delta -}{R-\overset{\displaystyle |}{\underset{\displaystyle R}{O}}: BX_3}$$

$$\text{8-IV} \qquad\qquad \text{8-V} \qquad\qquad\qquad \text{8-VI}$$

This charge separation can be achieved only by doing work against coulomb forces, which we must assume is more than compensated by the bond energy when a stable system results. However, if we take a case where one donor bond has been formed (structure 8-VI), then the second unshared pair on oxygen is further restrained by the positive charge on O that arises from the dative bond already formed. There is thus much more coulombic work to be done in forming a second dative bond—enough apparently to make this process energetically unfavorable. Steric hindrance between the first acceptor and a second would also militate against addition of a second acceptor. Note that this electrostatic argument is basically the same as that used to explain relative dissociation constants in polyfunctional acids.

8-10   The Elements of the Second Short Period

The elements of the second short period are Na, Mg, Al, Si, P, S, Cl, and Ar. Although their outer electronic structures are similar to those of the corresponding elements in the first short period, their chemistries differ considerably. In particular, the chemistries of Si, P, S, and Cl are largely different from their corresponding partner in the first short period. The elements of the second short period do, however, give a better guide to the chemistries of the heavier elements in their respective groups than do the elements of the first short period that start the groups. This is especially the case for the nonmetallic elements. The reasons for this are as follows:

1. It is not generally favorable to form $p\pi$–$p\pi$ multiple bonds such as $Si{=}Si$, $Si{=}O$, or $P{=}P$. Most likely, this occurs because, in order to approach

close enough to get good overlap of $p\pi$ atomic orbitals, the heavier atoms would encounter large repulsive forces due to overlapping of their filled inner shells. The small, compact inner shell of the elements from the second row (that is, just $1s^2$) does not produce this repulsion.

The result is that, as we have seen, the nature of the elements of the second short period is strikingly different from that of the elements of the first short period. As a striking example, consider the vast chemistry of carbon associated with multiple bonds such as $C{=}C$, $C{\equiv}C$, $C{=}O$, $C{=}N$, and so on. In contrast, silicon displays less tendency to form multiple bonds of this type, and although some compounds containing double bonds such as $Si{=}Si$, $Si{=}P$, and $P{=}P$ are being prepared and studied, the substances are stable only when sterically encumbered by very bulky substituents so that the double bonds are *kinetically* stable. An example is $[(CH_3)_3Si]_3CP{=}PC[Si(CH_3)_3]_3$. Here we also note that whereas CO_2 is a gas, SiO_2 (quartz) is an infinite polymer or network substance.

2. Although in certain types of compounds of P, S, and Cl such as Cl_3PO, Cl_2SO, SO_2, ClO_4^-, ClO_2, and so on, there is some multiple bonding, this occurs by an entirely different mechanism involving d orbitals. The low-lying $3d$ orbitals can be utilized not only for $p\pi$–$d\pi$ multiple bonding, but also for additional bond formation. The octet rule now no longer holds rigorously and is indeed commonly violated.

3. The possiblity of using the $3d$ orbitals then allows promotion to valence states leading to formation of five or six bonds. Hence, we find compounds such as PCl_5 or SF_6 and silicon can form species with five and six coordination also as in SiF_6^{2-}. For silicon, even where there is some analogy with carbon chemistry, as in compounds with single bonds, the reactions and mechanisms operating in silicon chemistry may be vastly different. A simple example is the unreactivity of CCl_4 toward water, whereas $SiCl_4$ is instantly hydrolyzed.

4. The shapes of molecules and the nature of the bonds also differ. Recall the discussion from Chapter 2 concerning VSEPR geometries.

5. Even the cation- and the anion-forming elements differ. Thus while beryllium forms only $[Be(H_2O)_4]^{2+}$, the magnesium ion is $[Mg(H_2O)_6]^{2+}$, and there are substantial differences between the chemistries of Li and Na. Aluminum is an electropositive metal totally different from boron, although in certain covalent compounds there are some similarities. For Group VIIB(17), the Cl—Cl bond strength is actually higher than that of F_2, and Cl_2 is much less reactive. In addition, solid chlorides commonly have structures that are quite different from the corresponding fluorides. The structures of ionic chlorides are much closer to those given by sulfides.

8-11 The Remainder of the Nontransition Elements

The elements of the first and especially the second short period just discussed give some guide to the chemistries of the remaining elements in their respective groups. The main features are as follows.

Group IA(1)

All the elements (Table 8-1) are highly electropositive giving $+1$ ions. Of all the groups in the periodic table, these metals show most clearly the effect of

Table 8-1   Some Properties of Group IA(1) Elements

Element	Electron Configuration	mp, °C	Ionic Radius, Å	E^0, V^a	Ionization Enthalpy, kJ mol^{-1}
Li	[He]$2s^1$	180	0.60	−3.0	520
Na	[Ne]$3s^1$	98	0.96	−2.7	496
K	[Ar]$4s^1$	64	1.33	−2.9	419
Rb	[Kr]$5s^1$	39	1.48	−3.0	403
Cs	[Xe]$6s^1$	29	1.69	−3.0	376
Fr^b	[Rn]$7s^1$	—	—	—	—

^{a}For $M^+(aq) + e^- = M(s)$.

^{b}All isotopes are radioactive with short half-lives.

increasing size and mass on chemical properties. Thus, as examples, the following *decrease* from Li to Cs: (a) melting points and heat of sublimation of the metals; (b) lattice energies of salts except those with very small anions (because of irregular radius ratio effects); (c) effective hydrated radii and hydration energies; and (d) strength of covalent bonds in M_2 molecules.

Group IIA(2) and IIB(12)

Some properties of the elements are given in Table 8-2. Calcium, Sr, Ba, and Ra are also highly electropositive forming +2 ions. Systematic group trends are again shown, for example, by increasing insolubilities of sulfates, increasing thermal stabilities of carbonates or nitrates and decreasing hydration energies of the ions in solution.

Zinc, Cd, and Hg are in Group IIB(12). They have two s electrons outside filled d shells since they follow Cu, Ag, and Au, respectively, after the first, second, and third transition series elements. The chemistries of Zn and Cd are quite similar, but the polarizing power of the M^{2+} ions is larger than would be predicted by comparing the radii with those of the Mg to Ra group. This can

Table 8-2   Some Properties of Group IIA(2) and IIB(12) Elements

Element	Electron Configuration	mp, °C	Ionic Radius M^{2+}, Å	E^0, V^a	ΔH(kJ mol^{-1}) for $M(g) \rightarrow M^{2+}(g) + 2e^-$
Be	[He]$2s^2$	1280	0.31	−1.85	2657
Mg	[Ne]$3s^2$	650	0.65	−2.37	2188
Ca	[Ar]$4s^2$	840	0.99	−2.87	1735
Sr	[Kr]$5s^2$	770	1.13	−2.89	1609
Ba	[Xe]$6s^2$	725	1.35	−2.90	1463
Ra	[Rn]$7s^2$	700	1.40	−2.92	1484
Zn	[Ar]$3d^{10}4s^2$	420	0.74	−0.76	2632
Cd	[Kr]$4d^{10}5s^2$	320	0.97	−0.40	2492
Hg	[Xe]$4f^{14}5d^{10}6s^2$	−39	1.10	+0.85	2805

^{a}For $M^{2+}(aq) + 2e^- = M(s)$.

be associated with the greater ease of distortion of the filled d shell compared with the noble gas shell of the Mg to Ra ions. Zinc and Cd are quite electropositive, resembling Mg in their chemistry, although there is a greater tendency to form complexes with NH_3, halide ions, and CN^-.

Mercury is unique. It has a high *positive* potential, and the Hg^{2+} ion does *not* resemble Zn^{2+} or Cd^{2+}. For example, the formation constants for, say, halide ions, are orders of magnitude greater than for Cd^{2+}. Mercury also readily forms the dimercury ion, which has a metal–metal bond, ^+Hg—Hg^+.

Group IIIA(3) and Group IIIB(13)

Some properties of the elements are given in Table 8-3. This group is quite a numerous one, since it contains the Group IIIA(3) elements, Sc, Y, La, and Ac, and the Group IIIB(13) elements, Al, Ga, In, and Tl. In addition, all of the lanthanide elements could be included, since their chemistry is similar to that of the Group IIIA(3) elements.

However, we consider the lanthanides separately because of their special position in the periodic table. Notice that in the Sc to Ac group the three-valence electrons are d^1s^2 compared with s^2p^1 for the Al to Tl group. Despite this occupancy of the d levels, the elements show no transition metal-like chemistry. They are highly electropositive metals, and their chemistry is primarily one of the $+3$ ions that have the noble gas configuration.

Scandium with the smallest ionic radius has chemical behavior intermediate between that of Al, which has a considerable tendency to covalent bond formation, and the mainly ionic natures of the heavier elements.

Gallium, In, and Tl, like Al are borderline between ionic and covalent in compounds, even though the metals are quite electropositive and they form M^{3+} ions.

The $+1$ state becomes progressively more stable as the group is descended, and for Tl the Tl^I–Tl^{III} relationship is a dominant factor of the chemistry. The occurrence of an oxidation state two units below the group valence is sometimes attributed to the *inert pair effect*, which first makes itself evident here. It could

Table 8-3 Some Properties of the Group IIIA(3) and IIIB(13) Elements

Element	Electron Configuration	mp, °C	Ionic Radius, Å[c]	E^0, V[a]
Sc	$[Ar]3d^14s^2$	1540	0.81	-1.88
Y	$[Kr]4d^15s^2$	1500	0.93	-2.37
La	$[Xe]5d^16s^2$	920	1.15	-2.52
Ac[b]	$[Rn]6d^17s^2$	1050	1.11	~ -2.6
Al	$[Ne]3s^23p^1$	660	0.50	-1.66
Ga	$[Ar]3d^{10}4s^24p^1$	30	0.62	-0.53
In	$[Kr]4d^{10}5s^25p^1$	160	0.81	-0.34
Tl	$[Xe]4f^{14}5d^{10}6s^26p^1$	300	0.95	$+0.72$

[a] For $M^{3+}(aq) + 3e^- = M(s)$.
[b] Isotopes are all radioactive.
[c] For M^{3+}.

be considered to apply in the low reactivity of mercury, but it is more pronounced still in Groups IVB(14) and VB(15). The term refers to the resistance of a pair of s electrons to be lost or to participate in covalent bond formation. Thus Hg is difficult to oxidize, allegedly because it contains only an inert pair ($6s^2$), Tl forms Tl^I rather than Tl^{III} because of the inert pair in the valence shell ($6s^26p$), and so on. The concept of the inert pair tells us little, if anything, about the ultimate reasons for the stability of lower oxidation states. It is a useful label.

Group IVB(14)

Some properties of the elements are given in Table 8-4. Note that we restrict our attention to Group IVB(14), since Group IVA(4) comprises the transition metals Ti, Zr, and Hf, whose chemistries we shall consider separately. This pattern holds true for the remaining Groups VB(15)–VIIB(17).

There is no more striking an example of the enormous discontinuity in properties between the elements of the first and second short periods (followed by a relatively smooth change toward metallic character for the remaining members of the group) than that provided by Group IVB(14). Carbon is nonmetallic, as is silicon, but little of the chemistry of silicon can be inferred from that of carbon. Germanium is much like silicon, although it shows much more metallic behavior in its chemistry. Tin and lead are metals, and both have some metal-like chemistry, especially in the divalent state.

The main chemistry in the IV oxidation state for all the elements is essentially one that involves covalent bonds and molecular compounds. Typical examples are $GeCl_4$ and $PbEt_4$. There is a decrease in the tendency to *catenation,* which is such a feature of carbon chemistry, in the order C ≫ Si > Ge ≃ Sn ≃ Pb. This is partly due to the diminishing strength of the C—C, Si—Si, and the like, bonds (Table 8-4). The strengths of covalent bonds to other atoms also generally decrease in going from C to Pb.

Now let us look at the *divalent state.* Although in CO the *oxidation* state of C is *formally* taken to be two, this *is* only a formalism and carbon uses more than two valence electrons in bonding. True divalence is found only in *carbenes* such as $:CF_2$, and these species are very reactive due to the accessibility of the sp^2 hybridized lone pair. The divalent compounds of the other Group IVB(14) elements can be regarded as carbenelike in the sense that they are angular

Table 8-4   Some Properties of Group IVB(14) Elements

Element	Electron Configuration	mp, °C	Covalent Radius, Å	Self-Bond Energy, kJ mol⁻¹
C	$[He]2s^22p^2$	>3550	0.77	356
Si	$[Ne]3s^23p^2$	1410	1.17	210–250
Ge	$[Ar]3d^{10}4s^24p^2$	940	1.22	190–210
Sn	$[Kr]4d^{10}5s^25p^2$	232	1.40	105–145
Pb	$[Xe]4f^{14}5d^{10}6s^26p^2$	327	1.44	–

with a lone pair and can readily undergo an oxidative–addition reaction (see also Chapter 30) to give two new bonds to the element, for example,

$$\begin{array}{c} R \\ \diagdown \\ \diagup C^{II}: \;+\; X\!-\!Y \;=\; \\ R \end{array} \qquad \begin{array}{c} R \quad X \\ \diagdown \;\diagup \\ \overset{IV}{C} \\ \diagup \;\diagdown \\ R \quad Y \end{array} \qquad (8\text{-}11.1)$$

The increase in stability of the divalent state cannot be attributed to ionization energies as they are very similar in all cases. Factors that doubtless govern the relative stabilities are (i) promotion energies, (ii) bond strengths in covalent compounds, and (iii) lattice energies in ionic compounds.

For CH_4, the factor that stabilizes CH_4 relative to $CH_2 + H_2$ despite the much higher promotional energy required in forming CH_4 is the great strength of C—H bonds. If we now have a series of reactions

$$MX_2 + X_2 = MX_4 \qquad (8\text{-}11.2)$$

in which the M—X bond energies are decreasing, as they do from Si → Pb, then it is possible that bond energy may become too small to compensate for the M^{II}—M^{IV} promotion energy and MX_2 then becomes the more stable.

The change in this group is shown by the reactions:

$$GeCl_2 + Cl_2 = GeCl_4 \qquad \text{(Very rapid at 25 °C)} \qquad (8\text{-}11.3)$$

$$SnCl_2 + Cl_2 = SnCl_4 \qquad \text{(Slow at 25 °C)} \qquad (8\text{-}11.4)$$

$$PbCl_2 + Cl_2 = PbCl_4 \qquad \text{(Only under forcing condition)} \qquad (8\text{-}11.5)$$

Also, even $PbCl_4$ decomposes readily while $PbBr_4$ and PbI_4 do not exist, probably because of the reducing power of Br^- and I^-.

It is difficult to give any rigorous argument on lattice energy effects, since there is no evidence for the existence of M^{4+} ions and in only a few compounds are there even Pb^{2+} ions.

Group VB(15)

Some properties of the Group VB(15) elements are given in Table 8-5.

Like nitrogen, phosphorus is essentially covalent in all its chemistry but

Table 8-5 Some Properties of Group VB(15) Elements

Element	Electron Configuration	mp, °C	Covalent Radius, Å	Ionic Radius, Å
P	$[Ne]3s^23p^3$	44	1.10	2.12 (P^{3-})
As	$[Ar]3d^{10}4s^24p^3$	814 (36 atm)	1.21	
Sb	$[Kr]4d^{10}5s^25p^3$	603	1.41	0.92 (Sb^{3+})
Bi	$[Xe]4f^{14}5d^{10}6s^26p^3$	271	1.52	1.08 (Bi^{3+})

arsenic, antimony, and bismuth show increasing tendencies to cationic behavior. Although electron gain to achieve the electronic structure of the next noble gas is conceivable (as in N^{3-}), considerable energies are involved so that anionic compounds are rare. Similarly, loss of valence electrons is difficult because of high ionization energies. There are no $+5$ ions and even the $+3$ ions are not simple, being SbO^+ and BiO^+. BiF_3 seems predominantly ionic.

The increasing metallic character is shown by the oxides that change from acidic for phosphorus to basic for bismuth, and by halides that have increasing ionic character.

Group VIB(16)

Table 8-6 gives some properties of these elements. The atoms of this group form compounds that feature:

1. The chalcogenide ions, *e.g.* S^{2-}, Se^{2-}, in salts of highly electropositive elements.
2. Two electron-pair bonds, as in H_2S or $SeCl_2$.
3. Anions containing one bond, as in HS^-.
4. Monocations containing three covalent bonds, as in sulfonium cations, R_3S^+.
5. Compounds in which the Group VIB(16) element has the IV or VI oxidation state, with four, five, or six covalent bonds, as for $SeCl_4$, SeF_5^-, and TeF_6.

We have already pointed out that, from top to bottom in the group, atomic size increases and electronegativity decreases. Also, the general trend down the group is for

1. Decreasing stability of the hydrides, H_2E.
2. Increasing metallic character of the elements themselves.
3. Increasing tendency to form anionic complexes such as $SeBr_6^{2-}$, $TeBr_6^{2-}$, and PoI_6^{2-}.

Group VIIB(17)

Some properties of the Group VIIB(17) elements are given in Table 8-7.

The halogen atoms are only one electron short of the noble gas configuration, and the elements form the anion X^- or a single covalent bond. Their chemistries are completely nonmetallic. The changes in behavior with increas-

Table 8-6 Some Properties of Group VIB(16) Elements

Element	Electron Configuration	mp, °C	Covalent Radius, Å	Ionic (X^{2-}) Radius, Å
S	$[Ne]3s^23p^4$	119	1.03	1.90
Se	$[Ar]3d^{10}4s^24p^4$	217	1.17	2.02
Te	$[Kr]4d^{10}5s^25p^4$	450	1.37	2.22
Po	$[Xe]4f^{14}5d^{10}6s^26p^4$	254	—	2.30

Table 8-7 Some Properties of Group VIIB(17) Elements

Element	Electron Configuration	mp, °C	bp, °C	Radius X^-, Å	Covalent Radius, Å
F	$[He]2s^22p^5$	-233	-118	1.19	0.71
Cl	$[Ne]3s^23p^5$	-103	-34.6	1.70	0.97
Br	$[Ar]3d^{10}4s^24p^5$	-7.2	58.8	1.87	1.14
I	$[Kr]4d^{10}5s^25p^5$	113.5	184.3	2.12	1.33
At^a	$[Xe]4f^{14}5d^{10}6s^26p^5$	—	—	—	—

^{a}All isotopes are radioactive with short half-lives.

ing size are progressive and, with the exception of the Li–Cs group, there are closer similarities within the group than in any other in the periodic table.

The halogens can form compounds in higher formal oxidation states, mainly in halogen fluorides such as ClF_3, ClF_5, BrF_5, and IF_7 and oxo compounds.

No evidence exists for cationic behavior with ions of the type X^+. However, Br_2^+, I_2^+, Cl_3^+, and Br_3^+ and several iodine cations are known. When a halogen forms a bond to another atom more electronegative than itself, for example, ICl, the bond will be polar with a positive charge on the heavier halogen.

8-12 The Transition Elements of the *d* and *f* Blocks

The transition elements may be strictly defined as those that, *as elements*, have partly filled *d* or *f* shells. We adopt a broader definition and include also elements that have partly filled *d* or *f* shells *in compounds*. This means that we treat the *coinage metals*, Cu, Ag, and Au, as transition metals, since Cu^{II} has a $3d^9$ configuration, Ag^{II} has a $4d^9$ configuration, and Au^{III} has a $5d^8$ configuration. Appropriately we also consider these elements as transition elements because their chemical behavior is quite similar to that of other transition elements.

There are thus 61 transition elements, counting the heaviest ones through atomic number 109. Those through number 104 have certain common properties:

1. They are all metals.
2. They are practically all hard, strong, high-melting, high-boiling metals that conduct heat and electricity well.
3. They form alloys with one another and with other metallic elements.
4. Many of them are sufficiently electropositive to dissolve in mineral acids, although a few are "noble"—that is, they have such low electrode potentials that they are unaffected by simple acids.
5. With very few exceptions, they exhibit variable valence, and their ions and compounds are colored in one if not all oxidation states.
6. Because of partially filled shells they form at least some paramagnetic compounds.

This large number of transition elements is subdivided into three main groups: (a) the main transition elements or *d*-block elements, (b) the lanthanide elements, and (c) the actinide elements.

The main transition group or *d* block includes those elements that have partially filled *d* shells only. Thus, the element scandium, with the outer electron configuration $4s^23d$, is the lightest member. The eight succeeding elements, the *first transition series*, Ti, V, Cr, Mn, Fe, Co, Ni, and Cu, all have partly filled $3d$ shells either in the ground state of the free atom (all except Cu) or in one or more of their chemically important ions (all except Sc). At zinc the configuration is $3d^{10}4s^2$; and this element forms no compound in which the $3d$ shell is ionized, nor does this ionization occur in any of the next nine elements. It is not until we come to yttrium, with ground-state outer electron configuration $5s^24d$, that we meet the next transition element. The following eight elements, Zr, Nb, Mo, Tc, Ru, Rh, Pd, and Ag, all have partially filled $4d$ shells whether in the free element (all but Ag) or in one or more of the chemically important ions (all but Y). This group of nine elements constitutes the *second transition series*.

Again there follows a sequence of elements in which there are never *d*-shell vacancies under chemically significant conditions until we reach the element lanthanum, with an outer electron configuration in the ground state of $6s^25d$. Now, if the pattern we have observed twice before were to be repeated, there would follow 8 elements with enlarged, but not complete, sets of $5d$ electrons. This does not happen, however. The $4f$ shell now becomes slightly more stable than the $5d$ shell and, through the next 14 elements, electrons enter the $4f$ shell until at lutetium it becomes filled. Lutetium thus has the outer electron configuration $4f^{14}5d6s^2$. Since both La and Lu have partially filled *d* shells and no other partially filled shells, it might be argued that both of them should be considered as *d*-block elements. However, for chemical reasons, it would be unwise to classify them in this way, since all of the 15 elements La ($Z = 57$) through Lu ($Z = 71$) have very similar chemical and physical properties, those of lanthanum being in a sense prototypal; hence, these elements are called the *lanthanides*.

The shielding of one *f* electron by another from the effects of the nuclear charge is quite weak on account of the shapes of the *f* orbitals. Hence, with increasing atomic number and nuclear charge, the effective nuclear charge experienced by each $4f$ electron increases. This causes a shrinkage in the radii of the atoms or ions as one proceeds from La to Lu (see Table 26-1). This accumulation of successive shrinkages is called the *lanthanide contraction*. It has a profound effect on the radii of subsequent elements, which are smaller than might have been anticipated from the increased mass. Thus Zr^{4+} and Hf^{4+} have almost identical radii despite the atomic numbers of 40 and 72, respectively.

For practical purposes, the *third transition series* begins with hafnium, having the ground-state outer electron configuration $6s^25d^2$, and embraces the elements Ta, W, Re, Os, Ir, Pt, and Au, all of which have partially filled $5d$ shells in one or more chemically important oxidation states as well as (excepting Au) in the neutral atom.

Continuing on from mercury, which follows gold, we come via the noble gas radon and the radioelements Fr and Ra to Ac, with the outer electron configuration $7s^2 6d$. Here we might expect, by analogy to what happened at lanthanum, that in the following elements electrons would enter the $5f$ orbitals, producing a lanthanidelike series of 15 elements. What actually occurs is not as simple. Although, immediately following lanthanum, the $4f$ orbitals become decisively more favorable than the $5d$ orbitals for the electrons entering in the succeeding elements, there is apparently not so great a difference between the $5f$ and $6d$ orbitals until later. Thus, for the elements immediately following Ac, and their ions, there may be electrons in the $5f$ or $6d$ orbitals, or both. Since it appears that later on, after 4 or 5 more electrons have been added to the Ac configuration, the $5f$ orbitals do become definitely the more stable, and since the elements from about americium on do show moderately homologous chemical behavior, it has become accepted practice to call the 15 elements beginning with Ac the *actinide elements*.

There is an important distinction, based on electronic structures, between the three classes of transition elements. For the d-block elements the partially filled shells are d shells, $3d$, $4d$, or $5d$. These d orbitals project well out to the periphery of the atoms and ions so that the electrons occupying them are strongly influenced by the surroundings of the ion and, in turn, are able to influence the environments very significantly. Thus, many of the properties of an ion with a partly filled d shell are quite sensitive to the number and arrangement of the d electrons present. In marked contrast to this, the $4f$ orbitals in the lanthanide elements are rather deeply buried in the atoms and ions. The electrons that occupy them are largely screened from the surroundings by the overlying shells ($6s$, $5p$) of electrons, and therefore reciprocal interactions of the $4f$ electrons and the surroundings of the atom or the ion are of relatively little chemical significance. This is why the chemistry of all the lanthanides is so homologous, whereas there are seemingly erratic and irregular variations in chemical properties as one passes through a series of d-block elements. The behavior of the actinide elements lies between those of the two types described previously because the $5f$ orbitals are not so well shielded as are the $4f$ orbitals, although they are not so exposed as are the d orbitals in the d-block elements.

STUDY GUIDE

Scope and Purpose

We have examined the periodic table and the positions of the elements in it, taking the opportunity to compare and contrast the properties of the elements in their uncombined states, as well as the various tendencies of the elements to form particular types of compounds. The student should note, especially, the highly useful and systematic manner in which the electron configurations of the elements correlate with the positions of the elements in the periodic table, and with the properties of the elements and their typical compounds.

Study Questions

A. Review

1. Which elements are (at 25 °C and 1-atm pressure)

   (a) gases   (b) liquids   (c) solids melting below 100 °C?

2. Why is white phosphorus much more chemically reactive than black phosphorus?

3. Draw the structure of the most stable form of sulfur.

4. Draw the structure for carbon in (a) diamond, (b) graphite. What is the nature of C—C bonding in the two allotropes?

5. Write down the electronic structures of the elements of the first short period, then answer the following questions.

   (a) What is the first ionization energy of Li (approximately)?

   (b) Why does Be not form a 2+ ion in solids?

   (c) Why is there a discontinuity between the ionization energy of N and O?

   (d) How do the electron attachment energies vary from Li to F?

   (e) Which of the elements can form anions?

6. Why is dinitrogen normally unreactive?

7. What is the octet rule? Why does it apply only to elements of the first short period?

8. What are Lewis acids and Lewis bases? Give two examples of each.

9. Why is there no silicon analog of graphite?

10. What are the main trends in properties of the alkali *metals*?

11. List the elements of Groups IIA(2) and IIB(12). Compare their main chemical features.

12. Give the electronic structures of

    Sc and Ti
    Y   and Zr
    La and Hf

    Why are there 14 other elements between La and Hf?

13. How do the following elements attain the noble gas configuration?

    (a) N   (b) S

14. Why are Cu, Ag, and Au considered as transition metals?

15. List the common features of transition metals.

16. What are the main groups of transition metals? Write out their names and give the electronic structures of the first, the middle, and the last.

17. What is an icosahedron? For which element is it the most characteristic structural feature?

18. What are the principal properties and structural types of the metals?

19. On what electronic process does the chemistry of hydrogen depend? Explain.

20. Why is carbon unique in forming chains of single bonds in compounds?

21. What is the lanthanide contraction and what is its main effect?

22. What are the actinide elements and what relation do they bear to the lanthanide elements?

B. Additional Exercises

1. Use MO theory to explain the bonding in N_2, O_2, and F_2. Why is oxygen paramagnetic?

2. Why is the bond energy of F_2 much less than that of Cl_2?

3. Correlate the Lewis diagrams in the compounds "BH_3," CH_4, NH_3, OH_2, and HF with their chemistries.

4. Predict the products of the following acid–base reactions:

(a) $BF_3 + F^-$ (e) $Na_2O + H_2O$

(b) $BF_3 + N(CH_3)_3$ (f) $SO_2 + H_2O$

(c) $Ni(CN)_2 + CN^-$ (g) $SO_3 + H_2O$

(d) $AlCl_3 + Cl^-$

5. Make diagrams of the $d\pi-p\pi$ bonds in Cl_3PO, Cl_2SO, SO_2, SO_4^{2-}, ClO_2, ClO_4^-, and PO_4^{3-}. Start by drawing the Lewis diagram for each and then designate the $p\pi$-donor atoms (and their donor orbitals) and the $d\pi$-acceptor atoms (and their acceptor orbitals),

6. Why is CH_2 unstable while $PbCl_2$ is stable? Compare also the stabilities of $GeCl_2$ and $SnCl_2$.

7. Why are the chemical consequences of partially filled d orbitals so much more pronounced for the d-block elements than the consequences of partially filled f orbitals for the f-block elements?

SUPPLEMENTARY READING

Cotton, S. A. and Hart, F. A., *The Heavy Transition Elements,* Wiley, New York, 1975.

Cowley, A. H., "Stable Compounds with Double Bonding between the Heavier Main-Group Elements," *Acc. Chem. Res.,* **1984,** *17,* 386.

Donohue, J., *The Structures of the Elements,* Wiley, New York, 1974.

Parish, R. V., *The Metallic Elements,* Longman, New York, 1977.

Powell, P. and Timms, P., *The Chemistry of the Non-Metals,* Chapman and Hall, London, 1974.

Raabe, G. and Michl, J., "Multiple Bonding to Silicon," *Chem. Rev.,* **1985,** *85,* 419.

Sanderson, R. T., *Chemical Periodicity,* Van Nostrand-Reinhold, New York, 1960.

Steudel, R., *Chemistry of the Non-Metals,* Walter de Gruyter, Berlin, 1977.

part 2

THE MAIN GROUP ELEMENTS

chapter 9

HYDROGEN

9-1 Introduction

Hydrogen (not carbon) forms more compounds than any other element. For this and other reasons, many aspects of hydrogen chemistry are treated elsewhere in this book. Protonic acids and the aqueous hydrogen ion have already been discussed in Chapter 7. In this chapter we examine certain topics that most logically should be considered here.

Three isotopes of hydrogen are known ^1H, ^2H (deuterium or D), and ^3H (tritium or T). Although isotope effects are greatest for hydrogen, justifying the use of distinctive names for the two heavier isotopes, the chemical properties of H, D, and T are essentially identical except in matters such as rates and equilibrium constants of reactions. The normal form of the element is the diatomic molecule; the various possibilities are H_2, D_2, T_2, HD, HT, DT.

Naturally occurring hydrogen contains 0.0156% deuterium, while tritium (formed continuously in the upper atmosphere in nuclear reactions induced by cosmic rays) occurs naturally in only minute amounts that are believed to be of the order of 1 in 10^{17} and is radioactive (β^-, 12.4 yr).

Deuterium as D_2O is separated from water by fractional distillation or electrolysis and is available in ton quantities for use as a moderator in nuclear reactors. Deuterium oxide is also useful as a source of deuterium in deuterium-labeled compounds.

Molecular hydrogen is a colorless, odorless gas (fp 20.28 K) virtually insoluble in water. It is most easily prepared by the action of dilute acids on metals such as Zn or Fe and by electrolysis of water.

Industrially, hydrogen is obtained by steam re-forming of methane or light petroleums over a promoted nickel catalyst at ca. 750 °C. The process is complex but the main reaction is

$$CH_4 + H_2O \rightleftharpoons CO + 3H_2 \qquad \Delta H = 205 \text{ kJ mol}^{-1} \qquad (9\text{-}1.1)$$

This is followed by the water–gas shift reaction (Eq. 9-1.2) over iron and copper catalysts. The mixtures of CO and H_2 that are produced in reaction 9-1.1 are called synthesis gas, which finds application as a reducing agent. The proportion of hydrogen in synthesis gas mixtures is increased by reaction 9-1.2, and the CO_2 by-product can be removed by scrubbing with K_2CO_3 solution. Small amounts of CO and CO_2 that remain (and act as poisons in some subsequent uses of hydrogen) are catalytically converted to methane (which is usually innocuous) according to reactions 9-1.3 and 9-1.4:

$$CO + H_2O \rightleftharpoons CO_2 + H_2 \qquad \Delta H = -42 \text{ kJ mol}^{-1} \qquad (9\text{-}1.2)$$

$$CO + 3H_2 \rightleftharpoons CH_4 + H_2O \qquad (9\text{-}1.3)$$

$$CO_2 + 4H_2 \rightleftharpoons CH_4 + 2H_2O \qquad (9\text{-}1.4)$$

Hydrogen is not exceptionally reactive. It burns in air to form water and will react explosively with oxygen and the halogens under certain conditions. At high temperatures, the gas will reduce many oxides to lower oxides (e.g., Eq. 9-1.5):

$$2MO_2 + H_2 \rightarrow M_2O_3 + H_2O \qquad (9\text{-}1.5)$$

or to the metal:

$$MO_2 + 2H_2 \longrightarrow M + 2H_2O \qquad (9\text{-}1.6)$$

$$M_2O_3 + 3H_2 \longrightarrow 2M + 3H_2O \qquad (9\text{-}1.7)$$

$$MO + H_2 \longrightarrow M + H_2O \qquad (9\text{-}1.8)$$

In the presence of suitable catalysts and above room temperature, hydrogen reacts with N_2 to form NH_3. With electropositive metals and with most non-metals it forms hydrides (Section 9-6). Hydrogen serves as a reducing agent for a variety of inorganic and organic substances, but requires a suitable catalyst, the reduction of olefins by hydrogen over Pt being an example.

The dissociation of H_2 is highly endothermic (Eq. 9-1.9), and this accounts in part for its rather low reactivity at low temperatures:

$$H_2 = 2H \qquad \Delta H = 434.1 \text{ kJ mol}^{-1} \qquad (9\text{-}1.9)$$

9-2 The Bonding of Hydrogen

The chemistry of hydrogen depends mainly on the three electronic processes discussed in Chapter 8, namely, (1) loss of a valence electron to give H^+, (2) acquisition of an electron to give H^-, and (3) formation of a single covalent bond as in CH_4.

However, hydrogen has additional unique bonding features. The nature of the proton and the complete absence of any shielding of the nuclear charge by electron shells allow other forms of chemical activity that are either unique to hydrogen or particularly characteristic of it. Some of these are the following, which we shall discuss in some detail subsequently.

1. The formation of numerous compounds, often nonstoichiometric, with metallic elements. They are generally called hydrides but cannot be regarded as simple saline hydrides (Section 9-6).

2. The formation of hydrogen bridge bonds in electron-deficient compounds such as structure 9-I and transition metal complexes such as structure 9-II.

$$
\begin{array}{ccc}
\text{H} \quad \text{H} \quad \text{H} & & \left[\begin{array}{c} \text{O} \quad\quad \text{O} \\ \text{C} \quad \text{CO} \quad \text{C} \quad \text{CO} \\ \text{OC—Cr—H—Cr—CO} \\ \text{O} \quad \text{C} \quad \text{O} \quad \text{C} \\ \text{O} \quad\quad \text{O} \end{array} \right]^{-} \\
\text{B} \quad\quad \text{B} & & \\
\text{H} \quad \text{H} \quad \text{H} & & \\
9\text{-}I & & 9\text{-}II
\end{array}
$$

The best-studied example of bridge bonds is provided by diborane, structure 9-I, and related compounds (Chapter 12). The electronic nature of such bridge bonds was discussed in Chapter 3.

3. The hydrogen bond is important not only because it is essential to an understanding of much other hydrogen chemistry but also because it is one of the most intensively studied examples of intermolecular attraction. Hydrogen bonds dominate the chemistry of water, aqueous solutions, hydroxylic solvents, and OH-containing species generally, and they are of crucial importance in biological systems, being responsible, among other things, for the linking of polypeptide chains in proteins and the base pairs of nucleic acids.

9-3   The Hydrogen Bond

When hydrogen is bonded to another atom, X, mainly F, O, N, or Cl such that the X—H bond is quite polar with H bearing a partial positive charge, it can interact with another negative or electron-rich atom, Y, to form what is called a hydrogen bond (H bond), written as

$$X\text{—}H\text{···}Y$$

Although the details are subject to variation, and controversy, it is generally believed that typical hydrogen bonds are due largely to electrostatic attraction of H and Y. The X—H distance becomes slightly longer, but this bond remains essentially a normal two-electron bond. The H---Y distance is generally much longer than that of a normal covalent H—Y bond.

In the case of the very strongest hydrogen bonds, the X—Y distance becomes quite short and the X—H and Y—H distances come close to being equal. In these cases there are presumably covalent and electrostatic components in both the X—H and Y—H bonds.

Experimental evidence for hydrogen bonding came first from comparisons of the physical properties of hydrogen compounds. Classic examples are the apparently abnormally high boiling points of NH_3, H_2O, and HF (Fig. 9-1), which imply association of these molecules in the liquid phase. Other properties

Figure 9-1   Periodic trends in the boiling points of some molecular hydrides.

such as heats of vaporization provided further evidence for association. Although physical properties reflecting association are still a useful tool in detecting hydrogen bonding, the most satisfactory evidence for solids comes from X-ray and neutron-diffraction crystallographic studies, and for solids, liquids, and solutions from infrared and nuclear magnetic resonance spectra.

Structural evidence for hydrogen bonds is provided by the X—Y distances, which are shorter than the expected van der Waals contact when a hydrogen bond exists. For instance, in crystalline $NaHCO_3$ there are four kinds of O---O distances between HCO_3^- ions with values of 3.12, 3.15, 3.19, and 2.55 Å. The first three are about equal to twice the van der Waals radius of oxygen, but the last one indicates a hydrogen bond, O—H---O. When an X—H group enters into hydrogen bonding, the X—H stretching band in the infrared spectrum is lowered in frequency, broadened, and increased in integrated intensity. These changes afford a very useful means of studying H bonding in solution.

The enthalpies of hydrogen bonds are relatively small in most instances: 20–30 kJ mol^{-1}, as compared with covalent bond enthalpies of 200 kJ mol^{-1}, and up. Nevertheless, these bonds can have a profound effect on the properties and chemical reactivity of substances in which they occur. This is clear from Fig. 9-1, where water, for example, would boil at about − 100 °C instead of + 100 °C if hydrogen bonds did not play their role. Obviously life itself—as we know it—depends on the existence of hydrogen bonds.

9-4   Ice and Water

The structure of water is very important since it is the medium in which so much chemistry, including the chemistry of life, takes place. The structure of ice is of interest for clues about the structure of water. There are nine known modifications of ice, the stability of each depending on temperature and pressure. The ice formed in equilibrium with water at 0 °C and 1 atm is called ice I and has the structure shown in Fig. 9-2. There is an infinite array of oxygen

Figure 9-2   The structure of ice I. Only the oxygen atoms are shown. The O · · · O distances are 2.75 Å.

atoms, each tetrahedrally surrounded by four others with hydrogen bonds linking each pair.

The structural nature of liquid water is still controversial. The structure is not random, as in liquids consisting of more-or-less spherical nonpolar molecules; instead, it is highly structured owing to the persistence of hydrogen bonds; even at 90 °C only a few percent of the water molecules appear not to be hydrogen bonded. Still, there is considerable disorder, or randomness, as befits a liquid.

In an attractive, though not universally accepted, model of liquid water the liquid consists at any instant of an imperfect network, very similar to the network of ice I, but differing in that (a) some interstices contain water molecules that do not belong to the network but, instead, disturb it; (b) the network is patchy and does not extend over long distances without breaks; (c) the short-range ordered regions are constantly disintegrating and re-forming (they are "flickering clusters"); and (d) the network is slightly expanded compared with ice I. The fact that water has a slightly higher density than ice I may be attributed to the presence of enough interstitial water molecules to more than offset the expansion and disordering of the ice I network. This model of water receives support from X-ray scattering studies.

9-5   Hydrates and Water Clathrates

Solids that consist of molecules of a compound together with water molecules are called *hydrates*. The majority contain discrete water molecules either bound to cations through the oxygen atom or bound to anions or other electron-rich atoms through hydrogen bonds, or both, as is shown in Fig. 9-3. In many cases when the hydrate is heated above 100 °C, the water can be driven off leaving

Figure 9-3 Three principal ways in which water molecules are bound in hydrates: (*a*) through oxygen to cations, (*b*) through hydrogen to anions, (*c*) a combination of the preceding two.

the *anhydrous* compound. However, there are many cases where something other than, or in addition to, water is driven off. For example, many hydrated chlorides give off HCl and a basic or oxo chloride is left:

$$\text{ScCl}_3 \cdot 6\text{H}_2\text{O} \xrightarrow{\text{Heat}} \text{ScOCl} + 2\text{HCl(g)} + 5\text{H}_2\text{O(g)} \tag{9-5.1}$$

Water also forms compounds called *gas hydrates,* which are actually a type of clathrate compound. A clathrate (from the Latin clathratus, meaning "enclosed or protected by crossbars or gratings") is a substance in which one component crystallizes in a very open structure that contains holes or channels in which atoms or small molecules of the second component can be trapped. There are a number of substances, other than water, for example, *p*-quinol, $\text{C}_6\text{H}_4(\text{OH})_2$, and urea, that can form clathrates.

There are two common gas hydrate structures, both cubic. In one, the unit cell contains 46 molecules of H_2O connected to form six medium-size and two small cages. This structure is adopted when atoms (Ar, Kr, Xe) or relatively small molecules (e.g., Cl_2, SO_2, CH_3Cl) are used, generally at pressures greater than 1 atm for the gases. Complete filling of only the medium cages by atoms or molecules, X, would give a composition $\text{X} \cdot 7.67\text{H}_2\text{O}$, while complete filling of all eight cages would lead to $\text{X} \cdot 5.76\text{H}_2\text{O}$. In practice, complete filling of all cages of one or both types is seldom attained, and these formulas therefore represent limiting rather than observed compositions; for instance, the usual formula for chlorine hydrate is $\text{Cl}_2 \cdot 7.30\text{H}_2\text{O}$. The second structure, often formed in the presence of larger molecules of liquid substances (and thus sometimes called the liquid hydrate structure) such as chloroform and ethyl chloride, has a unit cell containing 136 water molecules with 8 large cages and 16 smaller ones. The anesthetic effect of substances such as chloroform may be due to the formation of liquid hydrate crystals in brain tissue.

A third notable class of clathrate compounds, salt hydrates, is formed when tetraalkylammonium or sulfonium salts crystallize from aqueous solution with high water content, for example, $[(\text{C}_4\text{H}_9)_4\text{N}]\text{C}_6\text{H}_5\text{CO}_2 \cdot 39.5\text{H}_2\text{O}$ or $[(\text{C}_4\text{H}_9)_3\text{S}]\text{F} \cdot 20\text{H}_2\text{O}$. The structures of these substances are very similar to the gas and liquid hydrate structures in a general way although different in detail. These structures consist of frameworks constructed mainly of hydrogen-bonded water molecules but apparently including also the anions (e.g., F^-) or parts of the anions (e.g., the O atoms of the benzoate ion). The cations and parts of the anions (e.g., the C_6H_5C part of the benzoate ion) occupy cavities in an incomplete and random way.

9-6   Binary Hydrides

Compounds of hydrogen may all be called hydrides, although this term is best reserved for those that are neither organic compounds nor acids. As we might expect, they are of various types, as is indicated in Fig. 9-4.

The most electropositive elements, the alkali metals and larger alkaline earth metals, form hydrides with considerable ionic character, called *saline* (saltlike) *hydrides.* They may be thought of as containing metal cations and H^- ions. Their ionic nature is shown by the facts that they conduct electricity just below or at their melting points and, when they are dissolved in molten halides, hydrogen is evolved at the positive electrode. The ionic radius of H^- lies between those of F^- and Cl^-. The alkali metal hydrides, LiH to CsH, all have the NaCl structure.

The saline hydrides are prepared by direct reaction of the metals with hydrogen at 300 to 700 °C. They are quite reactive toward water and air (except for LiH). All are powerful reductants or hydrogenation reagents.

Among the covalent hydrides are many molecular compounds, including the H_2X compounds of Group VIB(16), the H_3X compounds of Group VB(15), and the H_4X compounds of Group IVB(14), $LiAlH_4$, and the many hydrogen compounds formed by boron, all of which are discussed in appropriate subsequent chapters.

The transition metal hydrides are very diverse in their properties. Many are formed by direct action of H_2 on the metals. The best known and most important ones are formed by the lanthanides, the actinides, and the elements of Groups IVA(4) and VA(5). For the most part, these are nonstoichiometric black solids, typical compositions being $LaH_{2.87}$, $YbH_{2.55}$, $TiH_{1.7}$, and $ZrH_{1.9}$. Uranium forms a well-defined stoichiometric hydride, UH_3, which is a useful reactant for preparing other uranium compounds.

These lanthanide and actinide hydrides appear to be mainly ionic in nature, but no entirely satisfactory detailed description of them has yet been developed. The Group IVA(4) and VA(5) materials are even less well understood.

H																	He
Li	Be																Ne
Na	Mg										B	C	N	O	F		Ar
K	Ca	Sc	Ti	V	Cr	Mn	Fe	Co	Ni	Cu	Zn	Al	Si	P	S	Cl	
Rb	Sr	Y	Zr	Nb	Mo	Tc	Ru	Rh	Pd	Ag	Cd	Ga	Ge	As	Se	Br	Kr
Cs	Ba	La–Lu	Hf	Ta	W	Re	Os	Ir	Pt	Au	Hg	In	Sn	Sb	Te	I	Xe
Fr	Ra	Ac			U,Pu							Tl	Pb	Bi	Po	At	Rn
Saline hydrides		Transition metal hydrides										Borderline hydrides		Covalent hydrides			

Figure 9-4   A classification of the binary hydrides. For the transition elements, in addition to the simple binary hydrides, complex molecules or ions containing M—H bonds are also known.

Of the remaining transition metals, only palladium and some of its alloys seem to form definite hydride phases.

STUDY GUIDE

Study Questions

A. Review

1. What are the three isotopes of hydrogen called? What are their approximate natural abundances? Which one is radioactive?
2. What is the chief large scale use for D_2O?
3. What is one thing that helps to explain the relatively low reactivity of elemental hydrogen?
4. What are the three principal electronic processes that lead to formation of compounds by the hydrogen atom?
5. When a hydrogen bond is symbolized by X—H---Y, what do the solid and dotted lines represent? Which distance is shorter?
6. How does hydrogen-bond formation affect the properties of HF, H_2O, and NH_3? Compared with what?
7. What is the usual range of enthalpies of a hydrogen bond?
8. Describe the main features of the structure of ice I. How is the structure of water believed to differ from that?
9. In what two principal ways is water bound in salt hydrates?
10. Can it safely be assumed that whenever a salt hydrate is heated at 100 to 120 °C the corresponding anhydrous salt will remain?
11. What is the true nature of so-called chlorine hydrate, $Cl_2 \cdot 7.3H_2O$?
12. What is a saline hydride? What elements form them? Why are they believed to contain cations and H^- ions?

B. Additional Exercises

1. Suggest a means of preparing pure HD.
2. It is believed that the shortest H bonds become symmetrical. How must the conventional description (X—H---Y) be modified to cover this situation?
3. Which H bond would you expect to be stronger, and why?

    S—H---O   or   O—H---S

4. Prepare a qualitative Born–Haber cycle to explain why only the most electropositive elements form saline hydrides.
5. Complete and balance the following reactions featuring hydrides:
    (a) $CaH_2 + H_2O \rightarrow$
    (b) $B_2H_6 + NaH \rightarrow$
    (c) $SiCl_4 + LiAlH_4$ to give silane, SiH_4
    (d) $Al_2Cl_6 + LiH$ to give $LiAlH_4$
6. The boiling points of the hydrogen halides follow the trend   HF(20 °C) > HCl(−85 °C) < HBr(−67 °C) < HI(−36 °C). Explain.

7. The three different aspects of the chemistry of hydrogen can be illustrated by the reactivity of water with NaH, CH_4, and HCl. Explain.

8. Compare the bonding in "BH_3" and BCl_3. Why is BCl_3 monomeric and "BH_3" dimeric?

9. Suggest a synthesis of H_2Se and H_2S; of $NaBH_4$ and $LiAlH_4$; of HCl and HI; of NaH and CaH_2.

10. Prepare an MO description of the linear and symmetrical hydrogen bond in $[F-H-F]^-$ using the $1s$ atomic orbital on the central hydrogen atom and ligand group orbitals (formed from appropriately oriented $2p$ atomic orbitals) on the two fluorine atoms. Prepare the MO energy-level diagram that accompanies these three molecular orbitals and add the proper number of electrons to it. What is the bond order in each $F-H$ half?

SUPPLEMENTARY READING

Bau, R., Ed., *Transition Metal Hydrides,* ACS Advances in Chemistry Series No. 167, American Chemical Society, Washington, D.C., 1978.

Cotton, F. A. and Wilkinson, G., *Advanced Inorganic Chemistry, Fourth Edition,* Wiley-Interscience, New York, 1980, p. 252.

Evans, E. A., *Tritium and Its Compounds, Second Edition,* Halstead-Wiley, New York, 1974.

Franks, F., Ed., *Water, A Comprehensive Treatise,* Vol. 1, Plenum, New York, 1972.

Libowitz, G. C., *The Solid State Chemistry of Binary Hydrides,* Benjamin, Menlo Park, CA, 1965.

Muetterties, E. L., Ed.; *Transition Metal Hydrides,* Dekker, New York, 1971.

Moore, R. A., Ed., *Water and Aqueous Solutions: Structures, Thermodynamics, and Transport Processes,* Wiley, New York, 1972.

Pimentel, G. C. and McClellan, A. L., *The Hydrogen Bond,* Freeman, San Francisco, 1960.

Shaw, B. L., *Inorganic Hydrides,* Pergamon, Elmsford, NY, 1967.

Vinogradov, S. N., *Hydrogen Bonding,* Van Nostrand-Reinhold, New York, 1971.

Wiberg, E. and Amberger, E., *Hydrides,* Elsevier, New York, 1971.

chapter 10

THE GROUP IA(1) ELEMENTS: LITHIUM, SODIUM, POTASSIUM, RUBIDIUM, AND CESIUM

10-1 Introduction

Sodium and potassium are abundant (2.6 and 2.4%, respectively) in the lithosphere. There are vast deposits of rock salt (NaCl) and $KCl \cdot MgCl_2 \cdot 6H_2O$ (carnallite) resulting from evaporation of lagoons over geologic time. The Great Salt Lake of Utah and the Dead Sea in Israel are examples of evaporative processes at work now. Lithium, Rb, and Cs have much lower abundances and occur in a few silicate minerals.

The element francium has only very short-lived isotopes that are formed in natural radioactive decay series or in nuclear reactors. Tracer studies show that the ion behaves as expected from the position of Fr in Group IA(1).

Sodium and its compounds are of great importance. The metal, as Na—Pb alloy, is used to make tetraalkylleads (Section 29-9), and there are other industrial uses. The hydroxide, carbonate, sulfate, tripolyphosphate, and silicate are among the top 50 industrial chemicals.

Potassium salts, usually sulfate, are used in fertilizers. The main use for lithium is as a metal in the synthesis of lithium alkyls (Section 29-3).

Both Na^+ and K^+ are of physiological importance in animals and plants; cells can differentiate between Na^+ and K^+ probably by some type of complexing mechanism. Lithium salts are used in the treatment of certain mental disorders.

Some properties of the elements were given in Table 8-1. The low ionization enthalpies and the fact that the resulting M^+ ions are spherical and of low polarizability leads to a chemistry of +1 ions. The high second ionization enthalpies preclude the formation of +2 ions. Despite the essentially ionic nature of Group IA(1) compounds, some degree of covalent bonding can occur. The diatomic molecules of the elements, for example, Na_2, are covalent. In some chelate and organometallic compounds, the M—O, M—N, and M—C bonds have a slight covalent nature. The tendency to covalency is greatest for the ion with the greatest polarizing power, that is, Li^+. The charge–radius ratio for Li^+, which is similar to that for Mg^{2+}, accounts for the similarities in their chemistry where Li^+ differs from the other members.

Some other ions that have $+1$ charge and radii similar to those of the alkalis may have similar chemistry. The most important are:

1. Ammonium and substituted ammonium ions. The solubilities and crystal structures of salts of NH_4^+ resemble those of K^+.
2. The Tl^+ ion can resemble either Rb^+ or Ag^+; its ionic radius is similar to that of Rb^+ but it is more polarizable.
3. Spherical, $+1$ complex ions such as $(\eta^5-C_5H_5)_2Co^+$ (Chapter 29).

10-2 Preparation and Properties of the Elements

Lithium and Na are obtained by electrolysis of fused salts or of low-melting eutectics such as $CaCl_2 + NaCl$. Because of their low melting points and ready vaporization K, Rb, and Cs cannot readily be made by electrolysis, but are obtained by treating molten chlorides with Na vapor. The metals are purified by distillation. Lithium, Na, K, and Rb are silvery but Cs has a golden-yellow cast. Because there is only one valence electron per metal atom, the binding energies in the close-packed metal lattices are relatively weak. The metals are hence very soft with low melting points. The Na—K alloy with 77.2% K has a melting point of -12.3 °C.

Lithium, Na, or K may be dispersed on various solid supports, such as Na_2CO_3, kieselguhr, and the like, by melting. They are used as catalysts for various reactions of alkenes, notably the dimerization of propene to 4-methyl-1-pentene. Dispersions in hydrocarbons result from high-speed stirring of a suspension of the melted metal. These dispersions may be poured in air, and they react with water with effervescence. They may be used where sodium shot or lumps would react too slowly.

The metals are highly electropositive (Table 8-1) and react directly with most other elements and many compounds on heating. Lithium is usually the least, and Cs the most reactive.

Lithium is only slowly attacked by water at 25 °C and will not replace the weakly acidic hydrogen in $C_6H_5C{\equiv}CH$, whereas the other alkali metals will do so. However, Li is uniquely reactive with N_2, slowly at 25 °C but rapidly at 400 °C, forming a ruby-red crystalline nitride, Li_3N. Like Mg, which gives Mg_3N_2, lithium can be used to absorb N_2.

With water, Na reacts vigorously, K inflames, and Rb and Cs react explosively; large lumps of Na may also react explosively. Lithium, Na, and K can be handled in air although they tarnish rapidly. The others must be handled under argon.

A fundamental difference attributable to cation size is shown by the reaction with O_2. In air or O_2 at 1 atm the metals burn. Lithium gives only Li_2O with a trace of Li_2O_2. Sodium normally gives the peroxide, Na_2O_2, but it will take up further O_2 under pressure and heat to give the superoxide, NaO_2. Potassium, Rb, and Cs form the superoxides MO_2. The increasing stability of the per- and superoxides as the size of the alkali ions increases is a typical example of the stabilization of larger anions by larger cations through lattice-energy effects, as is explained in Section 4-6.

The metals react with alcohols to give the alkoxides, and Na or K in C_2H_5OH or *t*-butanol is commonly used in organic chemistry as a reducing agent and a source of the nucleophilic RO^- ions.

Sodium and the other metals dissolve with much vigor in mercury. Sodium amalgam (Na/Hg) is a liquid when low in sodium, but is solid when rich in sodium. It is a useful reducing agent and can be used for aqueous solutions.

10-3   Solutions of the Metals in Liquid Ammonia and Other Solvents

The Group IA(1) metals, and to a lesser extent Ca, Sr, Ba, Eu, and Yb, are soluble in ammonia giving solutions that are blue when dilute. These solutions conduct electricity and the main current carrier is the solvated electron. While the lifetime of the solvated electron in water is very short, in very pure liquid ammonia it may be quite long (<1% decomposition per day).

In *dilute solutions* the main species are metal ions, M^+, and electrons, both solvated. The broad absorption around 15,000 Å, which accounts for the common blue color, is due to the solvated electrons. Magnetic and electron spin resonance studies show the presence of individual electrons, but the decrease in paramagnetism with increasing concentration suggests that the electrons can associate to form diamagnetic electron pairs. Although there may be other equilibria, the data can be accommodated by the equilibria:

$$Na(s) \text{ (dispersed)} \rightleftharpoons Na \text{ (in solution)} \rightleftharpoons Na^+ + e^- \qquad (10\text{-}3.1)$$

$$2e^- \rightleftharpoons e_2^{2-} \qquad (10\text{-}3.2)$$

The most satisfactory models of the solvated electron assume that the electron is not localized but is "smeared out" over a large volume so that the surrounding molecules experience electronic and orientational polarization. The electron is trapped in the resultant polarization field, and repulsion between the electron and the electrons of the solvent molecules leads to the formation of a cavity within which the electron has the highest probability of being found. In ammonia this is estimated to be approximately 3.0–3.4 Å in diameter; this cavity concept is based on the fact that solutions are of much lower density than the pure solvent, that is, they occupy far greater volume than that expected from the sum of the volumes of metal and solvent.

As the concentration of metal increases, metal ion clusters are formed. Above 3 *M* concentration, the solutions are copper colored with a metallic luster. Physical properties, such as their exceedingly high electrical conductivities, resemble those of liquid metals. More is said about this in Section 10-7.

The metals are also soluble to varying degrees in other amines, hexamethylphosphoramide, $OP(NMe_2)_3$, and in ethers such as THF or diglyme giving blue solutions.

The ammonia and amine solutions are widely used in organic and inorganic synthesis. (Lithium in methylamine or ethylenediamine can reduce aromatic rings to cyclic monoolefins.) Sodium in liquid ammonia is the most widely used of such reducing agents. The blue solution is moderately stable at temperatures where ammonia is still a liquid, but reaction to give the amide (Eq. 10-3.3),

$$Na + NH_3(\ell) = NaNH_2 + \tfrac{1}{2}H_2 \qquad (10\text{-}3.3)$$

can occur photochemically and is catalyzed by transition metal salts. Thus sodium amide is prepared by treatment of Na with ammonia in the presence of a trace of iron(III) chloride. Primary and secondary amines react similarly, giving alkylamides (Eq. 10-3.4),

$$Li(s) + CH_3NH_2(\ell) \longrightarrow LiNHCH_3(s) + \tfrac{1}{2}H_2 \qquad (10\text{-}3.4)$$

and dialkylamides (Eq. 10-3.5), respectively.

$$Li(s) + Et_2NH(\ell) \longrightarrow LiNEt_2(s) + \tfrac{1}{2}H_2 \qquad (10\text{-}3.5)$$

The lithium dialkylamides are used to make compounds with $M\text{—}NR_2$ bonds (Section 24-7).

   The formation of the amides of K, Rb, and Cs is reversible owing to the favorable potential for half-reaction 10-3.6.

$$e^- + NH_3 = NH_2^- + \tfrac{1}{2}H_2 \qquad K = 5 \times 10^4 \qquad (10\text{-}3.6)$$

The similar reactions for Li and Na are irreversible, owing to the insolubility of the latter amides in ammonia:

$$Na^+(am) + e^-(am) + NH_3(\ell)$$
$$= NaNH_2(s) + \tfrac{1}{2}H_2 \qquad K = 3 \times 10^9 \quad (10\text{-}3.7)$$

where am denotes a solution in ammonia.

COMPOUNDS OF THE GROUP IA(1) ELEMENTS

10-4 Binary Compounds

The metals react directly with most other elements to give binary compounds or alloys. Many of these are described under the appropriate element. The most important are the oxides (M_2O), peroxides (M_2O_2), and superoxides (MO_2). Although all three types can be obtained for each alkali metal, indirect methods are often required. The direct reactions of the metals with an excess of O_2 give different products, depending on the metal: lithium forms the oxide predominantly, along with traces of the peroxide; sodium forms the peroxide preferentially, with traces of the oxide; potassium, rubidium, and cesium form superoxides.

All three types of compounds between oxygen and an alkali metal are readily hydrolyzed:

$$\text{Oxides} \qquad M_2O + H_2O \; = 2M^+ + 2\,OH^- \qquad (10\text{-}4.1)$$

$$\text{Peroxides} \qquad M_2O_2 + 2H_2O = 2M^+ + 2\,OH^- + H_2O_2 \quad (10\text{-}4.2)$$

$$\text{Superoxides} \qquad 2MO_2 + 2H_2O = O_2 + 2M^+$$
$$+ \; 2\,OH^- + H_2O_2 \quad (10\text{-}4.3)$$

10-5   Hydroxides

These are white, very deliquescent crystalline solids; NaOH (mp 318 °C) and KOH (mp 360 °C). The solids and their aqueous solutions absorb CO_2 from the atmosphere. They are freely soluble exothermically in water and in alcohols and are used whenever strong alkali bases are required.

10-6   Ionic Salts

Salts of virtually all acids are known; they are usually colorless, crystalline, ionic solids. Color arises from colored anions, except where defects induced in the lattice, for example, by radiation, may cause *color centers*, through electrons being trapped in holes (cf. ammonia solutions cited previously).

The properties of a number of *lithium compounds* differ from those of the other Group IA(1) elements but resemble those of Mg^{2+} compounds. Many of these anomalous properties arise from the very small size of Li^+ and its effect on lattice energies, as explained in Section 4-6. In addition to examples cited there, we note that LiH is stable to approximately 900 °C while NaH decomposes at 350 °C. Li_3N is stable, whereas Na_3N does not exist at 25 °C. Lithium hydroxide decomposes at red heat to Li_2O, whereas the other hydroxides MOH sublime unchanged; LiOH is also considerably less soluble than the other hydroxides. The carbonate, Li_2CO_3, is thermally less stable relative to Li_2O and CO_2 than are other alkali metal carbonates. The solubilities of Li^+ salts resemble those of Mg^{2+}. Thus LiF is sparingly soluble (0.27 g/100 g H_2O at 18 °C) and is precipitated from ammoniacal NH_4F solutions; LiCl, LiBr, LiI and, especially $LiClO_4$ are soluble in ethanol, acetone, and ethyl acetate; LiCl is soluble in pyridine.

The alkali metal salts are generally characterized by high melting points, by electrical conductivity of the melts, and by ready solubility in water. They are seldom hydrated when the anions are small, as in the halides, because the hydration energies of the ions are insufficient to compensate for the energy required to expand the lattice. The Li^+ ion has a large hydration energy, and it is often hydrated in its solid salts when the same salts of other alkalis are unhydrated, $LiClO_4\cdot3H_2O$. For salts of *strong* acids, the Li salt is usually the *most* soluble in water of the alkali metal salts, whereas for *weak* acids the Li salts are usually *less* soluble than those of the other elements.

There are few important *precipitation reactions* of the ions. One example is the precipitation by methanolic solutions of 4,4'-diaminodiphenylmethane (L) of Li and Na salts, for example, NaL_3Cl. Generally the larger the M^+ ion the more numerous are its insoluble salts. Thus Na has few insoluble salts; the mixed Na—Zn and Na—Mg uranyl acetates [e.g., $NaZn(UO_2)_3(CH_3CO_2)_9 \cdot 6H_2O$], which may be precipitated almost quantitatively from dilute acetic acid solutions, are useful for analysis. Salts of the heavier ions, K^+, Rb^+, and Cs^+, with large anions such as ClO_4^-, $[PtCl_6]^{2-}$, $[Co(NO_2)_6]^{3-}$, and $B(C_6H_5)_4^-$ are relatively insoluble and form the basis for gravimetric analysis.

10-7 Solvation and Complexation of Alkali Ions

For these cations, as for others, solvation must be considered from two points of view. First there is the primary hydration shell, which is the number of solvent molecules directly coordinated, and second there is the solvation number, which is the total number of solvent molecules on which the ion exercises a substantial restraining influence. Most important is the primary hydration shell.

For Li^+ a primary hydration shell of four tetrahedrally arranged H_2O molecules is observed in various crystalline salts and probably occurs in solution. The ions Na^+ and K^+ may also have fourfold primary hydration; Rb^+ and Cs^+ probably coordinate six H_2O molecules. However, electrostatic forces operate beyond the primary hydration sphere and additional layers of water molecules are bound. The extent of this secondary hydration appears to vary *inversely* with the size of the bare cation. Thus, as the *crystal radii increase,* the total hydration numbers, hydrated radii, and hydration energies all *decrease.* As hydrated radii decrease, ionic mobilities increase. These trends can be observed in the data of Table 10-1.

These trends play a role in the behavior of the alkali ions in ion exchange materials and in their passage through cell walls and other biological membranes, although doubtless other factors than size and hydration numbers are also important. In a cation exchange resin, two cations compete for attachment at anionic sites as in the equilibrium:

$$A^+(aq) + [B^+R^-](s) = B^+(aq) + [A^+R^-](s) \qquad (10\text{-}7.1)$$

where R represents the resin and A^+ and B^+ the cations. Such equilibria can

Table 10-1 Data on the Hydration of Aqueous Group IA(1) Ions

	Li^+	Na^+	K^+	Rb^+	Cs^+
Pauling radii,[a] Å	0.60	0.96	1.33	1.48	1.69
Hydrated radii (approximately), Å	3.40	2.76	2.32	2.28	2.28
Approximate hydration numbers[b]	25.3	16.6	10.5	10.0	9.9
Hydration energies, kJ mol^{-1}	519	406	322	293	264
Ionic mobilities (at ∞ dilution, 18 °C)	33.5	43.5	64.6	67.5	68

[a] From Table 4-2.

[b] From transference data.

be measured quite accurately, and the order of preference of the alkali cations is usually $Li^+ < Na^+ < K^+ < Rb^+ < Cs^+$, although irregular behavior does occur in some cases. The usual order may be explained if we assume that the binding force is essentially electrostatic and that under ordinary conditions the ions within the waterlogged resin are hydrated approximately as they are outside it. Then the ion with the smallest hydrated radius (which is the one with the largest "naked" radius) will be able to approach most closely to the negative site of attachment and will hence be held most strongly according to the Coulomb law.

Ethers, polyethers, and especially cyclic polyethers are particularly suited to solvate Na^+ and other alkali ions. Examples are THF, the "glyme" solvents, which are linear polyethers, for example, $CH_3O(CH_2CH_2O)_nCH_3$, and the macrocyclic *"crown ethers"* such as cyclohexyl-18-crown-6, (structure 10-I). For this ether, bonding constants increase in the order $Li^+ < Na^+, Cs^+ < Rb^+ < K^+$.

The bonding of the alkali metal cation into the cavity of the cyclic polyether is largely electrostatic, and a close match between the size of the cation and the size of the cyclic polyether is important if the cation is to be tightly bound.

Even more potent and selective agents for binding alkali ions (and others) are the *cryptates,* which differ from the crown ethers in two ways. First, they incorporate nitrogen as well as oxygen atoms. Second, they are polycyclic and, hence, are able to surround a metal ion. One of the cryptates is structure 10-II, (2,2,2-crypt), and the structure of a representative complex is shown in Fig. 10-1.

10-I

10-II

When a solution of sodium in ethylamine is cooled in the presence of 2,2,2-crypt, the compound $[Na(2,2,2-crypt)]^+Na^-$ (Fig. 10-2), which is stable at $-10\,°C$, crystallizes. Although reaction 10-7.2

$$2Na(g) = Na^+(g) + Na^-(g) \qquad (10\text{-}7.2)$$

is endothermic by 438 kJ mol^{-1}, the lattice energy and the complexation of the sodium cation by the cryptate overcome this endothermicity and stabilize the sodide (Na^-) ion. Other less stable alkalide anions have been prepared, e.g., $[K(2,2,2-crypt)]^+K^-$. The *alkalides* are yellow-brown, and diamagnetic. A similar series of *electrides* is known. These are black, paramagnetic, and have the formula M^+ (crown) e^-. The structures of the electrides are similar to those of the alkalides. The electride Cs^+ (crown) e^- has a cavity of radius 2.4 Å that holds the electron instead of the Cs^- as in the ceside.

Figure 10-1   The structure of the cation in the thiocyanate salt [Rb(2,2,2-crypt)]SCN·H$_2$O. [Reproduced by permission from M. R. Truter, *Chem. Br.* **1971**, 203.]

= Na⁻

Figure 10-2   Part of the unit cell of the crystalline sodide [Na(2,2,2-crypt)]⁺Na⁻ showing a single sodium cation at the center of the 2,2,2-crypt ligand and the six nearest neighbor Na⁻ (sodide) anions. [Reprinted in part with permission from F. J. Tehan, B. L. Barnett, and J. L. Dye, *J. Am. Chem. Soc*, **1974**, *96*, 7203–7208, and used with permission.]

Figure 10-3 The structure of the nonactin complex of K$^+$. [Reproduced by permission from D. A. Fenton, *Chem. Soc. Rev.*, **1977**, *6*, 325–343.]

Naturally occurring small cyclic polypeptides can also act to encapsulate metal ions, and these play a part in transporting alkali (and alkaline earth) ions across membranes in living systems. Perhaps the best-known examples of such cyclic polypeptides are valinomycin (structure 10-III) and nonactin (shown in Fig. 10-3 as the K$^+$ complex).

10-III

10-8 Organometallic Compounds

Lithium Alkyls and Aryls

One of the most important areas of chemistry for the Group IA(1) elements is that of their organic compounds. This is especially true of Li, whose alkyls and aryls find extensive use as alkylating and arylating agents. Organolithium compounds resemble, in their reactions, Grignard reagents, although the lithium reagents are generally more reactive.

Lithium alkyls and aryls are best prepared as in Eq. 10-8.1

$$C_2H_5Cl + 2Li \longrightarrow C_2H_5Li + LiCl \tag{10-8.1}$$

using alkyl or aryl chlorides in benzene or petroleum solvents. Methyllithium may also be prepared at low temperatures in hexane as insoluble white crystals from the exchange between butyllithium and methyl iodide:

$$C_4H_9Li + CH_3I \longrightarrow CH_3Li(s) + C_4H_9I \tag{10-8.2}$$

Organolithium compounds all react rapidly with oxygen and water, and are usually spontaneously flammable in air.

Organolithium compounds are among the few alkali metal compounds that have properties—solubility in hydrocarbons and other nonpolar liquids and high volatility—typical of covalent substances. They are generally liquids or low melting solids, and molecular association is an important structural feature. For example, in the crystals of methyllithium (Fig. 10-4), the lithium atoms are associated in a tetrahedral unit with methyl groups symmetrically capping each triangular face of the Li_4 tetrahedron. A similar aggregation occurs for lithium alkoxides (LiOR) and dialkylamides ($LiNR_2$).

In solution, the lithium alkyls are also aggregated, but the extent of aggregation depends on the solvent and the steric nature of the organic group. It is not surprising that the wide variations in reactivities of Li alkyls depend, then, on these differences in aggregation and other ion-pairing interactions. An example is benzyllithium, which is monomeric in THF and reacts as a benzylating agent some 10^4 times as fast as methylation by the tetrameric methyllithium.

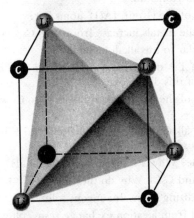

Figure 10-4 The structure of solid $(CH_3Li)_4$, showing the tetrahedral arrangement of Li atoms and the face-capping positions of the methyl groups. The structure may be regarded to be roughly that of a cube.

Organosodium and Organopotassium Compounds

These are all appreciably ionic and are not soluble to any extent in hydrocarbons. They are exceedingly reactive, being sensitive to air and water. Although alkyl and aryl derivatives can be prepared *in situ* for use as reactive intermediates, they are seldom isolated.

Some of the most important compounds are those formed by the more acidic hydrocarbons such as cyclopentadiene (Eq. 10-8.3),

$$3C_5H_6 + 2Na \longrightarrow 2C_5H_5^-Na^+ + C_5H_8 \qquad (10\text{-}8.3)$$

and acetylenes (Eq. 10-8.4).

$$RC\equiv CH + Na \longrightarrow RC\equiv C^-Na^+ + \tfrac{1}{2}H_2 \qquad (10\text{-}8.4)$$

Reactions 10-8.3 and 10-8.4 are best performed using sodium dispersed in THF, glyme, or DMF. The ionic products of reactions 10-8.3 and 10-8.4 are useful as reagents for the synthesis of transition metal organometallic derivatives.

STUDY GUIDE

Study Questions

A. Review

1. Why are the alkali metals soft and volatile?
2. Why are they highly electropositive?
3. Write down the electronic structure of francium.
4. Why are the first ionization energies of the Group IA(1) atoms low?
5. Why does the chemical reactivity of the metals increase from Li to Cs?
6. What other ions have properties similar to the alkali metal ions?
7. How does the charge-radius ratio of Li$^+$ differ from those of the other Group IA(1) ions? List some consequences of this difference.
8. How do the reactivity and the nature of the products vary from Li to Cs when the alkali metals react with oxygen?
9. What is the nature of the solutions of alkali metals in liquid ammonia? What is the chief reaction by which they decompose?
10. How would you make lithium hydride? Why is it more stable than NaH?
11. Draw the crystal structures of NaCl and CsCl. Why do they differ?
12. Why is sodium peroxide a useful oxidizing agent in aqueous solution?
13. In what order are the M$^+$ ions eluted from a cation exchange resin column?
14. Why is LiF almost insoluble in water, whereas LiCl is soluble, not only in water, but in acetone?
15. What is (a) a crown ether, (b) a cryptate?
16. Why are lithium salts commonly hydrated and those of the other alkali ions usually anhydrous?
17. How would you extinguish a sodium fire in the laboratory?

B. Additional Exercises

1. Vapors of the alkali metals contain ~1% diatomic molecules. Discuss the bonding in such molecules using the MO approach. Why do the dissociation energies of the diatomic alkali metal molecules decrease with increasing Z?

2. Anhydrous KOH in THF is one of the strongest known bases and will deprotonate exceedingly weak acids. Why? (Compare the solvation of KOH by water and by THF.)

3. The formation constant for the 1:1 complex between K^+ and cyclohexyl-18-crown-6 is much larger than the values for the other alkali metal cations. Estimate from this the size of the "hole" available for the cations in this ligand.

4. Why is there so little variation in the standard potentials for reduction of the Group IA(1) cations?

5. Which ligand would you expect more favorably to complex with K^+, cyclohexyl-18-crown-6 (structure 10-I) or 2,2,2-crypt (structure 10-II)? Why?

6. Write balanced chemical equations for the electrolysis of (a) NaCl in water, (b) molten NaCl, (c) tetraethylammonium chloride in water, (d) molten tetraethylammonium chloride.

7. Complete and balance equations for the following reactions involving the metals and the ions of Group IA(1).

(a) $KCl + Na$

(b) $Li + N_2$

(c) $Na + O_2$

(d) $Cs + O_2$

(e) $K + C_2H_5OH$

(f) $Li + HNEt_2$

(g) $Li + HN(SiMe_3)_2$

(h) $RbO_2 + H_2O$

(i) $Li_2O + H_2O$

(j) $KOH + CO_2$

(k) $K^+ + B(C_6H_5)_4^-$

(l) $Li + ClC_6H_5$

(m) $C_4H_9Li + CH_3I$

(n) $CH_3Li + [W(CO)_5Cl]^-$

8. If a crown ether were to be modified by replacing some or all oxygens with sulfur, would such a complexing agent favor K^+ or Ag^+? Explain.

C. Questions from the Literature of Inorganic Chemistry

1. Consider the paper by H. K. Frendsdorf, *J. Am. Chem. Soc*, **1971**, *93*, 600–606, and references cited therein, regarding the stability constants of cyclic polyether complexes with alkali cations.

   (a) Draw the structures of the crown ethers in Table II of this paper.

   (b) What relationship exists between stability constants for the complexes in methanol, cation radius, and ring size of the various crown ethers?

   (c) How do the potassium complexes of nonactin and valinomycin compare with the potassium complexes of 24-crown-8 and 30-crown-10, as inferred from stability constants?

   (d) Why are the stability constants for crown ether–alkali metal complexes in water lower than stability constants in methanol?

2. Consider the paper by B. Van Eck, Dinh Le Long, D. Issa, and J. L. Dye, *Inorg. Chem.*, **1982**, *21*, 1966–1970.

   (a) The analysis of the crystalline alkalides that are featured in this work was performed by reacting the samples with water. Write a balanced chemical equation for the reaction that takes place.

(b) The H_2 evolved during analysis was compared with the total titratable base that was present after reaction with water. Why? For K^+crypt-2,2,2·Na^-, how many equivalents of titratable base are released per equivalent of hydrogen upon reaction with water?

(c) Why are the sodides the easiest crystals to prepare and the most stable of the alkalide compounds?

3. Consider the work: E. C. Alyea, D. C. Bradley, and R. G. Copperthwaite, *J. Chem. Soc., Dalton Trans.,* **1972,** *1580–1584.*

(a) Draw Lewis diagrams for the lithium derivatives of $[N(SiMe_3)_2]^-$, which are used as reagents in this paper.

(b) Suggest a synthesis of the lithium bis(trimethylsilyl)amido reagents, $Li[N(SiMe_3)_2]$.

(c) What is the likely coordination geometry of the metal complexes of Table 2?

(d) What reactions were used to synthesize the complexes of Table 2? Write balanced chemical equations.

(e) What π-delocalizations do the authors mention involving the N and Si atoms of the silylamide ligands? Show with orbital diagrams how π overlap within the $(Si)_2N$—M framework may take place. To what extent is Sc^{3+} believed to be involved in such π bonding? Why?

(f) Show with orbital diagrams both the M π donation and π acceptance that the authors discuss. For which metals is each form of π bonding apparent?

(g) What would be the likely reaction of such ML_3 complexes with water?

SUPPLEMENTARY READING

The Alkali Metals, Spec. Publ. No. 22, The Chemical Society, London, 1967.

Bach, R. O., *Lithium. Current Applications in Science, Medicine, and Technology,* Wiley, New York, 1985.

Dietrich, B., "Coordination-Chemistry of Alkali and Alkaline-Earth Cations with Macrocyclic Ligands," *J. Chem. Educ.,* **1985,** *63,* 954.

Dye, J. L., "Electrides, Negatively Charged Metal Ions, and Related Phenomena," in *Progress in Inorganic Chemistry,* Vol. 32, S. Lippard, Ed., Wiley-Interscience, New York, 1984.

Dunitz, J. D. et al., Eds., *Structure and Bonding,* Vol. 16, Springer-Verlag, Berlin, 1973.

Fenton, D. E., "Across the Living Barrier," *Chem. Soc. Rev.,* **1977,** *16,* 325–343.

Jolly, W. L., *Metal–Ammonia Solutions,* Dowden, Hutchinson, and Ross, Stroudsburg, 1972.

Jortner, J. and Kestner, N. R., Eds., *Electrons in Liquids; The Nature of Metal Ammonia Solutions,* Springer-Verlag, Berlin, 1973.

Kapoor, P. N. and Mehrotra, R. C., "Coordination Compounds of the Alkali and Alkaline Earth Elements with Covalent Characteristics," *Coord. Chem. Rev.,* **1974,** *14,* 1.

Langer, A. W., Ed., "Polyamine-Chelated Alkali Metal Compounds," *Advances in Chemistry Series,* No. 130; American Chemical Society, 1974.

Oliver, J. P., "Organoalkalimetal Compounds," *International Review of Science, Inorganic Chemistry Series 2,* Vol. 4, B. J. Aylett, Ed., Buttersworths, London, 1979, pp. 1–40.

Wakefield, B. J., *The Chemistry of Organolithium Compounds,* Pergamon Press, New York, 1974.

chapter 11

THE GROUP IIA(2) ELEMENTS: BERYLLIUM, MAGNESIUM, CALCIUM, STRONTIUM, AND BARIUM

11-1 Introduction

Beryllium occurs in the mineral *beryl*, $Be_3Al_2(SiO_3)_6$. Beryllium compounds are exceedingly toxic, especially if inhaled, whereby they cause degeneration of lung tissue similar to miners' silicosis; they must be handled with great care. The element has only minor technical importance.

Magnesium, Ca, Sr, and Ba are widely distributed in minerals and in the sea. There are substantial deposits of limestone ($CaCO_3$), dolomite ($CaCO_3 \cdot MgCO_3$), and carnallite ($KCl \cdot MgCl_2 \cdot 6H_2O$). Less abundant are strontianite ($SrSO_4$) and barytes ($BaSO_4$). All isotopes of radium are radioactive. ^{226}Ra, α, 1600 yr, which occurs in the ^{238}U decay series was first isolated by Pierre and Marie Curie from the uranium ore, pitchblende. It was collected from solutions by coprecipitation with $BaSO_4$ and the nitrates subsequently fractionally crystallized. Its use in cancer therapy has been supplanted by other forms of radiation.

The positions of the Group IIA(2) elements and of the related Group IIB(12) (Zn, Cd, Hg) elements in the periodic table and some of their properties have been given in Chapter 8.

The atomic radii are smaller than those of the Li to Cs group as a result of the increased nuclear charge (cf. Table 4-2). The number of bonding electrons in the metals is now two, so that these have higher melting and boiling points and densities. The ionization enthalpies are higher than those of Group IA(1) atoms and their enthalpies of vaporization are higher. Nevertheless, the high lattice energies and high hydration energies of M^{2+} ions compensate for these increases. The metals are hence electropositive with high chemical reactivities and standard electrode potentials. Born–Haber cycle calculations show that MX compounds would be unstable, in the sense that the following reactions should have very large negative enthalpies:

$$2MX = M + MX_2 \qquad (11\text{-}1.1)$$

Figure 11-1 The infinite chain structure of BeX_2 compounds, X = F, Cl, CH_3, whereby each Be atom achieves a coordination number of four.

Because of its exceptionally small atomic radius and high enthalpies of ionization and sublimation, the lattice or hydration energies are insufficient in the case of beryllium to provide complete charge separation. Thus even BeF_2 and BeO show evidence of covalent character, and covalent compounds with bonds to carbon are quite stable. In both these respects Be resembles Zn. Note that to form two covalent bonds, promotion from the $2s^2$ to the $2s2p$ configuration is required. Thus BeX_2 molecules should be linear, but since such molecules are coordinatively unsaturated they exist only in the gas phase. In condensed phases fourfold coordination is achieved by:

1. Polymerization to give chains with bridge groups as in $(BeF_2)_n$, $(BeCl_2)_n$, or $[Be(CH_3)_2]_n$, Fig. 11-1.
2. Formation of a covalent lattice as in BeO or BeS, which have the wurtzite, ZnO, or zinc blende, ZnS, structures (see Fig. 4-1.)
3. Interaction of BeX_2 as a Lewis acid with solvents to give four-coordinate compounds like $BeCl_2(OEt_2)_2$.
4. Interaction of BeX_2 with anions to give anionic species like BeF_4^{2-}.

The cation $[Be(H_2O)_4]^{2+}$ has its water molecules very firmly bound, but because of the high charge and small size, dissociation of protons occurs readily.

The second member of Group IIA(2), magnesium, is intermediate in behavior between beryllium and the remainder of the group whose chemistry is almost entirely ionic in nature. The Mg^{2+} ion has high polarizing ability, and there is a decided tendency to nonionic behavior. Magnesium readily forms bonds to carbon (Section 29-5). Like $Be(OH)_2$, $Mg(OH)_2$ is sparingly soluble in water while the other hydroxides are water soluble and highly basic.

Calcium, Sr, Ba, and Ra form a closely related group where the chemical and physical properties change systematically with increasing size. Examples are increases from Ca to Ra in (a) the electropositive nature of the metal—cf. $E°$, Table 8-2, (b) hydration energies of salts, (c) insolubility of most salts, notably sulfates, and (d) thermal stabilities of carbonates and nitrates. As in Group IA(1), the larger cations can stabilize large anions such as O_2^{2-}, O_2^-, and I_3^- (cf. Section 4-6).

Because of similarity in charge and radius, the +2 ions of the lanthanides (Section 26-5) resemble the Sr to Ra ions. Thus europium, which forms an insoluble sulfate, $EuSO_4$, sometimes occurs in Group IIA(2) minerals.

11-2 Beryllium and Its Compounds

The *metal*, obtained by Ca or Mg reduction of $BeCl_2$, is very light and has been used for "windows" in X-ray apparatus. The absorption of electromagnetic radiation depends on the electron density in matter, and Be has the lowest stopping power per unit of mass thickness of all constructional materials.

The metal, or the hydroxide, dissolve in strong base to give the beryllate ion, $[Be(OH)_4]^{2-}$, behavior comparable to that of Al and $Al(OH)_3$. In strongly acid solutions of noncomplexing acids, the aquo ion is $[Be(OH_2)_4]^{2+}$. Solutions of Be salts are acidic, due to hydrolysis, where the initial reaction

$$[Be(H_2O)_4]^{2+} = [Be(H_2O)_3OH]^+ + H^+ \qquad (11\text{-}2.1)$$

is followed by further polymerization reactions. In fluoride solutions the $[BeF_4]^{2-}$ ion is formed. This tetrahedral ion behaves in crystals much like SO_4^{2-}; thus $PbBeF_4$ and $PbSO_4$ have similar structures and solubilities.

Beryllium chloride forms long chains in the crystal, and this compound and the similar methyl $[Be(CH_3)_2]_n$ are cleaved by donor molecules to give complexes such as $BeCl_2(OR_2)_2$. This Lewis acid behavior is also typical of Mg, Zn, and Al halides and alkyls.

Inhalation of beryllium or beryllium compounds can cause serious respiratory disease and soluble compounds may produce dermatitis on contact with the skin. Appropriate precautions should be taken in handling the element and its compounds.

MAGNESIUM, CALCIUM, STRONTIUM, BARIUM, AND RADIUM

11-3 The Elements and Their Properties

Magnesium

Magnesium is produced in several ways. The important sources are dolomite rock and seawater, which contains 0.13% Mg. Dolomite is first calcined to give a CaO/MgO mixture from which the calcium can be removed by ion exchange using seawater. The equilibrium is favorable because the solubility of $Mg(OH)_2$ is lower than that of $Ca(OH)_2$

$$Ca(OH)_2 \cdot Mg(OH)_2 + Mg^{2+} \longrightarrow 2Mg(OH)_2 + Ca^{2+} \qquad (11\text{-}3.1)$$

The most important processes for obtaining the metal are (a) the electrolysis of fused halide mixtures (e.g., $MgCl_2 + CaCl_2 + NaCl$) from which the least electropositive metal, Mg, is deposited, and (b) the reduction of MgO or of calcined dolomite ($MgO \cdot CaO$). The latter is heated with ferrosilicon:

$$CaO \cdot MgO + FeSi = Mg + \text{silicates of Ca and Fe} \qquad (11\text{-}3.2)$$

and the Mg is distilled out. MgO can be heated with coke at 2000 °C and the metal deposited by rapid quenching of the high-temperature equilibrium that lies well to the right:

$$MgO + C \rightleftharpoons Mg + CO \qquad (11\text{-}3.3)$$

Magnesium is greyish white and has a protective surface oxide film. Thus it is not attacked by water, despite the favorable potential, unless amalgamated.

It is, however, readily soluble in dilute acids. It is used in light constructional alloys and for the preparation of Grignard reagents (Section 29-5) by inter-action with alkyl or aryl halides in ether solution. It is essential to life because it occurs in chlorophyll (cf. Section 31-4).

Calcium

Calcium, Sr, and Ba are made only on a relatively small scale by reduction of the halides with Na. They are soft and silvery, resembling Na in their reactiv-ities, although somewhat less reactive. Calcium is used for the reduction to the metal of actinide and lanthanide halides and for the preparation of CaH_2, a useful reducing agent.

11-4   Binary Compounds

Oxides

The oxides, MO, are obtained by roasting of the carbonates; CaO is made in huge amounts for cement.

Magnesium oxide is relatively inert, especially after ignition at high tem-peratures, but the other oxides react with H_2O, evolving heat, to form the hydroxides. They absorb CO_2 from the air. Magnesium hydroxide is insoluble in water ($\sim 1 \times 10^{-4}$ g/L at 20 °C) and can be precipitated from Mg^{2+} solutions; it is a much weaker base than the Ca to Ra hydroxides, although it has no acidic properties and unlike $Be(OH)_2$ is insoluble in an excess of hydroxide. The Ca to Ra hydroxides are all soluble in water, increasingly so with increasing atomic number [$Ca(OH)_2$, ~ 2 g/L; $Ba(OH)_2$, ~ 60 g/L at ~ 20 °C], and all are strong bases.

Halides

The anhydrous halides can be made by dehydration (Section 20-3) of the hydrated salts. Magnesium and Ca halides readily absorb water. The ability to form hydrates, as well as the solubilities in water, decrease with increasing size, and Sr, Ba, and Ra halides are normally anhydrous. This is attributed to the fact that the hydration energies decrease more rapidly than the lattice energies with increasing size of M^{2+}.

The fluorides vary in solubility in the reverse order, that is, Mg < Ca < Sr < Ba, because of the small size of the F^- relative to the M^{2+} ion. The lattice energies decrease unusually rapidly because the large cations make contact with one another without at the same time making contact with the F^- ions.

All the halides appear to be essentially ionic. On account of its dispersion and transparency properties, CaF_2 is used for prisms in spectrometers and for cell windows (especially for aqueous solutions). It is also used to provide a stabilizing lattice for trapping lanthanide +2 ions (Section 26-5).

Other Compounds

The metals, like the alkalis, react with many other elements. Compounds such as phosphides, silicides, or sulfides are mostly ionic and are hydrolyzed by water.

Calcium *carbide*, obtained by reduction of the oxide with carbon in an electric furnace is an acetylide $Ca^{2+}C_2^{2-}$. It used to be employed as a source of acetylene:

$$Ca^{2+}C_2^{2-} + 2H_2O \longrightarrow Ca(OH)_2 + HC{\equiv}CH \qquad (11\text{-}4.1)$$

The binary hydrides MH_2 are ionic, apart from MgH_2, which is more covalent in nature. CaH_2 reacts smoothly with water and is used as a drying agent for organic solvents and for gases.

11-5 Oxo Salts, Ions, and Complexes

All the elements form *oxo salts,* those of Mg and Ca often being hydrated. The carbonates are all rather insoluble in water and the solubility products decrease with increasing size of M^{2+}; $MgCO_3$ is used in stomach powders to absorb acid. The same solubility order applies to the *sulfates;* magnesium sulfate which, as Epsom salt, $MgSO_4 \cdot 7H_2O$, is used as a mild laxative in "health" salts, is readily soluble in water. Calcium sulfate has a hemihydrate $2CaSO_4 \cdot H_2O$ (plaster of Paris) which readily absorbs more water to form the very sparingly soluble $CaSO_4 \cdot 2H_2O$ (gypsum), while Sr, Ba, and Ra sulfates are insoluble and anhydrous. $BaSO_4$ is accordingly used for "barium meals" as it is opaque to X-rays and provides a suitable shadow in the stomach. The *nitrates* of Sr, Ba, and Ra are also anhydrous and the last two can be precipitated from cold aqueous solution by the addition of fuming nitric acid. *Magnesium perchlorate* is used as a drying agent, but contact with organic materials must be avoided because of the hazard of explosions.

For water, acetone, and methanol solutions, nmr studies have shown that the coordination number of Mg^{2+} is six, although in ammonia it appears to be five. The $[Mg(H_2O)_6]^{2+}$ ion is not acidic and in contrast to $[Be(H_2O)_4]^{2+}$ can be dehydrated fairly readily: It occurs in a number of crystalline salts.

Only Mg^{2+} and Ca^{2+} show any appreciable tendency to form *complexes* and in solution, with a few exceptions, these are of oxygen ligands. $MgBr_2$, MgI_2, and $CaCl_2$ are soluble in alcohols and polar organic solvents. Adducts such as $MgBr_2(OEt_2)_2$ and $MgBr_2(THF)_4$ can be obtained.

Oxygen chelate complexes, among the most important being those with ethylenediaminetetraacetate (EDTA) type ligands, readily form in alkaline aqueous solution. For example:

$$Ca^{2+} + EDTA^{4-} = [Ca(EDTA)]^{2-} \qquad (11\text{-}5.1)$$

The cyclic polyethers and related nitrogen compounds form strong complexes and salts can be isolated. The complexing of calcium by $EDTA^{4-}$ and also by polyphosphates is of importance, not only for removal of Ca^{2+} from water but also for the volumetric estimation of Ca^{2+}.

Both Mg^{2+} and Ca^{2+} have important biological roles (Chapter 31). The tetrapyrrole systems in chlorophyll form an exception to the rule that complexes of Mg (and the other elements) with nitrogen ligands are weak.

STUDY GUIDE

Study Questions

A. Review

1. Name the important minerals of the Group IIA(2) elements.
2. Why do these metals have higher melting points than the alkali metals?
3. Why does beryllium tend to form covalent compounds?
4. Why do linear molecules X—Be—X exist only in the gas phase?
5. Which compound, when dissolved in water, would give the most acid solution, $BeCl_2$ or $CaCl_2$?
6. Draw the structures of $BeCl_2$ and $CaCl_2$ in the solid state.
7. How is magnesium made?
8. What are the properties of the hydroxides, $M(OH)_2$?
9. How do the solubilities of (a) hydroxides, (b) chlorides, and (c) sulfates vary in Group IIA(2)?
10. What and where are the Dolomites from which $MgCO_3 \cdot CaCO_3$ gets its name?
11. What is an important fact about berylium compounds from a safety point of view?
12. Compare the physical properties of Be, Mg, Ca, and Sr.
13. Do the alkaline earth cations form many complexes? Which cations tend most to do so and what are the best complexing agents?
14. What are the main types of compounds formed by the alkaline earth elements? Are they generally soluble in water?

B. Additional Exercises

1. Beryllium readily forms a compound of stoichiometry $Be_4O(CO_2CH_3)_6$. Write a likely structure for this compound.
2. Write a balanced chemical equation for the synthesis of hydrogen peroxide using barium oxide.
3. Why do you think that the usual coordination numbers for Be^{2+} and Mg^{2+} are four and six, respectively?
4. The hydroxide of beryllium (actually a hydrous metal oxide) is a white, gelatinous substance that is amphoteric. Write balanced chemical equations for its reaction with H^+ and with OH^-.
5. Why does the increase in the number of valence electrons for the alkaline earth metals over that for the alkali metals give the alkaline earths higher melting points, higher boiling points, and higher densities?
6. Write balanced equations for one method of preparation of each of the metals of this group.

7. Describe the bonding in the chain-like $[Be(CH_3)_2]_n$.

8. Describe the bonding in $BeCl_2(g)$ and $[BeCl_2]_n(s)$.

C. Problems from the Literature of Inorganic Chemistry

1. Consider the paper by R. Aruga, *Inorg. Chem.*, **1980**, *19*, 2895–2896.

(a) What are the three series or behaviors in stability constants that are listed in the introduction?

(b) How is each series distinguished?

(c) Into which series do the Group IIA(2) cation complexes of iminodiacetate fit? of thiosulfate? of sulfate? of malate?

(d) For which behavior (series) is entropy an important factor in determining the stability of the complexes?

SUPPLEMENTARY READING

Bell, N. A., "Beryllium Halides and Complexes," *Adv. Inorg. Chem. Radiochem.*, **1972**, *14*, 225.

Dietrich, B., "Coordination-Chemistry of Alkali and Alkaline-Earth Cations with Macrocyclic Ligands," *J. Chem. Educ.*, **1985**, *63*, 954.

Everest, D. A., *The Chemistry of Beryllium*, Elsevier, Amsterdam, 1964.

Hughes, M. N. and Birch, N. J., "IA and IIA Cations in Biology," *Chem. Br.*, **1982**, 196–198.

Kapoor, P. N. and Mehrotra, R. C., "Coordination Compounds of Alkali and Alkaline Earth Elements with Covalent Characteristics," *Coord. Chem. Rev.*, **1974**, *14*, 1.

Spiro, T. G., Ed., *Calcium in Biology*, Wiley-Interscience, New York, 1983.

Wacker, W. E. C., *Magnesium and Man*, Harvard University Press, Cambridge, MA, 1980.

chapter 12

BORON

12-1 Introduction

The principal ores of boron are borates such as:

Ulexite   {NaCa[$B_5O_6(OH)_6$]·$5H_2O$}
Borax   {Na_2[$B_4O_5(OH)_4$]·$8H_2O$}
Colemanite   {Ca_2[$B_3O_4(OH)_3$]$_2$·$2H_2O$}
Kernite   {Na_2[$B_4O_5(OH)_4$]·$2H_2O$}

The structures of borate minerals are complex and diverse, but they characteristically contain trigonal BO_3 or tetrahedral BO_4 units in large boron–oxygen anions. Some oxygen atoms in borate minerals are monoprotonated to give hydroxyl groups, while others are diprotonated to give waters of hydration. The cations in such minerals are usually alkali or alkaline earth cations. The structure of the borate anion in borax is shown in Fig. 12-1. Borax occurs in large deposits in the Mojave Desert of California and is the major source of boron.

No ionic compounds involving simple B^{3+} boron cations are formed because the ionization enthalpies for boron are so high that lattice energies or hydration enthalpies cannot offset the energy required for formation of a cation. Boron does form three covalent bonds using sp^2 hybrid orbitals in a trigonal plane. All such BX_3 compounds are coordinatively unsaturated and act as strong Lewis acids; interaction with Lewis bases (molecules or ions) gives tetrahedral adducts such as BF_3·OEt_2, BF_4^-, and BPh_4^-. The formation of such Lewis acid–base adducts requires a change to sp^3 hybridization for boron.

Another major feature of boron chemistry is the preponderance of compounds consisting of boron atoms in closed polyhedra or in open, basketlike arrangements. Often the structures are seen to be derivatives or fragments of the icosahedron. The frameworks of such molecules may include atoms other than boron, for example, carbon, and many of those with carbon (the carboranes) form complexes with transition metals.

Among the Group IIIB(13) elements, it is the chemistry of boron that is unique. The chemistry of boron has only a few features in common with that of aluminum. The main resemblances to silicon and differences from the more metallic aluminum are as follows:

1. The oxide B_2O_3 and $B(OH)_3$ are acidic. $Al(OH)_3$ is a basic hydroxide although it shows weak amphoteric properties, dissolving in strong NaOH.

Figure 12-1 The structure of the borate anion, $[B_4O_5(OH)_4]^{2-}$, in the mineral borax, showing two tetrahedral and two trigonal boron atoms.

2. Borates and silicates are built on similar structural principles with sharing of oxygen atoms so that complicated chain, ring, or other structures result.

3. The halides of B and Si (except BF_3) are readily hydrolyzed. The Al halides are solids and only partly hydrolyzed by water. All act as Lewis acids.

4. The hydrides of B and Si are volatile, spontaneously flammable, and readily hydrolyzed. Aluminum hydride is a polymer $(AlH_3)_n$.

12-2 Isolation of the Element

Boron forms a number of allotropes that are difficult to purify because of the high melting points of the solids (e.g., 2250 °C for the β-rhombohedral form) and because of the corrosive nature of the liquid. Boron is made in 95–98% purity as an amorphous powder by reduction of the oxide B_2O_3 with Mg

$$B_2O_3 + 3Mg \longrightarrow 2B + 3MgO \qquad (12\text{-}2.1)$$

followed by washing of the powder with NaOH, HCl, and HF. Other electropositive metals may be used in place of Mg. Purer forms of the element are available from the reductions of boron trihalides with zinc at 900 °C, as in Eq. 12-2.2:

$$2BCl_3 + 3Zn \longrightarrow 3ZnCl_2 + 2B \qquad (12\text{-}2.2)$$

or from reductions with hydrogen over hot tantalum metal as a catalyst, as in

Eq. 12-2.3:

$$2BX_3 + 3H_2 \longrightarrow 6HX + 2B \qquad (12\text{-}2.3)$$

The several allotropes of crystalline boron all have structures built up of B_{12} icosahedra (structure 8-II), one form differing from another by the manner in which these icosahedra are packed into the unit cell.

Crystalline boron is very inert and is attacked only by hot concentrated oxidizing agents. Amorphous boron is more reactive. With ammonia for instance, amorphous boron at white heat gives $(BN)_x$, a slippery white solid with a layer structure resembling that of graphite, but with hexagonal rings of alternating B and N atoms.

12-3   Oxygen Compounds of Boron

Almost all of the naturally occurring forms of boron are the oxygen-containing borate minerals. Endless varieties of organic derivatives containing boron–oxygen bonds are known; the chief examples that include trigonal boron are the orthoborates, $B(OR)_3$; the acyl borates, $B(OCOR)_3$; the peroxo borates, $B(OOR)_3$; and the boronic acids, $RB(OH)_2$. It is appropriate to consider that these are derivatives of boric acid, $B(OH)_3$.

Boric Acid

From borates, or by hydrolysis of boron trihalides, the acid $B(OH)_3$ can be obtained as white needles. The $B(OH)_3$ units are linked together by hydrogen bonds to form infinite layers of nearly hexagonal symmetry. The layers are 3.12-Å apart, and the crystals are readily cleaved along interlayer planes. Some reactions of boric acid are given in Fig. 12-2.

Figure 12-2   Some reactions of boric acid.

Boric acid is moderately soluble in water, where it acts as a weak Lewis acid towards OH$^-$

$$B(OH)_3 + H_2O = B(OH)_4^- + H^+ \qquad pK = 9.0 \qquad (12\text{-}3.1)$$

The B(OH)$_4^-$ ion occurs in many borate-type minerals, but most borates (especially those formed by fusion of boric acid with metal oxides) have complex structures such as the ring anion, structure 12-I. Boric acid and borates form very stable complexes with 1,2-diols, as in structure 12-II:

12-I   12-II

The concentration of boric acid can be determined by complexation with a diol such as glycerol (Eq. 12-3.2)

$$(12\text{-}3.2)$$

followed by titration with NaOH.

The fusion of the acid gives the oxide B$_2$O$_3$ as a glass. The melt readily dissolves metal oxides to give borate glasses. It also reacts with silica to give the borosilicate glass known as Pyrex.

Esterification of boric acid by alcohols with sulfuric acid gives B(OR)$_3$, which can be coordinated in ethers by H$^-$ to give the useful reducing agents [HB(OR)$_3$]$^-$. The reactivity and selectivity of the latter can be controlled by changing the R groups.

12-4 The Trihalides of Boron

Boron trifluoride is a pungent, colorless gas (bp -101 °C) that is obtained by heating B$_2$O$_3$ with NH$_4$BF$_4$ or CaF$_2$ and concentrated H$_2$SO$_4$; it is commercially available in tanks.

Boron trifluoride is one of the strongest Lewis acids known and reacts readily with most Lewis bases such as ethers, alcohols, amines, or water to give adducts, and with F^- to give the tetrafluoroborate ion, BF_4^-. The diethyletherate, $(C_2H_5)_2OBF_3$, a viscous liquid, is available commercially. Unlike the other halides, BF_3 is only partially hydrolyzed by water:

$$4BF_3 + 6H_2O = 3H_3O^+ + 3BF_4^- + B(OH)_3 \qquad (12\text{-}4.1)$$

$$BF_4^- + H_2O = [BF_3OH]^- + HF \qquad (12\text{-}4.2)$$

Because of this, and its potency as a Lewis acid, BF_3 is widely used to promote various organic reactions. Examples are

(a) Ethers or alcohols + acids $\rightarrow$ esters + H_2O or ROH.

(b) Alcohols + benzene $\rightarrow$ alkylbenzenes + H_2O.

(c) Polymerization of alkenes and alkene oxides such as propylene oxide.

(d) Friedel–Crafts-like acylations and alkylations.

In (a) and (b) the effectiveness of BF_3 must depend on its ability to form an adduct with one or both of the reactants, thus lowering the activation energy of the rate-determining step in which H_2O or ROH is eliminated by breaking of C—O bonds. In reactions of type (d), intermediates may be characterized at low temperatures. Thus the interaction of benzene and C_2H_5F proceeds as in Eq. 12-4.3. It is clear that BF_3 is not actually a catalyst, since it must be present in stoichiometric amount and is consumed in removing HF as HBF_4.

$$(12\text{-}4.3)$$

Fluoroboric acid solutions are formed on dissolving $B(OH)_3$ in aqueous HF

$$B(OH)_3 + 4HF = H_3O^+ + BF_4^- + 2H_2O \qquad (12\text{-}4.4)$$

The commercial solutions contain 40% acid. Fluoroboric acid is a strong acid and cannot, of course, exist as HBF_4. The ion is tetrahedral and fluoroborates resemble the corresponding perchlorates in their solubilities and crystal structures. Like ClO_4^- and PF_6^- the anion has a low tendency to act as a ligand toward metal ions in *aqueous* solution. In nonaqueous media, there is evidence for complex formation.

Boron trichloride (bp 12 °C) and the *bromide* (bp 90 °C) are obtained by direct interaction at elevated temperatures. They fume in moist air and are violently hydrolyzed by water:

$$BCl_3 + 3H_2O = B(OH)_3 + 3HCl \qquad (12\text{-}4.5)$$

The rapid hydrolysis supports other evidence that these halides are stronger Lewis acids than BF_3.

Reactions of the Trihalides of Boron

As has already been mentioned, the boron trihalides are Lewis acids, and they readily react with Lewis bases to form adducts. Two other important reactions that we shall consider are halide exchange among the trihalides themselves, and the elimination of HX from adducts of the trihalides when an acidic hydrogen is available.

Formation of Adducts with Lewis Bases

Even the weakest of bases will form adducts with the trihalides of boron. Ethers, amines, phosphines, alcohols, anions, carbon monoxide, and the like all form adducts by donation of an electron pair to boron. The rehybridization of boron that accompanies adduct formation results in a loss in BX double-bond character, as shown in Fig. 12-3. When the Lewis donor is trimethylamine, the enthalpy change for adduct formation as in Eq. 12-4.6:

$$BX_3 + :N(CH_3)_3 \longrightarrow X_3B \leftarrow N(CH_3)_3 \qquad (12\text{-}4.6)$$

is most negative for BBr_3 and least negative for BF_3. We would expect that the higher electronegativity of fluorine should enhance the stability of the trimethylamine adduct with BF_3. Since the enthalpy of adduct formation is least favorable with BF_3, however, it is concluded that the loss in BX double-bond character upon rehybridization to form an adduct is greater with BF_3 than in the other trihalides. From this we can conclude that the double-bond character in the trihalides follows the order $BF_3 > BCl_3 > BBr_3$, a trend opposite to that expected from the electronegativities of the halides. (Recall that the double bond in BX_3 results from donation of π-electron density from X into an empty $2p$ atomic orbital of an sp^2-hybridized boron atom. The π bond system in these sorts of molecules was discussed in Section 3-6.) Evidently the π-bond system in BF_3 is especially strong because of effective overlap between the boron $2p$ and the fluorine $2p$ atomic orbitals—overlap that is effective because of the closely matched energies and sizes of the orbitals. The $3p$ and $4p$ atomic orbitals of Cl and Br have the proper symmetry for π overlap with the $2p$ atomic orbital of B in the compounds BX_3, but the π overlap is less effective because the energies and sizes of the π-donor orbitals ($3p$ for chlorine

sp^2 Boron sp^3 Boron

Figure 12-3   The reaction of a trigonal trihalide of boron with a Lewis base, :D, to give a tetrahedral adduct. The rehybridization of boron that is required when :D disrupts the B—X π bond in the BX_3 reactant.

and $4p$ for bromine) are not well matched to those of the π-acceptor $(2p)$ orbital of boron.

Halide Exchange Reactions Among the Boron Trihalides

Mixtures of two different trihalides of boron undergo exchange of halide as illustrated in reaction 12-4.7:

$$BCl_3 + BBr_3 = BCl_2Br + BBr_2Cl \qquad (12\text{-}4.7)$$

The position of equilibrium in Eq. 12-4.7 lies mostly to the left, but small amounts of the exchange products can be detected spectroscopically. The trifluoride undergoes halide exchange less readily than BBr_3 and BCl_3. No intermediates have been detected, but it is reasonable to propose that the exchange involves the type of dimeric structure shown in structure 12-III. Such a dimer would be similar to Al_2Cl_6, structure 6-I.

12-III

Equilibria of the type illustrated by reaction 12-4.7 are established rapidly, and only small amounts of the exchange products can be detected. Attempts to isolate the exchange products from such systems are not successful because of the facile nature of the equilibria. Thus, no pure mixed halide of boron is known. A concerted mechanism as illustrated in structure 12-III would be consistent with all of the facts as long as the new, bridging BX bonds that form the dimer are weak.

Elimination Reactions of BX₃ Adducts

When an acidic hydrogen is present in an adduct of BX_3, elimination of HX is possible, as illustrated in the following reactions. Hydrolysis of BCl_3 by alcohols involves adduct formation followed by elimination of HCl as in reaction 12-4.8.

$$BCl_3 + C_2H_5OH \longrightarrow Cl_2B\text{---}OC_2H_5 + HCl \qquad (12\text{-}4.8)$$

Stepwise addition and elimination eventually leads to complete solvolysis as in Eq. 12-4.9:

$$BCl_3 + 3C_2H_5OH \longrightarrow B(OC_2H_5)_3 + 3HCl \qquad (12\text{-}4.9)$$

The dimethylamine adduct of BCl_3 undergoes elimination of HCl to give an aminoborane as in Eq. 12-4.10:

$$(CH_3)_2NH \rightarrow BCl_3 \longrightarrow (CH_3)_2N\text{---}BCl_2 + HCl \qquad (12\text{-}4.10)$$

Aminoboranes, and in particular, the nature of the BN bond in aminoboranes, will be discussed in Section 12-6.

12-5 The Hydrides of Boron

Boranes

Boron forms an extensive series of molecular hydrides called *boranes*. Typical ones are B_2H_6, B_4H_{10}, B_9H_{15}, $B_{10}H_{14}$, and $B_{20}H_{16}$. Boranes were first prepared between 1912 and 1936 by Alfred Stock who developed vacuum line techniques to handle these reactive materials. Stock's original synthesis—the reaction of Mg_3B_2 with acid—is now superseded for all but B_6H_{10}. Most syntheses now involve thermolysis of B_2H_6 under varied conditions, often in the presence of hydrogen.

The properties of some boranes are listed in Table 12-1. The nomenclature that is used for boranes is straightforward: the number of boron atoms is indicated by the prefix, and the number of hydrogen atoms is indicated parenthetically. For example, B_4H_{10} is *tetra*borane(10).

Diborane(6)

B_2H_6 is a gas (bp $-92.6\ °C$) that is spontaneously flammable in air and instantly hydrolyzed by water to H_2 and boric acid. It is obtained virtually quantitatively in ether, at room temperature, by the reaction of sodium borohydride with BF_3, as in reaction 12-5.1:

$$3NaBH_4 + 4BF_3 \longrightarrow 2B_2H_6 + 3NaBF_4 \qquad (12\text{-}5.1)$$

Laboratory quantities are best prepared by oxidation of sodium borohydride by iodine in diglyme, as in Eq. 12-5.2:

$$2NaBH_4 + I_2 \longrightarrow B_2H_6 + 2NaI + H_2 \qquad (12\text{-}5.2)$$

Industrial quantities are prepared at high temperatures by reduction with sodium hydride of BF_3:

$$2BF_3 + 6NaH \longrightarrow B_2H_6 + 6NaF \qquad (12\text{-}5.3)$$

Borane, BH_3, has only a transient existence in the thermal decomposition of diborane:

$$2B_2H_6 = BH_3 + B_3H_9 \qquad (12\text{-}5.4)$$

Reactions of diborane are discussed later in Section 12-5. It should be pointed out here that diborane is an extremely versatile reagent for the synthesis of organoboranes, which in turn are very useful intermediates in organic synthesis. Diborane is also a powerful reducing agent for some functional groups, for example, aldehydes and organic nitriles.

Higher Boranes

The heavier boranes, for example, B_6H_{10}, are mainly liquids whose flammability in air decreases with increasing molecular weight. One of the most important is decaborane, $B_{10}H_{14}$, a solid (mp $99.7\ °C$) that is stable in air and only slowly hydrolyzed by water. It is obtained by heating B_2H_6 at $100\ °C$ and

Table 12-1 Important Properties of Some Boranes

Formula	Name	Melting Point °C	Boiling Point °C	Reaction With Air at 25 °C	Thermal Stability	Reaction With Water
B_2H_6	Diborane(6)	−164.85	−92.59	Spontaneously flammable	Fairly stable at 25 °C	Instant hydrolysis
B_4H_{10}	Tetraborane(10)	−120	18	Not spontaneously flammable if pure	Decomposes fairly rapidly at 25 °C	Hydrolysis in 24 h
B_5H_9	Pentaborane(9)	−46.6	48	Spontaneously flammable	Stable at 25 °C; slow decomposition 150 °C	Hydrolyzed only on heating
B_5H_{11}	Pentaborane(11)	−123	63	Spontaneously flammable	Decomposes very rapidly at 25 °C	Rapid hydrolysis
B_6H_{10}	Hexaborane(10)	−62.3	108	Spontaneously flammable	Slow decomposition at 25 °C	Hydrolyzed only on heating
B_6H_{12}	Hexaborane(12)	−82.3	80–90	—	Liquid stable few hours at 25 °C	Quantitative, to give B_4H_{10}, $B(OH)_3$, H_2
B_8H_{12}	Octaborane(12)	−20	—	—	Decomposes above −20 °C	—
B_8H_{18}	Octaborane(18)	—	—	—	Unstable	—
B_9H_{15}	Enneaborane(15)	2.6	—	Stable	—	—
$B_{10}H_{14}$	Decaborane(14)	99.7	213 (extrap.)	Very stable	Stable at 150 °C	Slow hydrolysis

is an important starting material for the synthesis of the $B_{10}H_{10}^{2-}$ anion and carboranes discussed later.

Structure and Bonding in the Boranes

The structures of the boranes are unlike those of other hydrides such as those of carbon and are unique. A few of them are shown in Fig. 12-4. Observe that in none are there sufficient electrons to allow the formation of conven-

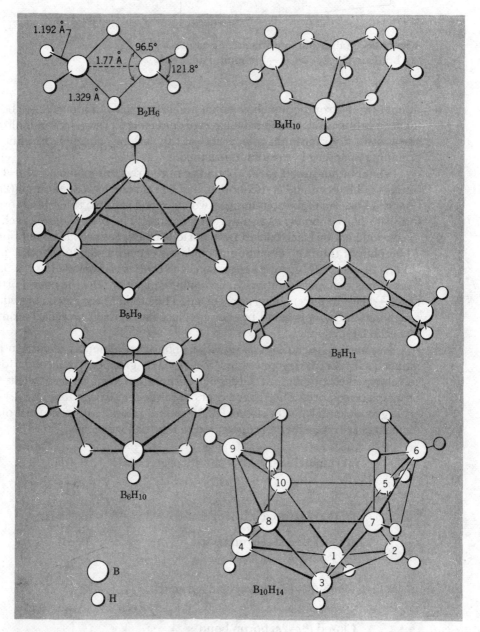

Figure 12-4 The structures of some boranes.

Figure 12-5   A diagram showing the formation of
two bridging (3c–2e) B—H—B bonds in diborane.

tional two-electron bonds between all adjacent pairs of atoms (2*c*–2*e* bonds).
There is thus the problem of electron deficiency. It was to rationalize the
structures of boranes that the earliest of the various concepts of multicenter
bonding (Chapter 3) were first developed.

For diborane itself (3*c*–2*e*) bonds are required to explain the B—H—B
bridges. The terminal B—H bonds may be regarded as conventional (2*c*–2*e*)
bonds. Thus, each boron atom uses two electrons and two roughly *sp*³ orbitals
to form (2*c*–2*e*) bonds to two hydrogen atoms. The boron atom in each BH₂
group still has one electron and two hybrid orbitals for use in further bonding.
The plane of the two remaining orbitals is perpendicular to the BH₂ plane.
When two such BH₂ groups approach each other as is shown in Fig. 12-5, with
hydrogen atoms also lying, as is shown, in the plane of the four empty orbitals,
two B—H—B (3*c*–2*e*) bonds are formed. The total of four electrons required
for these bonds is provided by the one electron carried by each H atom and
by each BH₂ group.

We have just seen that two structure–bonding elements are used in B₂H₆,
namely, (2*c*–2*e*) BH groups and (3*c*–2*e*) BHB groups. To account for the
structures and bonding of the higher boranes, these elements as well as three
others are required. The three others are (2*c*–2*e*) BB groups, (3*c*–2*e*) open
BBB groups, and (3*c*–2*e*) closed BBB groups. These five structure–bonding
elements are conveniently represented in the following way:

Terminal (2*c*–2*e*) boron–hydrogen bond   B—H

(3*c*–2*e*) Hydrogen bridge bond $\overset{\text{H}}{\underset{\text{B}\qquad\text{B}}{\frown}}$

(2*c*–2*e*) Boron–boron bond   B—B

Open (3*c*–2*e*) Boron bridge bond $\overset{\text{B}}{\underset{\text{B}\qquad\text{B}}{\frown}}$

Closed (3*c*–2*e*) boron bond $\underset{\text{B}\qquad\text{B}}{\overset{\text{B}}{\wedge}}$

Figure 12-6 Valence descriptions of some electron deficient boranes using Lipscomb's "semitopological" scheme.

By using these five elements, W. N. Lipscomb was able to develop "semitopological" descriptions of the structures and bonding in all of the boranes. The scheme is capable of elaboration into a comprehensive, semipredictive tool for correlating all the structural data. Figure 12-6 shows a few examples of its use to depict known structures.

The semitopological scheme does not always provide the best description of bonding in the boranes and related species such as the polyhedral borane anions and carboranes we discuss later. Where there is symmetry of a high order it is often better to think in terms of a highly delocalized MO description of the bonding. For instance, in B_5H_9 (Fig. 12-4) where the four basal boron atoms are equivalently related to the apical boron atom, it is *possible* to depict

a resonance hybrid involving the localized and B—B elements, namely:

but it is neater and simpler to formulate a set of seven five-center molecular orbitals with the lowest three occupied by electron pairs. When one approaches the hypersymmetrical species such as $B_{12}H_{12}^{2-}$, use of the full molecular symmetry in an MO treatment becomes the only practical course.

Reactions of the Boranes

The boranes undergo an impressive variety of reactions including oxidations to oxides, pyrolysis to higher boranes, attack by nucleophiles and electrophiles, reduction to borane anions, and reactions with bases such as OH^- and NH_3. In some cases it is useful to view at least the substitutions as being either reactions of terminal BH groups or of bridging BHB groups. We shall restrict our attention to three illustrative systems: diborane(6), B_2H_6; pentaborane(9), B_5H_9; and decaborane(14), $B_{10}H_{14}$.

Diborane(6), B_2H_6. Controlled pyrolysis of diborane leads to most of the higher boranes. Reaction with oxygen is extremely exothermic:

$$B_2H_6 + 3O_2 \longrightarrow B_2O_3 + 3H_2O \qquad \Delta H = -2160 \text{ kJ mol}^{-1} \qquad (12\text{-}5.5)$$

Reaction of diborane with water is instantaneous:

$$B_2H_6 + 6H_2O \longrightarrow 2B(OH)_3 + 6H_2 \qquad (12\text{-}5.6)$$

Diborane is also hydrolyzed by weaker acids such as alcohols, as in reaction 12-5.7:

$$B_2H_6 + 6ROH \longrightarrow 2B(OR)_3 + 6H_2 \qquad (12\text{-}5.7)$$

Reaction with HCl replaces a terminal H with Cl

$$B_2H_6 + HCl \longrightarrow B_2H_5Cl + H_2 \qquad (12\text{-}5.8)$$

and reaction with chlorine gives the trichloride, as in reaction 12-5.9.

$$B_2H_6 + 3Cl_2 \longrightarrow 2BCl_3 + 6HCl \qquad (12\text{-}5.9)$$

The electron deficient three-center, two-electron BHB bridges are sites of nucleophilic attack. Small amines such as NH_3, $MeNH_2$, and Me_2NH give unsymmetrical cleavage of diborane, as in reaction 12-5.10:

$$B_2H_6 + 2NH_3 \longrightarrow [H_2B(NH_3)_2]^+[BH_4]^- \qquad (12\text{-}5.10)$$

The boronium ion products, $[H_2BL_2]^+$, are tetrahedral, and can undergo substitution by other bases, as in reaction 12-5.11.

$$[H_2B(NH_3)_2]^+ + 2PR_3 \longrightarrow [H_2B(PR_3)_2]^+ + 2NH_3 \qquad (12\text{-}5.11)$$

Large amines such as Me_3N and pyridine give symmetrical cleavage of diborane, as in reaction 12-5.12:

$$B_2H_6 + 2NMe_3 \longrightarrow 2H_3B{\leftarrow}NMe_3 \qquad (12\text{-}5.12)$$

The amine borane products from symmetrical cleavage of diborane are Lewis base adducts of BH_3. Amine boranes will be discussed more in Section 12-6.

Reduction of diborane can be accomplished with sodium:

$$2B_2H_6 + 2Na \longrightarrow NaBH_4 + NaB_3H_8 \qquad (12\text{-}5.13)$$

or with sodium borohydride:

$$B_2H_6 + NaBH_4 \longrightarrow NaB_3H_8 + H_2 \qquad (12\text{-}5.14)$$

Reductions of diborane with sodium borohydride can also lead to higher borane anions, as in reaction 12-5.15:

$$2NaBH_4 + 5B_2H_6 \longrightarrow Na_2B_{12}H_{12} \qquad (12\text{-}5.15)$$

The polyhedral borane anion $B_{12}H_{12}{}^{2-}$ has icosahedral geometry. Other polyhedral borane anions and carboranes will be discussed shortly.

Pentaborane(9), B_5H_9. Pentaborane(9) has the structure shown in Fig. 12-4. The apical boron is bonded only to a terminal hydrogen atom, while each of the four basal borons is bonded to one terminal hydrogen atom and to two bridging hydrogen atoms. The relative electron deficiency in the basal plane is illustrated by reaction of B_5H_9 with base, as in Eq. 12-5.16:

$$B_5H_9 + NaH \longrightarrow Na^+B_5H_8^- + H_2 \qquad (12\text{-}5.16)$$

Higher boranes are even more acidic than B_5H_9. The anionic product of reaction 12-5.16 has the structure shown in structure 12-IV, where it can be seen

12-IV

that loss of one bridging hydrogen atom from the basal plane of B_5H_9 opens the base of the pyramid.

The $B_5H_8^-$ system is fluxional, though, and the basal boron atoms are indistinguishable using nmr techniques, as are the bridging hydrogen atoms.

The relatively electron-rich apical BH group of pentaborane(9) is susceptible to attack by electrophiles, as in reaction 12-5.17.

$$B_5H_9 + I_2 \longrightarrow B_5H_8I + HI \qquad (12\text{-}5.17)$$

Decaborane(14), $B_{10}H_{14}$. The structure of decaborane(14) is shown in Fig. 12-4. Four electron deficient bridging BHB groups cap the top of this icosahedral fragment, making this part of the molecule the preferred site for attack by nucleophiles. As for pentaborane(9), it is the bridging hydrogen atoms that are acidic:

$$B_{10}H_{14} + OH^- \longrightarrow B_{10}H_{13}^- + H_2O \qquad (12\text{-}5.18)$$

Reduction by sodium converts two of the bridging hydrogen atoms at the top of the molecule to terminal hydrogen atoms:

$$B_{10}H_{14} + 2Na \longrightarrow Na_2B_{10}H_{14} \qquad (12\text{-}5.19)$$

Nucleophiles react to give 6,9-disubstituted products as in Eqs. 12-5.20 to 12-5.22:

$$B_{10}H_{14} + 2CN^- \longrightarrow B_{10}H_{12}(CN)_2^{2-} + H_2 \qquad (12\text{-}5.20)$$

$$B_{10}H_{14} + 2CH_3CN \longrightarrow B_{10}H_{12}(NCCH_3)_2 + H_2 \qquad (12\text{-}5.21)$$

$$B_{10}H_{14} + 2PR_3 \longrightarrow B_{10}H_{12}(PR_3)_2 + H_2 \qquad (12\text{-}5.22)$$

In each such example, two bridging hydrogen atoms have migrated into the positions between boron atoms 5,10 and 7,8. Also, in a formal sense, the two terminal hydrogen atoms at boron atoms 6 and 9 have been replaced by the incoming nucleophile, and H_2 has been eliminated.

In contrast to reactions with nucleophiles, decaborane(14) reacts with electrophiles to give 2,4- or 1,3-disubstituted products. An example is shown in reaction 12-5.23.

$$B_{10}H_{14} + I_2 \longrightarrow 2,4\text{-}I_2B_{10}H_{12} + H_2 \qquad (12\text{-}5.23)$$

Charge distribution calculations using MO theory indicate that considerable excess negative charge should be assigned to boron atoms 1, 2, 3, and 4, with positive charge assigned to the electron deficient positions elsewhere in the molecule. It is thus gratifying that experiments show consistently that only positions 1, 2, 3, and 4 can be substituted electrophilically.

The Tetrahydroborate Ion, BH_4^-

The tetrahydroborate ion, BH_4^-, is the simplest of a number of borohydride anions. It is of great importance as a reducing agent and source of H^- ion both in inorganic and organic chemistry; derivatives such as $[BH(OMe)_3]^-$ and $[BH_3CN]^-$ are also useful, the latter because it can be used in acidic solutions.

Borohydrides of many metals have been made and some representative syntheses are

$$4NaH + B(OMe)_3 \xrightarrow{\sim 250\ ^\circ C} NaBH_4 + 3NaOCH_3 \qquad (12\text{-}5.24)$$

Figure 12-7 The structure of Zr $(BH_4)_4$. (Taken from Bird, P. H. and Churchill, M. R., *J. Chem. Soc., Chem. Commun.,* **1967,** 403, and used with permission.)

$$NaH + B(OMe)_3 \xrightarrow{\text{THF}} NaBH(OMe)_3 \tag{12-5.25}$$

$$2LiH + B_2H_6 \xrightarrow{\text{Ether}} 2LiBH_4 \tag{12-5.26}$$

$$AlCl_3 + 3NaBH_4 \xrightarrow{\text{Heat}} Al(BH_4)_3 + 3NaCl \tag{12-5.27}$$

$$UF_4 + 2Al(BH_4)_3 \longrightarrow U(BH_4)_4 + 2AlF_2BH_4 \tag{12-5.28}$$

The most important salt is $NaBH_4$. It is a white crystalline solid, stable in dry air, and nonvolatile. It is insoluble in diethyl ether but dissolves in water, THF, and ethyleneglycol ethers from which it can be crystallized.

Many borohydrides are ionic, containing the tetrahedral BH_4^- ion. However BH_4^- can serve as a ligand, interacting more or less covalently with metal ions, by bridging hydrogen atoms. Thus in $(Ph_3P)_2CuBH_4$ there are two Cu—H—B bridges, whereas in $Zr(BH_4)_4$, each BH_4 forms three bridges to Zr as shown in Fig. 12-7. These M—H—B bridges are $(3c–2e)$ bonding systems.

Polyhedral Borane Anions and Carboranes

The polyhedral borane anions have the formula $B_nH_n^{2-}$. The carboranes may be considered to be *formally* derived from $B_nH_n^{2-}$ by replacement of BH^- by the isoelectronic and isostructural CH. Thus two replacements lead to neutral molecules, $B_{n-2}C_2H_n$. Carboranes or derivatives with $n = 5$ to $n = 12$ are known, in some of which two or more isomers may be isolated. Sulfur and phosphorus derivatives can also be obtained, PH^+, for example, replacing CH or BH^-.

Geometrically there are two broad classes of compounds:

1. Those in which the boron atom framework closes in on itself to form a polyhedron. These are *closo* (Greek for cage) compounds.
2. Those frameworks that are open or incomplete polyhedra. These are *nido* (nest) compounds, which have one missing vertex, and *arachno* (spider web) compounds, which two missing vertices.

Some of the *closo* boranes and carboranes are shown in Fig. 12-8.

$B_nH_n^{2-}$ Ions. The most stable and best studied are $B_{10}H_{10}^{2-}$ and $B_{12}H_{12}^{2-}$, which can be synthesized by the reactions

$$B_{10}H_{14} + 2R_3N \xrightarrow{150\ °C} 2(R_3NH)^+ + B_{10}H_{10}^{2-} + H_2 \qquad (12\text{-}5.29)$$

$$6B_2H_6 + 2R_3N \xrightarrow{150\ °C} 2(R_3NH)^+ + B_{12}H_{12}^{2-} + 11H_2 \qquad (12\text{-}5.30)$$

The most important general reaction of the anions is attack by electrophilic reagents such as Br^+, $C_6H_5N_2^+$, RCO^+ in strongly acid media. $B_{10}H_{10}^{2-}$ is more susceptible to substitution than is $B_{12}H_{12}^{2-}$.

$B_{n-2}C_2H_n$ Carboranes. The most important carboranes are 1,2- and 1,7-dicarba-*closo*-dodecaborane, $B_{10}C_2H_{12}$, and their *C*-substituted derivatives. The 1,2 isomer may be obtained by the reactions

$$B_{10}H_{14} + 2R_2S = B_{10}H_{12}(R_2S)_2 + H_2 \qquad (12\text{-}5.31)$$

$$B_{10}H_{12}(R_2S)_2 + RC{\equiv}CR' = 1,2\text{-}B_{10}H_{10}C_2RR' + 2R_2S + H_2 \qquad (12\text{-}5.32)$$

On heating at 450 °C the 1,2 isomer rearranges to the 1,7 isomer.

Derivatives may be obtained from $B_{10}C_2H_{12}$ by replacement of the CH hydrogen atoms by Li. The dilithio derivatives react with many other reagents (Scheme 12-1) where a self-explanatory abbreviation is used for $B_{10}H_{10}C_2$.

Scheme 12-1

An enormous number of compounds have been made, one of the main motives being the incorporation of the thermally stable carborane residues into high polymers such as silicones in order to increase the thermal stability. Chlorinated carboranes can be obtained directly from $B_{10}C_2H_{10}R_2$.

$B_9C_2H_{13-n}^{n-}$ Carborane Anions. When the 1,2- and 1,7-dicarba-*closo*-dodecaboranes are heated with alkoxide ions, degradation occurs to form iso-

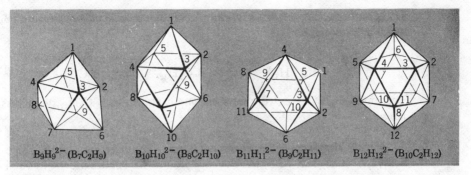

$B_9H_9^{2-}$ $(B_7C_2H_9)$ $B_{10}H_{10}^{2-}$ $(B_8C_2H_{10})$ $B_{11}H_{11}^{2-}$ $(B_9C_2H_{11})$ $B_{12}H_{12}^{2-}$ $(B_{10}C_2H_{12})$

Figure 12-8 The structures and the numbering schemes of some *closo* polyhedral borane anions ($B_nH_n^{2-}$) and the isoelectronic and isostructural carboranes ($B_{n-2}C_2H_n$), which are neutral.

meric *nido*-carborane anions, $B_9C_2H_{12}^-$

$$B_{10}C_2H_{12} + EtO^- + 2EtOH = B_9C_2H_{12}^- + B(OEt)_3 + H_2 \quad (12\text{-}5.33)$$

This removal of a BH^{2+} unit from $B_{10}C_2H_{12}$ may be interpreted as a nucleophilic attack at the most electron-deficient boron atoms of the carborane. Molecular orbital calculations show that the C atoms in carboranes have considerable electron-withdrawing power. The most electron-deficient B atoms are those adjacent to carbon. In $1,2\text{-}B_{10}C_2H_{12}$ these will be in positions three and six while in $1,7\text{-}B_{10}C_2H_{12}$ they will be at positions two and three.

While alkoxide ion attack produces only $B_9C_2H_{12}^-$, use of the very strong base NaH forms the $B_9C_2H_{11}^{2-}$ ions:

$$B_9C_2H_{12}^- + NaH = Na^+ + B_9C_2H_{11}^{2-} + H_2 \quad (12\text{-}5.34)$$

The structures of the isomeric $B_9C_2H_{11}^{2-}$ ions are shown in Fig. 12-9. The $B_9C_2H_{11}^{2-}$ ions are very strong bases and readily acquire H^+ to give $B_9C_2H_{12}^-$.

○ B

◑ C

(3) Open position left by the removal B atom 3

Figure 12-9 The isomeric *nido*-1,2- and *nido*-1,7-carborane anions, $B_9C_2H_{11}^{2-}$.

These, in turn, can be protonated to form the neutral *nido*-carboranes $B_9C_2H_{13}$, which are strong acids.

$$B_9C_2H_{11}{}^{2-} \stackrel{H^+}{\rightleftharpoons} B_9C_2H_{12}{}^{-} \stackrel{H^+}{\rightleftharpoons} B_9C_2H_{13} \qquad (12\text{-}5.35)$$

Heating $B_9C_2H_{13}$ gives yet another *closo*-carborane, $B_9C_2H_{11}$, with loss of hydrogen.

Metal Complexes of Carborane Anions. The open pentagonal faces of the $B_9C_2H_{11}{}^{2-}$ ions (Fig. 12-9) were recognized by M. F. Hawthorne in 1964 to bear a strong resemblance structurally and electronically to the cyclopentadienyl ion, $C_5H_5^-$. The latter forms strong bonds to transition metals, as we discuss in Chapter 29.

Interaction of $Na_2B_9C_2H_{11}$ with metal compounds such as those of Fe^{2+} or Co^{3+} thus leads to species isoelectronic with ferrocene, $(C_5H_5)_2Fe$, or the cobalticinium ion, $(C_5H_5)_2Co^+$, namely, $(B_9C_2H_{11})_2Fe^{2-}$ and $(B_9C_2H_{11})_2Co^-$, respectively. The iron complex undergoes reversible oxidation like ferrocene:

$$[(C_5H_5)_2Fe^{III}]^+ + e^- = [(C_5H_5)_2Fe^{II}]^0 \qquad (12\text{-}5.36)$$

$$[(B_9C_2H_{11})_2Fe]^- + e^- = [(B_9C_2H_{11})_2Fe]^{2-} \qquad (12\text{-}5.37)$$

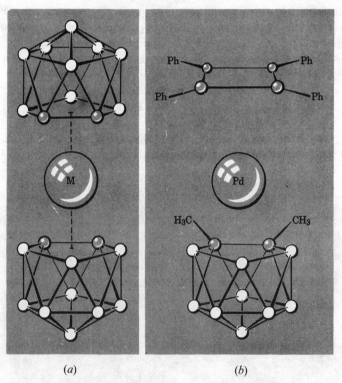

(a) (b)

Figure 12-10 (a) The general structure of bis(dicarbollide) metal complexes. (b) An example of a mono(dicarbollide) complex of palladium.

The formal nomenclature for the $B_9C_2H_{11}{}^{2-}$ ion and its complexes is unwieldy and the trivial name "*dicarbollide*" ion was proposed (from the Spanish *olla* for pot, referring to the potlike shape of the B_9C_2 cage).

The structures of two types of bis(dicarbollide) metal complexes are shown in Fig. 12-10. While some complexes have a symmetrical "sandwich" structure [Fig. 12-10(*a*)] others have the metal disposed unsymmetrically.

Finally, comparable with η^5-$C_5H_5Mn(CO)_3$ (Chapter 29), there are mixed complexes with only one dicarbollide unit and other ligands such as CO, Ph_4C_4, C_5H_5, and so on, [Fig. 12-10(*b*)].

12-6 Boron-Nitrogen Compounds

Here we describe three types of B—N compounds, each analogous to C—C compounds, but with some differences. Since the covalent radius and the electronegativity of carbon are each intermediate between those of B and N, it is to be expected that C—C compounds will be similar to, but less polar than, their isoelectronic B—N counterparts. We shall consider amineboranes (analogous to alkanes), aminoboranes (analogous to alkenes), and borazines (analogous to benzenes).

Amine Boranes

Amine boranes are Lewis acid–base adducts containing a boron–nitrogen donor bond. Both boron and nitrogen are typically tetrahedral, and the B—N bond length is comparable to the C-C bond lengths found in simple alkanes such as ethane. Amine boranes are formed by symmetrical cleavage of diborane or by reaction of ammonium salts as in Eq. 12-6.1:

$$[H_3NR]Cl + LiBH_4 \longrightarrow RH_2N{\rightarrow}BH_3 + LiCl + H_2 \quad (12\text{-}6.1)$$

The B—N bond strength varies from one adduct to another. The weakest B—N bonds are represented

$$\underset{12\text{-}V}{-\!\!\!\underset{/}{\overset{\textstyle \diagup}{N}}\!\!\rightarrow\! B\!\!\underset{\diagdown}{\overset{\textstyle \diagup}{-}}} \qquad \underset{12\text{-}VI}{-\!\!\!\underset{/}{\overset{\textstyle \diagup}{N}}\!\!\overset{+}{-}\! \overset{-}{B}\!\!\underset{\diagdown}{\overset{\textstyle \diagup}{-}}}$$

as in structure 12-V, where an arrow indicates a slight donor → acceptor interaction. More complete sharing of nitrogen electrons with boron is represented by structure 12-VI, which is expected to be polar.

Steric hindrance can prevent the formation of some adducts, for example, 2,6-dimethylpyridine with trimethylborane. Bridged diadducts can be obtained, as in reaction 12-6.2:

$$B_2H_6 + en \longrightarrow \underset{\underset{H_3B}{\downarrow}}{H_2N}\overbrace{\qquad\qquad}^{}\underset{\underset{BH_3}{\downarrow}}{NH_2} \qquad (12\text{-}6.2)$$

The chief reaction of amine boranes is elimination either of HX or of RH, to give aminoboranes.

Aminoboranes

Aminoboranes are B—N compounds that are analogous to alkenes. Boron is trigonal in aminoboranes, and the three substituents at boron are planar, or very nearly so. Two resonance forms may be written, structures 12-VII and 12-VIII.

$$\text{\Large B—N} \longleftrightarrow \text{\Large B=N}$$

12-VII   12-VIII

In most aminoboranes there is something less than a full double bond between boron and nitrogen, but in some cases high barriers to rotation about the B—N bond indicate that the B—N bond order exceeds 1.0. The multiple bond in aminoboranes is formed by overlap of atomic p orbitals as shown in Fig. 12-11. Average rotational barriers are lower in bis(amino)boranes, indicating competition between the two nitrogen π donors for the empty p orbital of boron. Rotational barriers are lower still for tris(amino)boranes.

Aminoboranes are synthesized by reduction of ammonium salts with tetrahydroborate reagents as in reaction 12-6.1 (followed by dehydrohalogenation of the intermediate amine borane), or by treatment of certain aminoboranes with Grignard reagents, as in Eq. 12-6.3:

$$R_2\ddot{N}\text{—}BCl_2 + 2R'MgX \longrightarrow R_2\ddot{N}\text{—}BR'_2 + 2MgXCl \qquad (12\text{-}6.3)$$

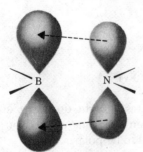

Figure 12-11 The formation of a π bond in aminoboranes as a result of donation of electrons from a filled p orbital on nitrogen to an empty p orbital on boron.

The sequence of reactions 12-6.4 to 12-6.6 serves as a useful example.

$$Me_2HN: + BCl_3 \longrightarrow Me_2HN{\rightarrow}BCl_3 \qquad (12\text{-}6.4)$$

$$Me_2HN{\rightarrow}BCl_3 \longrightarrow Me_2\overset{+}{N}{=}\overset{-}{B}Cl_2 + HCl \qquad (12\text{-}6.5)$$

$$Me_2\overset{+}{N}{=}\overset{-}{B}Cl_2 + 2EtMgCl \longrightarrow Me_2\overset{+}{N}{=}\overset{-}{B}Et_2 + 2MgCl_2 \qquad (12\text{-}6.6)$$

The chief reaction (other than substitution) of aminoboranes is condensation to cyclic systems, as in formation of a dimer, structure 12-IX.

$$
\begin{array}{ccc}
R & & Cl \\
| & & | \\
R\text{---}N & \text{---} & B\text{---}Cl \\
\downarrow & & \uparrow \\
Cl\text{---}B & \text{---} & N\text{---}R \\
| & & | \\
Cl & & R \\
\end{array}
$$

12-IX

Condensation of aminoboranes to cyclic trimers, when accompanied by elimination of either HX or RH, leads to the borazine derivatives.

Borazines

One of the most interesting B—N compounds is *borazine*, $B_3N_3H_6$, structure 12-X.

$$
\begin{array}{c}
\text{H} \\
\text{B} \\
HN \quad\quad NH \\
HB \quad\quad BH \\
N \\
H
\end{array}
$$

12-X

It has an obvious formal resemblance to benzene, and the physical properties of the compounds are similar. However, borazine is much more reactive than benzene and readily undergoes addition reactions such as in Eq. 12-6.7:

$$B_3N_3H_6 + 3HX \longrightarrow (\text{---}H_2N\text{---}BHX\text{---})_3$$

$$X = Cl, OH, OR, \text{ and so on} \qquad (12\text{-}6.7)$$

which do not occur with benzene. Borazine also decomposes slowly and may be hydrolyzed to NH_3 and boric acid at elevated temperatures. As with benzene, π complexes with transition metals may be obtained (Chapter 29); thus hexamethylborazine gives structure 12-XI:

$$\text{12-XI}$$

Borazine and substituted borazines may be synthesized by reactions such as 12-6.8 to 12-6.11.

$$3\ NH_4Cl + 3\ BCl_3 \xrightarrow[140\ °C]{C_6H_5Cl}$$

$$\nearrow B_3N_3H_6 \quad (12\text{-}6.8)$$
$$NaBH_4$$
$$CH_3MgBr$$
$$\searrow B_3N_3H_3(CH_3)_3 \quad (12\text{-}6.9)$$

$$CH_3NH_2 + BCl_3 \xrightarrow[C_6H_5Cl]{Boiling} Cl_3B\cdot NH_2CH_3 \quad (12\text{-}6.10)$$
$$(mp\ 126\text{–}128\ °C)$$

$$3\ Cl_3B\cdot NH_2CH_3 + 6(CH_3)_3N \xrightarrow{Toluene}$$

$$6(CH_3)_3NHCl + \quad (12\text{-}6.11)$$

$$(mp\ 153\text{–}156\ °C)$$

STUDY GUIDE

Study Questions

A. Review

1. Draw the structure of the B_{12} unit that is found in elemental boron.
2. Draw the structures of the cyclic borate anion in $K_3B_3O_6$ and the chain borate anion in $Mg_2B_2O_5$. Indicate the hybridization at each atom in these borate anions.

3. How does boric acid ionize in water? How strong an acid is it?

4. Why is the activity of boric acid increased by the addition of glycerol?

5. How would one best prepare BF_3 in the laboratory?

6. Why is BBr_3 a better Lewis acid than BF_3?

7. Draw the structure of diborane and describe its bonding.

8. Give equations for one useful synthesis of diborane(6).

9. How is sodium borohydride (or tetrahydroborate) prepared?

B. Additional Exercises

1. Review each of the structures of the boron hydrides that have been presented in this chapter and decide which can properly be thought of as a fragment of the icosahedron.

2. The borate anion, $[B_5O_6(OH)_4]^-$, has one tetrahedral boron and four trigonal boron atoms, and has two six-membered rings. Draw the structure.

3. Review the reactions of diborane and prepare the same sort of "reaction wheel" for it that has already been prepared for boric acid (Fig. 12-2).

4. Explain why the barriers to rotation around the B—N bond in the following aminoboranes display the trend $H_2B(—NR_2) > HB(—NR_2)_2 > B(—NR_2)_3$.

5. Propose a structure for the anion $B_3H_8^-$ featured in reactions 12-5.13 and 12-5.14.

6. Draw the structure of the disubstituted product from the reaction of decaborane(14) with CN^-.

7. What are the hybridizations and the geometries of the C and O atoms in the organic derivatives $B(OR)_3$, $B(OCOR)_3$, and $B(OOR)_3$?

8. What is the structure of the anion formed upon deprotonation of decaborane(14)? Which are the acidic hydrogens in decaborane(14) and why?

9. Predict the products of the following reactions:
   (a) $BF_3 + OEt_2$ (b) $BF_3 + H_2O$
   (c) $BCl_3 + ROH$ (d) $B_2H_6 + HCl$
   (e) $B_{10}H_{14} + NR_3$ (f) $B_{10}H_{14} + I_2$
   (g) $LiH + B_2H_6$ (h) $NH_4Cl + LiBH_4$
   (i) $Me_2N—BCl_2 + PhMgBr$ (j) $B_3N_3H_6 + H_2O$
   (k) $B_3N_3H_6 + HBr$ (l) $(Cl—B)_3(NH)_3 + EtMgBr$

10. Suggest a series of reactions for the synthesis of
    (a) Borazine, beginning with boron trichloride.
    (b) Decaborane(14), starting with diborane.
    (c) $[H_2B(NMe_3)_2]^+$, starting with diborane.
    (d) Diethylaminodichloroborane, starting with BCl_3.
    (e) B-Trichloro-N-trimethyl borazine, starting with BCl_3.

11. Suggest a reason for the greater reactivity of borazine than benzene towards addition of HX.

12. Draw the structure of $(Ph_3P)_2CuBH_4$. Carefully show the geometry at P, Cu, and B.

13. Consider the semitopological diagram of $B_{10}H_{14}$ in Fig. 12-6. Account for all of the electrons in the molecule by listing the number of each that is involved in (a) terminal BH groups, (b) bridging BHB groups, (c) open BBB bridge groups, (d) two-electron BB bonds, and (e) closed BBB bonds.

C. Problems from the Literature of Inorganic Chemistry

1. Consider the paper by R. W. Parry, R. W. Rudolph, and D. F. Shriver, *Inorg. Chem.*, **1964**, *3*, 1479–1483.

   (a) Write balanced equations for the symmetrical and unsymmetrical cleavage reactions of tetraborane(10) by a general nucleophile, L.

   (b) Write balanced equations for the symmetrical and unsymmetrical cleavage reactions of tetraborane(10) by $NaBH_4$.

   (c) Write the balanced equations for the symmetrical and unsymmetrical cleavage of tetraborane(10) by $NaBD_4$, and account for the predicted percentage of D label in the products for each case.

   (d) Why have the authors so carefully argued against "exchange" in such reactions or among the reaction products?

   (e) What are the products of the cleavage of tetraborane(10) by NH_3?

2. Consider the comparison of amine boranes and borazines made by O. T. Beachley, Jr., and B. Washburn, *Inorg. Chem.*, **1975**, *14*, 120–123.

   (a) Write balanced chemical equations to represent the reactions that were employed to synthesize

      (i) $H_2ClB \cdot N(CH_3)_3$ and $H_2BrB \cdot N(CH_3)_2H$

      (ii) $H_2CH_3B \cdot N(CH_3)_3$ and $H_2CH_3B \cdot N(CH_3)_2H$

      (iii) $H_2(CN)B \cdot N(CH_3)_3$ and $H_2(CN)B \cdot N(CH_3)_2H$

   (b) Draw the Lewis diagram for each adduct mentioned in (a).

   (c) What reaction takes place between $HgBr_2$ and (i) $H_3B \cdot N(CH_3)_3$ (ii) $H_3B_3N_3H_3$?

   (d) What reaction takes place between AgCN and (i) $H_3B_3N_3H_3$ at 0 °C (ii) $H_3B \cdot N(CH_3)_3$ at 130 °C?

   (e) What mechanistic interpretation do the authors give to the facts in (c)?

   (f) How do π- and σ-bond effects combine in the borazine ring to make the BH group sufficiently hydridic to react with $HgCl_2$?

   (g) What suggestion do the authors make to explain the facts in (d)?

3. Methylation at boron of the *closo*-carborane, $2,4\text{-}C_2B_5H_7$, has been studied by J. F. Ditter, E. B. Klusmann, R. E. Williams, and T. Onak, *Inorg. Chem.*, **1976**, *15*, 1063–1065.

   (a) When methylation was performed with methylchloride in the presence of an excess of $AlCl_3$, which boron atom(s) was methylated to give (i) $MeC_2B_5H_6$ via monomethylation (ii) $Me_2C_2B_5H_5$ via dimethylation (iii) $Me_3C_2B_5H_4$ via trimethylation?

   (b) What do the facts in (a) suggest about the relative availability of electrons (as judged by readiness to react with electrophilic reagents) at the different boron atoms in $C_2B_5H_7$?

   (c) How does its position in the cage influence the electron availability at a boron atom, according to these authors?

SUPPLEMENTARY READING

Brown, H. C., *Boranes in Organic Chemistry*, Cornell University Press, Ithaca, 1972.

Brown, H. C., *Organic Syntheses via Boranes*, Wiley, New York, 1975.

Greenwood, N. N., *Boron*, Pergamon Press, Elmsford, NY, 1975.

Grimes, R. N., *Carboranes*, Academic, New York, 1971.

Grimes, R. N., Ed., *Metal Interactions with Boron Clusters*, Plenum, New York, 1982.

Muetterties, E. L., Ed., *The Chemistry of Boron and its Compounds*, Wiley, New York, 1967.

Muetterties, E. L. Ed., *Boron Hydride Chemistry*, Academic, New York, 1975.

Muetterties, E. L. and Knoth, W. H., *Polyhedral Boranes*, Dekker, New York, 1968.

Niedenzu, K. and Dawson, J. W., *Boron–Nitrogen Compounds*, Springer-Verlag, New York, 1965.

chapter 13

THE GROUP IIIB(13) ELEMENTS: ALUMINUM, GALLIUM, INDIUM, AND THALLIUM

13-1 Introduction

Aluminum is the commonest metallic element in the earth's crust and occurs in rocks such as felspars and micas. More accessible deposits are hydrous oxides such as bauxite ($Al_2O_3 \cdot nH_2O$) and cryolite (Na_3AlF_6). Gallium and In occur only in traces in Al and Zn ores. Thallium, also a rare element, is recovered from flue dusts from the roasting of pyrite and other sulfide ores.

Aluminum metal has many uses and some salts such as the sulfate (ca. 10^8 kg/yr in the USA) are made on a large scale. Gallium finds some use in solid state devices as GaAs. Thallium is used mainly as the Tl^{III} carboxylates in organic synthesis.

The position of the elements and their relation to the Sc, Y, La group is discussed in Chapter 8, where Table 8-3 gives some important properties of the elements.

The elements are more metallic than boron, and the chemistry in compounds is more ionic. Nevertheless, many of the compounds are on the borderline of ionic–covalent character. All four elements give trivalent compounds, but the univalent state becomes increasingly important for Ga, In, and Tl. For Tl the two states are about equally important and the redox system Tl^{I}–Tl^{III} dominates the chemistry. The Tl^+ ion is well defined in solutions.

The main reason for the existence of the univalent state is the decreasing strengths of bonds in MX_3; thus, for the chlorides, the mean bond energies are Ga, 242; In, 206; Tl, 153 kJ mol^{-1}. There is hence an increasing drive for reaction 13-1.1 to occur.

$$MX_3 = MX + X_2 \qquad (13\text{-}1.1)$$

The compounds MX_3 or MR_3 resemble similar BX_3 compounds in that they are Lewis acids, with strengths decreasing in the order   B > Al > Ga > In ~ Tl. However, while all BX_3 compounds are planar monomers, the halides of the other elements have crystal structures in which the coordination number is increased to four or six. Also the lower alkyls of Al are dimers, while Lewis acid adducts may also be five-coordinate like $(Me_3N)_2AlH_3$.

Each of the elements forms an aquo ion, $[M(H_2O)_6]^{3+}$, and gives simple salts and complex compounds in virtually all of which the metals are octahedrally coordinated.

13-2 Occurrence, Isolation, and Properties of the Elements

Aluminum is prepared on a vast scale from bauxite, $Al_2O_3 \cdot nH_2O$ ($n = 1$–3). This is purified by dissolution in aqueous NaOH and reprecipitation as $Al(OH)_3$ using CO_2. The dehydrated product is dissolved in molten cryolite and the melt at 800 to 1000 °C is electrolyzed. Aluminum is a hard, strong, white metal. Although highly electropositive, it is nevertheless resistant to corrosion because a hard, tough film of oxide is formed on the surface. Thick oxide films are often electrolytically applied to aluminum, a process called anodizing; the fresh films can be colored by pigments. Aluminum is soluble in dilute mineral acids, but is "passivated" by concentrated HNO_3. If the protective effect of the oxide film is broken, for example, by scratching or by amalgamation, rapid attack even by water can occur. The metal is readily attacked by hot aqueous NaOH, halogens, and various nonmetals.

Gallium, indium, and *thallium* are usually obtained by electrolysis of aqueous solutions of their salts; for Ga and In this possibility arises because of large overvoltages for hydrogen evolution of these metals. They are soft, white, comparatively reactive metals, dissolving readily in acids. Thallium dissolves only slowly in H_2SO_4 or HCl, since the Tl^I salts formed are only sparingly soluble. Gallium, like Al, is soluble in aqueous NaOH. The elements react rapidly at room temperature, or on warming, with the halogens and with nonmetals such as sulfur.

13-3 Oxides

The only oxide of aluminum is *alumina*, Al_2O_3. However, this simplicity is compensated by the occurrence of polymorphs and hydrated materials whose nature depends on the conditions of preparation. There are two forms of anhydrous Al_2O_3, namely, α-Al_2O_3 and γ-Al_2O_3. Other trivalent metals (e.g., Ga, Fe) form oxides that crystallize in these same two structures. Both have close-packed arrays of oxide ions but differ in the arrangement of the cations.

α-Al_2O_3 is stable at high temperatures and also indefinitely metastable at low temperatures. It occurs in nature as the mineral corundum and may be prepared by heating γ-Al_2O_3 or any hydrous oxide above 1000 °C. Gamma-Al_2O_3 is obtained by dehydration of hydrous oxides at low temperatures ($\sim$450 °C). Alpha-Al_2O_3 is hard and is resistant to hydration and to attack by acids. Gamma-Al_2O_3 readily absorbs water and dissolves in acids; the aluminas used for chromatography and conditioned to different reactivities are γ-Al_2O_3. Large quantities of α-Al_2O_3 are used in industry as a support material for heterogeneous catalysts.

There are several hydrated forms of alumina of stoichiometries from $AlO \cdot OH$ to $Al(OH)_3$. Addition of ammonia to a boiling solution of an aluminum salt produces a form of $AlO \cdot OH$ known as *boehmite*. A second form of $AlO \cdot OH$ occurs in nature as the mineral *diaspore*. The true *hydroxide*, $Al(OH)_3$, is obtained as a crystalline white precipitate when CO_2 is passed into alkaline "aluminate" solutions.

Gallium and indium oxides are similar, but Tl gives only brown-black Tl_2O_3, which decomposes to Tl_2O at 100 °C.

The elements form *mixed oxides* with other metals. Aluminum oxides containing only traces of other metal ions include ruby (Cr^{3+}) and blue sapphire (Fe^{2+}, Fe^{3+}, and Ti^{4+}). Synthetic ruby, blue sapphire, and white sapphire (gem-quality corundum) are manufactured in large quantities. Mixed oxides containing macroscopic proportions of other elements include the minerals *spinel* ($MgAl_2O_4$) and *crysoberyl* ($BeAl_2O_4$). The *spinel structure* is important as a prototype for many other $M^{II}M^{III}_2O_4$ compounds. Compounds such as $NaAlO_2$, which can be made by heating Al_2O_3 with sodium oxalate at 1000 °C, are also ionic mixed oxides.

13-4   Halides

All four halides of each element are known, with one exception. The compound TiI_3, obtained by adding iodine to thallium(I) iodide, is not thallium(III) iodide, but rather thallium(I) triiodide, $Tl^I(I_3)$. This situation may be compared with the nonexistence of iodides of other oxidizing cations such as Cu^{2+} and Fe^{3+}, except that here a lower-valent compound fortuitously has the same stoichiometry as the higher-valent one. The coordination numbers of the halides are shown in Table 13-1. The fluorides of Al, Ga, and In are ionic and high melting (>950 °C), whereas the chlorides, bromides, and iodides have lower melting points. There is some correlation between melting points and coordination number, since the halides with coordination number four consist of discrete dinuclear molecules (Fig. 13-1) and the melting points are low. Thus, the three chlorides have the following melting points $AlCl_3$, 193 °C (at 1700 mm); $GaCl_3$, 78 °C; $InCl_3$, 586 °C. In the vapor, aluminum chloride also is dimeric so that there is a radical change of coordination number on vaporization. The dimer structures persist in the vapor phase at temperatures close to the boiling points but at higher temperatures dissociation occurs, giving triangular monomers analogous to the boron halides.

Table 13-1 Coordination Numbers of Metal Atoms in Group IIIB(13) Halides

	F	Cl	Br	I
Al	6	6	4	4
Ga	6	4	4	4
In	6	6	6	4
Tl	6	6	4	

Figure 13-1 The structures of Al_2Br_6 and In_2I_6.

The covalent halides dissolve readily in nonpolar solvents such as benzene, in which they are dimeric. As Fig. 13-1 shows, the configuration of halogen atoms about each metal atom is distorted tetrahedral. The formation of such dimers is attributable to the tendency of the metal atoms to complete their octets.

The thallium(III) halides vary considerably in thermal stability. Although TlF_3 is stable to 500 °C, $TlCl_3$ loses chlorine at about 40 °C forming TlCl, while $TlBr_3$ loses Br_2 at even lower temperatures to give first "$TlBr_2$," which is actually $Tl^I[Tl^{III}Br_4]$.

The trihalides (fluorides excepted) are strong Lewis acids, and this is one of the most important aspects of their chemistry, as well as that of other MR_3 compounds, such as the alkyls and AlH_3. Adducts are formed quite readily with Lewis bases (including halide ions), the dimeric halides being cleaved thereby to give products such as $Cl_3AlN(CH_3)_3$ and $AlCl_4^-$.

Aluminum chloride and bromide especially are used as catalysts (Friedel–Crafts type) in a variety of reactions. The formation of $AlCl_4^-$ or $AlBr_4^-$ ions is essential to the catalytic action, since in this way carbonium ions are formed (Eq. 13-4.1):

$$RCOCl + AlCl_3 = RCO^+ + AlCl_4^- \quad \text{(ion pair)} \qquad (13\text{-}4.1)$$

and made available for reaction as in Eq. 13-4.2:

$$RCO^+ + C_6H_6 \longrightarrow [RCOC_6H_6]^+ \longrightarrow RCOC_6H_5 + H^+ \qquad (13\text{-}4.2)$$

13-5 The Aqua Ions, Oxo Salts, and Aqueous Chemistry

The elements Al, Ga, In, and Tl form well-defined octahedral aqua ions, $[M(H_2O)_6]^{3+}$, and many salts containing these ions are known, including hydrated halides, sulfates, nitrates, and perchlorates. Phosphates are sparingly soluble.

In aqueous solution, the octahedral ions $[M(H_2O)_6]^{3+}$ are quite acidic. For reaction 13-5.1

$$[M(H_2O)_6]^{3+} = [M(H_2O)_5(OH)]^{2+} + H^+ \qquad (13\text{-}5.1)$$

the constants are $K_a(\text{Al})$, 1.12×10^{-5}; $K_a(\text{Ga})$, 2.5×10^{-3}; $K_a(\text{In})$, 2×10^{-4}; and $K_a(\text{Tl})$, $\sim 7 \times 10^{-2}$. Although little emphasis can be placed on the exact numbers, the orders of magnitude are important, for they show that aqueous solutions of the M^{III} salts are subject to extensive hydrolysis. Indeed, salts of weak acids—sulfides, carbonates, cyanides, acetates, and the like—cannot exist in contact with water.

In addition to this hydrolysis reaction there is also a dimerization as in reaction 13-5.2:

$$2\text{AlOH}^{2+}(\text{aq}) = [\text{Al}_2(\text{OH})_2]^{4+}(\text{aq}) \qquad K = 600\ M^{-1}\ (30\ °\text{C}) \qquad (13\text{-}5.2)$$

More complex species of the general formula $\text{Al}[\text{Al}_3(\text{OH})_8]_m^{m+3}$ have also been postulated and some, such as $[\text{Al}_{13}\text{O}_4(\text{OH})_{24}(\text{H}_2\text{O})_{12}]^{7+}$, have been identified in crystalline basic salts.

An important class of aluminum salts, the *alums*, are structural prototypes and give their name to a large number of analogous salts formed by other elements. They have the general formula $\text{MAl}(\text{SO}_4)_2 \cdot 12\text{H}_2\text{O}$ in which M is practically any common univalent, monatomic cation except for Li^+, which is too small to be accommodated without loss of stability of the structure. The crystals are made up of $[\text{M}(\text{H}_2\text{O})_6]^+$, $[\text{Al}(\text{H}_2\text{O})_6]^{3+}$, and two SO_4^{2-} ions. Salts of the same type, $\text{M}^I\text{M}^{III}(\text{SO}_4)_2 \cdot 12\text{H}_2\text{O}$, having the same structures are formed by other M^{3+} ions, including those of Ti, V, Cr, Mn, Fe, Co, Ga, In, Rh, and Ir. All such compounds are referred to as alums. The term is used so generally that those alums containing aluminum are redundantly designated aluminum alums.

Thallium carboxylates, particularly the acetate and trifluoroacetate, which can be obtained by dissolution of the oxide in the acid, are extensively used in organic synthesis. The trifluoroacetate will directly thallate (cf. mercuration, Chapter 29) aromatic compounds to give aryl thallium ditrifluoroacetates, for example, $\text{C}_6\text{H}_5\text{Tl}(\text{OOCCF}_3)_2$. It also acts as an oxidant, converting para substituted phenols into *p*-quinones, for example.

The hydroxides of *aluminates and gallates* are amphoteric:

$$\text{Al}(\text{OH})_3(\text{s}) = \text{Al}^{3+} + 3\ \text{OH}^- \qquad K \approx 5 \times 10^{-33} \qquad (13\text{-}5.3)$$

$$\text{Al}(\text{OH})_3(\text{s}) = \text{AlO}_2^- + \text{H}^+ + \text{H}_2\text{O} \qquad K \approx 4 \times 10^{-13} \qquad (13\text{-}5.4)$$

$$\text{Ga}(\text{OH})_3(\text{s}) = \text{Ga}^{3+} + 3\ \text{OH}^- \qquad K \approx 5 \times 10^{-37} \qquad (13\text{-}5.5)$$

$$\text{Ga}(\text{OH})_3(\text{s}) = \text{GaO}_2^- + \text{H}^+ + \text{H}_2\text{O} \qquad K \approx \quad 10^{-15} \qquad (13\text{-}5.6)$$

Like the oxides these also dissolve in bases as well as in acids. By contrast the oxides and hydroxides of In and Tl are purely basic. According to Raman spectra, the main aluminate species from pH 8 to 12 appears to be an OH bridged polymer with octahedral Al, but at pH > 13 and concentrations below $1.5\ M$ the tetrahedral $\text{Al}(\text{OH})_4^-$ ion is present. Above $1.5\ M$ there is condensation to give the ion $[(\text{HO})_3\text{AlOAl}(\text{OH})_3]^{2-}$. This occurs in the crystalline salt $\text{K}_2[\text{Al}_2\text{O}(\text{OH})_6]$ and has an angular Al—O—Al bridge.

Figure 13-2 The cubic structure of cryolite Na_3AlF_6.

13-6 Coordination Compounds

The trivalent elements form four-, five- and six-coordinate complexes, which may be cationic, like $[Al(H_2O)_6]^{3+}$ or $[Al(OSMe_2)_6]^{3+}$, neutral, for example, $AlCl_3(NMe_3)_2$, or anionic, like $[AlF_6]^{3-}$ and $[In(SO_4)_2]^-$.

One of the most important salts is *cryolite* whose structure (Fig. 13-2) is adopted by many other salts that contain small cations and large octahedral anions and, with reversal of cations and anions, by many salts of the same type as $[Co(NH_3)_6]I_3$. It is closely related to the structures adopted by many compounds of the types $M_2^+[AB_6]^{2-}$ and $[XY_6]^{2+}Z_2^-$. The last two structures are essentially the fluorite (or antifluorite) structures (see Fig. 4-1), except that the anions (or cations) are octahedra whose axes are oriented parallel to the cube edges. The relationship of the two structures can be seen in Fig. 13-2, since the Na^+ ions have been indicated by both open $\bigcirc$ and marked $\otimes$ circles. If all of the marked circles (one at the center and one on each of the cube edges) in Fig. 13-2 are removed, the cryolite structure reduces to the $M_2^+[AB_6]^{2-}$ fluorite-type structure.

Many of the important octahedral complexes are those containing chelate rings, typical ones containing β-diketones, pyrocatechol (structure 13-I), dicarboxylic acids (structure 13-II), and 8-quinolinol (structure 13-III). The

$$\left[\left(\begin{array}{c}\text{O}\\\text{O}\end{array}\right)M\right]_3^{3-} \qquad \left[\left(\begin{array}{c}\text{O}=\text{C}-\text{O}\\\text{O}=\text{C}-\text{O}\end{array}\right)M\right]_3^{3-} \qquad \left(\begin{array}{c}\text{O}\\\text{N}\end{array}\right)M$$

13-I   13-II   13-III

neutral complexes are soluble in organic solvents, but insoluble in water. The acetylacetonates have low melting points (<200 °C) and vaporize without decomposition. The anionic complexes are isolated as the salts of large univalent cations. The 8-quinolinolates are used for analytical purposes.

The four elements form *alkoxides,* but only those of aluminum are important. The isopropoxide is widely used in organic chemistry to catalyze the reduction of aldehydes and ketones by alcohols or vice versa (Meerwein–Ponndorf–Oppenauer–Verley reactions). Alkoxides can be made by reactions 13-6.1 and 13-6.2:

$$\text{Al} + 3\text{ROH} \xrightarrow[\text{catalyst, warm}]{1\% \text{ HgCl}_2 \text{ as}} (\text{RO})_3\text{Al} + \tfrac{3}{2}\text{H}_2 \qquad (13\text{-}6.1)$$

$$\text{AlCl}_3 + 3\text{RONa} \xrightarrow{\text{ROH}} (\text{RO})_3\text{Al} + 3\text{NaCl} \qquad (13\text{-}6.2)$$

The alkoxides hydrolyze vigorously in water. The *tert*-butoxide is a cyclic dimer (structure 13-IV) in solvents, whereas the isopropoxide is tetrameric

13-IV   13-V

(structure 13-V) at ordinary temperatures but trimeric at elevated temperatures. Terminal and bridging alkoxyl groups can be distinguished by nmr spectra. Other alkoxides form dimers and trimers.

13-7 Complex Hydrides

Important hydrides of Al are the salts containing the tetrahedral anion AlH_4^-, which is similar in some ways to BH_4^-. Gallium also forms a tetrahydrido anion. The thermal and chemical stabilities of these tetrahydrido anions vary with the ability of the MH_3 groups to act as a H^- acceptor as in reaction 13-7.1.

$$\text{MH}_3 + \text{H}^- = \text{MH}_4^- \qquad (13\text{-}7.1)$$

The order is B > Al > Ga. Thus LiGaH$_4$ decomposes slowly even at 25 °C to LiH, Ga, and H$_2$ and is a milder reducing agent than LiAlH$_4$. Similarly, although BH_4^- is stable in water, the Al and Ga salts are rapidly and often explosively hydrolyzed by water:

$$MH_4^- + 4H_2O = 4H_2 + M(OH)_3 + OH^- \qquad (13\text{-}7.2)$$

The most important compound is *lithium tetrahydridoaluminate*, which is widely used in both organic and inorganic chemistry as a reducing agent. It accomplishes many otherwise tedious or difficult reductions, for example, —CO_2H to —CH_2OH. It is a nonvolatile, crystalline solid, white when pure but usually grey. It is stable below 120 °C and is soluble in diethyl ether, THF, and glymes.

Both aluminum and gallium salts are made by reaction of the chloride with lithium hydride as in reaction 13-7.3:

$$4LiH + MCl_3 \xrightarrow{Et_2O} LiMH_4 + 3LiCl \qquad (13\text{-}7.3)$$

The sodium salt can be obtained by direct interactions of the elements, as in reaction 13-7.4:

$$Na + Al + 2H_2 \xrightarrow[150\ °C/2000\ psi]{THF} NaAlH_4 \qquad (13\text{-}7.4)$$

$NaAlH_4$ is precipitated by the addition of toluene, and it can be converted to the lithium salt by recrystallization in the presence of LiCl from ether, as in Eq. 13-7.5:

$$NaAlH_4 + LiCl \xrightarrow{Et_2O} NaCl(s) + LiAlH_4 \qquad (13\text{-}7.5)$$

13-8 Lower Valent Compounds

Since the outer electron configuration is ns^2np^1, univalent compounds are, in principle, possible. Aluminum forms such species only at high temperature in the gas phase, for example,

$$AlCl_3(s) + 2Al(s) \rightleftharpoons 3AlCl(g) \qquad (13\text{-}8.1)$$

Some gallium(I) and indium(I) compounds are known, the so-called dichloride "$GaCl_2$" being actually $Ga^I[Ga^{III}Cl_4]$.

Thallium has a well-defined unipositive state. In aqueous solution it is distinctly more stable than Tl^{III}

$$Tl^{3+} + 2e^- = Tl^+ \qquad E^0 = +1.25\ V \qquad (13\text{-}8.2)$$

The Tl^+ ion is not very sensitive to pH, although the Tl^{3+} ion is extensively hydrolyzed to $TlOH^{2+}$ and the colloidal oxide even at pH 1–2.5. The redox potential is, hence, very dependent on pH as well as on the presence of complexing anions. For example, the presence of Cl^- stabilizes Tl^{3+} more (by formation of complexes) than Tl^+ and the potential is thereby lowered.

The colorless Tl^+ ion has a radius of 1.54 Å, comparable to those of K^+, Rb^+, and Ag^+ (1.44, 1.58, and 1.27 Å). Thus it resembles the alkali ions in some ways and the Ag^+ ion in others. It may replace K^+ in certain enzymes and has potential use as a probe for potassium. In crystalline salts, the Tl^+ ion is usually six or eight coordinate. The yellow hydroxide is unstable, giving the black oxide, Tl_2O, at about 100 °C. The oxide and hydroxide are soluble in water giving strongly basic solutions. These absorb carbon dioxide from the air, although TlOH is a weaker base than KOH. Many thallium(I) salts, for example, Tl_2SO_4, Tl_2CO_3, or $TlCO_2CH_3$, have solubilities somewhat lower than those of the corresponding K^+ salts, but otherwise they are similar to and quite often isomorphous with them. Thallium(I) fluoride is soluble in water but the other halides are sparingly soluble. Thallium(I) chloride also resembles AgCl in being photosensitive and darkening on exposure to light, but differs in being insoluble in ammonia. All thallium compounds are exceedingly poisonous.

STUDY GUIDE

Study Questions

A. Review

1. What is bauxite, and how is it purified for Al production?
2. Why is aluminum resistant to air and water, even though it is very electropositive?
3. What is the formula and structure of (a) corundum, (b) the mineral spinel?
4. What is the structure of the trihalide dimers, M_2X_6? What happens to these molecules at high temperatures?
5. What is an alum? What species are present in a crystalline alum?
6. For cryolite, give the formula, structure, and chief industrial use.
7. Compare the properties of B_2O_3 and Al_2O_3.
8. How is $LiAlH_4$ prepared? Why does it explode with water, while $NaBH_4$ does not?
9. Write equations to show that the hydroxides of Al and Ga are amphoteric.

B. Additional Exercises

1. Discuss the reasons why $Tl^{III}I_3$ is unstable relative to Tl^II_3, whereas the opposite is true for Al, Ga, and In.
2. How might one establish that the true nature of "$GaCl_2$" is actually $Ga^I[Ga^{III}Cl_4]$?
3. Interaction of Al with alcohols using $HgCl_2$ as a catalyst gives alkoxides of Al that are tetrameric in solution. Write a structure for the aluminum–isopropoxide tetramer.
4. Show, with equations, how $AlCl_3$ functions as a Friedel–Crafts catalyst.
5. Why is the Tl^+/Tl^{3+} electrochemical potential sensitive to pH and to the presence of complexing anions?
6. Explain the preference shown in Table 13-1 of six coordination for fluorides and chlorides *versus* four coordination for bromides and iodides.

C.   Questions from the Literature of Inorganic Chemistry

1. Complexes of the type $InCl_3 \cdot 3L$ and $TlX_3 \cdot 2L$ were studied by B. F. G. Johnson and R. A. Walton, *Inorg. Chem.*, **1966**, *5*, 49–53.

    (a) Write balanced equations for the reactions that were employed in the syntheses of these two types of compounds.

    (b) Suggest a structure for $TlCl_4^-$, for $TlCl_3 \cdot 2py$, and for $InCl_3 \cdot 3py$.

2. What evidence do the authors present for the presence of a metal–metal bond in the compound $Ga_2I_4 \cdot 2(diox)$? See J. C. Beamish, R. W. H. Small, and I. J. Worrall, *Inorg. Chem.*, **1979**, *18*, 220–223.

3. Consider the paper by E. R. Alton, R. G. Montemayer, and R. W. Parry, *Inorg. Chem.*, **1974**, *13*, 2267–2270.

    (a) Which of the Lewis bases featured in this study ($:PF_3$, $:PCl_3$, $:C{\equiv}O:$, or $:NH_3$) form complexes with the Lewis acids (i) BF_3 (ii) $AlCl_3$ (iii) Me_3Al?

    (b) What conclusions in reference to σ-base strength do the authors reach for PF_3 versus CO?

    (c) What is the *distortion energy* that the authors mention, and how can this concept be used to explain a higher stability for $F_3P:AlCl_3$ than for $F_3P:BF_3$?

SUPPLEMENTARY READING

Carty, A. J. and Tuck, D. J., "Coordination Chemistry of Indium," *Prog. Inorg. Chem.*, **1975**, *19*, 243.

Cucinella, S., Mazzei, A., and Marconi, W., "Synthesis and Reactions of Aluminum Hydride Derivatives," *Inorg. Chim. Acta Rev.*, **1970**, *4*, 51.

Greenwood, N. N., "The Chemistry of Gallium," *Adv. Inorg. Chem. Radiochem.*, **1963**, *5*, 91.

Lee, A. G., *The Chemistry of Thallium*, Elsevier, Amsterdam, 1971.

Lee, A. G., "Coordination Chemistry of Thallium (I)," *Coord. Chem. Rev.*, **1972**, *8*, 289.

Olah, G. A., *Friedel–Crafts Chemistry*, Wiley, New York, 1973.

Sheka, I. A., Chans, I. S., and Mityureva, T. T., *The Chemistry of Gallium*, Elsevier, Amsterdam, 1966.

Walton, R. A., "Coordination Complexes of the Thallium(III) Halides and Their Behavior in Non-Aqueous Media," *Coord. Chem. Rev.*, **1971**, *6*, 1–25.

chapter **14**

CARBON

14-1 Introduction

There are more known compounds of carbon than of any other element except hydrogen. Most are best regarded as organic chemicals. In this chapter we consider certain compounds traditionally considered "inorganic" and in Chapter 29 we discuss organometallic or, more precisely, organoelement compounds in which there are bonds to carbon such as Fe—C, P—C, Si—C, Al—C, and so on.

The electronic structure of C in its ground state is $1s^2 2s^2 2p^2$ so that to accommodate the normal four covalence the atom must be promoted to a valence state $2s2p_x2p_y2p_z$ (see Section 3-2). The ion C^{4+} does not arise in any normal chemical process, but C^{4-} may possibly exist in some carbides of the most electropositive metals.

Some cations, anions, and radicals have been detected as transient species in organic reactions, and certain stable species of these types are known. The ions are known as *carbonium* ions, for example, $(C_6H_5)_3C^+$ or *carbanions*, for example, $(NC)_3C^-$. They can be stable only when the charge is extensively delocalized onto the attached groups.

Divalent carbon species or *carbenes* ($:CR_1R_2$) play a role in many reactions, but they are highly reactive. They can be trapped by binding to transition metals and many metal carbene compounds are known (Section 29-17).

The divalent species of some other Group IVB(14) elements such as $:SiF_2$ or $:SnCl_2$ can be considered to have carbene-like behavior.

A unique feature of carbon is its propensity for bonding to itself in chains or rings, not only with single bonds, C—C, but also containing multiple bonds, C=C or C≡C. Sulfur and silicon are the elements next most inclined to *catenation*, as this self-binding is called, but they are far inferior to carbon. The reason for the thermal stability of carbon chains is the intrinsic high strength of the C—C single bond, 356 kJ mol^{-1}. The Si—Si bond (226 kJ mol^{-1}) is weaker but another important factor is that Si—O bonds (368 kJ mol^{-1}) are much stronger than C—O bonds (336 kJ mol^{-1}). Hence, given the necessary activation energy, compounds with Si—Si links are converted very exothermically into ones with Si—O bonds.

14-2   Allotropy of Carbon: Diamond and Graphite

The two best-known forms of carbon, diamond and graphite, differ in their physical and chemical properties because of differences in the arrangement and bonding of the atoms (Section 8-5). Diamond (3.51 g cm^{-3}) is denser than graphite (2.22 g cm^{-3}), but graphite is more stable, by 2.9 kJ mol^{-1} at 300 K and 1-atm pressure. From the densities, it follows that to transform graphite into diamond, pressure must be applied. From the thermodynamic properties of the allotropes it is estimated that they would be in equilibrium at 300 K under a pressure of ~15,000 atm. Because equilibrium is attained extremely slowly at this temperature, the diamond structure persists under ordinary conditions.

Diamonds can be produced from graphite only by the action of high pressure, and high temperatures are necessary for an appreciable rate of conversion. Naturally occurring diamonds must have been formed when those conditions were provided by geological processes.

Only in 1955 was a successful synthesis of diamonds from graphite reported. Although graphite can be directly converted into diamond at ca. 3000 K and pressures above 125 kbar, in order to obtain useful rates of conversion, a transition metal catalyst such as Cr, Fe, or Pt is used. It appears that a thin film of molten metal forms on the graphite, dissolving some and reprecipitating it as diamond, which is less soluble. Diamonds up to 0.1 carat (20 mg) of high industrial quality can be routinely produced at competitive prices. Some gem quality diamonds have also been made but the cost, thus far, has been prohibitive. Diamond will burn in air at 600 to 800 °C but its chemical reactivity is much lower than that of graphite or amorphous carbon.

Graphite

The many forms of amorphous carbon, such as charcoals, soot, and lampblack, are all actually microcrystalline forms of graphite. The physical properties of such materials are mainly determined by the nature and extent of their surface areas. The finely divided forms, which present relatively vast surfaces with only partially saturated attractive forces, readily absorb large amounts of gases and solutes from solution. Active carbons impregnated with palladium, platinum, or other metals are widely used as industrial catalysts.

An important aspect of graphite technology is the production of very strong fibers by pyrolysis, at 1500 °C or above, of oriented organic polymer fibers, for example, those of polyacrylonitrile, polyacrylate esters, or cellulose. When incorporated into plastics the reinforced materials are light and of great strength. Other forms of graphite such as foams, foils, or whiskers can also be made.

The loose layered structure of graphite allows many molecules and ions to penetrate the layers to form what are called *intercalation* or *lamellar compounds*. Some of these may be formed spontaneously when the reactant and graphite are brought together. Examples of reactants are the alkali metals, halogens, and metal halides and oxides, for example, $FeCl_3$ and MoO_3.

Carbides

The direct interaction of carbon with metals or metal oxides at high temperatures gives compounds generally called carbides. Those of electropositive metals behave as though they contain C^{4-} or C_2^{2-} ions, and react with water to give hydrocarbons, for example,

$$Al_4C_3 + 12H_2O = 4Al(OH)_3 + 3CH_4 \qquad (14\text{-}2.1)$$

$$Ca^{2+}C_2^{2-} + 2H_2O = Ca(OH)_2 + HC{\equiv}CH \qquad (14\text{-}2.2)$$

Transition metals give *interstitial carbides* in which carbon atoms occupy octahedral holes in close-packed arrays of metal atoms. Such materials are commonly very hard, electrically conducting, and have very high melting points (3000–4800 °C). The smaller metals Cr, Mn, Fe, Co, and Ni give carbides that are intermediate between typically ionic and interstitial carbides and these are hydrolyzed by water or dilute acids.

Silicon and boron form SiC and B_4C, which are also extremely hard, infusible, and chemically inert. Silicon carbide has a diamond-like structure in which C and Si atoms are each tetrahedrally surrounded by four of the other kind. Under the name *carborundum* it is used in cutting tools and abrasives.

14-3 Carbon Monoxide

This colorless toxic gas (bp − 190 °C) is formed when carbon is burned in a deficiency of oxygen. At all temperatures there is the equilibrium

$$2CO(g) = C(s) + CO_2(g) \qquad (14\text{-}3.1)$$

but it is rapidly attained only at elevated temperatures. Carbon monoxide is made commercially along with hydrogen (Section 9-1) by steam reforming or partial combustion of hydrocarbons and by reaction 14-3.2:

$$CO_2 + H_2 = CO + H_2O \qquad (14\text{-}3.2)$$

A mixture of CO and H_2 ("synthesis gas") is very important commercially, being used in the hydroformylation process (Section 30-9) and for the synthesis of methanol. Carbon monoxide is also formed when carbon is used in reduction processes, for example, of phosphate rock to give phosphorus (Section 17-2), in automobile exhausts, and the like. Carbon monoxide is also released by certain marine plants and it occurs naturally in the atmosphere.

Carbon monoxide is formally the anhydride of formic acid (HCO_2H), but this is not an important aspect of its chemistry. Although CO is an exceedingly weak base, one of its important properties is the ability to act as a ligand toward transition metals. The metal—CO bond involves a certain type of multiple bonding, $d\pi–p\pi$ bonding discussed in Chapter 28. The toxicity of CO arises from this ability to bind to the Fe atom in hemoglobin (Section 31-4) in the blood. Only iron and nickel react directly with CO (Chapter 28) under practical conditions.

14-4   Carbon Dioxide and Carbonic Acid

Carbon dioxide is present in the atmosphere (300 ppm), in volcanic gases, and in supersaturated solution in certain spring waters. It is released on a large scale by fermentation processes, limestone calcination, and all forms of combustion of carbon and carbon compounds. It is involved in geochemical cycles as well as in photosynthesis. In the laboratory it can be made by the action of heat or acids on carbonates. Solid carbon dioxide (sublimes $-78.5\ °C$) or "dry ice" is used for refrigeration.

Carbon dioxide is the anhydride of the most important simple acid of carbon, *carbonic acid*. For many purposes, the following acid dissociation constants are given for aqueous carbonic acid:

$$\frac{[H^+][HCO_3^-]}{[H_2CO_3]} = 4.16 \times 10^{-7}$$

$$\frac{[H^+][CO_3^{2-}]}{[HCO_3^-]} = 4.84 \times 10^{-11}$$

The equilibrium quotient in the first equation is incorrect because not all the CO_2 dissolved and undissociated is present as H_2CO_3. The greater part of the dissolved CO_2 is only loosely hydrated, so that the correct first dissociation constant, using the real concentration of H_2CO_3, has the much larger value of about 2×10^{-4}, more in keeping (see Section 7-12) with the structure $(HO)_2CO$.

The rate at which CO_2 comes into equilibrium with H_2CO_3 and its dissociation products when passed into water is measurably slow. This is why we can distinguish analytically between H_2CO_3 and the loosely hydrated $CO_2(aq)$. This slowness is of great importance in biological, analytical, and industrial chemistry.

The slow reaction can be shown by addition of a saturated aqueous solution of CO_2, on the one hand, and of dilute acetic acid, on the other, to solutions of dilute NaOH containing phenolphthalein indicator. The acetic acid neutralization is instantaneous, whereas with the CO_2 neutralization, it takes several seconds for the color to fade.

The hydration of CO_2 occurs by two paths. For pH $<$ 8, the principal mechanism is direct hydration of CO_2 according to Eq. 14-4.1, followed by a rapid acid–base reaction to give bicarbonate:

$$CO_2 + H_2O = H_2CO_3 \qquad \text{(Slow)} \qquad (14\text{-}4.1)$$

$$H_2CO_3 + OH^- = HCO_3^- + H_2O \qquad \text{(Instantaneous)} \qquad (14\text{-}4.2)$$

The rate law for this process is first order:

$$\frac{-d[CO_2]}{dt} = k_{CO_2}[CO_2] \qquad k_{CO_2} = 0.03\ \text{s}^{-1} \qquad (14\text{-}4.3)$$

At pH > 10, the predominant reaction of CO_2 is by direct attack with OH^-, as in reaction 14-4.4, followed by a rapid acid–base reaction to give carbonate:

$$CO_2 + OH^- = HCO_3^- \qquad \text{(Slow)} \qquad (14\text{-}4.4)$$

$$HCO_3^- + OH^- = CO_3^{2-} + H_2O \qquad \text{(Instantaneous)} \qquad (14\text{-}4.5)$$

for which the rate law is

$$\frac{-d[CO_2]}{dt} = k_{OH^-}[OH^-][CO_2] \qquad k_{OH^-} = 8500 \text{ M}^{-1}\text{s}^{-1} \qquad (14\text{-}4.6)$$

Because k_{OH^-} is so much larger than k_{CO_2}, it can be considered that the mechanism given by reactions 14-4.4 and 14-4.5 represents base catalysis of the CO_2 hydrolysis mechanism given by Eqs. 14-4.1 and 14-4.2. In the pH range 8–10, both mechanisms operate.

For each hydration process there is a corresponding dehydration reaction:

$$H_2CO_3 \longrightarrow H_2O + CO_2 \qquad k_{H_2CO_3} = 20 \text{ s}^{-1} \qquad (14\text{-}4.7)$$

$$HCO_3^- \longrightarrow CO_2 + OH^- \qquad k_{HCO_3^-} = 2 \times 10^{-4} \text{ s}^{-1} \qquad (14\text{-}4.8)$$

Hence, for the overall equilibrium represented by Eq. 14-4.9:

$$H_2CO_3 \rightleftharpoons CO_2 + H_2O \qquad (14\text{-}4.9)$$

the equilibrium constant can be determined to be

$$K = \frac{[CO_2]}{[H_2CO_3]} = \frac{k_{H_2CO_3}}{k_{CO_2}} = \text{ca. } 660 \qquad (14\text{-}4.10)$$

It follows from the large value of K in Eq. 14-4.10 that the true ionization constant of H_2CO_3, K_a, is greater than the apparent constant as noted previously.

14-5   Compounds with C—N Bonds; Cyanides and Related Compounds

An important area of "inorganic" carbon chemistry is that of compounds with C—N bonds. The most important species are the cyanide, cyanate, and thiocyanate ions and their derivatives.

Cyanogen, (CN)₂. This flammable gas (bp −21 °C) is stable despite the fact that it is highly endothermic ($\Delta H_f^\circ = 297$ kJ mol^{-1}). It can be obtained by catalytic gas phase oxidation of HCN by NO_2

$$2HCN + NO_2 \longrightarrow (CN)_2 + NO + H_2O \qquad (14\text{-}5.1)$$

$$NO + \tfrac{1}{2}O_2 \longrightarrow NO_2 \qquad (14\text{-}5.2)$$

Cyanogen can also be obtained from CN^- by aqueous oxidation using Cu^{2+} (cf. the Cu^{2+}–I^- reaction):

$$Cu^{2+} + 2CN^- \longrightarrow CuCN + \tfrac{1}{2}(CN)_2 \qquad (14\text{-}5.3)$$

or acidified peroxodisulfate. Dry $(CN)_2$ is made by the reaction:

$$Hg(CN)_2 + HgCl_2 \longrightarrow Hg_2Cl_2 + (CN)_2 \qquad (14\text{-}5.4)$$

Although pure $(CN)_2$ is stable, the impure gas may polymerize at 300 to 500 °C. Cyanogen dissociates into CN radicals and, like halogens, can oxidatively add to lower-valent metal atoms (Chapter 30) giving dicyano complexes, for example,

$$(Ph_3P)_4Pd + (CN)_2 \longrightarrow (Ph_3P)_2Pd(CN)_2 + 2Ph_3P \qquad (14\text{-}5.5)$$

A further resemblance to the halogens is the disproportionation in basic solution:

$$(CN)_2 + 2OH^- \longrightarrow CN^- + OCN^- + H_2O \qquad (14\text{-}5.6)$$

Thermodynamically this reaction can occur in acid solution but is rapid only in base. A stoichiometric mixture of O_2 and $(CN)_2$ burns producing one of the hottest flames (ca. 5050 K) known from a chemical reaction.

Hydrogen Cyanide. HCN, like the hydrogen halides, is a covalent, molecular substance, but capable of dissociation in aqueous solution. It is an extremely poisonous (though less so than H_2S), colorless gas and is evolved when cyanides are treated with acids. Liquid HCN (bp 25.6 °C) has a very high dielectric constant (107 at 25 °C) that is due (as for H_2O) to association of the polar molecules by hydrogen bonding. Liquid HCN is unstable and can polymerize violently in the absence of stabilizers. In aqueous solutions polymerization is induced by ultraviolet light.

Hydrogen cyanide is thought to have been one of the small molecules in the earth's primeval atmosphere and to have been an important source or intermediate in the formation of biologically important chemicals. For example, under pressure, with traces of water and ammonia, HCN pentamerizes to adenine.

In aqueous solution, HCN is a very weak acid, $pK_{25°C} = 9.21$, and solutions of soluble cyanides are extensively hydrolyzed, but the pure liquid is a strong acid.

Hydrogen cyanide is made industrially from CH_4 and NH_3 by the reactions

$$2CH_4 + 3O_2 + 2NH_3 \xrightarrow[> 800\,°C]{\text{Catalyst}} 2HCN + 6H_2O \qquad (14\text{-}5.7)$$

$$\Delta H = -475 \text{ kJ mol}^{-1}$$

or

$$CH_4 + NH_3 \xrightarrow[\text{Pt}]{1200\,°C} HCN + 3H_2 \qquad \Delta H = +240 \text{ kJ mol}^{-1} \qquad (14\text{-}5.8)$$

Hydrogen cyanide has many industrial uses. It may be added directly to alkenes; for example, butadiene gives adiponitrile, $NC(CH_2)_4CN$ (for nylon), in the presence of zero-valent Ni alkylphosphite catalysts that operate by oxidative–addition and transfer reactions (Chapter 30).

Cyanides. Sodium cyanide is manufactured by the fusion of calcium cyanamide with carbon and sodium carbonate:

$$CaCN_2 + C + Na_2CO_3 \longrightarrow CaCO_3 + 2NaCN \qquad (14\text{-}5.9)$$

The cyanide is leached with water. The $CaCN_2$ is made in an impure form contaminated with CaO, CaC_2, C, and so on, by the interaction:

$$CaC_2 + N_2 \xrightarrow{\text{ca. } 1100\ ^\circ C} CaNCN + C \qquad (14\text{-}5.10)$$

The linear NCN^{2-} ion is isostructural and isoelectronic with CO_2. Cyanamide itself, H_2NCN, can be made by acidification of CaNCN. The commercial product is the dimer, $H_2NC(=NH)NHCN$, which also contains much of the tautomer containing the substituted *carbodiimide group*, $H_2N-C(=NH)-N=C=NH$. Organocarbodiimides are important synthetic reagents in organic chemistry and $CH_3N=C=NCH_3$ is stable enough to be isolated.

Sodium cyanide can also be obtained by the reaction

$$NaNH_2 + C \xrightarrow{500\text{--}600\ ^\circ C} NaCN + H_2 \qquad (14\text{-}5.11)$$

Cyanides of electropositive metals are water soluble but those of Ag^I, Hg^I, and Pb^{II} are very insoluble. The cyanide ion is of great importance as a ligand (Chapter 28), and many cyano complexes are known of transition metals, Zn, Cd, Hg, and so on; some, like $Ag(CN)_2^-$ and $Au(CN)_2^-$, are of technical importance and others are employed analytically. The complexes sometimes resemble halogeno complexes, for example, $Hg(CN)_4^{2-}$ and $HgCl_4^{2-}$, but other types exist. Fusion of alkali cyanides with sulfur gives the *thiocyanate* ion, SCN^-.

14-6   Compounds with C—S Bonds

Carbon disulfide, CS_2, is a very toxic liquid (bp 46 °C), usually pale yellow and is prepared on a large scale by the interaction of methane and sulfur over silica or alumina catalysts at ~1000 °C.

$$CH_4 + 4S = CS_2 + 2H_2S \qquad (14\text{-}6.1)$$

In addition to its high flammability in air, CS_2 is a very reactive molecule and has an extensive chemistry, much of it organic in nature. It is used to prepare carbon tetrachloride industrially:

$$CS_2 + 3Cl_2 \longrightarrow CCl_4 + S_2Cl_2 \qquad (14\text{-}6.2)$$

Carbon disulfide is one of the small molecules that readily undergo the "insertion reaction" (Chapter 30) where the $-S-\overset{\overset{\textstyle \|}{\textstyle }}{C}-$ group is inserted be-

$$\overset{\|}{S}$$

tween Sn—N, Co—Co, or other bonds. Thus with titanium dialkylamides, dithiocarbamates are obtained:

$$Ti(NR_2)_4 + 4CS_2 \longrightarrow Ti(S_2CNR_2)_4 \qquad (14\text{-}6.3)$$

The CS_2 molecule can also serve as a ligand, being either bound as a donor through sulfur or added oxidatively (Chapter 30) to give a three-membered ring as in structure 14-I:

$$
\begin{array}{c}
Ph_3P \qquad S \\
\diagdown \diagup\diagdown \\
Pt \\
\diagup \diagdown \diagup \\
Ph_3P \qquad C \\
\diagdown\diagdown \\
S
\end{array}
$$

14-I

Important reactions of CS_2 involve nucleophilic attacks on carbon by the ions RO^- and HS^- and by primary or secondary amines, which lead, in basic solution, respectively, to xanthates, thiocarbonates, and dithiocarbamates, for example:

$$
\left.\begin{array}{l}
RO^- \\[4pt]
HS^- \\[4pt]
R_2HN
\end{array}\right\} +
\begin{array}{c}
S \\
\| \\
C \\
\| \\
S
\end{array}
\longrightarrow
\left\{\begin{array}{ll}
ROCS_2^- & \text{Xanthate} \qquad (14\text{-}6.4) \\[4pt]
CS_3^{2-} & \text{Thiocarbonate} \qquad (14\text{-}6.5) \\[4pt]
R_2NCS_2^- & \text{Dithiocarbamate} \qquad (14\text{-}6.6)
\end{array}\right.
$$

Dithiocarbamates are normally prepared as Na salts by the action of primary or secondary amines on CS_2 in the presence of NaOH. The Zn, Mn, and Fe dithiocarbamates are used as agricultural fungicides, and Zn salts are used as accelerators in the vulcanization of rubber.

Dithiocarbamates form many complexes with metals. The CS_2^- group in dithiocarbamates, as well as in xanthates, thioxanthates, and thiocarbonates, is usually chelated (as in structure 14-II), but monodentate and bridging dithiocarbamates are known.

$$
\begin{array}{c}
\qquad S \\
\qquad \diagup \diagdown \\
M \qquad C-X \\
\qquad \diagdown \diagup \\
\qquad S
\end{array}
\qquad
\begin{array}{l}
X = NHR \text{ or } NR_2, \\[4pt]
\qquad OR \text{ or } SR, \\[4pt]
\qquad O, S, \text{ or } S-S
\end{array}
$$

14-II

On oxidation of aqueous solutions by H_2O_2, Cl_2, or $S_2O_8{}^{2-}$, *thiuram disulfides* are obtained, for example,

$$I_2 + 2Me_2NCS_2^- \longrightarrow \underset{\underset{S}{\|}}{Me_2NC}-S-S-\underset{\underset{S}{\|}}{CNMe_2} + 2I^- \qquad (14\text{-}6.7)$$

Thiuram disulfides, which are strong oxidants, are used as polymerization initiators (for, when heated, they give radicals) and as vulcanization accelerators. Tetraethylthiuram disulfide is "Antabuse," the agent for rendering the body allergic to ethanol.

STUDY GUIDE

Scope and Purpose

Most of the chemistry of the element carbon constitutes the field of organic chemistry. The inorganic chemist, however, is legitimately concerned with certain aspects that are very important and that have traditionally not been included in the realm of organic chemistry. These include nearly all of the chemistry of the element itself, of compounds in which carbon is combined with metals and metalloids, and much of the chemistry of the simple, binary compounds with nonmetals (oxides, cyanides, halides). The field of organometallic chemistry, which we examine in Chapters 29 and 30, is a truly interdisciplinary one.

Study Questions

A. Review

1. The electronic structure of C in its ground state is $1s^2 2s^2 2p_x 2p_y$. Why does carbon usually form four single bonds and not two?

2. Give examples of a stable carbonium ion, a carbanion, and a free radical. What is a carbene?

3. What is meant by catenation? Why does silicon have much less tendency to catenation than carbon? Could the same be said for nitrogen?

4. Describe the synthesis and main properties of diamond.

5. What is graphite? Draw its structure and explain why its properties differ from those of diamond.

6. List ways in which CO can be made.

7. List ways in which CO_2 can be made.

8. On which side is the equilibrium in the reaction:

$$CO_2(aq) + 2H_2O \rightleftharpoons H_3O^+ + HCO_3^-$$

9. Why does $CaCO_3$ dissolve to some extent in CO_2 saturated water? Write balanced equations for the reactions involved.

10. How could you make cyanogen in the laboratory? Write balanced equations.

11. List similarities between $(CN)_2$ and CN^- and Cl_2 and Cl^-.

12. Why are solutions of KCN in water alkaline?

13. Give the industrial synthesis and major properties of hydrogen cyanide.

14. How is CS_2 prepared? Write equations for its reaction with C_2H_5ONa in ethanol and with $(C_2H_5)_2NH$ in the presence of aqueous NaOH.

15. How would you convert $BaCO_3$ labeled with ^{13}C or ^{14}C, which is the usual source of labeled carbon compounds, to (a) $Ni(^*CO)_4$, (b) $^*C_2H_2$, (c) $^*CH_4$, (d) $^*CS_2$, and (e) $^*CH_3OH$?

B. Additional Exercises

1. The C—C bond length in graphite is 1.42 Å. How does this compare with the C—C bond length in (a) diamond, (b) ethylene, and (c) benzene? What do you expect is the C—C bond order in graphite? Explain.

2. Write down the structures, the Lewis diagrams, and the molecular orbitals for the isoelectronic molecules carbon dioxide and allene. What sort of differences in chemistry do you expect?

3. HCN can give on polymerization dimers, trimers, tetramers, pentamers, and polymers. Write some plausible structures for these molecules.

4. Explain why HCN is a weak acid in aqueous solution yet as the pure liquid it is a strong acid. Recall the material of Chapter 7.

5. Zinc dithiocarbamates are dimeric. Propose a structure.

6. Draw the Lewis diagrams for each reactant and product of reaction 14-6.3.

7. Identify the oxidizing and reducing agents in reactions 14-5.1 and 14-5.2. Draw the Lewis diagram for each reactant and product.

SUPPLEMENTARY READING

Ansell, M. F., "Diamond Cleavage," *Chem. Br.*, **1984,** 1017–1021.

Cotton, F. A. and Wilkinson, G., *Advanced Inorganic Chemistry*, 4th ed., Wiley-Interscience, New York, 1980.

Walker, P. L., Ed., *Chemistry and Physics of Carbon*, Vols. I and II, Dekker, New York, 1966.

chapter 15

THE GROUP IVB(14) ELEMENTS: SILICON, GERMANIUM, TIN, AND LEAD

15-1 Introduction

Silicon is second only to oxygen in its natural abundance (ca. 28% of the earth's crust) and occurs in a great variety of silicate minerals and as quartz, SiO_2.

Germanium, tin, and lead are rare elements (ca. $10^{-3}\%$). Tin and lead have been known since antiquity because of the ease with which they are obtained from their ores.

Cassiterite, SnO_2, occurs mixed in granites, sands, and clays. Lead occurs mainly as *galena*, PbS.

Germanium was discovered in 1886 following the prediction of its existence by Dimitri Mendeleev. It occurs widely but in small amounts and is recovered from coal and zinc ore concentrates.

The main use of Ge, Sn, and Pb is as the metals, but alkyltin and alkyllead compounds are made on a large scale (Chapter 29).

The position of the elements in the periodic table and some general features, including the reasons for the existence of the lower II oxidation state, were discussed in Section 8-11. Some properties of the elements were given in Table 8-4.

Multiple Bonding

Unlike carbon, these elements do not normally form stable $p\pi-p\pi$ multiple bonds. Thus, although stoichiometric similarities may occur, for example, the pairs CO_2, SiO_2 and $(CH_3)_2CO$, $(CH_3)_2SiO$, there is no structural or chemical similarity between them. Carbon dioxide is a gas, properly written $O{=}C{=}O$, whereas SiO_2 is a giant molecule with each Si atom singly bound to four oxygen atoms giving linked SiO_4 tetrahedra (Section 5-4). Despite this absence of $p\pi-p\pi$ bonding, the elements can use d orbitals in multiple bonding. Thus certain structural and chemical features of Si and Ge compounds, particularly those with SiO and SiN bonds, are best explained by some double-bond character of the $p\pi-d\pi$ type. For example, $N(SiH_3)_3$ is planar, whereas $N(CH_3)_3$ is pyramidal; this can be ascribed to $p\pi-d\pi$ bonding involving a filled nitrogen $2p_z$ orbital overlapping with empty silicon $3d_{xz}$ orbitals (Fig. 15-1).

Figure 15-1 The formation of a $d\pi-p\pi$ bond between Si and N atoms in trisilylamine.

Stereochemistry in the IV State

Unlike carbon, the compounds of these elements can have five, six and, in $Pb(O_2CMe)_4$ and $Sn(NO_3)_4$, eight coordination. Examples are

five coordination:	$Me_3SnCl(py)$	SiF_5^-
six coordination:	$SnCl_4(py)_2$	$[Ge(C_2O_4)_3]^{2-}$
	$[Si(acac)_3]^+$	$[PbCl_6]^{2-}$

The II-Oxidation State

In many of the compounds of Sn^{II} and to a lesser extent of Ge^{II} and Pb^{II} the lone pair of electrons has important structural and chemical consequences.

First, the structures are such that the lone pairs appear to be occupying a bond position. Thus the $SnCl_3^-$ ion is pyramidal with a lone-pair like NH_3 (Section 16-1). Second, tin(II) compounds, especially $SnCl_2$ and $SnCl_3^-$ can act as donors toward transition metals as in the complex $[Pt^{II}(SnCl_3)_5]^{3-}$.

15-2 Isolation and Properties of the Elements

Silicon is obtained in the ordinary commercial form by reduction of SiO_2 with carbon or CaC_2 in an electric furnace. Similarly, Ge is prepared by reduction of GeO_2 with C or H_2. Silicon and Ge are used as semiconductors, especially in transistors. For this purpose, exceedingly high purity ($<10^{-9}$ atom % of impurities) is essential, and special methods are required to obtain usable materials. The element is first converted to the tetrachloride, which is reduced back to the metal by hydrogen at high temperatures. After casting into rods it is *zone refined*. A rod of metal is heated near one end so that a cross-sectional wafer of molten silicon is produced. Since impurities are more soluble in the melt than they are in the solid they concentrate in the melt, and the melted zone is then caused to move slowly along the rod by moving the heat source. This carries impurities to the end. The process may be repeated. The impure end is then removed. Super-pure Ge is made in a similar way.

Tin and lead are obtained by reduction of the oxide or sulfide with carbon.

The metals can be dissolved in acid and deposited electrolytically to effect further purification.

Silicon is ordinarily rather unreactive. It is attacked by halogens giving tetrahalides, and by alkalis giving solutions of silicates. It is not attacked by acids except hydrofluoric; presumably the stability of $[SiF_6]^{2-}$ provides the driving force here.

Germanium is somewhat more reactive than silicon and dissolves in concentrated H_2SO_4 and HNO_3. Tin and lead dissolve in several acids and are rapidly attacked by halogens. They are slowly attacked by cold alkali, rapidly by hot, to form stannates and plumbites. Lead often appears to be more noble and unreactive than would be indicated by its standard potential of -0.13 V. This low reactivity can be attributed to a high overvoltage for hydrogen and also, in some instances, to insoluble surface coatings. Thus lead is not dissolved by dilute H_2SO_4 and concentrated HCl.

15-3   Hydrides, MH$_4$

These are colorless gases. Only *monosilane*, SiH_4, is of any importance. This spontaneously flammable gas is prepared by the action of $LiAlH_4$ on SiO_2 at 150–170 °C or by reduction of $SiCl_4$ with $LiAlH_4$ in an ether. Although stable to water and dilute acids, rapid base hydrolysis gives hydrated SiO_2 and H_2.

Substituted silanes with organic groups are of great importance, as are some closely related tin compounds (Chapter 29). The most important reaction of compounds with Si—H bonds, such as $HSiCl_3$ or $HSi(CH_3)_3$, is the Speier or hydrosilation reaction of alkenes:

$$RCH{=}CH_2 + SiHCl_3 \longrightarrow RCH_2CH_2SiCl_3 \qquad (15\text{-}3.1)$$

This reaction, which employs chloroplatinic acid as a catalyst, is commercially important for the synthesis of precursors to silicones.

15-4   Chlorides, MCl$_4$

Chlorination of the hot Group IVB(14) elements gives colorless liquids, MCl_4, except $PbCl_4$, which is yellow. $PbCl_4$ may also be prepared by reaction 15-4.1:

$$PbO_2 + 4HCl \longrightarrow PbCl_4 + 2H_2O \qquad (15\text{-}4.1)$$

The tetrachlorides are hydrolyzed by water eventually to hydrous oxides, but limited hydrolysis may give oxochlorides. In aqueous HCl, the tetrachlorides of Sn and Pb give chloroanions, $[MCl_6]^{2-}$.

$GeCl_4$ differs from $SiCl_4$ in that the former can be distilled and separated from concentrated HCl, whereas the silicon tetrachloride is immediately hydrolyzed by water.

The principal uses of $SiCl_4$ and $GeCl_4$ are in the synthesis of pure Si and Ge. Additional uses of $SiCl_4$ and $SnCl_4$ are in syntheses of organometallic compounds (Chapter 29).

15-5 Oxygen Compounds

Silica

Pure SiO_2 occurs in two forms, *quartz* and *cristobalite*. The Si is always tetrahedrally bound to four oxygen atoms but the bonds have considerable ionic character. In cristobalite the silicon atoms are placed as are the carbon atoms in diamond, with the oxygen atoms midway between each pair. In quartz, there are helices so that enantiomorphic crystals occur, and these may be easily recognized and separated mechanically.

Quartz and cristobalite can be interconverted when heated. These processes are slow because the breaking and re-forming of bonds is required and the activation energy is high. However, the rates of conversion are profoundly affected by the presence of impurities, or by the introduction of alkali metal oxides.

Slow cooling of molten SiO_2 or heating any solid form to the softening temperature gives an amorphous material that is glassy in appearance and is indeed a glass in the general sense, that is, a material with no long-range order but, instead, a disordered array of polymeric chains, sheets, or three-dimensional units.

Silica is relatively unreactive towards Cl_2, H_2, acids, and most metals at 25 °C or even at slightly elevated temperatures but is attacked by F_2, aqueous HF, alkali hydroxides, and fused carbonates.

Aqueous HF gives solutions containing fluorosilicates, for example, $[SiF_6]^{2-}$. The *silicates* have been discussed in Section 5-4. The fusion of excess alkali carbonates with SiO_2 at ~1300 °C gives water-soluble products commercially sold as a syrupy liquid that has many uses. Aqueous sodium silicate solutions appear to contain the ion $[SiO_2(OH)_2]^{2-}$ but, depending on the pH and concentration, polymerized species are also present.

The basicity of the dioxides increases, SiO_2 being purely acidic, GeO_2 less so, SnO_2 amphoteric, and PbO_2 somewhat more basic. When SnO_2 is made at high temperatures or by dissolving Sn in hot concentrated nitric acid, it is, like PbO_2, remarkably inert to attack.

Only lead forms a stable oxide containing both Pb^{II} and Pb^{IV}, namely, Pb_3O_4, which is a bright red powder known commercially as red lead. It is made by heating PbO and PbO_2 together at 250 °C. Although it behaves chemically as a mixture of PbO and PbO_2, the crystal contains $Pb^{IV}O_6$ octahedra linked in chains by sharing opposite edges. The chains are linked by Pb^{II} atoms each bound to three O atoms.

There are no true hydroxides and the products of hydrolysis of the hydrides or halides, and the like, are best regarded as hydrous oxides.

15-6   Complex Compounds

Most of the complex species contain halide ions or donor ligands that are O, N, S, or P compounds.

Anionic Complexes

Silicon forms only fluoroanions, normally $[SiF_6]^{2-}$, whose high formation constant accounts for the incomplete hydrolysis of SiF_4 in water, according to Eq. 15-6.1:

$$2SiF_4 + 2H_2O = SiO_2 + [SiF_6]^{2-} + 2H^+ + 2HF \qquad (15\text{-}6.1)$$

The ion is usually made by dissolving SiO_2 in aqueous HF and is stable even in basic solution. Under selected conditions and with cations of the right size, the $[SiF_5]^-$ ion can be isolated, for example,

$$SiO_2 + HF(aq) + R_4N^+Cl^- \xrightarrow{CH_3OH} [R_4N][SiF_5] \qquad (15\text{-}6.2)$$

By contrast with $[SiF_6]^{2-}$, the $[GeF_6]^{2-}$ and $[SnF_6]^{2-}$ ions are hydrolyzed by bases; $[PbF_6]^{2-}$ ion is hydrolyzed even by water.

Although Si does not, the other elements give chloroanions, and all the elements form oxalato ions $[M(ox)_3]^{2-}$.

Cationic Complexes

The most important are those of chelating uninegative oxygen ligands such as the acetylacetonates, for example, $[Ge(acac)_3]^+$.

The tetrahalides act as Lewis acids; $SnCl_4$ is a good Friedel–Crafts catalyst. The *adducts* are 1:1 or 1:2 but it is not always clear in the absence of X-ray evidence whether they are neutral, that is, MX_4L_2, or whether they are salts, for example, $[MX_2L_2]X_2$. Some of the best defined are the pyridine adducts, for example, *trans*-$(py)_2SiCl_4$.

Alkoxides, Carboxylates, and Oxo Salts

All four elements form alkoxides. Those of silicon, for example, $Si(OC_2H_5)_4$, are the most important; the surface of glass or silica can also be alkoxylated. Alkoxides are normally obtained by the standard method, solvolysis of chlorides, as in Eq. 15-6.3:

$$MCl_4 + 4ROH + 4 \text{ amine} \longrightarrow M(OR)_4 + 4 \text{ amine·HCl} \qquad (15\text{-}6.3)$$

Silicon alkoxides are hydrolyzed by water, eventually to hydrous silica. Of the carboxylates, *lead tetraacetate* is the most important as it is used in organic chemistry as a strong but selective oxidizing agent. It is made by dissolving Pb_3O_4 in hot glacial acetic acid or by electrolytic oxidation of Pb^{II} in acetic acid. In oxidations the attacking species is probably $Pb(OOCMe)_3^+$, which is isoelectronic with the similar oxidant, $Tl(OOCMe)_3$, but this is not always so and some oxidations are free radical in nature. The trifluoroacetate is a white solid, which will oxidize even heptane to give the $ROOCCF_3$ species whence the alcohol ROH is obtained by hydrolysis; benzene similarly gives phenol.

Tin(IV) sulfate, $Sn(SO_4)_2 \cdot 2H_2O$, can be crystallized from solutions obtained by oxidation of Sn^{II} sulfate; it is extensively hydrolyzed in water.

Tin(IV) nitrate is a colorless volatile solid made by interaction of N_2O_5 and $SnCl_4$; it contains bidentate NO_3^- groups giving dodecahedral coordination. The compound reacts with organic matter.

15-7 The Divalent State
Silicon

Divalent silicon species are thermodynamically unstable under normal conditions. However, several species, notably SiF_2, have been identified in high temperature reactions and trapped by chilling to liquid nitrogen temperatures. Thus at ca. 1100 °C and low pressures, the following reaction goes in ca. 99.5% yield

$$SiF_4 + Si \rightleftharpoons 2SiF_2 \qquad (15\text{-}7.1)$$

SiF_2 is stable for a few minutes at 10^{-4} cm pressure; the molecule is angular and diamagnetic. When the frozen compound warms, it gives fluorosilanes up to $Si_{16}F_{34}$.

Germanium

Germanium dihalides are stable. GeF_2 is a white crystalline solid obtained by the action of anhydrous HF on Ge at 200 °C; it is a fluorine bridged polymer with approximately tbp coordination of Ge. Germanium dichloride, $GeCl_2$, gives salts of the $GeCl_3^-$ ion similar to those of Sn noted in the next section.

Tin

The most important compounds are SnF_2 and $SnCl_2$, which are obtained by heating Sn with gaseous HF or HCl. The fluoride is sparingly soluble in water and is used in fluoride-containing toothpastes. Water hydrolyzes $SnCl_2$ to a basic chloride, but from dilute acid solutions $SnCl_2 \cdot 2H_2O$ can be crystallized. Both halides dissolve in solutions containing an excess of halide ion, thus:

$$SnF_2 + F^- = SnF_3^- \qquad pK \approx 1 \qquad (15\text{-}7.2)$$

$$SnCl_2 + Cl^- = SnCl_3^- \qquad pK \approx 2 \qquad (15\text{-}7.3)$$

In aqueous fluoride solutions SnF_3^- is the major species, but the ions SnF^+ and $Sn_2F_5^-$ can be detected.

The halides dissolve in donor solvents such as acetone, pyridine, or DMSO, to give pyramidal adducts, for example, $SnCl_2OC(CH_3)_2$.

The very air-sensitive tin(II) ion, Sn^{2+}, occurs in acid perchlorate solutions, which may be obtained by reduction of copper(II) perchlorate as in Eq. 15-7.4:

$$Cu(ClO_4)_2 + Sn/Hg = Cu + Sn^{2+} + 2ClO_4^- \qquad (15\text{-}7.4)$$

Hydrolysis gives $[Sn_3(OH)_4]^{2+}$, with $SnOH^+$ and $[Sn_2(OH)_2]^{2+}$ in minor amounts:

$$3Sn^{2+} + 4H_2O \rightleftharpoons [Sn_3(OH)_4]^{2+} + 4H^+ \qquad \log K = -6.77 \quad (15\text{-}7.5)$$

The trimeric, probably cyclic, ion appears to provide the nucleus of several basic tin(II) salts obtained from aqueous solutions at fairly low pH. Thus the nitrate appears to be $Sn_3(OH)_4(NO_3)_2$ and the sulfate, $Sn_3(OH)_2OSO_4$. All Sn^{II} solutions are readily oxidized by oxygen and, unless stringently protected from air, normally contain some Sn^{IV}. The chloride solutions are often used as mild reducing agents:

$$SnCl_6^{2-} + 2e^- = SnCl_3^- + 3Cl^- \qquad (15\text{-}7.6)$$
$$E^0 = \text{ca. } 0.0 \text{ V } (1 \, M \text{ HCl}, 4 \, M \text{ Cl}^-)$$

Lead

Of the four elements, only lead has a well-defined cationic chemistry. The lead(II) ion, Pb^{2+}, is partially hydrolyzed in water:

$$Pb^{2+} + H_2O = PbOH^+ + H^+ \qquad \log K \approx -7.9 \qquad (15\text{-}7.7)$$

In concentrated solutions and on addition of base, polymeric ions that contain three, four, and six Pb atoms are formed. The crystalline "basic" salt

$$[Pb_6O(OH)_6]^{4+}(ClO_4^-)_4 \cdot H_2O$$

has the cluster structure in Fig. 15-2. The O atom lies at the center of the middle tetrahedron, while the OH groups lie on the faces of the outer tetrahedra.

Most lead salts are only sparingly soluble in water and some, for example,

Figure 15-2   The three face-sharing tetrahedra of Pb atoms in the $Pb_6O(OH)_6^{4+}$ cluster.

$PbSO_4$ or $PbCrO_4$, are insoluble. The common soluble salts are $Pb(NO_3)_2$ and $Pb(CO_2Me)_2 \cdot 2H_2O$, which is incompletely ionized in water. The halides are always anhydrous and in solution form complex species PbX^+, PbX_3^-, and so on, except for the fluoride where only PbF^+ occurs.

STUDY GUIDE

Study Questions

A. Review

1. Why is CO_2 a gas and SiO_2 a giant molecule?
2. Explain what is meant by $d\pi - p\pi$ bonding.
3. Why does tin form divalent inorganic compounds more easily than silicon?
4. How is super pure Ge made from GeO_2?
5. Write balanced equations for the synthesis of SiH_4 and for its hydrolysis by aqueous KOH.
6. Why is CCl_4 unreactive to H_2O, whereas $SiCl_4$ is rapidly hydrolyzed?
7. Why is SiF_4 incompletely hydrolyzed by water?
8. Explain the nature of zeolites and of molecular sieves.
9. Why does silicon have much less tendency to form bonds to itself than does carbon?
10. How is lead tetraacetate made?
11. What is red lead?
12. What is the nature of Sn^{II} in aqueous chloride solution?

B. Additional Exercises

1. Explain why H_3SiNCS has a linear SiNCS group, whereas in H_3CNCS the CNC group is angular.
2. Why are silanols such as $(CH_3)_3SiOH$ stronger acids than their carbon analogs?
3. List the various types of geometries among the compounds of the tetravalent Group IVB(14) elements and give examples. For each example, give the structural classification for the Group IVB(14) atom, according to the AB_xE_y scheme of Chapter 3.
4. What methods could one use to determine the nature of 1:1 and 1:2 adducts of $SnCl_4$ with neutral donors?
5. Why can Sn^{II} compounds such as $SnCl_3^-$ act as donors (ligands) to transition metals?
6. The single-bond energies for the elements of the first and second short periods follow the trends   C > Si; N < P; O < S; F < Cl. Why is the first pair in the list apparently anomalous?
7. Predict the relative π-bond strength between B and N in the two compounds bis(trimethylsilyl)aminoborane and bis(t-butyl)aminoborane. Explain your answer in terms of the π orbitals that are involved.
8. Draw the π-bond system that is responsible for the planarity of trisilylamine.
9. Draw the Lewis diagrams and discuss the geometries of $SnCl_2$, $SnCl_3^-$, and $[Pt(SnCl_3)_5]^{3-}$.

10. Balance the equation for the reaction of $SiCl_4$ with $LiAlH_4$.

11. Use Valence Shell Electron Pair Repulsion theory to compare the bond angles in the pyramidal ions SnF_3^-, $SnCl_3^-$, and $GeCl_3^-$.

C. Questions from the Literature of Inorganic Chemistry

1. Let the paper by R. H. Nielson and R. L. Wells, *Inorg. Chem.*, **1977**, *16*, 7–11, serve as a basis for the following questions:

(a) What typical values for B—N rotational barriers does one expect for mono-, bis-, and tris-aminoboranes?

(b) Why should studies of rotational barriers in these aminoboranes indicate the relative extent of π bonding between boron and an *N*-trimethylsilyl, an *N*-trimethylgermyl, and an *N*-trimethylstannyl substituent?

(c) Both a steric and a competitive π-bonding argument can be given to explain the trends reported here. Elaborate.

2. Consider the paper by D. Kummer and T. Seshadri, *Angew. Chem. Int. Ed. Eng.*, **1975**, *14*, 699–700.

(a) Determine the oxidation state of Si and draw the Lewis diagram for each of the Si-containing compounds mentioned in this article.

(b) Predict the geometry for each of these compounds.

3. Compare and contrast the structure of and the bonding in two different classes of Sn^{IV} compounds as presented in

(a) R_2SnX_2
   N. W. Alcock and J. F. Sawyer, *J. Chem. Soc., Dalton Trans.*, **1977**, 1090–1095.

(b) $SnCl_4(PR_3)_2$
   G. G. Mather, G. M. McLaughlin, and A. Pidcock, *J. Chem. Soc., Dalton Trans.*, **1973**, 1823–1827.

4. Consider the compounds $M[CH(Me_3Si)_2]_2$, where M = Ge, Sn, or Pb, as described by J. D. Cotton, P. J. Davidson, and M. F. Lappert, *J. Chem. Soc., Dalton Trans.*, **1976**, 2275–2285.

(a) Draw the Lewis diagram of these substances.

(b) Explain (and give an example of) each of the four types of reactions mentioned for these substances.

SUPPLEMENTARY READING

Breck, D. W., *Molecular Sieves*, Wiley, New York, 1973.

Burger, H. and Eugen, R., "The Chemistry of Lower-Valent Silicon," *Topics in Current Chemistry*, No. 5, Springer-Verlag, Berlin, 1974.

Davidov, V. I., *Germanium*, Gordon and Breach, New York, 1966.

Donaldson, J. D., "The Chemistry of Divalent Tin," *Prog. Inorg. Chem.*, **1967**, *8*, 287.

Drake, J. E. and Riddle, C., "Volatile Compounds of the Hydrides of Silicon and Germanium with Elements of Groups V and VI," *Q. Rev.*, **1970**, *24*, 263.

Eaborn, C., *Organosilicon Compounds*, Butterworths, London, 1960.

Ebsworth, E. A. V., *Volatile Silicon Compounds*, Pergamon Press, Elmsford, NY, 1963.

Ebsworth, E. A. V., *The Organometallic Compounds of the Group IV Elements*, G. Mac-Diarmid, Ed., Dekker, New York, 1968.

Glocking, F., *The Chemistry of Germanium*, Academic, New York, 1969.

Lesbre, M., Mazerolles, P., and Satge, J., *The Organic Compounds of Germanium*, Wiley, New York, 1971.

Margrave, J. L. and Wilson, P. W., "Silicon Difluoride, Its Reactions and Properties," *Acc. Chem. Res.*, **1971,** *4*, 145.

Noll, W. et al., *Chemistry and Technology of Silicones*, Academic, New York, 1968.

Raabe, G. and Michl, J., "Multiple Bonding to Silicon," *Chem. Rev.*, **1985,** *85*, 419–509.

Shapiro, H. and Frey, F. W., *The Organic Compounds of Lead*, Wiley, New York, 1968.

Zuckerman, J. J., Ed., "Organotin Compounds: New Chemistry and Applications," *Advances in Chemistry Series*, No. 157, American Chemical Society, 1976.

chapter 16

NITROGEN

16-1 Introduction

The nitrogen atom, $1s^2 2s^2 2p_x 2p_y 2p_z$, can complete its valence shell in the following ways:

1. Electron gain to form the nitride ion N^{3-}; this ion is found only in saltlike nitrides of the most electropositive metals.
2. Formation of electron-pair bonds: (a) single bonds as in NH_3, or (b) multiple bonds as in $:N{\equiv}N:$, $-\dot{N}{=}\dot{N}-$, or NO_2.
3. Formation of electron-pair bonds with electron gain as in NH_2^- or NH^{2-}.
4. Formation of electron-pair bonds with electron loss as in the tetrahedral ammonium and substituted ammonium ions, $[NR_4]^+$.

Among those compounds of nitrogen having covalent bonds, the following structural types (recall Chapter 3) are common: AB_4 (as in tetrahedral NR_4^+); AB_3E (as in pyramidal NR_3); AB_2E_2 (as in bent NR_2^-); AB_3 (as in planar NO_3^-); AB_2E (as in bent $R_2C{=}N{-}OH$); and ABE (N_2). There are a few stable species in which, formally, the nitrogen valence shell is incomplete. Nitroxides, $R_2\dot{N}{=}\ddot{O}$, NO, and NO_2 are the best examples; these have unpaired electrons and are paramagnetic.

Three-Covalent Nitrogen

The molecules NR_3 are pyramidal; the bonding is best considered as involving sp^3 hybrid orbitals so that the lone pair occupies the fourth position. There are three points of note:

1. As a result of the nonbonding electron pair, all NR_3 compounds behave as Lewis bases and they give donor–acceptor complexes with Lewis acids, for example, $F_3B{\leftarrow}NMe_3$ and they act as ligands toward transition metal ions as in, for example, $[Co(NH_3)_6]^{3+}$.
2. Pyramidal molecules, $NRR'R''$, should be chiral. Optical isomers cannot be isolated, however, because such molecules very rapidly undergo a motion known as *inversion* in which the N atom oscillates through the plane of the three R groups, much as an umbrella can turn inside out (Fig. 16-1). The energy barrier for this process is only ca. 24 kJ mol^{-1}.
3. There are a very few cases where three-covalent nitrogen is planar; in these cases multiple bonding is involved as we discussed for $N(SiMe_3)_3$,

Figure 16-1 Diagram illustrating the inversion of NH_3.

in Section 15-1. The *N*-centered triangular metal complexes such as $[NIr_3(SO_4)_6(H_2O)_3]^{4-}$ are similar.

N—N Single-Bond Energy

The N—N single bond is quite weak. If we compare the single-bond energies:

$H_3C—CH_3$	$H_2N—NH_2$	$HO—OH$	$F—F$	Units
350	160	140	150	$kJ\ mol^{-1}$

it is clear that there is a profound drop between C and N. This difference is probably attributable to the effects of repulsion between nonbonding lone pairs. The result is that unlike carbon, nitrogen has little tendency to catenation.

Multiple Bonds

The propensity of nitrogen, like carbon, to form $p\pi–p\pi$ multiple bonds is a feature that distinguishes it from phosphorus and the other Group VB(15) elements. Thus nitrogen as the element is dinitrogen, N_2, with a very high bond strength and a short internuclear distance (1.094 Å), whereas phosphorus forms P_4 molecules or infinite layer structures in which there are only single bonds (Section 8-5).

Where a nitrogen atom forms one single and one double bond, nonlinear molecules result, as shown in structures 16-I to 16-IV.

Each nitrogen atom in these structures is of the AB_2E type, uses sp^2 hybrid orbitals, and forms a π bond using the unhybridized $2p$ orbital.

In the oxo anions NO_2^- (AB_2E) and NO_3^- (AB_3), there are multiple bonds that may be formulated in either resonance or MO terms, as discussed in Chapter 3.

16-2 Occurrence and Properties of the Element

Nitrogen occurs in nature mainly as dinitrogen, N_2 (bp 77.3 K), which comprises 78% by volume of the earth's atmosphere. The isotopes ^{14}N and ^{15}N have an absolute ratio $^{14}N/^{15}N = 272.0$. Compounds enriched in ^{15}N are used in tracer studies.

The heat of dissociation of N_2 is extremely large:

$$N_2(g) = 2N(g) \qquad \Delta H = 944.7 \text{ kJ mol}^{-1} \qquad K_{25\,°C} = 10^{-120} \qquad (16\text{-}2.1)$$

The great strength of the $N{\equiv}N$ bond is principally responsible for the chemical inertness of N_2 and for the fact that most simple nitrogen compounds are endothermic even though they may contain strong bonds. Dinitrogen is notably unreactive in comparison with isoelectronic, triply bonded systems such as $X{-}C{\equiv}C{-}X$, $:C{\equiv}O:$, $X{-}C{\equiv}N:$, and $X{-}N{\equiv}C:$. Both $-C{\equiv}C-$ and $-C{\equiv}N$ groups can act as donors by using their π electrons, whereas N_2 does not. It can, however, form complexes similar to those formed by CO, although to a much more limited extent, in which there are $M{\leftarrow}N{\equiv}N:$ and $M{\leftarrow}C{\equiv}O:$ configurations (Chapter 28).

Nitrogen is obtained by liquefaction and fractionation of air. It usually contains some argon and, depending on the quality, upwards of ~30 ppm of oxygen. Spectroscopically pure N_2 is made by thermal decomposition of sodium or barium azide:

$$2NaN_3 \longrightarrow 2Na + 3N_2 \qquad (16\text{-}2.2)$$

The only reactions of N_2 at room temperature are with metallic Li to give Li_3N, with certain transition metal complexes, and with nitrogen fixing bacteria, either free living or symbiotic on root nodules of clover, peas, beans, and the like. The mechanism by which these bacteria fix N_2 is unknown.

At elevated temperatures nitrogen becomes more reactive, especially when catalyzed, typical reactions being:

$$N_2(g) + 3H_2(g) = 2NH_3(g) \qquad\qquad K_{25\,°C} = 10^3 \text{ atm}^{-2} \qquad (16\text{-}2.3)$$

$$N_2(g) + O_2(g) = 2NO(g) \qquad\qquad K_{25\,°C} = 5 \times 10^{-31} \qquad (16\text{-}2.4)$$

$$N_2(g) + 3Mg(s) = Mg_3N_2(s) \qquad\qquad\qquad (16\text{-}2.5)$$

$$N_2(g) + CaC_2(s) = C(s) + CaNCN(s) \qquad\qquad (16\text{-}2.6)$$

16-3 Nitrides

Nitrides of electropositive metals have structures with discrete nitrogen atoms and can be regarded as ionic, for example, $(Ca^{2+})_3(N^{3-})_2$, $(Li^+)_3N^{3-}$, and so on. Their ready hydrolysis to ammonia and metal hydroxides is consistent with this. Such nitrides are prepared by direct interaction or by loss of ammonia from amides on heating, for example:

$$3Ba(NH_2)_2 \longrightarrow Ba_3N_2 + 4NH_3 \qquad (16\text{-}3.1)$$

Many transition metal *nitrides* are often nonstoichiometric and have nitrogen atoms in the interstices of close-packed arrays of metal atoms. Like the similar carbides or borides they are hard, chemically inert, high melting, and electrically conducting.

There are numerous covalent *nitrides* (BN, S_4N_4, P_3N_5, etc.), and their properties vary greatly depending on the element with which nitrogen is combined. These are, therefore, discussed more fully under the appropriate element.

16-4 Nitrogen Hydrides

Ammonia

Ammonia, NH_3, is formed by the action of a base on an ammonium salt:

$$NH_4X + OH^- \longrightarrow NH_3 + H_2O + X^- \qquad (16\text{-}4.1)$$

Industrially ammonia is made by the Haber process in which the reaction

$$N_2(g) + 3H_2(g) = 2NH_3(g) \qquad \Delta H = -46 \text{ kJ mol}^{-1} \qquad (16\text{-}4.2)$$
$$K_{25\,°C} = 10^3 \text{ atm}^{-2}$$

is carried out at 400 to 500 °C and pressures of 10^2 to 10^3 atm in the presence of a catalyst. Although the equilibrium is most favorable at low temperature, even with the best catalysts elevated temperatures are required to obtain a satisfactory rate. The best catalyst is α-iron containing some oxide to widen the lattice and enlarge the active interface.

Ammonia is a colorless, pungent gas (bp -33.35 °C). The liquid has a large heat of evaporation (1.37 kJ g^{-1} at the boiling point) and can be handled in ordinary laboratory equipment. Liquid NH_3 resembles water in its physical behavior, being highly associated via strong hydrogen bonding. Its dielectric constant (~22 at -34 °C; cf. 81 for H_2O at 25 °C) is sufficiently high to make it a fair ionizing solvent. Its self-ionization has been discussed previously (Section 7-3).

Liquid NH_3 has lower reactivity than H_2O toward electropositive metals and dissolves many of them (Section 10-3).

Because $NH_3(\ell)$ has a much lower dielectric constant than water, it is a better solvent for organic compounds but generally a poorer one for ionic inorganic compounds. Exceptions occur when complexing by NH_3 is superior to that by water. Thus AgI is exceedingly insoluble in water but very soluble in NH_3. Primary solvation numbers of cations in NH_3 appear similar to those in H_2O, for example, 5.0 ± 0.2 and 6.0 ± 0.5 for Mg^{2+} and Al^{3+}, respectively.

Ammonia burns in air

$$4NH_3(g) + 3O_2(g) = 2N_2(g) + 6H_2O(g) \qquad K_{25 °C} = 10^{228} \qquad (16\text{-}4.3)$$

Reaction 16-4.3 is the thermodynamically favored one under normal conditions. However, at 750 to 900 °C, in the presence of a platinum or a platinum–rhodium catalyst, reaction of ammonia with oxygen can be made to give NO instead of N_2, as in Eq. 16-4.4:

$$4NH_3 + 5O_2 = 4NO + 6H_2O \qquad K_{25 °C} = 10^{168} \qquad (16\text{-}4.4)$$

thus affording a useful synthesis of NO. The latter reacts with an excess of O_2 to produce NO_2, and the mixed oxides can be absorbed in water to form nitric acid:

$$2NO + O_2 \longrightarrow 2NO_2 \qquad\qquad (16\text{-}4.5)$$

$$3NO_2 + H_2O \longrightarrow 2HNO_3 + NO \qquad \text{and so on} \qquad (16\text{-}4.6)$$

Thus the sequence in industrial utilization of atmospheric nitrogen is as follows:

$$N_2 \xrightarrow[\substack{\text{Haber}\\\text{process}}]{H_2} NH_3 \xrightarrow[\substack{\text{Ostwald}\\\text{process}}]{O_2} NO \xrightarrow{O_2 + H_2O} HNO_3(aq) \qquad (16\text{-}4.7)$$

Ammonia is extremely soluble in water. Although aqueous solutions are generally referred to as solutions of the weak base, NH_4OH, called *ammonium hydroxide*, undissociated NH_4OH probably does not exist. The solutions are best described as $NH_3(aq)$, with the equilibrium written as

$$NH_3(aq) + H_2O = NH_4^+ + OH^- \qquad K_{25 °C} = \frac{[NH_4^+][OH^-]}{[NH_3]} \qquad (16\text{-}4.8)$$

$$= 1.77 \times 10^{-5}(pK_b = 4.75)$$

Ammonium Salts

Stable crystalline salts of the tetrahedral NH_4^+ ion are mostly water soluble. Ammonium salts generally resemble those of potassium and rubidium in solubility and structure, since the three ions are of comparable (Pauling) radii: $NH_4^+ = 1.48$ Å, $K^+ = 1.33$ Å, $Rb^+ = 1.48$ Å. Salts of strong acids are fully ionized, and the solutions are slightly acidic:

$$NH_4Cl = NH_4^+ + Cl^- \qquad K \approx \infty \qquad (16\text{-}4.9)$$

$$NH_4^+ + H_2O = NH_3 + H_3O^+ \qquad K_{25 °C} = 5.5 \times 10^{-10} \qquad (16\text{-}4.10)$$

Thus, a 1 M solution will have a pH of ~4.7. The constant for the second reaction is sometimes called the hydrolysis constant; however, it may equally well be considered as the acidity constant of the cationic acid NH_4^+, and the system regarded as an acid–base system in the following sense:

$$NH_4^+ + H_2O = H_3O^+ + NH_3(aq) \qquad (16\text{-}4.11)$$

$$\underset{\text{Acid}}{} \quad \underset{\text{Base}}{} \quad \underset{\text{Acid}}{} \quad \underset{\text{Base}}{}$$

Many ammonium salts volatilize with dissociation around 300 °C, for example:

$$NH_4Cl(s) = NH_3(g) + HCl(g) \qquad \Delta H = 177 \text{ kJ mol}^{-1}$$

$$K_{25\,°C} = 10^{-16} \qquad (16\text{-}4.12)$$

$$NH_4NO_3(s) = NH_3(g) + HNO_3(g) \qquad \Delta H = 171 \text{ kJ mol}^{-1} \qquad (16\text{-}4.13)$$

Salts that contain oxidizing anions may decompose when heated, with oxidation of the ammonia to N_2O or N_2 or both. For example:

$$(NH_4)_2Cr_2O_7(s) = N_2(g) + 4H_2O(g) + Cr_2O_3(s) \qquad (16\text{-}4.14)$$

$$\Delta H = -315 \text{ kJ mol}^{-1}$$

$$NH_4NO_3(\ell) = N_2O(g) + 2H_2O(g) \qquad (16\text{-}4.15)$$

$$\Delta H = -23 \text{ kJ mol}^{-1}$$

Hydrazine

Hydrazine, N_2H_4, may be thought of as derived from ammonia by replacement of a hydrogen atom by the —NH_2 group. It is a bifunctional base:

$$N_2H_4(aq) + H_2O = N_2H_5^+ + OH^- \qquad K_{25\,°C} = 8.5 \times 10^{-7} \qquad (16\text{-}4.16)$$

$$N_2H_5^+(aq) + H_2O = N_2H_6^{2+} + OH^- \qquad K_{25\,°C} = 8.9 \times 10^{-15} \qquad (16\text{-}4.17)$$

and two series of hydrazinium salts are obtainable. Those of $N_2H_5^+$ are stable in water while those of $N_2H_6^{2+}$ are extensively hydrolyzed. Salts of $N_2H_6^{2+}$ can be obtained by crystallization from aqueous solution containing a large excess of the acid, since they are usually less soluble than the monoacid salts.

Anhydrous N_2H_4 is a fuming colorless liquid (bp 114 °C). It is surprisingly stable in view of its endothermic nature ($\Delta H_f^\circ = 50 \text{ kJ mol}^{-1}$). It burns in air with considerable evolution of heat.

$$N_2H_4(\ell) + O_2(g) = N_2(g) + 2H_2O(\ell) \qquad \Delta H^\circ = -622 \text{ kJ mol}^{-1} \qquad (16\text{-}4.18)$$

Aqueous hydrazine is a powerful reducing agent in basic solution, normally being oxidized to nitrogen. Hydrazine is made by the interaction of aqueous ammonia with sodium hypochlorite:

$$NH_3 + NaOCl \longrightarrow NaOH + NH_2Cl \qquad \text{(Fast)} \qquad (16\text{-}4.19)$$

$$NH_3 + NH_2Cl + NaOH \longrightarrow N_2H_4 + NaCl + H_2O \qquad (16\text{-}4.20)$$

However, there is a competing reaction that is rather fast once some hydrazine has been formed:

$$2NH_2Cl + N_2H_4 \longrightarrow 2NH_4Cl + N_2 \qquad (16\text{-}4.21)$$

To obtain appreciable yields, it is necessary to add gelatine. This sequesters heavy-metal ions that catalyze the parasitic reaction; even the part per million or so of Cu^{2+} in ordinary water will almost completely prevent the formation of hydrazine if no gelatine is used. Since simple sequestering agents such as EDTA are not as beneficial as gelatine, the latter is assumed to have a catalytic effect as well.

Hydroxylamine

Hydroxylamine, NH_2OH, is a weaker base than NH_3

$$NH_2OH(aq) + H_2O = NH_3OH^+ + OH^- \qquad K_{25\,°C} = 6.6 \times 10^{-9}$$

$$(16\text{-}4.22)$$

It is prepared by reduction of nitrates or nitrites either electrolytically or with SO_2, under controlled conditions. Hydroxylamine is a white unstable solid. In aqueous solution or as its salts $[NH_3OH]Cl$ or $[NH_3OH]_2SO_4$ it is used as a reducing agent.

Azides

Sodium azide can be obtained by the reaction

$$3NaNH_2 + NaNO_3 \xrightarrow{175\,°C} NaN_3 + 3NaOH + NH_3 \qquad (16\text{-}4.23)$$

Heavy metal azides are explosive and lead or mercury azide have been used in detonation caps. The azide ion, which is linear and symmetrical, behaves rather like a halide ion and can act as a ligand in metal complexes. The pure acid, HN_3, is a dangerously explosive liquid.

16-5   Nitrogen Oxides

Dinitrogen Monoxide (Nitrous Oxide)

Nitrous oxide, N_2O, is obtained by thermal decomposition of molten ammonium nitrate:

$$NH_4NO_3 \xrightarrow{250\,°C} N_2O + 2H_2O \qquad (16\text{-}5.1)$$

The contaminants are NO (which can be removed by passage through ferrous sulfate solution), and 1–2% of nitrogen.

Nitrous oxide has the linear structure NNO. It is relatively unreactive, being inert to the halogens, alkali metals, and ozone at room temperature. On heating, it decomposes to N_2 and O_2. At elevated temperatures, it will react with the alkali metals and with many organic compounds. It will oxidize some low-valent transition metal complexes and itself forms the complex, $[Ru(NH_3)_5N_2O]^{2+}$. It is used as an anaesthetic.

Nitrogen Monoxide (Nitric Oxide)

Nitric oxide, NO, is formed in many reactions involving reduction of nitric acid and solutions of nitrates and nitrites. For example, with 8 M nitric acid:

$$8HNO_3 + 3Cu \longrightarrow 3Cu(NO_3)_2 + 4H_2O + 2NO \qquad (16\text{-}5.2)$$

Reasonably pure NO is obtained by the aqueous reactions:

$$2NaNO_2 + 2NaI + 4H_2SO_4 \longrightarrow$$
$$I_2 + 4NaHSO_4 + 2H_2O + 2NO \qquad (16\text{-}5.3)$$

$$2NaNO_2 + 2FeSO_4 + 3H_2SO_4 \longrightarrow Fe_2(SO_4)_3 + 2NaHSO_4$$
$$+ 2H_2O + 2NO \qquad (16\text{-}5.4)$$

or, using molten salts,

$$3KNO_2(\ell) + KNO_3(\ell) + Cr_2O_3(s) \longrightarrow 2K_2CrO_4(s, \ell) + 4NO \qquad (16\text{-}5.5)$$

Nitric oxide reacts instantly with O_2

$$2NO + O_2 \longrightarrow 2NO_2 \qquad (16\text{-}5.6)$$

It is oxidized to nitric acid by strong oxidizing agents; the reaction with permanganate is quantitative and provides a method of analysis. It is reduced to N_2O by SO_2 and to NH_2OH by Cr^{2+}, in acid solution in both cases.

Nitric oxide is thermodynamically unstable and at high pressures it readily decomposes in the range 30–50 °C:

$$3NO \longrightarrow N_2O + NO_2 \qquad (16\text{-}5.7)$$

The NO molecule is paramagnetic with the electron configuration

$$(\sigma_1)^2(\sigma_2)^2(\sigma_3)^2(\pi)^4(\pi^*)^1$$

The electron in the π^* orbital is relatively easily lost to give the *nitrosonium ion*, NO^+, which forms many salts. Because the electron removed comes out of an antibonding orbital, the bond is stronger in NO^+ than in NO; the bond length decreases by 0.09 Å and the vibration frequency rises from 1840 cm^{-1} in NO to 2150–2400 cm^{-1} (depending on environment) in NO^+.

The ion is formed when N_2O_3 or N_2O_4 is dissolved in concentrated sulfuric acid:

$$N_2O_3 + 3H_2SO_4 = 2NO^+ + 3HSO_4^- + H_3O^+ \qquad (16\text{-}5.8)$$

$$N_2O_4 + 3H_2SO_4 = NO^+ + NO_2^+ + 3HSO_4^- + H_3O^+ \qquad (16\text{-}5.9)$$

The compound $NO^+HSO_4^-$, nitrosonium hydrogen sulfate, is an important intermediate in the lead-chamber process for manufacture of sulfuric acid.

Nitric oxide forms many complexes with transition metals (Chapter 28) some of which can be considered to arise from NO^+.

Nitrogen Dioxide (NO_2) and Dinitrogen Tetroxide (N_2O_4)

The two oxides, NO_2 and N_2O_4, exist in a strongly temperature-dependent equilibrium

$$2NO_2 \rightleftharpoons N_2O_4 \qquad (16\text{-}5.10)$$

Brown   Colorless

paramagnetic   diamagnetic

both in solution and in the gas phase. In the solid state, the oxide is wholly N_2O_4. In the liquid phase, partial dissociation occurs; it is pale yellow at the freezing point ($-11.2\,°C$) and contains 0.01% of NO_2, which increases to 0.1% in the deep red-brown liquid at the boiling point, $21.15\,°C$. Dissociation is complete in the vapor above $140\,°C$. Nitrogen dioxide has an unpaired electron. The other "free radical" molecules, NO and ClO_2 (Section 20-4), have little tendency to dimerize, and the difference may be that in NO_2 the electron is localized mainly on the N atom. The dimer has three isomeric forms of which the most stable and normal form has the planar structure O_2N-NO_2. The N—N bond is rather long, $1.75\,\text{Å}$, as would be expected from its weakness. The dissociation energy of N_2O_4 is only $57\ kJ\ mol^{-1}$.

Mixtures of the two oxides are obtained by heating metal nitrates, by oxidation of NO, and by reduction of nitric acid and nitrates by metals and other reducing agents. The gases are highly toxic and attack metals rapidly. They react with water as in Eq. 16-5.11:

$$2NO_2 + H_2O = HNO_3 + HNO_2 \qquad (16\text{-}5.11)$$

The nitrous acid decomposes, particularly when warmed:

$$3HNO_2 = HNO_3 + 2NO + H_2O \qquad (16\text{-}5.12)$$

Thermal decomposition of NO_2 takes place above $150\,°C$ according to Eq. 16-5.13:

$$2NO_2 \rightleftharpoons 2NO + O_2 \qquad (16\text{-}5.13)$$

The oxides are fairly strong oxidizing agents in aqueous solution, comparable in strength to bromine:

$$N_2O_4(g) + 2H_{(aq)}^+ + 2e^- = 2HNO_{2(aq)} \qquad E^0 = +1.07 \text{ V} \qquad (16\text{-}5.14)$$

An equilibrium mixture of the oxides, *nitrous fumes*, is used in organic chemistry as a selective oxidizing agent, the oxidation proceeding through an initial hydrogen abstraction to give HONO according to Eq. 16-5.15:

$$RH + NO_2 = R\cdot + HONO \qquad (16\text{-}5.15)$$

Liquid N_2O_4 can be used as a solvent and has been utilized to make anhydrous nitrates and nitrate complexes. Thus Cu dissolves in N_2O_4 to give $Cu(NO_3)_2\cdot N_2O_4$, which looses N_2O_4 on heating to give $Cu(NO_3)_2$.

In solvents such as anhydrous HNO_3, N_2O_4 dissociates ionically as in Eq. 16-5.16:

$$N_2O_4 = NO^+ + NO_3^- \qquad (16\text{-}5.16)$$

Dinitrogen Trioxide

Dinitrogen trioxide, N_2O_3, formally the anhydride of nitrous acid, is obtained by interaction of stoichiometric amounts of NO and O_2, or of NO and N_2O_4. It is an intensely blue liquid or a pale blue solid. The stable form has a weak N—N bond. It exists only at low temperature, and readily dissociates to give NO and NO_2 as in Eq. 16-5.17:

$$N_2O_3 = NO + NO_2 \qquad (16\text{-}5.17)$$

Dinitrogen Pentoxide

This oxide, N_2O_5, forms unstable colorless crystals. It is made by reaction 16-5.18:

$$2HNO_3 + P_2O_5 = 2HPO_3 + N_2O_5 \qquad (16\text{-}5.18)$$

N_2O_5 is the anhydride of nitric acid. In the solid state it exists as the nitronium nitrate, $NO_2^+ NO_3^-$.

16-6 The Nitronium Ion

Just as NO readily loses its odd electron, so does NO_2. The *nitronium* ion, NO_2^+, is involved in the dissociation of HNO_3, in solutions of nitrogen oxides in acids, and in nitration reactions of aromatic compounds. Indeed, it was studies on nitration reactions that lead to proper recognition of the importance of NO_2^+ as the attacking species.

The nitronium ion is formed in ionizing solvents such as H_2SO_4, CH_3NO_2, or CH_3CO_2H by ionizations such as

$$2HNO_3 = NO_2^+ + NO_3^- + H_2O \qquad (16\text{-}6.1)$$

$$HNO_3 + H_2SO_4 = NO_2^+ + HSO_4^- + H_2O \qquad (16\text{-}6.2)$$

The actual nitration process can then be formulated

$$(16\text{-}6.3)$$

Nitronium salts can be readily isolated. They are thermally stable but rapidly hydrolyzed. Typical preparations are

$$N_2O_5 + HClO_4 = NO_2^+ClO_4^- + HNO_3 \qquad (16\text{-}6.4)$$

$$HNO_3 + 2SO_3 = NO_2^+HS_2O_7^- \qquad (16\text{-}6.5)$$

16-7 Nitrous Acid

Solutions of the weak acid, HONO ($pK_a = 3.3$), are made by acidifying cold solutions of nitrites. The aqueous solution can be obtained free of salts by the reaction

$$Ba(NO_2)_2 + H_2SO_4 \longrightarrow 2HNO_2 + BaSO_4(s) \qquad (16\text{-}7.1)$$

The pure liquid acid is unknown, but it can be obtained in the vapor phase. Even aqueous solutions of nitrous acid are unstable and decompose rapidly when heated:

$$3HNO_2 \rightleftharpoons H_3O^+ + NO_3^- + 2NO \qquad (16\text{-}7.2)$$

Nitrites of the alkali metals are prepared by heating the nitrates with a reducing agent such as carbon, lead, iron, or the like. They are very soluble in water. Nitrites are very toxic but have been used for preservation of ham and other meat products; there is evidence that they can react with proteins to give carcinogenic nitrosoamines.

The main use of nitrites is to generate nitrous acid for the synthesis of organic diazonium compounds from primary aromatic amines. Organic derivatives of the NO_2 group are of two types: nitrites (R—ONO) and nitro compounds (R—NO_2). Similar isomerism occurs in metal complexes where the NO_2^- ligand can be coordinated to a metal either through the nitrogen atom (i.e., the nitro ligand) or through the oxygen atom (i.e., the nitrito ligand), as has already been discussed in Chapter 6.

16-8 Nitrogen Halides

Of the binary halides we have NF_3, NF_2Cl, $NFCl_2$, and NCl_3. There are also N_2F_2, N_2F_4, and the halogen azides XN_3 ($X = F$, Cl, Br, I). With the exception of NF_3, the halides are reactive, some of them explosively, for example, $NFCl_2$. Only the fluorides are important.

Interaction of NF_3, F_2, and a strong Lewis acid such as BF_3, AsF_5, or SbF_5 gives salts of the ion NF_4^+. Such reactions are performed at low temperature, under high pressures, with UV light, as in Eq. 16-8.1:

$$NF_3 + F_2 + BF_3 \longrightarrow NF_4^+BF_4^- \qquad (16\text{-}8.1)$$

Compounds of NF_4^+ are ionic, and other salts may similarly be prepared, namely, those of AsF_6^- and SnF_6^{2-}. The perchlorate may be prepared by low-temperature ($-78\,°C$) metathesis in liquid HF, as in Eq. 16-8.2:

$$NF_4^+SbF_6^- + CsClO_4 \longrightarrow CsSbF_6(s) + NF_4^+ClO_4^- \qquad (16\text{-}8.2)$$

NF_4^+ is one of the strongest oxidizers known.

The oxohalides (or the nitrosyl halides), XNO, where $X = F$, Cl, or Br are obtained by reaction of the halogens with NO as in Eq. 16-8.3:

$$2NO + X_2 \longrightarrow 2XNO \qquad (16\text{-}8.3)$$

All three of the nitrosyl halides are powerful oxidants, able to attack many metals, and all decompose on treatment with water producing HNO_3, HNO_2, NO, and HX.

STUDY GUIDE

Study Questions

A. Review

1. Give the electronic structure of the nitrogen atom and list the ways by which the octet can be completed in forming compounds of nitrogen. Give examples.

2. Draw the Lewis diagrams and explain the geometry and hybridization at each atom in NO_2^-, NO_3^-, NO_2^+, NO^+, NO, N_2, N_3^-, FNO, and N_2O.

3. Write balanced equations for the synthesis of nitric acid from NH_3 and O_2.

4. Write equations for the action of heat on (a) $NaNO_3$, (b) NH_4NO_3, (c) $Cu(NO_3)_2 \cdot nH_2O$, (d) N_2O, and (e) N_2O_3.

5. How is hydrazine prepared?

6. Write balanced equations for three different preparations of nitric oxide.

7. How is the nitronium ion prepared? Explain its significance in the nitration of aromatic hydrocarbons.

8. In acid solution we have

$$HNO_2 + H^+ + e^- \longrightarrow NO + H_2O \qquad E^0 = 1.0 \text{ V}$$

Write balanced equations for the reactions of nitrous acid with (a) I^-, (b) Fe^{2+}, (c) $C_2O_4^{2-}$.

9. How can NO_2^- and NO_3^- be bonded to transition metal complexes?

10. Write balanced equations for the hydrolysis of (a) calcium nitride, (b) lithium nitride, (c) dinitrogen pentoxide, and (d) dinitrogen trioxide.

11. Draw Lewis diagrams for the radicals NO and NO_2. Explain the formation of the N—N bond in N_2O_3 and in N_2O_4.

B. Additional Exercises

1. Use MO theory to compare the electronic structures of CO, N_2, CN^-, and NO^+. Why does nitrogen form complexes with metals less readily than CO?

2. Why does nitrogen form only a diatomic molecule unlike phosphorus and other elements of Group VB(15)?

3. Nitrogen trichloride is an extremely dangerous explosive oil, but NF_3 is a stable gas that reacts only above 250 °C. Explain this difference.

4. Three isomers of N_2O_4 are known. Draw likely structures for them.

5. Determine the oxidation numbers of the atoms in the molecules and ions found in the following: Eqs. 16-6.1, 16-5.16, 16-5.13, 16-5.7, 16-5.1, 16-4.13, 16-4.4, and 16-2.4. Which of these are redox reactions?

6. Show with drawings how hybrid orbitals overlap in the formation of the σ-bond framework in each of the following molecules and ions: (a) N_2, (b) N_3^-, (c) NO_2^-, and (d) ClNO.

7. Show with drawings the hybrid orbitals that house lone pairs of electrons in the molecules and ions of Problem 6. Be careful to show the geometry correctly, including the likely position of the lone electrons in the molecules and ions, and specify the type of hybrid that is used in each case.

8. Show with drawings the formation of the π-bond system in the molecules and ions of Problem 6.

9. Complete and balance the following equations.

(a) $Li + N_2$	(b) $Cu + NO_2$
(c) $C + NO_2$	(d) $H_2O_2 + NO_2$
(e) $O_3 + NO_2$	(f) $H_2 + NO_2$
(g) $HI + HNO_2$	

10. Draw the Lewis diagrams for N_2F_2 and N_2F_4, each of which has a nitrogen–nitrogen linkage. Classify each nitrogen atom according to the AB_xE_y scheme of Chapter 3 and give the hybridization for each nitrogen.

11. Give the AB_xE_y classification (Chapter 3) for each oxide mentioned in Section 16-5.

C. Questions from the Literature of Inorganic Chemistry

1. Hydrolysis of dinitrogen trioxide is described in the paper by G. Y. Markovits, S. E. Schwartz, and L. Newman, *Inorg. Chem.*, **1981**, *20*, 445–450.

   (a) Draw the Lewis diagrams, discuss the geometry, and assign an oxidation number to each atom in the substances found in reactions (1), (2), and (3).

   (b) What evidence do the authors cite for an equilibrium in which N_2O_3 is formed from nitrous acid in acidic medium?

(c) How is Eq. (15) obtained?

(d) The authors report a value for $\Delta G_f°[N_2O_3(aq)]$. How was this number calculated?

(e) Of reactions (1), (2), (3), (9), and (13), which represent disproportionation, hydrolysis, and/or acid–base type reactions?

2. Consider the paper by K. O. Christe, C. J. Schack, and R. D. Wilson in *Inorg. Chem.*, **1977**, *16*, 849–854.

(a) What is the nature of solid SnF_4, and why is it not a good Lewis acid?

(b) What reaction takes place in liquid HF solvent between KF and SnF_4?

(c) Draw the Lewis diagrams and predict the geometries of NF_4^+, BF_4^-, $(SnF_4)_x$, SnF_5^-, and $[SnF_6]^{2-}$.

(d) What reaction takes place in liquid HF solvent between NF_4BF_4 and SnF_4?

(e) Why does NF_4SnF_5 not react with a second equivalent of NF_4BF_4 to form $(NF_4)_2SnF_6$?

3. Some reaction chemistry of NF_4^+ is reported by K. O. Christe, W. W. Wilson, and R. D. Wilson in *Inorg. Chem.*, **1980**, *19*, 1494–1498.

(a) Write balanced equations for the reactions in anhydrous HF solvent between NF_4^+ and (i) ClO_4^-, (ii) BrO_4^-, and (iii) HF_2^-.

(b) Write balanced equations for the reactions in BrF_5 solvent between NF_4^+ and (i) BrF_4^- and (ii) BrF_4O^-.

SUPPLEMENTARY READING

Bottomley, F. and Burns, R. C., *Treatise on Dinitrogen Fixation*, Wiley, New York, 1979.

Chatt, J. C., da C. Pina, L. M., and Richards, R. L., *New Trends in Nitrogen Fixation*, Academic, New York, 1980.

Colburn, C. B., Ed., *Developments in Inorganic Nitrogen Chemistry*, Vols. 1 and 2, Elsevier, Amsterdam, 1966 and 1973.

Griffith, W. P., "Transition-Metal Nitrido Complexes," *Coord. Chem. Rev.*, **1972**, *8*, 369–396.

Jolly, W. L., *The Inorganic Chemistry of Nitrogen*, Benjamin, New York, 1964.

Smith, P. A. S., *The Open-Chain Chemistry of Organic Nitrogen Compounds*, Vols. 1 and 2, Benjamin, New York, 1966.

Wright, A. N. and Winkler, C. A., *Active Nitrogen*, Academic, New York, 1968.

chapter 17

THE GROUP VB(15) ELEMENTS: PHOSPHORUS, ARSENIC, ANTIMONY, AND BISMUTH

17-1 Introduction

Phosphorus occurs mainly in minerals of the *apatite* family, $Ca_9(PO_4)_6 \cdot CaX_2$; X = F, Cl, or OH, which are the main component of amorphous phosphate rock, millions of tons of which are processed annually. Arsenic, Sb, and Bi occur mainly as sulfide minerals such as *mispickel* (FeAsS) or *stibnite* (Sb_2S_3).

Some properties of the elements are given in Table 8-5, and some general features and trends are noted in Chapter 8.

The valence shells of the atoms, ns^2np^3, are similar to the electron configuration of N, but beyond the similarity in stoichiometries of compounds such as NH_3, PH_3, and so on, there is little resemblance between even P and N in their chemistries. Phosphorus is a true nonmetal in its chemistry but As, Sb, and Bi show an increasing trend to metallic character and cationic behavior.

The principal factors responsible for the differences between nitrogen and phosphorus group chemistry are those responsible for the C to Si differences, namely, (a) the diminished ability of the second-row element to form $p\pi-p\pi$ multiple bonds, and (b) the possibility of utilizing the lower-lying $3d$ orbitals.

The first explains features such as the fact that nitrogen forms esters O=NOR, whereas phosphorus gives $P(OR)_3$. Nitrogen oxides and oxoacids all involve multiple bonds (Section 16-1), whereas the phosphorus oxides have single P—O bonds as in P_4O_6 and phosphoric acid is $PO(OH)_3$ in contrast to $NO_2(OH)$.

The utilization of d orbitals has three effects. First, it allows some $p\pi-d\pi$ bonding as in R_3P=O or R_3P=CH_2. Thus amine oxides, R_3NO, have only a single canonical structure, $R_3\overset{+}{N}$—$\overset{-}{O}$, and are chemically reactive, while P—O bonds are shorter than expected for the sum of single bond radii, indicating multiple bonding, and are very strong, ca. 500 kJ mol^{-1}. Second, there is the possibility of expansion of the valence shell, whereas nitrogen has a covalency maximum of four. Thus we have compounds such as PF_5, PPh_5, $P(OMe)_6^-$, and PF_6^-.

Notice that for many of the five-coordinate species, especially of phosphorus, the energy difference between the trigonal-bipyramidal and square-pyramidal configurations is small and that such species are usually stereochemically nonrigid (Section 6-6).

When higher coordination numbers occur for the elements in the III oxidation state, as in $[SbF_5]^{2-}$, the structures take the form of a square pyramid. As was discussed in Chapter 3, AB_5E systems such as these accommodate one lone pair (E), in addition to the five peripheral atoms (B), at the central atom (A).

Finally, while trivalent nitrogen and the other elements in compounds such as NEt_3, PEt_3, $AsPh_3$, and so on have lone pairs and act as donors, there is a profound difference in their donor ability toward transition metals. This follows from the fact that although NR_3 has no low-lying acceptor orbitals, the others do have such orbitals, namely, the empty d orbitals. These can accept electron density from filled metal d orbitals to form $d\pi$–$d\pi$ bonds, as we shall discuss in detail later (Section 28-15).

17-2 The Elements

Phosphorus is obtained by reduction of phosphate rock with coke and sand in an electric furnace. Phosphorus distills and is condensed under water as P_4. Phosphorus allotropes have been discussed (Section 8-4).

$$2Ca_3(PO_4)_2 + 6SiO_2 + 10C = P_4 + 6CaSiO_3 + 10CO \qquad (17\text{-}2.1)$$

P_4 is stored under water to protect it from air in which it will inflame. Red and black P are stable in air but will burn on heating. P_4 is soluble in CS_2, benzene, and similar organic solvents; it is very poisonous.

Arsenic, Sb, and *Bi* are obtained as the metals (Section 8-5) by reduction of their oxides with carbon or hydrogen. The metals burn on heating in oxygen to give the oxides.

All the elements react readily with halogens but are unaffected by nonoxidizing acids. Nitric acid gives, respectively, phosphoric acid, arsenic acid, antimony trioxide, and bismuth nitrate, which well illustrates the increasing metallic character as the group is descended.

Interaction with various metals and nonmetals gives phosphides, arsenides, and the like, which may be ionic, covalent polymers or metal-like solids. Gallium arsenide (GaAs)—one of the so-called III–V compounds of a Group IIIB(13) and a Group VB(15) element—has semiconductor properties similar to those of Si and Ge.

17-3 Hydrides, EH₃

The stability of these EH_3 gases decreases in the series NH_3, PH_3, AsH_3, SbH_3, and BiH_3. The last two in the series are very unstable thermally. The average bond energies are N—H, 391; P—H, 322; As—H, 247; and Sb—H, 255 kJ mol^{-1}.

Phosphine, PH_3, is made by the action of acids on zinc phosphide. Pure PH_3

is not spontaneously flammable, but it often inflames owing to traces of P_2H_4 or P_4 vapor. It is exceedingly poisonous. Because of poor ability to enter into H bonding, it is not associated in the liquid state, in contrast to the behavior of ammonia. Phosphine is sparingly soluble in water, and it is a very weak base. The proton affinities of PH_3 and NH_3 differ considerably, as indicated by the relative values of $\Delta H°$ for reactions 17-3.1 and 17-3.2.

$$PH_3(g) + H^+(g) = PH_4^+(g) \qquad \Delta H° = -770 \text{ kJ mol}^{-1} \qquad (17\text{-}3.1)$$
$$NH_3(g) + H^+(g) = NH_4^+(g) \qquad \Delta H° = -866 \text{ kJ mol}^{-1} \qquad (17\text{-}3.2)$$

Although PH_3 is the weaker base, it does react with gaseous HI to give PH_4I as unstable colorless crystals. Phosphonium iodide, PH_4I, is completely hydrolyzed by water, as in Eq. 17-3.3:

$$PH_4I(s) + H_2O = H_3O^+ + I^- + PH_3(g) \qquad (17\text{-}3.3)$$

It is the low basicity of PH_3 that forces the equilibrium in Eq. 17-3.3 to lie far to the right. Phosphine is used industrially to make organophosphorus compounds (Chapter 29).

17-4   Halides (EX₃, EX₅) and Oxohalides

The trihalides, except PF_3, are obtained by direct halogenation, keeping the element in excess. An excess of the halogen gives EX_5. The trihalides are rapidly hydrolyzed by water and are rather volatile; the gaseous molecules have pyramidal structures. The chlorides and bromides, as well as PF_3 and PI_3, have molecular lattices. AsI_3, SbI_3, and BiI_3 have layer structures based on hexagonal close packing of iodine atoms with the Group IIIB(13) atoms in octahedral holes. Bismuth trifluoride, BiF_3, is known in two forms, in both of which Bi has coordination number eight, while SbF_3 has an intermediate structure in which SbF_3 molecules are linked through F bridges to give each Sb^{III} a very distorted octahedral environment.

Phosphorus trifluoride is a colorless, toxic gas, made by fluorination of PCl_3. It forms complexes with transition metals similar to those formed by carbon monoxide (Section 28-15). Unlike the other trihalides, PF_3 is hydrolyzed only slowly by water, but it is attacked rapidly by alkalis. It has no Lewis acid properties.

Phosphorus trichloride is a low-boiling liquid that is hydrolyzed by water to give phosphorous acid. It reacts with oxygen to give $OPCl_3$. Figure 17-1 illustrates some of the important reactions of PCl_3. Many of these reactions are typical of other EX_3 compounds and also, with obvious changes in formulas, of $OPCl_3$ and other oxo halides.

Arsenic trihalides are similar to those of phosphorus. Antimony trichloride, $SbCl_3$, differs in that it dissolves in a limited amount of water to give a clear solution that, on dilution, gives insoluble oxo chlorides such as SbOCl and $Sb_4O_5Cl_2$. No simple Sb^{3+} ions exist in the solutions. Bismuth trichloride, $BiCl_3$, a white, crystalline solid, is hydrolyzed by water to BiOCl but this reaction is

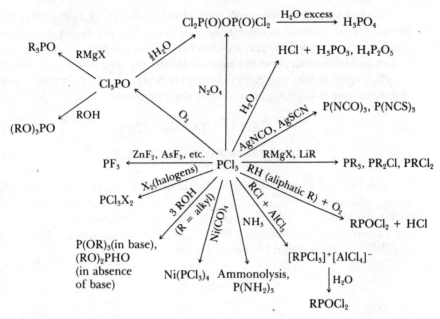

Figure 17-1 Some important reactions of PCl₃. Many of these are typical of other EX₃ and OEX₃ compounds.

reversible:

$$BiCl_3 + H_2O \rightleftharpoons BiOCl + 2HCl \qquad (17\text{-}4.1)$$

Phosphorus pentafluoride, PF₅, is prepared by the interaction of PCl₅ with CaF₂ at 300 to 400 °C. It is a very strong Lewis acid and forms complexes with amines, ethers, and other bases, as well as with F⁻, in which phosphorus becomes six coordinate. However, these organic complexes are less stable than those of BF₃ and are rapidly decomposed by water and alcohols. Like BF₃, PF₅ is a good catalyst, especially for ionic polymerization. Arsenic pentafluoride, AsF₅, is similar.

Antimony pentafluoride is a viscous liquid (bp 150 °C). Its association is due to polymerization through fluorine bridging. The crystal has cyclic tetramers. Its main use is in "superacids" (Section 7-13).

AsF₅, SbF₅, and PF₅ are potent fluoride ion acceptors, forming MF₆⁻ ions. The PF₆⁻ ion is a common and convenient *noncomplexing* anion.

Phosphorus (V) chloride has a trigonal-bipyramidal structure in the gas, melt, and solution in nonpolar solvents, but the solid is [PCl₄]⁺[PCl₆]⁻ and in polar solvents like CH₃NO₂ it is ionized. The tetrahedral PCl₄⁺ ion can be considered to arise here by transfer of Cl⁻ to the Cl⁻ acceptor, PCl₅. It is not therefore surprising that many salts of the PCl₄⁺ ion are obtained when PCl₅ reacts with other Cl⁻ acceptors, namely,

$$PCl_5 + TiCl_4 \longrightarrow [PCl_4{}^+]_2[Ti_2Cl_{10}]^{2-} \quad \text{and} \quad [PCl_4]^+[Ti_2Cl_9]^- \quad (17\text{-}4.2)$$

$$PCl_5 + NbCl_5 \longrightarrow [PCl_4]^+[NbCl_6]^- \qquad (17\text{-}4.3)$$

Solid *phosphorus pentabromide* is also ionic, but differs, being $PBr_4^+Br^-$. Antimony forms *antimony pentachloride,* which is a fuming liquid, colorless when pure, and usually yellow. It is a powerful chlorinating agent. Arsenic does not form a pentabromide, and the pentachloride decomposes above $-50°C$.

Phosphoryl halides are X_3PO, in which X may be F, Cl, or Br. The most important one is Cl_3PO, obtainable by the reactions

$$2PCl_3 + O_2 \longrightarrow 2Cl_3PO \qquad (17\text{-}4.4)$$

$$P_4O_{10} + 6PCl_5 \longrightarrow 10Cl_3PO \qquad (17\text{-}4.5)$$

The reactions of Cl_3PO are much like those of PCl_3 (Fig. 17-1). Hydrolysis by water yields phosphoric acid. Cl_3PO also has donor properties and many complexes are known, in which oxygen is the ligating atom.

The oxohalides SbOCl and BiOCl are precipitated when solutions of Sb^{III} and Bi^{III} in concentrated HCl are diluted.

17-5 Oxides

The oxides of the Group VB(15) elements clearly exemplify two important trends that are manifest to some extent in all groups of the periodic table: (1) the stability of the higher oxidation state decreases with increasing atomic number, and (2) in a given oxidation state the metallic character of the elements, and, therefore, the basicity of the oxides, increase with increasing atomic number. Thus, P^{III} and As^{III} oxides are acidic, Sb^{III} oxide is amphoteric, and Bi^{III} oxide is strictly basic.

Phosphorus pentoxide is so termed for historical reasons but its correct molecular formula is P_4O_{10} [Fig. 17-2(*a*)]. It is made by burning phosphorus in excess oxygen. It has at least three solid forms. Two are polymeric but one is a white, crystalline material that sublimes at 360 °C and 1 atm. Sublimation is an excellent method of purification, since the products of incipient hydrolysis, which are the commonest impurities, are comparatively nonvolatile. This form and the vapor consist of molecules in which the P atoms are at the corners of a tetrahedron with six oxygen atoms along the edges. The remaining four O atoms lie along extended threefold axes of the tetrahedron. The P—O—P bonds are single but the length of the four apical P—O bonds indicates $p\pi$–$d\pi$ bonding, that is, P=O.

P_4O_{10} is one of the most effective drying agents known at temperatures below 100 °C. It reacts with water to form a mixture of phosphoric acids whose composition depends on the quantity of water and other conditions. It will even extract the elements of water from many other substances themselves considered good dehydrating agents; for example, it converts pure HNO_3 into N_2O_5 and H_2SO_4 into SO_3. It also dehydrates many organic compounds, for example, converting amides into nitriles.

The *trioxide* is also polymorphous: one form contains discrete molecules, P_4O_6. The structure [Fig. 17-2(*b*)] is similar to that of P_4O_{10} except that the four nonbridging apical oxygen atoms in the latter are missing. P_4O_6 is a colorless, volatile compound that is formed in about 50% yield when P_4 is burned in a

Figure 17-2 The structure of (a) P_4O_{10} and (b) P_4O_6.

deficit of oxygen. As_4O_6 and Sb_4O_6 are similar to P_4O_6 both structurally and in their acidic nature. Bi_2O_3 and the hydroxide $Bi(OH)_3$ precipitated from bismuth(III) solution have no acidic properties.

17-6 Sulfides

Phosphorus and sulfur combine directly above 100 °C to give several sulfides, the most important being P_4S_3, P_4S_5, P_4S_7, and P_4S_{10}. Each compound is obtained by heating stoichiometric quantities of red P and sulfur. P_4S_3 is used in matches. It is soluble in organic solvents such as carbon disulfide and benzene. P_4S_{10} has the same structure as P_4O_{10}. The others also have structures based on a tetrahedral group of phosphorus atoms with P—S—P bridges or apical P═S groups. P_4S_{10} reacts with alcohols:

$$P_4S_{10} + 8ROH \longrightarrow 4(RO)_2P(S)SH + 2H_2S \qquad (17\text{-}6.1)$$

to give dialkyl and diaryl dithiophosphates that form the basis of many extreme-pressure lubricants, of oil additives, and of flotation agents.

Arsenic forms As_4S_3, As_4S_4, As_2S_3, and As_2S_5 by direct interaction. The last two can also be precipitated from hydrochloric acid solutions of As^{III} and As^V by hydrogen sulfide. As_2S_3 is insoluble in water and acids but is acidic dissolving in alkali sulfide solutions to give thio anions. As_2S_5 behaves similarly. As_4S_4, which occurs as the mineral *realgar,* has a structure with an As_4 tetrahedron.

Antimony forms Sb_2S_3 either by direct interaction or by precipitation with H_2S from Sb^{III} solutions; it dissolves in an excess of sulfide to give anionic thio complexes, probably mainly SbS_3^{3-}. Antimony trisulfide, Sb_2S_3, as well as Bi_2S_3, has a ribbonlike polymeric structure in which each Sb atom and each S atom is bound to three atoms of the opposite kind, forming interlocking SbS_3 and SSb_3 pyramids.

Bismuth gives dark brown Bi_2S_3 on treatment of Bi^{III} solutions with H_2S; it is not acidic.

Some of the corresponding selenides and tellurides of As, Sb, and Bi have been studied intensively as semiconductors.

17-7   The Oxo Acids

The nature and properties of the oxoanions of the Group VB(15) elements have been discussed in Chapter 5. Here we discuss only the important acids and some of their derivatives.

Phosphorous acid is obtained when PCl_3 or P_4O_6 are hydrolyzed by water. It is a deliquescent colorless solid (mp 70 °C, $pK = 1.8$). The acid and its mono and diesters differ from PCl_3 in that there are *four* bonds to P, one being P—H. The presence of hydrogen bound to P can be demonstrated by nmr or other spectroscopic techniques. Phosphorous acid is, hence, best written $HP(O)(OH)_2$ as in structure 17-I. Hypophosphorous acid, H_3PO_2, also has P—H bonds (structure 17-II). By contrast the triesters have only three bonds to phosphorus, thus being analogous to PCl_3. The trialkyl and aryl phosphites, $P(OR)_3$, have excellent donor properties toward transition metals and many complexes are known.

17-I   17-II

Phosphorous acid may be oxidized by chlorine or other agents to phosphoric acid, but the reactions are slow and complex. However, the triesters are quite readily oxidized and must be protected from air:

$$2(RO)_3P + O_2 = 2(RO)_3PO \qquad (17\text{-}7.1)$$

They also undergo the Michaelis–Arbusov reaction with alkyl halides, forming dialkyl phosphonates:

$$P(OR)_3 + R'X \longrightarrow [(RO)_3PR']X \longrightarrow RO\underset{\underset{\textstyle OR}{|}}{\overset{\overset{\textstyle O}{\|}}{P}}R' + RX \qquad (17\text{-}7.2)$$

Phosphonium
intermediate

Trimethylphosphite easily undergoes spontaneous isomerization to the dimethyl ester of methylphosphonic acid:

$$P(OCH_3)_3 \longrightarrow CH_3PO(OCH_3)_2 \qquad (17\text{-}7.3)$$

Orthophosphoric acid, H_3PO_4, commonly called phosphoric acid, is one of the oldest known and most important phosphorus compounds. It is made in vast quantities, usually as 85% syrupy acid, by the direct reaction of ground phosphate rock with sulfuric acid and also by the direct burning of phosphorus and subsequent hydration of P_4O_{10}. The pure acid is a colorless crystalline solid (mp 42.35 °C). It is very stable and has essentially no oxidizing properties below 350–400 °C. At elevated temperatures it is fairly reactive toward metals, which reduce it, and it will attack quartz. *Pyrophosphoric acid* is also produced:

$$2H_3PO_4 \longrightarrow H_2O + H_4P_2O_7 \qquad (17\text{-}7.4)$$

but this conversion is slow at room temperature.

The acid is tribasic: at 25 °C, $pK_1 = 2.15$, $pK_2 = 7.1$, $pK_3 \approx 12.4$. The pure acid and its crystalline hydrates have tetrahedral PO_4 groups connected by hydrogen bonds. Hydrogen bonding persists in the concentrated solutions and is responsible for the syrupy nature. For solutions of concentration less than ~50%, the phosphate anions are hydrogen bonded to the liquid water rather than to other phosphate anions.

Phosphates and the polymerized phosphate anions (for which the free acids are unknown) are discussed in Section 5-4. Large numbers of *phosphate esters* can be made by the reaction

$$OPCl_3 + 3ROH = OP(OR)_3 + 3HCl \qquad (17\text{-}7.5)$$

or by oxidation of trialkylphosphites. Phosphate esters such as tributylphosphate are used in the extraction of certain +4 metal ions (see Section 26-2) from aqueous solutions.

Phosphate esters are also of fundamental importance in living systems. It is because of this that their hydrolysis has been much studied. Triesters are attacked by OH^- at P and by H_2O at C, depending on pH.

$$OP(OR)_3 \quad \overset{^{18}OH^-}{\nearrow} \quad OP(OR)_2(^{18}OH) + RO^- \qquad (17\text{-}7.6)$$
$$\underset{H_2{}^{18}O}{\searrow} \quad OP(OR)_2(OH) + R^{18}OH \qquad (17\text{-}7.7)$$

Diesters, which are strongly acidic, are completely in the anionic form at normal (and physiological) pH's:

$$
\begin{array}{c}
O \\
\parallel \\
RO-P-OR' \\
\mid \\
OH
\end{array}
\rightleftharpoons R'OPO_2OR^- + H^+ \qquad K \approx 10^{-1.5} \qquad (17\text{-}7.8)
$$

They are thus relatively resistant to nucleophilic attack by either OH^- or H_2O, and this is why enzymic catalysis is indispensible to achieve useful rates of reaction.

Relatively little has been firmly established as yet concerning the mechanisms of most phosphate ester hydrolyses, especially the many enzymic ones. Two important possibilities are the following:

1. One-step nucleophilic displacement (S_N2) with inversion:

$$
H_2O(\text{or } OH^-) + \underset{\substack{\nearrow \quad \nwarrow \\ {}^-O \quad\quad OR'}}{\overset{\substack{O \\ \diagdown}}{P-OR}} \longrightarrow HO-\underset{\substack{\nearrow \quad \nwarrow \\ {}^-O \quad\quad OR'}}{\overset{\substack{O \\ \diagup}}{P}} + HOR \qquad (17\text{-}7.9)
$$

2. Release of a short-lived *metaphosphate* group, PO_3^-, which rapidly recovers the four-connected orthophosphate structure:

$$-O-\underset{O}{\overset{O}{P}}-O-\underset{O}{\overset{O}{P}}-O-\underset{\underset{H^+\ O^-\ H^+}{}}{\overset{O}{\underset{\|}{P}}}-OH \longrightarrow$$

$$-\underset{O}{\overset{O}{O}}PO\underset{O}{\overset{O}{P}}OH + PO_3^- \xrightarrow{H_2O} H_2PO_4^- \qquad (17\text{-}7.10)$$

17-8   Complexes of the Group VB(15) Elements

The main aqueous chemistry of Sb^{III} is in oxalato, tartrato, and similar hydroxy acid complexes.

The $[Sb(C_2O_4)_3]^{3-}$ ion forms isolable salts and has been shown to have the incomplete pentagonal-bipyramid structure (Fig. 17-3) with a lone pair at one axial position. The tartrate complexes of antimony(III) have been much studied, and have been used medicinally as "tartar emetic" for more than 300 years. The structure of the anion in this salt, $K_2[Sb_2(d\text{-}C_4H_2O_6)_2]\cdot 3H_2O$, is shown in Fig. 17-4.

Only for bismuth is there a true cationic chemistry. Aqueous solutions contain well-defined hydrated cations, but there is no evidence for a simple aquo ion $[Bi(H_2O)_n]^{3+}$. In neutral perchlorate solutions the main species is $[Bi_6O_6]^{6+}$ or its hydrated form, $[Bi_6(OH)_{12}]^{6+}$, and at a higher pH $[Bi_6O_6(OH)_3]^{3+}$ is formed. The $[Bi_6(OH)_{12}]^{6+}$ species contains an octahedron of Bi^{3+} ions with an OH^- bridging each edge.

Figure 17-3   The $[Sb(C_2O_4)_3]^{3-}$ ion. Two oxalato, $C_2O_4{}^{2-}$, ligands are bidentate and one is monodentate. The oxygen donor atoms form a pentagonal base to the pyramid that is capped by Sb^{3+}.

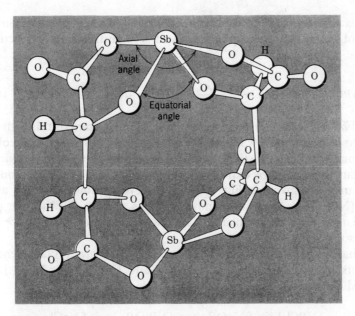

Figure 17-4 Geometry of the anion, $[Sb_2(C_4H_2O_6)_2]^{2-}$. Water molecules link the anion into sheets by hydrogen bonding to carboxylate carbon atoms. [Reproduced by permission from Tapscott, R. E., Belford, R. L., and Paul, I. C., *Coord. Chem. Rev.*, **1969**, *4*, 323.]

17-9 Phosphorus–Nitrogen Compounds

Many compounds are known with P—N and P=N bonds. R_2N—P bonds are particularly stable and occur widely in combination with bonds to other univalent groups, such as P—R, P—Ar, and P—halogen.

Phosphazenes are cyclic or chain compounds that contain alternating phosphorus and nitrogen atoms with two substituents on each phosphorus atom. The three main structural types are the cyclic trimer (structure 17-III), cyclic tetramer (structure 17-IV), and the oligomer or high polymer (structure 17-V). The alternating sets of single and double bonds in structures 17-III to 17-V are written for convenience but, in general, all P—N distances are found to be equal. It appears that they are of the order of ≈1.5, since their lengths, 1.56–1.61 Å, are appreciably shorter than expected (~1.80) for P—N single

17-III   17-IV   17-V

bonds. Hexachlorocyclotriphosphazene, $(NPCl_2)_3$, is a key intermediate in the synthesis of many other phosphazenes and is manufactured by reaction 17-9.1:

$$n\text{PCl}_5 + n\text{NH}_4\text{Cl} \xrightarrow{\text{in C}_2\text{H}_2\text{Cl}_4 \text{ or C}_6\text{H}_5\text{Cl}} (\text{NPCl}_2)_n + 4n\text{HCl} \quad (17\text{-}9.1)$$

Reaction 17-9.1 produces a mixture of cyclic $[NPCl_2]_n$ compounds with $n = 3$, $4, 5, \ldots$, as well as some low molecular weight linear polymers. Control of the reaction conditions can give 90% yields of either the compound with $n = 3$ or 4, which can be purified by extraction, recrystallization, or sublimation.

Structures are given in Fig. 17-5 of the cyclic trimer $[NPCl_2]_3$ and the tetramer $[NPClPh]_4$. Most six-membered rings such as $[NPX_2]_3$ are planar, while the larger rings are nonplanar. The fluoroderivatives, $[NPF_2]_n$, are planar, or nearly so, when $n = 3$–6.

The majority of the reactions of phosphazenes involve replacement of the substituents at phosphorus by nucleophiles (OH, OR, NR_2, or R, e.g.) to give substituted derivatives, as in reactions 17-9.2 to 17-9.4:

$$[NPCl_2]_3 + 6NaOR \longrightarrow [NP(OR)_2]_3 + 6NaCl \quad (17\text{-}9.2)$$

$$[NPCl_2]_3 + 6NaSCN \longrightarrow [NP(SCN)_2]_3 + 6NaCl \quad (17\text{-}9.3)$$

$$[NPF_2]_3 + 6PhLi \longrightarrow [NPPh_2]_3 + 6LiF \quad (17\text{-}9.4)$$

Hexachlorotriphosphazene, $[NPCl_2]_3$, is especially susceptible to hydrolysis as in Eq. 17-9.5:

$$[NPCl_2]_3 + 6H_2O \longrightarrow [NP(OH)_2]_3 + 6HCl \quad (17\text{-}9.5)$$

Hexachlorotriphosphazene undergoes a ring opening polymerization above 250 °C to give the linear polydichlorophosphazene represented in structure 17-VI. Although the dichloro polymer is hydrolytically unstable, it is readily converted, by reactions analogous to those of the cyclic trimer, to derivatives such as structures 17-VII and 17-VIII. The properties of such polymers depend largely on the nature of the groups attached to phosphorus. Especially

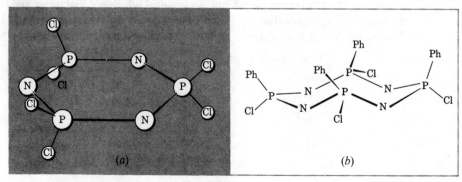

Figure 17-5   The structures of two representative cyclic phosphazenes (*a*) $[NPCl_2]_3$ and (*b*) all-*cis*-$[NPClPh]_4$.

stable fibers and useful elastomers are obtained when the substituents are the perfluoroalkoxy groups such as $CF_3(CF_2)_nCH_2O^-$ or the amides such as $NHMe^-$.

$$\left[\begin{array}{c} Cl \\ | \\ -N{=}P- \\ | \\ Cl \end{array}\right]_n \qquad \left[\begin{array}{c} OR \\ | \\ -N{=}P- \\ | \\ OR \end{array}\right]_n \qquad \left[\begin{array}{c} NR_2 \\ | \\ -N{=}P- \\ | \\ NR_2 \end{array}\right]_n$$

17-VI   17-VII   17-VIII

STUDY GUIDE

Study Questions

A. Review

1. Why does phosphorus form P_4 molecules while nitrogen is N_2?
2. How are white and red phosphorus obtained from phosphate rock?
3. What are the principal factors responsible for the differences between the chemistry of nitrogen and the chemistry of phosphorus?
4. Explain the differences in (a) basicity and (b) donor ability toward transition metals of NMe_3 and PMe_3.
5. Write balanced equations for the reactions:
   (i) $P_4 + HNO_3$ (ii) $AsCl_3 + H_2O$ (iii) $POCl_3 + H_2O$
   (iv) $P_4O_{10} + HNO_3$ (v) $P_4O_6 + H_2O$ (vi) Zn_3P + dilute HCl
6. How is PCl_5 made? What is its structure in solutions and in the solid state?
7. Draw the structures of P_4O_{10} and As_4O_6.
8. What happens when H_2S is passed into acidic (HCl) solution of trivalent P, As, Sb, and Bi?
9. What are the structures of (a) phosphorous acid and (b) triethylphosphite?
10. What is the Michaelis–Arbusov reaction?
11. Why is pure phosphoric acid syrupy?
12. What is the structure of "tartar emetic"?
13. What are phosphazenes and how are they made?
14. Describe the interaction of water with $SbCl_3$ and $BiCl_3$.
15. How is PF_5 prepared? Give its main chemical properties.
16. Compare the structure and properties of nitric and phosphoric acids.

B. Additional Exercises

1. Discuss the importance of $d\pi-p\pi$ bonding for phosphorus. Give examples, with explanations for differences between the chemistries of N and P.
2. NF_3 has no donor properties at all, but PF_3 forms numerous complexes with metals, for example, $Ni(PF_3)_4$. Explain.
3. P and Sb both form stable pentachlorides but As does not. Why?
4. Compare the oxides of N with those of P.

5. Show with drawings the formation of the π bonds in R_3PO and $R_3P{=}CH_2$. What is the geometry at P in each case?

6. Draw the Lewis diagrams and discuss the geometries in PF_3, PF_5, and PF_6^-.

7. Write balanced equations for the following reactions.

   (a) The hydrolysis of PCl_3.

   (b) Air oxidation of PCl_3.

   (c) The hydrolysis of $BiCl_3$.

   (d) A synthesis of triethylphosphine.

   (e) Oxidation of PCl_3 by F_2.

   (f) Methanolysis of trichlorophosphine oxide.

   (g) Dissolution of PCl_5 in polar solvents.

   (h) Ammonolysis of PCl_3.

   (i) The synthesis of hexachlorotriphosphazene.

8. Suggest a synthesis of $[NPMe_2]_3$ starting with PCl_5, NH_4Cl, and a Grignard reagent.

9. How many isomers are possible for the partially substituted cyclic trimer $N_3P_3F_2Cl_4$?

10. Discuss the changes in hybridization, oxidation state, and geometry (use the AB_xE_y classification scheme of Chapter 3 and VSEPR theory) that take place on forming

   (a) SbF_6^- from SbF_5 (b) PCl_4^+ from PCl_5

   (c) PCl_6^- from PCl_5 (d) $[SbF_5]^{2-}$ from SbF_5

11. Use the Lewis theory of acids and bases to discuss the reactions that are found in Problem 10.

C. Questions from the Literature of Inorganic Chemistry

1. Consider the paper by B. H. Christian, R. J. Gillespie, and J. F. Sawyer, *Inorg. Chem.*, **1981,** *20,* 3410–3420.

   (a) Salts of the cations $As_3S_4^+$ and $As_3Se_4^+$ have been prepared starting with As_4S_4 or As–Se alloys and using (as oxidants) the Lewis acids AsF_5 or SbF_5. Draw Lewis diagrams for the cations and anions that are formed in these reactions.

   (b) What (different) products were obtained upon oxidation of As_4F_4 by $SbCl_5$, Cl_2, or Br_2? Why?

   (c) How does the structure of the starting material As_4S_4 differ from its oxidized product, $As_3S_4^+$?

2. The dianion $[Sb_2OCl_6]^{2-}$ is described in a paper by M. Hall and D. B. Sowerby, *J. Chem. Soc., Chem. Commun.,* **1979,** 1134–1135.

   (a) How is this dianion uniquely different from other antimony chlorides or antimony oxide chlorides?

   (b) Show with drawings how each Sb^{III} center can be viewed as an AB_5E system (according to the classification of Chapter 3) in which the "sixth position" of a pseudooctahedron is occupied by a lone electron pair.

   (c) Is there evidence among the structural data (either in terms of bond angles or bond lengths) for the presence of a lone pair of electrons on each Sb^{III} center? Answer in terms of VSEPR theory (Chapter 3).

3. The structure of the ion $[SbCl_5]^{2-}$ was reported by R. K. Wismer and R. A. Jacobson, *Inorg. Chem.,* **1974,** *13,* 1678–1680.

   (a) Use VSEPR theory and the AB_xE_y classification that was presented in Chapter 3 to discuss the hybridizations and geometries around antimony in the compounds $SbCl_3$, $(NH_4)_2SbCl_5$, $(pyH)SbCl_4$, and $[Co(NH_3)_6][SbCl_6]$.

(b) In the crystals of K_2SbCl_5, the square-pyramidal $[SbCl_5]^{2-}$ units were found to be packed base to base. The short interion Sb–Sb distance indicates little *stereochemical effect* from a localized lone pair of electrons on Sb. Elaborate and explain.

4. Consider the work by P. Wisian-Neilson and R. H. Neilson, *J. Am. Chem. Soc.,* **1980,** *102,* 2848–2849.

   (a) What problems normally arise in the syntheses of *fully alkylated* polymeric dialkylphosphazenes, $[NPR_2]_n$, starting with $[NPCl_2]_n$ polymers and using Grignard reagents?

   (b) Compound 2 as reported in this work leads to fully alkylated polymers, $[NPR_2]_n$, without the problems mentioned in (a). Why? Show the elimination that must take place upon polymerization.

   (c) Draw the Lewis diagrams and discuss the hybridizations and geometries around all atoms in Compounds 1 and 2 of this paper.

   (d) Show at each Si, N, and P atom how a *p* or *d* orbital may become involved in a π-bond system in each Molecule 1 and 2.

   (e) Elimination reactions of Compound 1 gave a cyclic tetramer, $[NPMe_2]_4$. Show the necessary elimination reactions and draw the likely structure of the cyclized product.

SUPPLEMENTARY READING

Allcock, H. R., *Phosphorus–Nitrogen Compounds,* Academic, New York, 1972.

Allcock, H. R., "Inorganic Macromolecules," *Chem. & Eng. News,* **1985,** March 18, 22–36.

Corbridge, D. E. C., *The Structural Chemistry of Phosphorus,* Elsevier, Amsterdam, 1974.

Doak, G. O. and Freedman, L. D., *Organometallic Compounds of Arsenic, Antimony, and Bismuth,* Wiley, New York, 1970.

Emsley, J. and Hall, D., *The Chemistry of Phosphorus,* Harper & Row, New York, 1976.

Fluck, E., "The Chemistry of Phosphine," in *Topics in Current Chemistry,* Springer-Verlag, Berlin, 1973.

Goldwhite, H., *Introduction to Phosphorus Chemistry,* Cambridge University Press, Cambridge, 1981.

Mann, F. G. *Heterocyclic Derivatives of P, As, Sb, and Bi,* Wiley, New York, 1970.

McAuliffe, C. A. and Levason, W., *Phosphine, Arsine, and Stibine Complexes of the Transition Elements,* Elsevier, Amsterdam, 1979.

Toy, A. D. F., *The Chemistry of Phosphorus,* Pergamon Press, New York, 1975.

chapter 18

OXYGEN

18-1 Introduction

Oxygen compounds of all the elements except He, Ne, and possibly Ar are known. Molecular oxygen (dioxygen, O_2) reacts (at room temperature or on heating) with all other elements except the halogens, a few noble metals, and the noble gases.

The chemistry of oxygen involves the completion of the octet (neon configuration) by one of the following means:

1. Electron gain to form the oxide, O^{2-}.
2. Formation of two single covalent bonds, as in AB_2E_2 systems such as water and ethers.
3. Formation of a double bond, as in ABE_2 systems such as ketones or $Cl_4Re{=}O$.
4. Formation of a single bond, as well as electron gain, as in ABE_3 systems such as OH^- and RO^-.
5. Formation of three covalent bonds, as in AB_3E systems such as H_3O^+ and R_3O^+.
6. Formation in rare cases of four covalent bonds, as, for example, in $Be_4O(CH_3CO_2)_6$.

The wide range of physical properties shown by the binary oxides of the elements is due to the broad range of bond types from essentially ionic systems to essentially covalent ones. Thus we distinguish the highly ionic oxides (such as those of the alkali and alkaline earth metals) from the completely covalent, molecular oxides, such as CO_2. There are, however, intermediate cases such as the oxides of boron, aluminum, or silicon.

Ionic Oxides

The formation of the oxide ion from molecular oxygen requires ca. 1000 kJ mol^{-1}:

$$\tfrac{1}{2}O_2(g) = O(g) \qquad \Delta H = 248 \text{ kJ mol}^{-1} \qquad (18\text{-}1.1)$$

$$O(g) + 2e^- = O^{2-} \qquad \Delta H = 752 \text{ kJ mol}^{-1} \qquad (18\text{-}1.2)$$

In forming an ionic metal oxide, energy must also be expended to vaporize and to ionize the metal. Thus the stability of ionic metal oxides is a consequence only of the high lattice energies that are obtained with the small and highly charged oxide ion.

Where the lattice energy is not sufficient to offset the energies for ionization, and so on, oxides with substantial covalent character are formed. Examples of oxides with some covalent character are BeO, SiO_2, and oxides of boron such as B_2O_3.

Covalent or Molecular Oxides

Covalent or molecular oxides are compounds such as CO_2, SO_2, SO_3, NO_2, and so on, in which covalent bonding is dominant. Such compounds are well described by the AB_xE_y classification, as presented in Chapter 3, with some exceptions as noted in the following section. Use of the p orbitals in π bonding with other atoms is an important aspect in the bonding of molecular oxides. This may be $p\pi$–$p\pi$ bonding as in the ketones, ($R_2C{=}O$) or $p\pi$–$d\pi$ bonding as in phosphine oxides ($R_3P{=}O$).

ABE_3 Systems
Terminal oxygen atoms that bear three lone pairs of electrons are found in alkoxides (RO^-), and hydroxide (OH^-). Such oxygen atoms are considered to be sp^3 hybridized.

AB_2E_2 Systems
The compounds that fit into this class are usually angular due to the volume requirements of two lone pairs of electrons. Examples include water, alcohols, and ethers. The oxygen atoms are considered to be sp^3 hybridized, but there are wide variations from the tetrahedral bond angles due to electronic repulsions between the two lone pairs of electrons: H_2O (104.5°) and Me_2O (111°). Where the atoms bound to oxygen have d orbitals available, some $p\pi$–$d\pi$ character is often present in the bond to oxygen, and the B—A—B angles may be even larger, for example, the angle Si—O—Si in quartz is 142° and in H_3Si—O—SiH_3 it is $>150°$.

A linear B—A—B situation at oxygen occurs in some AB_2E_2 systems containing transition metals, for example, $[Cl_5Ru{-}O{-}RuCl_5]^{4-}$. The σ bonds to Ru are formed by sp hybrids on oxygen, thus leaving two pairs of π electrons on oxygen in p orbitals that are oriented perpendicular to the Ru—O—Ru axis. These filled p orbitals on oxygen interact with empty d orbitals on the Ru atoms, forming a π-bond system.

AB_3E Systems
The third example containing sp^3 hybridized oxygen atoms is that of the oxonium ions $:OH_3^+$ and $:OR_3^+$. The formation of oxonium ions is analogous to formation of ammonium ions, NH_4^+. Oxygen is less basic than nitrogen, and the oxonium ions are therefore less stable. Notice that ions of the type OH_4^{2+} are unlikely (even though $:OH_3^+$ still has a lone electron pair), because of

electrostatic repulsion of the $:OH_3^+$ ion towards another proton. As for $:NR_3$, the pyramidal $:OR_3^+$ ions undergo rapid inversion.

ABE₂ Systems

Oxygen atoms of this type include those of ketones, aldehydes, and other organic carbonyls. The oxygen atoms are sp^2 hybridized and have a roughly trigonal arrangement around the oxygen of the lone pairs E and the carbonyl carbon. The sp^2 hybridization of the carbon atom leaves one p orbital available for formation of a π bond perpendicular to the trigonal plane.

18-2   Occurrence, Properties, and Allotropy

Oxygen has three isotopes, ^{16}O (99.759%), ^{17}O (0.0374%), and ^{18}O (0.2039%). Fractional distillation of water allows concentrates containing up to 97 atom % ^{18}O or up to 4 atom % ^{17}O to be prepared. Oxygen-18 is used as a tracer in studying reaction mechanisms of oxygen compounds. Although ^{17}O has a nuclear spin ($\frac{5}{2}$), its low abundance means that, even when enriched samples are used, spectrum accumulation and/or the Fourier transform method are required. An example of ^{17}O resonance studies is the distinction between H_2O in a complex, for example, $[Co(NH_3)_5H_2O]^{3+}$, and solvent water.

Oxygen has two allotropes; dioxygen (O_2) and trioxygen or ozone (O_3). Dioxygen is paramagnetic in all phases and has the rather high dissociation energy of 496 kJ mol^{-1}. Simple valence bond theory predicts the electronic structure $:\ddot{O}{=}\ddot{O}:$ which, though accounting for the strong bond, fails to account for the paramagnetism. However, simple MO theory (Section 3-5) readily accounts for the triplet ground state having a double bond. There are several low-lying singlet states that are important in photochemical oxidations. Like NO, which has one unpaired electron in an antibonding (π^*) MO, oxygen molecules associate only weakly, and true electron pairing to form a symmetrical O_4 species does not occur even in the solid. Both liquid and solid O_2 are pale blue.

Ozone

The action of a silent electric discharge on O_2 produces O_3 in concentrations up to 10%. Ozone gas is perceptibly blue and is diamagnetic. Pure ozone obtained by fractional liquefaction of O_2—O_3 mixtures gives a deep blue, explosive liquid. The action of ultraviolet light on O_2 produces traces of O_3 in the upper atmosphere. The maximum concentration is at an altitude of ~25 km. It is of vital importance in protecting the earth's surface from excessive exposure to ultraviolet light. Ozone decomposes exothermically as in Eq. 18-2.1:

$$O_3 = \tfrac{3}{2}O_2 \qquad \Delta H = -142 \text{ kJ mol}^{-1} \qquad (18\text{-}2.1)$$

but it decomposes only slowly at 250 °C in the absence of catalysts and ultraviolet light.

The O_3 molecule is symmetrical and bent; $\angle O{-}O{-}O$, 117°; $O{-}O$,

1.28 Å. Since the O—O bond distances are 1.49 Å in HOOH (single bond) and 1.21 Å in O_2 (~ double bond), it is apparent that the O—O bonds in O_3 must have considerable double-bond character. In terms of a resonance description, this can be accounted for as in the resonance forms of structures 18-I and 18-II:

$$\overset{..}{\underset{}{O}}\overset{}{\underset{..}{O}}\overset{..}{\underset{}{O}} \longleftrightarrow \overset{..}{\underset{}{O}}\overset{}{\underset{..}{O}}\overset{..}{\underset{}{O}}$$

18-I   18-II

Chemical Properties of O_2 and O_3

Ozone is a much more powerful oxidizing agent than O_2 and reacts with many substances under conditions where O_2 will not. The reaction

$$O_3 + 2KI + H_2O \longrightarrow I_2 + 2KOH + O_2 \qquad (18\text{-}2.2)$$

is quantitative and can be used for analysis. Ozone is used for oxidations of organic compounds and in water purification. Oxidation mechanisms probably involve free radical chain processes as well as intermediates with —OOH groups. In acid solution, O_3 is exceeded in oxidizing power only by F_2, the perxenate ion $[H_2XeO_6]^{2-}$, atomic oxygen, OH radicals, and a few other such species.

The following potentials indicate the oxidizing strengths of O_2 and O_3 in ordinary aqueous solution:

$$O_2 + 4H^+(10^{-7} M) + 4e^- = 2H_2O \qquad E° = +0.815 \text{ V} \quad (18\text{-}2.3)$$

$$O_3 + 2H^+(10^{-7} M) + 2e^- = O_2 + H_2O \qquad E° = +1.65 \text{ V} \quad (18\text{-}2.4)$$

The first step in the reduction of O_2 in aprotic solvents such as DMSO and pyridine appears to be a one-electron step to give the superoxide anion:

$$O_2 + e^- = O_2^- \qquad (18\text{-}2.5)$$

whereas in aqueous solution a two-electron step occurs to give HO_2^-

$$O_2 + 2e^- + H_2O = HO_2^- + OH^- \qquad (18\text{-}2.6)$$

It can also be seen from the potential given for reaction 18-2.3 that neutral water saturated with O_2 is a fairly good oxidizing agent. For example, although Cr^{2+} is just stable toward oxidation in pure water, in oxygen-saturated water it is rapidly oxidized. Ferrous ion, Fe^{2+}, is oxidized (slowly in acid, but more rapidly in base) to Fe^{3+} in the presence of air, although in oxygen-free water it is quite stable, as shown by the potential for reaction 18-2.7:

$$Fe^{3+} + e^- = Fe^{2+} \qquad E° = +0.77 \text{ V} \qquad (18\text{-}2.7)$$

Many oxidations by oxygen in acid solution are slow, but the rates of oxidation may be vastly increased by catalytic amounts of transition metal ions, especially Cu^{2+} where a Cu^I–Cu^{II} redox cycle is involved.

The dioxygen molecule is readily soluble in organic solvents, and merely pouring these liquids in air serves to saturate them with O_2. This should be kept in mind when determining the reactivity of air-sensitive materials in solution in organic solvents.

Measurements of electronic spectra of alcohols, ethers, benzene, and even saturated hydrocarbons show that there is reaction of the charge-transfer type with the oxygen molecule. However, there is no true complex formation, since the heats of formation are negligible and the spectral changes are due to contact between the molecules at van der Waals distances. The classic example is that of *N,N*-dimethylaniline, which becomes yellow in air or oxygen but colorless again when the oxygen is removed. Such weak charge-transfer complexes make certain electronic transitions in molecules more intense; they are also a plausible first stage in photooxidations.

With certain transition metal complexes, O_2 adducts may be formed, sometimes reversibly (Section 18-7). Although the O_2 entity remains intact, the complexes may be described as having coordinated O_2^- or O_2^{2-} ions, bound to the metal in a three-membered ring or as a bridging group. Coordinated O_2 is more reactive than free O_2, and substances not directly oxidized under mild conditions can be attacked in the presence of metal complexes.

The Excited State Chemistry of Oxygen

As discussed in Chapter 3, the oxygen molecule contains two unpaired electrons in π^* molecular orbitals. This electron configuration gives rise to three electronic states, as shown in Table 18-1. The triplet state ($^3\Sigma_g^-$) is the ground state, but two excited states are also available at higher energies. These excited singlet states (especially $^1\Delta_g$) have sufficiently long lifetimes to allow them to be useful for reactions with a variety of substrates, where they cause specific oxidations, a very typical example being 1,4 addition to a 1,3-diene, as in reaction 18-2.8:

$$\text{||} \diagdown\diagup \text{||} + O_2(\text{Singlet}) \longrightarrow \begin{array}{c} \diagup \diagdown \\ \text{O—O} \end{array} \qquad (18\text{-}2.8)$$

Singlet oxygen molecules may be generated either by photochemical or chemical means. The photochemical route typically employs a sensitizer, which first absorbs energy from the light source and then transfers an appropriate amount of that energy to triplet oxygen to give an oxygen molecule in an excited (singlet) state. The sensitizer molecule or ion must be in an excited triplet state for this energy transfer to be spin allowed.

Table 18-1 The Three Electronic States Arising from the $(\pi^*)^2$ Electron Configuration of Molecular Oxygen

State	π_a^*	π_b^*	Energy
$^1\Sigma_g^+$	↑	↓	155 kJ ($\sim$13,000 cm^{-1})
$^1\Delta_g$	↑↓		92 kJ ($\sim$8,000 cm^{-1})
$^3\Sigma_g^+$	↑	↑	0 (Ground state)

The chemical generation of singlet oxygen may be accomplished as in reactions 18-2.9 and 18-2.10:

$$H_2O_2 + Cl_2 \longrightarrow 2Cl^- + 2H^+ + O_2 \tag{18-2.9}$$

$$H_2O_2 + ClO^- \longrightarrow Cl^- + H_2O + O_2 \tag{18-2.10}$$

which are accompanied by a red chemiluminescent glow.

18-3 Hydrogen Peroxide

Pure H_2O_2 is a colorless liquid (bp 152.1 °C, fp -0.41 °C). It resembles water in many of its physical properties and is even more highly associated via hydrogen bonding and 40% denser than is H_2O. It has a high dielectric constant, but its utility as an ionizing solvent is limited by its strong oxidizing nature and its ready decomposition in the presence of even traces of many heavy-metal ions according to the equation:

$$2H_2O_2 = 2H_2O + O_2 \qquad \Delta H = -99 \text{ kJ mol}^{-1} \tag{18-3.1}$$

In dilute aqueous solution it is more acidic than water:

$$H_2O_2 = H^+ + HO_2^- \qquad K_{20°C} = 1.5 \times 10^{-12} \tag{18-3.2}$$

The molecule H_2O_2 has a skew, chain structure (Fig. 18-1).

There are two methods for large-scale production of hydrogen peroxide. One is by autoxidation of an anthraquinol, such as 2-ethylanthraquinol:

$$\tag{18-3.3}$$

The resulting quinone is reduced with H_2 gas. The H_2O_2 is obtained as a 20% aqueous solution. Only O_2, H_2 and H_2O are required as raw materials.

An older and more expensive method is electrolytic oxidation of sulfuric acid or ammonium sulfate–sulfuric acid solutions to give peroxodisulfuric acid, which is then hydrolyzed to yield H_2O_2:

$$2HSO_4^- \longrightarrow HO_3S-O-O-SO_3H + 2e^- \tag{18-3.4}$$

$$H_2S_2O_8 + H_2O \longrightarrow H_2SO_5 + H_2SO_4 \qquad \text{(Rapid)} \tag{18-3.5}$$

$$H_2SO_5 + H_2O \longrightarrow H_2O_2 + H_2SO_4 \qquad \text{(Slow)} \tag{18-3.6}$$

Fractional distillation can then give 90–98% H_2O_2.

Figure 18-1 The structure of hydrogen peroxide.

The redox chemistry of H_2O_2 in aqueous solution is summarized by the
potentials:

$$H_2O_2 + 2H^+ + 2e^- = 2H_2O \qquad E° = 1.77 \text{ V} \qquad (18\text{-}3.7)$$

$$O_2 + 2H^+ + 2e^- = H_2O_2 \qquad E° = 0.68 \text{ V} \qquad (18\text{-}3.8)$$

$$HO_2^- + H_2O + 2e^- = 3OH^- \qquad E° = 0.87 \text{ V} \qquad (18\text{-}3.9)$$

These show that hydrogen peroxide is a strong oxidizing agent in either acid
or basic solution. It behaves as a reducing agent only toward very strong
oxidizing agents such as MnO_4^-.

Dilute or 30% hydrogen peroxide solutions are widely used as oxidants.
In acid solution, oxidations with hydrogen peroxide are slow, whereas in basic
solution, they are usually fast. Decomposition to H_2O and O_2, which may be
considered a self-oxidation, or disproportionation, occurs most rapidly in basic
solution; hence an excess of H_2O_2 may best be destroyed by heating in basic
solution.

Many reactions involving H_2O_2 (and also O_2) in solutions involve free
radicals. Metal-ion catalyzed decomposition of H_2O_2 and other reactions form
radicals of which HO_2 and OH are most important. The hydroperoxo radical,
HO_2, has been detected in aqueous solutions where H_2O_2 interacts with Ti^{3+},
Fe^{2+}, or Ce^{4+} ions.

18-4 Peroxides and Superoxides

These are substances that are derived formally from O_2^{2-} (peroxides) and
O_2^- (superoxides).

Ionic Peroxides

Ionic peroxides are formed by alkali metals, Ca, Sr, and Ba. Sodium peroxide
is made commercially by air oxidation of sodium. Sodium peroxide is a yellow
powder that is very hygroscopic, though thermally stable to 500 °C. It contains,
according to electron spin resonance (esr) studies, about 10% of the superoxide.

The ionic peroxides give H_2O_2 on reaction with water or dilute acids. All of the ionic peroxides are powerful oxidizing agents, converting organic materials to carbonate even at moderate temperatures. Sodium peroxide also vigorously oxidizes some metals, for example, Fe, which violently gives FeO_4^{2-}. The peroxides of the alkali metals also react with CO_2 according to Eq. 18-4.1 to give carbonates:

$$2CO_2(g) + 2M_2O_2 \longrightarrow 2M_2CO_3 + O_2 \qquad (18-4.1)$$

Peroxides may also act as reducing agents for such strongly oxidizing substances as permanganate.

Other electropositive metals such as Mg and the lanthanides also give peroxides; these are intermediate in character between the ionic ones and the essentially covalent peroxides of metals such as Zn, Cd, and Hg.

Many ionic peroxides form well-crystallized hydrates such as $Na_2O_2 \cdot 8H_2O$ and $M^{II}O_2 \cdot 8H_2O$. These contain discrete O_2^{2-} ions to which water molecules are hydrogen bonded, giving chains of the type shown in structure 18-III:

$$\cdots O_2^{2-} \cdots (H_2O_8) \cdots O_2^{2-} \cdots (H_2O)_8 \cdots$$

18-III

The formation of such stable hydrates accounts for the extreme hygroscopic nature of the crystalline peroxides.

Ionic Superoxides

Ionic superoxides, MO_2, are formed by the interaction of O_2 with K, Rb, or Cs as yellow to orange crystalline solids. NaO_2 can be obtained by reaction of Na_2O_2 with O_2 at 300 atm and 500 °C. LiO_2 cannot be isolated. Alkaline earth, Zn, and Cd superoxides occur only in small concentrations as solid solutions in the peroxides. The O_2^- ion has one unpaired electron. Superoxides are very powerful oxidizing agents. They react vigorously with water:

$$2O_2^- + H_2O = O_2 + HO_2^- + OH^- \qquad (18-4.2)$$

$$2HO_2^- = 2OH^- + O_2 \quad \text{(Slow)} \qquad (18-4.3)$$

The reaction with CO_2, which involves peroxocarbonate intermediates, is used for removal of CO_2 and regeneration of O_2 in closed systems (e.g., submarines). The overall reaction is

$$4MO_2(s) + 2CO_2(g) = 2M_2CO_3(s) + 3O_2(g) \qquad (18-4.4)$$

18-5 Other Peroxo Compounds

There are many *organic peroxides* and *hydroperoxides*. Peroxo carboxylic acids, for example, peracetic acid, $CH_3C(O)OOH$, can be obtained by the action of H_2O_2 on acid anhydrides. The peroxo acids are useful oxidants and sources of free radicals, for example, by treatment with $Fe^{2+}(aq)$. Benzoyl peroxide and cumyl hydroperoxide are moderately stable and widely used where free radical initiation is required, as in polymerization reactions.

Organic peroxo compounds are also obtained by *autoxidation* of ethers, alkenes, and the like, on exposure to air. Autoxidation is a free radical chain reaction initiated by radicals generated by interaction of oxygen and traces of metals such as Cu, Co, or Fe. The attack on specific reactive C—H bonds by a radical, $X\cdot$, gives first $R\cdot$ and then hydroperoxides that can react further:

$$RH + X^{\cdot} \longrightarrow R^{\cdot} + HX \qquad (18\text{-}5.1)$$

$$R^{\cdot} + O_2 \longrightarrow RO_2^{\cdot} \qquad (18\text{-}5.2)$$

$$RO_2^{\cdot} + RH \longrightarrow ROOH + R^{\cdot} \qquad (18\text{-}5.3)$$

Explosions can occur on distillation of oxidized solvents, and they should be washed with acidified $FeSO_4$ solution or, for ethers and hydrocarbons, passed through a column of activated alumina. Peroxides are absent when $Fe^{2+} + SCN^-$ reagent does not give a red color, indicative of the $Fe(SCN)^{2+}$ ion.

There are also many inorganic peroxo compounds where —O— is replaced by —O—O— groups, such as peroxodisulfuric acid, $(HO)_2S(O)OOS(O)(OH)_2$, mentioned previously. Potassium and ammonium peroxodisulfates (Section 19-5) are commonly used as a strong oxidizing agent in acid solution, for example, to convert C into CO_2, Mn^{2+} into MnO_4^-, or Ce^{3+} into Ce^{4+}. The last two reactions are slow and normally incomplete in the absence of silver ion as a catalyst.

It is important to make the distinction between true peroxo compounds, which contain —O—O— groups, and compounds that contain hydrogen peroxide of crystallization such as $2Na_2CO_3\cdot3H_2O_2$ or $Na_4P_2O_7\cdot nH_2O_2$.

18-6　The Dioxygenyl Cation

The interaction of PtF_6 with O_2 gives an orange solid, O_2PtF_6, isomorphous with $KPtF_6$, which contains the paramagnetic O_2^+ ion. This reaction was of importance in that it lead N. Bartlett to treat PtF_6 with xenon (Section 21-2). A number of other salts of the O_2^+ ion are known.

It is instructive to compare the various $O_2^{n\pm}$ species, since they provide an interesting illustration of the effect of varying the number of antibonding electrons on the length and stretching frequency of a bond, as the data in Table 18-2 show.

Table 18-2　Bond Values for Oxygen Species

Species	O—O distance Å	Number of π^* Electrons	$\nu_{O-O}(cm^{-1})$
O_2^+	1.12	1	1860
O_2	1.21	2	1556
O_2^-	1.33	3	1145
O_2^{2-}	1.49	4	~770

18-7 Dioxygen as a Ligand

Although the most common mode of reaction of molecular oxygen with transition metal complexes is oxidation (i.e., extraction of electrons from the metal or from its ligands), under appropriate circumstances the dioxygen molecule may, instead, become a ligand. Such reactions are termed **oxygenations,** because the dioxygen ligand retains its identity, whereas oxidation reactions are those in which the O_2 molecule loses its identity through reduction.

Oxygenation reactions are often reversible. That is, upon increasing temperature and/or reducing the partial pressure of O_2, the dioxygen ligand is lost by dissociation or by transfer to another acceptor (which may become oxidized). The process of reversible oxygenation plays an essential role in life processes. In man or other higher animals, oxygen molecules are "carried" from the lungs to the various tissues by hemoglobin and myoglobin molecules, in which $1:1$ O_2–Fe complexes are formed. In lower animals, there are molecules such as hemerythrins and hemocyanins that serve similar functions. More detail concerning these biological complexes will be given in Chapter 31.

Broadly speaking, there are two types of $1:1$ O_2–M complexes, the "end-on" and the "side-on" types, as shown in Fig. 18-2, types (a) and (b). In addition, there are many $1:2$ O_2–M complexes, as shown in Fig. 18-2, types (c) and (d). The hemoglobin and myoglobin complexes are of type (a), and there are a number of synthetic examples in which O_2 fills one position in an octahedral complex. Most of these can be considered to contain a coordinated superoxide ion, O_2^-, and thus have an unpaired electron formally present on the coordinated dioxygen unit. Many of these complexes form reversibly.

The "side-on" complexes, type (b) in Fig. 18-2, are also numerous. Many are formed reversibly, as with Vaska's compound in reaction 18-7.1:

$$
\begin{array}{ccc}
\underset{OC}{\overset{Ph_3P}{\diagdown}}Ir\underset{PPh_3}{\overset{Cl}{\diagup}} + O_2 \rightleftharpoons & \underset{OC}{\overset{Ph_3P}{\diagdown}}Ir\underset{PPh_3}{\diagup}\overset{O}{\underset{\diagdown}{\diagdown}}\overset{|}{\underset{O}{}}Cl
\end{array}
\tag{18-7.1}
$$

These are generally best regarded as peroxide complexes, that is, containing the O_2^{2-} ligand. The complexes in Fig. 18-2, types (c) and (d) are also best regarded as peroxide complexes.

Figure 18-2 The four structural types of dioxygen complexes.

STUDY GUIDE

Study Questions

A. Review

1. Give the electron configuration of the oxygen atom.
2. Give two examples of oxonium ions. What is their structure?
3. Describe the carbon–oxygen bond in acetone.
4. Describe the interaction with water of acidic, basic, and neutral oxides. Give two examples of each case.
5. Explain why the oxygen molecule is paramagnetic.
6. Write out the electron configurations of the two excited state singlets found in Table 18-1.
7. Describe the preparation in the laboratory of ozone.
8. How is hydrogen peroxide made?
9. Write balanced equations for the following reactions: (a) H_2O_2 and $KMnO_4$ in acidic solution; (b) $Fe(OH)_2$ and O_2 in basic solution; (c) sodium peroxide and CO_2; and (d) potassium superoxide and water.
10. What is the difference between oxygenation and oxidation?

B. Additional Exercises

1. Prepare MO energy-level diagrams for all of the ions O_2^{n+} that are chemically important, and determine the bond order and the expected magnetic moment (μ_{eff} in Bohr magnetons, as discussed in Chapter 2).
2. Classify the oxygen atoms in the following systems according to the AB_xE_y scheme of Chapter 3, and, where appropriate, discuss the geometry about oxygen in terms of the VSEPR theory:
   (a) O_2 and O_3 (b) O_2^- and O_2^{2-}
   (c) CH_3OH and H_2O (d) CO_2 and SO_3
   (e) H_2O_2 and OH^- (f) Me_2O and CH_3CO_2H
   (g) $CH_3C(O)OOH$ (h) peroxodisulfuric acid
3. Draw the orbitals as they interact to form the π-bond systems in
   (a) ketones   (b) carbonate ion
   (c) $[Cl_5Ru—O—RuCl_5]^{4-}$ (d) ozone
   (e) triphenyl phosphine oxide   (f) $H_3Si—O—SiH_3$
   (g) $OSCl_2$
4. Calculate the standard redox potential for the air oxidation of Fe^{2+} in aqueous solution.

C. Questions from the Literature of Inorganic Chemistry

1. Compare the structures and properties of two very different "reversible oxygen complexes" as reported by S. J. La Placa and J. A. Ibers, *J. Am. Chem. Soc.*, **1965**, *87*, 2581–2586, and as reported by A. L. Crumbliss and F. Basolo, *J. Am. Chem. Soc.*, **1970**, *92*, 55–60. See also L. Vaska, *Science*, **1963**, *140*, 809.
   (a) Should the oxygen ligands in these complexes be considered to be O_2, O_2^-, or O_2^{2-} ligands?

(b) How do magnetic data support or conflict with your answer to (a)?

(c) What should be the approximate O—O distances in the cobalt–O_2 compounds of Crumbliss? ˙

2. Consider the work by M. M. Morrison, J. L. Roberts, Jr., and D. T. Sawyer, *Inorg. Chem.*, **1979,** *18,* 1971–1973.

(a) What reaction takes place between OH^- and H_2O_2 in pyridine solution?

(b) What is formed upon electrochemical reduction of H_2O_2 in pyridine solution?

(c) After electrochemical reduction of H_2O_2 in pyridine solution, what reaction takes place between HO_2^- and H_2O_2?

(d) How are the reactions for (c) and (a) related?

(e) What role does solvent play in these reactions? What is different about these redox reactions in water and in pyridine?

SUPPLEMENTARY READING

Bailey, P. S., *Ozonation in Organic Chemistry*, Academic, New York, 1978.

Dotto, L. and Schiff, H., *The Ozone War,* Doubleday, New York, 1978.

Greenwood, G. and Hill, H. O. A., "Oxygen and Life," *Chem. Br.,* **1982,** 194.

Hayaishi, O., *Molecular Oxygen in Biology,* North-Holland, Amsterdam, 1974.

Hoare, P. J., *The Electrochemistry of Oxygen,* Wiley, New York, 1968.

Horvath, M., Bilitzky, L., and Huttner, J., *Ozone,* Elsevier, Amsterdam, 1985.

Murphy, J. S. and Orr, J. R., *Ozone Chemistry and Technology*, Franklin Institute Press, Philadelphia, 1975.

Patai, S., Ed., *The Chemistry of the Hydroxyl Group,* Wiley-Interscience, New York, 1971.

Schaap, A. P., Ed., *Singlet Molecular Oxygen,* Wiley, New York, 1976.

Severn, D., *Organic Peroxides,* Vols. I–III, Wiley-Interscience, New York, 1972.

Valentine, J. S., "The Dioxygen Ligand in Mononuclear Group VIII Transition Metal Complexes," *Chem. Rev.,* **1973,** *73,* 235.

Vaska, L., "Dioxygen Metal Complexes," *Acc. Chem. Res.,* **1976,** *9,* 175.

chapter 19

THE GROUP VIB(16) ELEMENTS: SULFUR, SELENIUM, TELLURIUM, AND POLONIUM

19-1 Introduction

The position of these elements in the periodic table has been discussed in Chapter 8, and some properties are listed in Table 8-6. These elements bear little resemblance to oxygen for the following reasons:

1. Sulfur, selenium, tellurium, and polonium have lower electronegativities than oxygen, and their compounds consequently have less ionic character. The relative stabilities of bonds to other elements are also different, and, in particular, the importance of hydrogen bonding is drastically lowered. Only very weak $S \cdots H-S$ bonds exist, and H_2S is totally different from H_2O (Chapter 7).

2. For sulfur particularly, as in other third-row elements, there is multiple $d\pi-p\pi$ bonding, but little if any $p\pi-p\pi$ bonding. The short $S-O$ distances in SO_4^{2-} (where s and p orbitals are used in σ bonding) is a result of multiple $d\pi-p\pi$ bond character. The latter arises from the flow of electrons from filled $p\pi$ orbitals on O atoms to empty $d\pi$ orbitals on S atoms.

3. Valence for S, Se, Te, and Po atoms is not confined to 2, and d orbitals can be utilized to form more than four bonds to other elements. Examples are SF_6 and $Te(OH)_6$.

4. Sulfur has a strong tendency to catenation, equaled or exceeded only by carbon. Sulfur forms compounds for which there are no O, Se, or Te analogs known. Examples are polysulfide ions, S_n^{2-}, polythionate ions, $[O_3S-S_n-SO_3]^{2-}$, and compounds of the type XS_nX, where $X = H$, Cl, CN, or NR_2.

The changes in the properties of compounds on going from S to Po can be associated with the increasing size of the atoms and with the decreasing electronegativity, from top to bottom in the group. Some examples of trends in properties of compounds that arise for these reasons are

(a) The decreasing stability of the hydrides, H_2E.

(b) The increasing tendency to form complex ions such as $SeBr_6^{2-}$.

(c) The appearance of metallic properties for Te and Po atoms. Thus the oxides MO_2 are ionic and basic, reacting with HCl to give the chlorides.

19-2 Occurrence and Reactions of the Elements

Sulfur occurs widely in nature as the element, as H_2S and SO_2, in metal sulfide ores, and as sulfates such as gypsum and anhydrite ($CaSO_4$), magnesium sulfate, and so on. Sulfur is obtained on a vast scale from natural hydrocarbon gases such as those in Alberta, Canada, which contain up to 30% H_2S; this is removed by interaction with SO_2, obtained from burning sulfur in air,

$$S + O_2 = SO_2 \tag{19-2.1}$$

$$2H_2S + SO_2 = 3S + 2H_2O \tag{19-2.2}$$

Selenium and tellurium are less abundant but frequently occur as selenide and telluride minerals in sulfide ores, particularly those of Ag and Au. They are recovered from flue dusts from combustion chambers for sulfide ores.

Polonium occurs in U and Th minerals as a product of radioactive decay series. The most accessible isotope, ^{210}Po (α, 138.4 days) can be made in gram quantities by irradiation of Bi in nuclear reactors:

$$^{209}Bi(n, \gamma)^{210}Bi \xrightarrow{\beta^-} {}^{210}Po \tag{19-2.3}$$

The Po can be separated by sublimation on heating. It is intensely radioactive and special handling techniques are required. The chemistry resembles that of Te but is somewhat more "metallic."

The physical properties and structures of the elements have been described (Chapter 8). On melting, S_8 first gives a yellow, transparent, mobile liquid that becomes dark and increasingly viscous above ca. 160 °C. The maximum viscosity occurs ca. 200 °C but on further heating the mobility increases until the boiling point, 444.6 °C, where the liquid is dark red. The "melting point" of S_8 is actually a decomposition point. Just after melting, rings with an average of 13.8 sulfur atoms are formed and at higher temperature, still larger rings. Then in the high viscosity region there are giant macromolecules that are probably chains with radical ends. At higher temperatures, highly colored S_3 and S_4 molecules are present to the extent of 1 to 3% at the boiling point. The nature of the physical changes and of the species involved are by no means fully understood.

Sulfur vapor contains S_8 and at higher temperatures S_2 molecules. The latter, like O_2, are paramagnetic with two unpaired electrons, and account for the blue color of the hot vapor.

Cyclosulfurs other than S_8, with ring sizes from S_6 to S_{20}, can be prepared by specific synthetic routes. They are all unstable in solution relative to S_8, but solutions of S_8 do contain, at equilibrium, about 0.3% S_6 and 0.8% S_7, both of which are much more reactive than S_8.

Sulfur, Se, and Te burn in air on heating to form the dioxides; they also react on heating with halogens, most metals, and nonmetals. They are attacked by hot oxidizing acids like H_2SO_4 or HNO_3.

In oleums (Section 7-11), S, Se, and Te dissolve to give highly colored solutions that contain cations in which the element is in a fractional oxidation state. Salts of these cations that have stoichiometries M_4^{2+}, M_8^{2+}, and M_{16}^{2+}

have been obtained by selective oxidation of the elements with SbF_5 or AsF_5 in liquid HF. For example,

$$S_8 + 3SbF_5 = S_8^{2+} + 2SbF_6^- + SbF_3 \tag{19-2.4}$$

or by reactions in molten $AlCl_3$, for example,

$$7Te + TeCl_4 + 4AlCl_3 = 2Te_4^{2+} + 4AlCl_4^- \tag{19-2.5}$$

The S_4^{2+}, Se_4^{2+}, and Te_4^{2+} ions are square (structure 19-I) and there is probably a six π-electron quasiaromatic system. The green Se_8^{2+} ion has a ring structure (structure 19-II). The S_{16}^{2+} and Se_{16}^{2+} ions have two M_8 rings joined together.

19-I

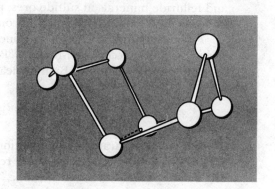

19-II

The reaction of sulfur with the double bonds of natural and synthetic rubbers, a process called vulcanization, is of great technical importance. It leads to formation of S bridges between carbon chains and, hence, to strengthening of rubber.

All reactions of S_8 must involve initial ring opening to give sulfur chains or chain compounds. Many reactions involve nucleophilic reactants, for example,

$$S_8 + 8CN^- \longrightarrow 8SCN^- \tag{19-2.6}$$

$$S_8 + 8Na_2SO_3 \longrightarrow 8Na_2S_2O_3 \tag{19-2.7}$$

$$S_8 + 8Ph_3P \longrightarrow 8Ph_3PS \tag{19-2.8}$$

Such reactions proceed by a series of steps such as:

$$S_8 + CN^- \longrightarrow SSSSSSSSCN^- \tag{19-2.9}$$

$$S_6\text{—}S\text{—}SCN^- + CN^- \longrightarrow S_6SCN^- + SCN^- \quad \text{and so on} \tag{19-2.10}$$

Sulfur–sulfur bonds occur in a variety of compounds, and —S—S— bridges are especially important in certain enzymes and other proteins.

19-3 Hydrides, EH₂

These are obtained by the action of acids on metal sulfides, selenides, or tellurides. They are extremely poisonous gases with revolting odors. The toxicity of H_2S far exceeds that of HCN. The thermal stability and bond strengths decrease down the series, whereas the acidity in water increases.

Hydrogen sulfide dissolves in water to give a solution ca. 0.1 M at 1 atm. Its dissociation constants are

$$H_2S + H_2O = H_3O^+ + SH^- \qquad K = 1 \times 10^{-7} \qquad (19\text{-}3.1)$$

$$SH^- + H_2O = H_3O^+ + S^{2-} \qquad K = \sim 10^{-14} \qquad (19\text{-}3.2)$$

Owing to this small second dissociation constant, essentially only SH^- ions are present in solutions of ionic sulfides, and S^{2-} occurs only in very alkaline solutions (>8 M NaOH) as

$$S^{2-} + H_2O = SH^- + OH^- \qquad K = \sim 1 \qquad (19\text{-}3.3)$$

The compounds H_2S_2 to H_2S_6 are generally known as sulfanes; they contain —SS— to —SSSSSS— chains. They can be obtained by reactions such as

$$2H_2S(\ell) + S_nCl_2 = 2HCl(g) + H_2S_{n+2}(\ell) \qquad (19\text{-}3.4)$$

The anions of the sulfanes (polysulfides, S_n^{2-}) are also easily obtained as salts. Examples are Na_2S_5, K_2S_6, and BaS_4. In addition, the S_4^{2-} and S_5^{2-} ions can serve as chelating ligands, in complexes such as $[Pt(S_5)_3]^{2-}$, whose structure is shown in Fig. 19-1. The latter is chiral and may be resolved into enantiomorphs.

Figure 19-1 A complex ion of Pt^IV in which the three S_5^{2-} ligands are each bidentate.

19-4 Halides and Oxohalides of Sulfur

Sulfur Fluorides

Direct fluorination of S_8 yields mainly SF_6 and traces of S_2F_{10} and SF_4. The *tetrafluoride*, SF_4 (bp $-30\,°C$) is evolved as a gas when SCl_2 is refluxed with NaF in acetonitrile at 78 to 80 °C.

$$3SCl_2 + 4NaF = SF_4 + S_2Cl_2 + 4NaCl \qquad (19\text{-}4.1)$$

SF_4 is extremely reactive, and instantly hydrolyzed by water to SO_2 and HF. It is a very selective fluorinating agent converting C=O and P=O groups smoothly into CF_2 and PF_2, and CO_2H and $P(O)OH$ groups into CF_3 and PF_3 groups.

Sulfur hexafluoride is very resistant to chemical attack. Because of its inertness, high dielectric strength, and molecular weight, it is used as a gaseous insulator in high-voltage generators and other electrical equipment. The low reactivity is presumably due to a combination of factors including high S—F bond strength, coordinative saturation, and steric hindrance at sulfur. The inertness of SF_6 is due to kinetic factors and not to thermodynamic stability, since its reaction with H_2O to give SO_3 and HF would be decidedly favorable ($\Delta G = -460$ kJ mol^{-1}).

Sulfur Chlorides

The chlorination of molten sulfur gives S_2Cl_2, an orange liquid of revolting smell. By using an excess of Cl_2, with traces of $FeCl_3$ or I_2 as catalyst, at room temperature, an equilibrium mixture of SCl_2 (ca. 85%) and S_2Cl_2 is obtained. The dichloride, SCl_2, readily loses chlorine within a few hours, as in the equilibrium of Eq. 19-4.2:

$$2SCl_2 = S_2Cl_2 + Cl_2 \qquad (19\text{-}4.2)$$

but it can be obtained pure as a dark red liquid by fractional distillation in the presence of PCl_5, which stabilizes SCl_2.

Sulfur chlorides are solvents for sulfur, giving dichlorosulfanes up to about $S_{100}Cl_2$, which are used in the vulcanization of rubber. They are also useful as mild chlorinating agents.

Thionyl chloride, $SOCl_2$, is obtained by reaction 19-4.3:

$$SO_2 + PCl_5 \longrightarrow SOCl_2 + POCl_3 \qquad (19\text{-}4.3)$$

It is a colorless fuming liquid (bp 80 °C) that is readily hydrolyzed as in Eq. 19-4.4:

$$SOCl_2 + H_2O \longrightarrow SO_2 + 2HCl \qquad (19\text{-}4.4)$$

Because the products of reactions such as Eq. 19-4.4 are volatile (and therefore easily removed), thionyl chloride is often used to prepare anhydrous chlorides, such as iron (III) chloride, as in reactions 19-4.5 and 19-4.6:

$$Fe(OH)_3 + 3SOCl_2 \longrightarrow 3SO_2 + 3HCl + FeCl_3 \qquad (19\text{-}4.5)$$

$$FeCl_3 \cdot 6H_2O + 6SOCl_2 \longrightarrow 6SO_2 + 12HCl + FeCl_3 \qquad (19\text{-}4.6)$$

Thionyl chloride has a pyramidal structure with sulfur at the apex. Sulfur can be considered to be sp^3 hybridized, and it should be classified as an AB_3E system. The presence of one lone pair on sulfur allows thionyl chloride to act as a weak Lewis base. Some $d\pi–p\pi$ bonding between S and O is present.

Sulfuryl chloride, SO_2Cl_2, is obtained by reaction 19-4.7:

$$SO_2 + Cl_2 \longrightarrow SO_2Cl_2 \qquad (19\text{-}4.7)$$

The reaction requires a catalyst such as $FeCl_3$. Sulfuryl chloride is a colorless liquid that fumes in moist air, due to hydrolysis. It finds use as a chlorinating agent for organic compounds. The structure of sulfuryl chloride may be considered to be derived from a tetrahedron.

19-5 Oxides and Oxo Acids

In Table 19-1 are listed the formulas and structures of the principal oxo acids of sulfur. In each case the sulfur may be considered to be roughly sp^3 hybridized and to fall into either classification AB_3E or AB_4. Extensive $d\pi–p\pi$ bonding between oxygen and sulfur is to be expected. We approach the chemistry of the acids by considering that they are derived from hydration of the acidic anhydrides SO_2 or SO_3 or by protonation of the corresponding anions (e.g., sulfates or sulfites, etc.).

The Dioxides

The *dioxides* are obtained by burning the elements in air. Sulfur dioxide is produced when many sulfides are heated in air. Selenium and tellurium dioxides are also obtained by treating the metals with hot nitric acid to form H_2SeO_3 and $2TeO_2 \cdot HNO_3$, respectively, and then heating these to drive off water or nitric acid.

Sulfur dioxide is a gas with a pungent smell. The molecule is angular. Liquid SO_2 dissolves many organic and inorganic substances and is used as a solvent for nmr studies as well as in preparative reactions. The liquid does not undergo self-ionization and its conductivity is mainly a reflection of the purity.

Sulfur dioxide has lone pairs and can act as a Lewis base. However, it also acts as a Lewis acid giving complexes, for example, with amines as in Me_3NSO_2 and with electron-rich transition metal complexes. In the crystalline compound $SbF_5 \cdot SO_2$, which is of interest because of the use of SO_2 as a solvent for super-acid systems (Section 7-13), the SO_2 is bound as in structure 19-III. The bonding in structure 19-IV differs in that the S atom is bound to the metal.

Table 19-1 The Principal Oxo Acids of Sulfur

Name	Formula	Structure[a]
Acids Containing One Sulfur Atom		
Sulfurous[b]	H_2SO_3	SO_3^{2-} (in sulfites)
Sulfuric	H_2SO_4	$\begin{array}{c} O \\ \parallel \\ O-S-OH \\ \mid \\ OH \end{array}$
Acids Containing Two Sulfur Atoms		
Thiosulfuric	$H_2S_2O_3$	$\begin{array}{c} OH \\ \mid \\ HO-S-S \\ \parallel \\ O \end{array}$
Dithionous[b]	$H_2S_2O_4$	$\begin{array}{c} O\quad O \\ \parallel\quad\parallel \\ HO-S-S-OH \end{array}$
Disulfurous[b]	$H_2S_2O_5$	$\begin{array}{c} O\quad O \\ \parallel\quad\parallel \\ HO-S-S-OH \\ \parallel \\ O \end{array}$
Dithionic	$H_2S_2O_6$	$\begin{array}{c} O\quad O \\ \parallel\quad\parallel \\ HO-S-S-OH \\ \parallel\quad\parallel \\ O\quad O \end{array}$
Disulfuric	$H_2S_2O_7$	$\begin{array}{c} O\qquad O \\ \parallel\qquad\parallel \\ HO-S-O-S-OH \\ \parallel\qquad\parallel \\ O\qquad O \end{array}$
Acids Containing Three or More Sulfur Atoms		
Polythionic	$H_2S_{n+2}O_6$	$\begin{array}{c} O\qquad O \\ \parallel\qquad\parallel \\ HO-S-S_n-S-OH \\ \parallel\qquad\parallel \\ O\qquad O \end{array}$
Peroxo Acids		
Peroxomonosulfuric	H_2SO_5	$\begin{array}{c} O \\ \parallel \\ HOO-S-OH \\ \parallel \\ O \end{array}$
Peroxodisulfuric	$H_2S_2O_8$	$\begin{array}{c} O\qquad\qquad O \\ \parallel\qquad\qquad\parallel \\ HO-S-O-O-S-OH \\ \parallel\qquad\qquad\parallel \\ O\qquad\qquad O \end{array}$

[a]In most cases the structure given is inferred from the structure of anions in salts of the acid.
[b]Free acid unknown.

19-III   19-IV

Metal–sulfur bonding appears to be general in transition metal species. Sulfur dioxide also undergoes "insertion" reactions (Chapter 30) with metal–carbon bonds, for example,

$$RCH_2HgOAc + SO_2 \longrightarrow RCH_2SO_2HgOAc \qquad (19\text{-}5.1)$$

$$(CH_3)_4Sn + SO_2 \longrightarrow (CH_3)_3SnSO_2CH_3 \qquad (19\text{-}5.2)$$

Sulfur dioxide is quite soluble in water; such solutions, which possess acidic properties, have long been referred to as solutions of *sulfurous acid*, H_2SO_3. However, H_2SO_3 is either not present or present only in infinitesimal quantities in such solutions. The so-called hydrate, $H_2SO_3 \cdot \sim 6H_2O$, is the gas hydrate (Section 9-5), $SO_2 \cdot \sim 7H_2O$. The equilibria in aqueous solutions of SO_2 are best represented as

$$SO_2 + xH_2O = SO_2 \cdot xH_2O \qquad \text{(hydrated } SO_2\text{)} \qquad (19\text{-}5.3)$$

$$[SO_2 \cdot xH_2O = H_2SO_3 \qquad K \ll 1] \qquad (19\text{-}5.4)$$

$$SO_2 \cdot xH_2O = HSO_3^- (aq) + H_3O^+ + (x - 2)H_2O \qquad (19\text{-}5.5)$$

and the first acid dissociation constant for "sulfurous acid" is properly defined as follows:

$$K_1 = \frac{[HSO_3^-][H^+]}{[\text{Total dissolved } SO_2] - [HSO_3^-] - [SO_3^{2-}]} = 1.3 \times 10^{-2} \qquad (19\text{-}5.6)$$

Although sulfurous acid does not exist, two series of salts, the *bisulfites*, containing HSO_3^-, and the *sulfites*, containing SO_3^{2-}, are well known. The SO_3^{2-} ion in crystals is pyramidal. Only the water-soluble alkali sulfites and bisulfites are commonly encountered.

Heating solid bisulfites or passing SO_2 into their aqueous solutions affords *pyrosulfites*:

$$2MHSO_3 \overset{\text{Heat}}{\rightleftharpoons} M_2S_2O_5 + H_2O \qquad (19\text{-}5.7)$$

$$HSO_3^- (aq) + SO_2 = HS_2O_5^- (aq) \qquad (19\text{-}5.8)$$

$$SO_2 + Na_2CO_3(aq) \xrightarrow{\text{Cold}} NaHSO_3(aq) \xrightarrow[\text{excess}]{SO_2 \text{ in}} Na_2S_2O_5$$

Figure 19-2   Some reactions of sulfites.

Whereas pyro acids, for example, pyrosulfuric, $H_2S_2O_7$, (Section 7-11) usually have oxygen bridges, the pyrosulfite ion has an unsymmetrical structure, $O_2S—SO_3$. Some important reactions of sulfites are shown in Fig. 19-2.

Solutions of SO_2 and of sulfites possess reducing properties and are often used as reducing agents:

$$SO_4^{2-} + 4H^+ + (x - 2)H_2O + 2e^- = SO_2 \cdot xH_2O \qquad E^0 = 0.17 \text{ V} \qquad (19\text{-}5.9)$$

$$SO_4^{2-} + H_2O + 2e^- = SO_3^{2-} + 2\ OH^- \qquad E^0 = -0.93 \text{ V} \qquad (19\text{-}5.10)$$

Selenium dioxide is a white volatile solid; the gas consists of discrete and symmetrically bent molecules very similar to those of SO_2. In the solid state, the molecules of SeO_2 associate through $O \rightarrow Se$ donor bonds. For TeO_2, this type of association through adduct formation is so strong that the compound is not volatile.

The Trioxides

Sulfur trioxide is obtained by reaction of SO_2 with O_2, a reaction that is thermodynamically very favorable but extremely slow in the absence of a catalyst such as platinum sponge, V_2O_5, or NO. Sulfur trioxide reacts vigorously with water to form sulfuric acid. Industrially, SO_3 is absorbed in concentrated H_2SO_4 to give oleum (Section 7-11), which is then diluted. Sulfur trioxide is used as such for preparing sulfonated oils and alkyl arenesulfonate detergents. It is also a powerful but generally indiscriminate oxidizing agent.

The SO_3 molecule, in the gas phase, has a planar, triangular structure involving both $p\pi–p\pi$ and $p\pi–d\pi$, S—O bonding and forms polymers in the solid state.

Sulfuric, Selenic, and Telluric Acids

Sulfuric acid has already been discussed in Chapter 7. *Selenic acid* is similar to H_2SO_4, including the isomorphism of the hydrates and salts. It differs in being less stable, evolving oxygen above 200 °C, and being a strong but usually not kinetically fast oxidizing agent,

$$SeO_4^{2-} + 4H^+ + 2e^- = H_2SeO_3 + H_2O \qquad E^0 = 1.15 \text{ V} \qquad (19\text{-}5.11)$$

Telluric acid, obtained by oxidation of Te or TeO_2 with H_2O_2 or other powerful oxidants, is very different in structure, being $Te(OH)_6$ in the crystal. It is a very weak dibasic acid, $K_1 \approx 10^{-7}$, and is also an oxidant. Most tellurates contain TeO_6 octahedra as in $K[TeO(OH)_5]$ or Hg_3TeO_6.

Thiosulfates

Thiosulfates are readily obtained by boiling solutions of sulfites with sulfur. The free acid is unstable at ordinary temperatures. The alkali thiosulfates are manufactured for use in photography where they are used to dissolve unreacted silver bromide from emulsion by formation of the complexes $[Ag(S_2O_3)]^-$ and $[Ag(S_2O_3)_2]^{3-}$; the thiosulfate ion also forms complexes with other metal ions.

The thiosulfate ion has the structure $S-SO_3^{2-}$, structure 19-V:

S—S = 2.01 Å
S—O = 1.47 Å

19-V

and may be considered to be derived from sulfate by replacement of an O atom by a S atom.

Dithionites

The reduction of sulfites in aqueous solutions containing an excess of SO_2, by zinc dust, gives ZnS_2O_4. The Zn^{2+} and Na^+ salts are commonly used as powerful and rapid reducing agents in alkaline solution:

$$2SO_3^{2-} + 2H_2O + 2e^- = 4HO^- + S_2O_4^{2-} \qquad E^0 = -1.12 \text{ V} \qquad (19\text{-}5.12)$$

In the presence of 2-anthraquinonesulfonate as a catalyst aqueous $Na_2S_2O_4$ efficiently removes oxygen from inert gases.

The dithionite ion has the structure $O_2S-SO_2^{2-}$, shown in 19-VI:

S—S = 2.39 Å
S—O = 1.51 Å

19-VI

with a long and weak S—S bond.

Dithionates

The dithionate ion has the staggered structure $O_3S-SO_3^{2-}$. The ion is usually obtained by oxidation of sulfite or SO_2 solutions with manganese(IV) oxide as in reaction 19-5.13:

$$MnO_2 + 2SO_3^{2-} + 4H^+ \longrightarrow Mn^{2+} + S_2O_6^{2-} + 2H_2O \quad (19\text{-}5.13)$$

The ion itself is stable and solutions of its salts may be boiled without decomposition. It resists reaction with most oxidizing and reducing agents and is therefore a useful counterion for precipitating complex cations. The free acid may be obtained by treatment of the anion in aqueous solution with sulfuric acid. Dithionic acid is a moderately strong acid that decomposes slowly in concentrated solution or when warmed. Other salts of dithionate (e.g., BaS_2O_6) may be obtained by titration of an aqueous solution of the acid with the appropriate base [e.g., $Ba(OH)_2$]. Such salts are frequently hydrated, barium dithionate being obtained as the dihydrate, $BaS_2O_6 \cdot 2H_2O$.

Polythionates

Polythionate anions have the general formula $[O_3SS_nSO_3]^{2-}$. The corresponding acids are not stable, decomposing rapidly into S, SO_2, and sometimes SO_4^{2-}. The well-established polythionate anions are those with $n = 1$–4. They are named according to the total number of sulfur atoms and are thus called: trithionate ($S_3O_6^{2-}$), tetrathionate ($S_4O_6^{2-}$), and so on. There is evidence for anions having chains with up to 20 sulfur atoms.

Tetrathionates are obtained by treatment of thiosulfates with iodine in the reaction used in the volumetric determination of iodine:

$$2S_2O_3^{2-} + I_2 \longrightarrow 2\,I^- + S_4O_6^{2-} \quad (19\text{-}5.14)$$

The structures of trithionate and tetrathionate are shown in structures 19-VII and 19-VIII, respectively.

$$\left[\begin{array}{c} O \diagdown \ \ S \diagup O \\ S \ \ \ S \\ O \ \ O \ \ O \ \ O \end{array} \right]^{2-} \qquad S\text{—}S = 2.15 \text{ Å}$$

19-VII

$$\left[\begin{array}{c} SO_3 \\ S\text{—}S \\ O \diagdown S \\ O \ \ \ \ O \end{array} \right]^{2-} \qquad \begin{array}{l} OS\text{—}S = 2.12 \text{ Å} \\ SS\text{—}S = 2.02 \text{ Å} \end{array}$$

19-VIII

Peroxodisulfates

The NH_4^+ or Na^+ salts are obtained by electrolysis of the corresponding sulfates at low temperatures and high current densities. The $S_2O_8^{2-}$ ion has the structure $O_3S—O—O—SO_3$, with approximately tetrahedral angles about each S atom.

The ion is one of the most powerful and useful of oxidizing agents:

$$S_2O_8^{2-} + 2e^- = 2SO_4^{2-} \qquad E^0 = 2.01 \text{ V} \qquad (19\text{-}5.15)$$

However, the reactions are complicated mechanistically. Oxidations by $S_2O_8^{2-}$ are slow and are usually catalyzed by addition of Ag^+, which is converted to Ag^{2+}, the actual oxidant.

STUDY GUIDE

Study Questions

A. Review

1. What are the principal forms in which sulfur occurs in nature?
2. Ordinary solid sulfur consists of what species? Summarize briefly what is observed when sulfur is heated from below its melting point to above its boiling point and explain the reasons for these changes.
3. What types of species are formed on dissolving S, Se, and Te in oleums or other superacids?
4. Discuss the aqueous chemistry of H_2S, SH^-, and S^{2-}.
5. What are the principal fluorides of sulfur?
6. Write equations for the preparations and for the reactions with water of thionyl chloride and sulfuryl chloride.
7. Write equations for the two most important reactions, or types of reaction, of SO_3.
8. Of what use(s) is SO_2?
9. Mention the chief similarities and differences among sulfuric, selenic, and telluric acids.
10. Give general formulas for three series of compounds that contain chains of more than two S atoms.

B. Additional Exercises

1. Compare the boiling points and the acid strengths in the series H_2X, where X = O through Te. Explain the trends.
2. Although SF_6 is unreactive, TeF_6 is hydrolyzed by water. Explain.
3. Describe the preparation and uses of SF_4 and SF_6.
4. Why is it that $SOCl_2$ can act both as a Lewis acid and as a Lewis base?
5. Predict the structure and describe the bonding in $SeOCl_2(py)_2$.
6. Unlike SO_2, SeO_2 is a solid with a chain structure. Draw a reasonable Lewis diagram for such a structure.

7. Draw Lewis diagrams for the following molecules and ions, giving the AB_xE_y classification, the hybridization, and the geometry at each sulfur atom:
   (a) $S_2O_3^{2-}$ (b) $S_2O_4^{2-}$
   (c) $S_2O_6^{2-}$ (d) SO_2
   (e) SO_3 (f) $SOCl_2$
   (g) SO_2Cl_2 (h) SCl_2
   (i) S_2Cl_2

8. The bond order of the S—O bond decreases in the series $OSF_2 > OSCl_2 > OSBr_2$. Explain.

9. Predict the structure of the adduct between $SbCl_5$ and $OPCl_3$.

10. Write a balanced equation for the dehydration of selenous acid.

11. Draw pictures representing the orbitals as they overlap in forming $p\pi$–$d\pi$ bonds in SO_3.

12. Prepare an MO energy-level diagram for the π-bond system in SO_3. Use the group orbital approach as described in Chapter 3, and construct π-molecular orbitals centered on the d atomic orbitals of S.

13. The S—O bond length in SO_4^{2-} is 1.44 Å and the S—O bond length in SO_3 is 1.42 Å. Compare these with the bond lengths given in the chapter for $S_2O_3^{2-}$, $S_2O_4^{2-}$, $S_3O_6^{2-}$, and $S_4O_6^{2-}$, and with the sum (S + S and S + O) of the S—S and the S—O covalent single-bond radii. Discuss the relative strengths of S—O and S—S bonds in these systems.

C. Questions from the Literature of Inorganic Chemistry

1. Consider the oxofluorides of Se and Te as reported by H. Oberhammer and K. Seppelt, *Inorg. Chem.*, **1979**, *18*, 2226–2229.
   (a) Draw the Lewis diagrams and discuss the hybridization and geometry (using the AB_xE_y classification and the VSEPR approach) of the following oxofluorides mentioned in this paper: SeO_2F_2, $SeOF_4$, $Se_2O_2F_8$, $Te_2O_2F_8$, $I_2O_4F_6$, F_5SOSF_5, and $F_5SeOSeF_5$.
   (b) In which compounds in (a) is $d\pi$–$p\pi$ bonding between O and Se (or Te) important? Explain.
   (c) What reason(s) do the authors give for the tendancy of $SeOF_4$ to dimerize giving $Se_2O_2F_8$? Explain.
   (d) Do you suppose $TeOF_4$ is stable? Explain.

2. Consider the adducts of SO_2 described by P. G. Eller and G. J. Kubas, *Inorg. Chem.*, **1978**, *17*, 894–897.
   (a) Does SO_2 serve as a Lewis acid or as a Lewis base in forming ISO_2^-?
   (b) Other adducts XSO_2^- were not isolated, but stabilities of the adducts were studied. How?
   (c) Draw the Lewis diagram for ISO_2^- and discuss the structural data presented in the article. Classify the S atom according to the AB_xE_y system.
   (d) What is the significance of the I—S distance found in this study? Compare this I—S distance with the sum $r_{cov}(I + S)$ and the sum $r_{vdw}(I + S)$. Is this a fully covalent I—S bond?

3. Consider the paper by C. J. Schack, R. D. Wilson, and J. F. Hon, *Inorg. Chem.*, **1972**, *11*, 208–209.

(a) Write balanced equations for every step in each synthesis of SeF_5Cl as reported in this paper.

(b) What is the equation representing the hydrolysis in aqueous hydroxide solution of SeF_5Cl? How was this hydrolysis used to analyze the compound?

(c) With what other compounds of S and Se do the authors suggest a similarity? On what basis are these comparisons made?

SUPPLEMENTARY READING

Bagnall, K. W., *The Chemistry of Se, Te, and Po,* Elsevier, Amsterdam, 1966.

Clive, D. L. J., *Modern Organo-Selenium Chemistry,* Pergamon Press, New York, 1978.

Cooper, W. C., *Tellurium,* Van Nostrand-Reinhold, New York, 1972.

Engelbrecht, E. and Sladky, F., "Selenium and Tellurium Fluorides," *Adv. Inorg. Chem. Radiochem.,* **1981,** *24,* 189.

Heal, H. G., *The Inorganic Heterocyclic Chemistry of Sulfur, Nitrogen, and Phosphorus,* Academic, London, 1981.

Heal, H. G., "Sulfur–Nitrogen Compounds," *Adv. Inorg. Chem. Radiochem.,* **1972,** *15,* 375.

Janickis, J., "Polythionates and Selenopolythionates," *Acc. Chem. Res.,* **1969,** *2,* 316.

Meyer, B., "Elemental Sulfur," *Chem. Rev.,* **1976,** *76,* 367.

Nickless, G., Ed., *Inorganic Sulfur Chemistry,* Elsevier, Amsterdam, 1968.

Oae, S., *The Organic Chemistry of Sulfur,* Plenum, New York, 1977.

Roy, A. B. and Trudinger, P. A., *The Biochemistry of Inorganic Compounds of Sulfur,* Cambridge University Press, Cambridge, 1970.

chapter 20

THE HALOGENS: FLUORINE, CHLORINE, BROMINE, IODINE, AND ASTATINE

20-1 Introduction

With the exception of He, Ne, and Ar, all of the elements in the periodic table form halides. Ionic or covalent halides are among the most important and common compounds. They are often the easiest to prepare and are widely used as source materials for the synthesis of other compounds. Where an element has more than one valence, the halides are often the best known and most accessible compounds in all of the oxidation states. There is also an extensive and varied chemistry of organic halogen compounds; the fluorine compounds, especially where F completely replaces H, have unique properties.

The position of the elements in the periodic table is outlined in Section 2-5, and some properties are listed in Table 8-7. For the element *astatine*, named from the Greek for "unstable," the longest lived isotope has a half-life of only 8.3 h. As far as can be ascertained by tracer studies, At behaves like I but is perhaps somewhat less electronegative. It is made by the cyclotron reaction $^{209}Bi(\alpha, 2n)^{211}At$.

20-2 Occurrence, Isolation, and Properties of the Elements

Fluorine occurs widely, for example, as CaF_2 (*fluorspar*), Na_3AlF_6 (*cryolite*), and $3Ca_3(PO_4)_2Ca(F, Cl)_2$ (*fluorapatite*). It is more abundant than chlorine. Fluorine was first isolated in 1886 by H. Moissan. The element is obtained by electrolysis of molten fluorides. The most commonly used electrolyte is $KF \cdot 2-3HF$ (mp 70–100 °C). As the electrolysis proceeds the melting point increases but the electrolyte is readily regenerated by resaturation with HF from a storage tank. Fluorine cells are constructed of steel, Cu, or Ni–Cu alloy, which become coated with an unreactive layer of fluoride. The cathodes are steel or Cu, the anodes ungraphitized carbon. Although F_2 is often handled in metal apparatus, it can be handled in glass provided traces of HF, which attacks glass rapidly, are removed by passing the gas through anhydrous NaF or KF with which HF forms the bifluorides, MHF_2.

Fluorine is the most chemically reactive of all the elements and combines directly at ordinary or elevated temperatures with all the elements other than O_2, He, Ne, and Kr, often with extreme vigor. It also attacks many other compounds, breaking them down to fluorides; organic materials often inflame and burn in F_2.

The great reactivity of F_2 is in part attributable to the low dissociation energy (Table 1-1) of the F—F bond, and the fact that reactions of atomic fluorine are strongly exothermic. The low F—F bond energy is probably due to repulsion between nonbonding electrons. A similar effect may account for the low bond energies in H_2O_2 and N_2H_4.

Chlorine occurs as NaCl, KCl, $MgCl_2$, and so on, in seawater, salt lakes, and as deposits originating from the prehistoric evaporation of salt lakes. Chlorine is obtained by electrolysis of brine using a mercury anode in which sodium dissolves:

$$Na^+ + e^- = Na \tag{20-2.1}$$

$$Cl^- = \tfrac{1}{2}Cl_2 + e^- \tag{20-2.2}$$

Until recently, this was generally done using a mercury anode, which entailed a hazard because of the loss of Hg to the environment. A newer process employing membrane cells does not require mercury.

Chlorine is a greenish gas. It is moderately soluble in water, with which it reacts as in Eq. 20-2.3:

$$Cl_2 + H_2O = HCl + HOCl \tag{20-2.3}$$

Bromine occurs as bromides, in much smaller amounts along with chlorides. Bromine is obtained from brines by the reaction

$$2Br^- + Cl_2 \xrightarrow{\text{pH} \sim 3.5} 2Cl^- + Br_2 \tag{20-2.4}$$

It is swept out in a current of air. Bromine is a dense, mobile, dark red liquid at room temperature. It is moderately soluble in water and miscible with non-polar solvents such as CS_2 and CCl_4.

Iodine occurs as iodide in brines and as iodate in Chile saltpeter (guano, $NaNO_3$). Various forms of marine life concentrate iodine. Production of I_2 involves either oxidizing I^- or reducing iodates to I^- followed by oxidation. MnO_2 in acid solutions is commonly used as the oxidant.

Iodine is a black solid with a slight metallic luster. At atmospheric pressure it sublimes without melting. It is readily soluble in nonpolar solvents such as CS_2 and CCl_4. Such solutions are purple, as is the vapor. In polar solvents, unsaturated hydrocarbons, and liquid SO_2, brown or pinkish-brown solutions are formed. These colors indicate the formation of weak complexes $I_2 \cdots S$ known as *charge-transfer complexes*. The bonding energy results from partial transfer of charge in the sense $I_2^- S^+$. The complexes of I_2 and also of Br_2, Cl_2, and ICl can sometimes be isolated as crystalline solids at low temperatures.

Iodine forms a blue complex with starch, in which the iodine forms linear I_5^- ions in channels in the polysaccharide amylose.

20-3 Halides

There are almost as many ways of classifying halides as there are types of halides. Binary halides may form simple molecules, or complex, infinite arrays. For ionic compounds some common types of lattices are given in Chapter 4 and some general points on halides are discussed in Section 5-5. Other types of halide compounds include oxide halides such as $VOCl_3$, hydroxy halides, organohalides, and so on. The covalent and ionic radii are given in Table 8-7.

Preparation of Anhydrous Halides

1. *Direct interaction of the elements with halogens.* The halogens are normally used for most elements. HF, HCl, and HBr may also be used for metals.

Direct fluorination normally gives fluorides in the higher oxidation states. Most metals and nonmetals react very vigorously with F_2; with nonmetals such as P_4, the reaction may be explosive. For rapid formation in dry reactions of *chlorides, bromides,* and *iodides* elevated temperatures are usually necessary. For metals, the reaction with Cl_2 and Br_2 may be more rapid when THF or some other ether is used as a reaction medium; the halide is then obtained as a solvate.

2. *Dehydration of hydrated halides.* The dissolution of metals, oxides, or carbonates in aqueous halogen acids followed by evaporation or crystallization gives hydrated halides. These can sometimes be dehydrated by heating in vacuum, but this often leads to impure products or oxohalides. Dehydration of chlorides can be effected by thionyl chloride, and halides in general can be treated with 2,2-dimethoxypropane:

$$CrCl_3 \cdot 6H_2O + 6SOCl_2 \xrightarrow{\text{Reflux}} CrCl_3 + 12HCl + 6SO_2 \quad (20\text{-}3.1)$$

$$MX_n \cdot mH_2O \quad \text{in} \quad CH_3C(OCH_3)_2CH_3 \longrightarrow$$
$$MX_n + m(CH_3)_2CO + 2mCH_3OH \quad (20\text{-}3.2)$$

The acetone and methanol products of reaction 20-3.2 may solvate the halide products, but the solvents can easily be removed by gentle heating or at reduced pressures.

3. *Treatment of oxides with other halogen compounds.* Oxides may often be treated with halogen-containing compounds to replace oxygen with halogen, as in the following reactions:

$$NiO + ClF_3 \longrightarrow NiF_2 + \cdots \quad (20\text{-}3.3)$$

$$Pr_2O_3 + 6NH_4Cl \xrightarrow{300\,°C} 3PrCl_3 + 3H_2O + 6NH_3 \quad (20\text{-}3.4)$$

$$Sc_2O_3 + CCl_4 \xrightarrow{600\,°C} ScCl_3 + \cdots \quad (20\text{-}3.5)$$

4. *Halogen exchange.* Many halides react to exchange halogen with (a) elemental halogens, (b) acid halides, (c) halide salts, or (d) an excess of another halogen-containing substance. Chlorides can often be converted to either bromides (by KBr) or especially to iodides (by KI), using acetone, in which KCl is less soluble. Halogen exchange is especially important for the synthesis of fluorides from chlorides, using various metal fluorides such as CoF_3 or AsF_5.

This type of replacement is used extensively in the synthesis of organic fluorine compounds, as discussed in Section 20-7.

Another fluorinating agent that has special advantages is SbF_3, which is used along with $SbCl_5$ as a catalyst in reaction 20-3.6:

$$PhCCl_3 + SbF_3 \longrightarrow PhCF_3 + SbCl_3 \qquad (20\text{-}3.6)$$

Molecular Halides

Most of the electronegative elements, and the metals in high oxidation states, form molecular halides. These are gases, liquids, or volatile solids with molecules held together only by van der Waals forces. There is probably a rough correlation between increasing metal to halogen covalence and increasing tendency to the formation of molecular compounds. Thus the molecular halides are sometimes also called the covalent halides. The designation molecular is preferable, since it states a fact.

The formation of halide bridges between two or, less often, three other atoms is an important structural feature. Between two metal atoms, the most common situation involves two halogen atoms, but examples with one and three bridge atoms are known. Such bridges used to be depicted as involving a covalent bond to one metal atom and donation of an electron pair to the other as in structure 20-I, but structural data show that the two bonds to each bridging halogen atom are equivalent as in structure 20-II. Molecular orbital theory provides a simple, flexible formulation in which the M—X—M group is treated as a three-center, four-electron group.

With Cl^- and Br^-, bridges are characteristically bent, whereas fluoride bridges may be either bent or linear. Thus, in BeF_2 there are infinite chains, ---BeF_2BeF_2---, with bent bridges, similar to the situation in $BeCl_2$. On the other hand, transition metal pentahalides afford a notable contrast. While the pentachlorides dimerize with bent M—Cl—M bridges (structure 20-II), the pentafluorides form cyclic tetramers with linear M—F—M bridges (structure 20-III). The fluorides probably adopt the tetrameric structures with linear bridges, in part because the smaller size of F than of Cl would introduce excessive metal–metal repulsion in a bent bridge.

20-I   20-II   20-III

Molecular fluorides of both metals and nonmetals are usually gases or volatile liquids. Their volatility is due to the absence of intermolecular bonding other than van der Waals forces, since the polarizability of fluorine is very low and no suitable outer orbitals exist for other types of attraction. Where the central atom has suitable vacant orbitals available, and especially if the polarity of the single bonds M—F would be such as to leave a considerable charge on M, as in, say, SF_6, multiple bonding can occur using filled p orbitals of fluorine for overlap with vacant orbitals of the central atom. This multiple bonding is a major factor in the shortness and high strength of many bonds of fluorine. Because of the high electronegativity of fluorine the bonds in these compounds tend to be very polar. Because of the low dissociation energy of F_2 and the relatively high energy of many bonds to F (e.g., C—F, 486; N—F, 272; P—F, 490 kJ mol^{-1}), molecular fluorides are often formed very exothermically.

The high electronegativity of fluorine often has a profound effect on the properties of molecules in which several F atoms occur. Representative are facts such as (a) CF_3CO_2H is a strong acid; (b) $(CF_3)_3N$ and NF_3 have no basicity; and (c) CF_3 derivatives in general are attacked much less readily by electrophilic reagents in anionic substitutions than are CH_3 compounds. The CF_3 group may be considered as a kind of large pseudohalogen with an electronegativity about comparable to that of Cl.

A fairly general property of molecular halides is their easy hydrolysis, for example,

$$BCl_3 + 3H_2O \longrightarrow B(OH)_3 + 3H^+ + 3Cl^- \qquad (20\text{-}3.7)$$

$$PBr_3 + 3H_2O \longrightarrow HPO(OH)_2 + 3H^+ + 3Br^- \qquad (20\text{-}3.8)$$

$$SiCl_4 + 4H_2O \longrightarrow Si(OH)_4 + 4H^+ + 4Cl^- \qquad (20\text{-}3.9)$$

Where the maximum covalency is attained, as in CCl_4 or SF_6, the halides may be quite inert towards water. However, this is a result of kinetic and not thermodynamic factors. For instance, for CF_4, the equilibrium for hydrolysis as in Eq. 20-3.10

$$CF_4(g) + 2H_2O(\ell) = CO_2(g) + 4HF(g) \qquad (20\text{-}3.10)$$

is thermodynamically favorable ($K_{eq} = 10^{23}$), but the rate of hydrolysis is negligible because there is no site for attack by water at carbon. The necessity for means of attack is also illustrated by the fact that SF_6 is not hydrolyzed, whereas SeF_6 and TeF_6 are hydrolyzed at 25 °C. Attack by a nucleophile (and expansion of the coordination sphere) is possible only for Se and Te, not S.

20-4   Halogen Oxides

Oxygen fluorides have been studied as potential rocket fuel oxidizers. Oxygen difluoride, OF_2, is obtained as a pale yellow gas on passing F_2 gas rapidly through a 2% NaOH solution. Dioxygen difluoride, O_2F_2, is an unstable orange-yellow solid made by the action of electric discharges on F_2–O_2 mixtures; O_2F_2 is an extremely potent oxidizing and fluorinating agent.

Chlorine oxides are reactive, and tend to explode. None can be obtained by direct reaction of Cl_2 and O_2. The *dioxide*, ClO_2, is a powerful oxidant and is used diluted with air commercially, for example, for bleaching wood pulp. It is always made "on site" by reaction 20-4.1:

$$2NaClO_3 + SO_2 + H_2SO_4 = 2ClO_2 + 2NaHSO_4 \qquad (20\text{-}4.1)$$

or by reduction of $KClO_3$ with moist oxalic acid at 90 °C, an additional product being carbon dioxide. Cl_2O is used as a selective and powerful chlorinating agent for organic compounds. It can also be passed into lime water to make $Ca(OCl)_2$, a safe and useful bleaching agent.

Iodine pentoxide is the anhydride of iodic acid, and it can be prepared by dehydration of iodic acid at elevated temperatures, as in reaction 20-4.2:

$$2HIO_3 \underset{\substack{H_2O, \\ \text{Fast}}}{\overset{240\,°C}{\rightleftharpoons}} I_2O_5 + H_2O \qquad (20\text{-}4.2)$$

Iodine pentoxide is an oxidizing agent that can be used in the determination of CO, as in Eq. 20-4.3:

$$5CO + I_2O_5 = I_2 + 5CO_2 \qquad (20\text{-}4.3)$$

where the liberated iodine is determined by iodometry. Iodine pentoxide has a three-dimensional network structure with O_2I—O—IO_2 units linked by strong intermolecular $I \cdots O$ interactions.

20-5 The Oxo Acids

The chemistry of the halogen oxo acids is complicated. Solutions of the acids and several of the anions may be obtained by interaction of the free halogens with water or aqueous bases. In this section the term halogen refers to Cl, Br, and I only; fluorine forms only FOH as discussed in the following section.

Reaction of Halogens with H_2O and OH^-

The potentials and equilibrium constants necessary to understand these systems can be derived from data given in Table 20-1.

The halogens are all soluble in water to some extent. However, in such solutions there are species other than solvated halogen molecules, since a *disproportionation* reaction occurs *rapidly*:

$$X_2(g,\ell,s) = X_2(aq) \qquad K_1 \qquad (20\text{-}5.1)$$

$$X_2(aq) = H^+ + X^- + HOX \qquad K_2 \qquad (20\text{-}5.2)$$

The values of K_1 are: Cl_2, 0.062; Br_2, 0.21; I_2, 0.0013. The values of K_2 computed from the potentials in Table 20-1 are 4.2×10^{-4} for Cl_2, 7.2×10^{-9}

Table 20-1   Standard Potentials (in Volts) for Reactions of Halogen Compounds

Reaction	Cl	Br	I
(1) $H^+ + HOX + e^- = \frac{1}{2}X_2(g,\ell,s) + H_2O$	1.63	1.59	1.45
(2) $3H^+ + HXO_2 + 3e^- = \frac{1}{2}X_2(g,\ell,s) + 2H_2O$	1.64	—	—
(3) $6H^+ + XO_3^- + 5e^- = \frac{1}{2}X_2(g,\ell,s) + 3H_2O$	1.47	1.52	1.20
(4) $8H^+ + XO_4^- + 7e^- = \frac{1}{2}X_2(g,\ell,s) + 4H_2O$	1.42	1.59	1.34
(5) $\frac{1}{2}X_2(g,\ell,s) + e^- = X^-$	1.36	1.07	0.54^a
(6) $XO^- + H_2O + 2e^- = X^- + 2\,OH^-$	0.89	0.76	0.49
(7) $XO_2^- + 2H_2O + 4e^- = X^- + 4\,OH^-$	0.78	—	—
(8) $XO_3^- + 3H_2O + 6e^- = X^- + 6\,OH^-$	0.63	0.61	0.26
(9) $XO_4^- + 4H_2O + 8e^- = X^- + 8\,OH^-$	0.56	0.69	0.39

^{a}Indicates that I^- can be oxidized by oxygen in aqueous solution.

for Br_2, and 2.0×10^{-13} for I_2. We can also estimate from

$$\tfrac{1}{2}X_2 + e^- = X^- \tag{20-5.3}$$

and

$$O_2 + 4H^+ + 4e^- = 2H_2O \qquad E^\circ = 1.23 \text{ V} \tag{20-5.4}$$

that the potentials for the reactions

$$2H^+ + 2X^- + \tfrac{1}{2}O_2 = X_2 + H_2O \tag{20-5.5}$$

are -1.62 V for fluorine, -0.13 V for chlorine, 0.16 V for bromine, and 0.69 V for iodine.

Thus for saturated solutions of the halogens in water at 25 °C we have the results shown in Table 20-2. There is an appreciable concentration of HOCl in a saturated aqueous solution of Cl_2, a smaller concentration of HOBr in a saturated solution of Br_2, but only a negligible concentration of HOI in a saturated solution of I_2.

Hypohalous Acids

The colorless, very unstable gas, FOH, is made by passing F_2 over ice and collecting the gas in a trap. It reacts rapidly with water. The other XOH compounds are also unstable. They are known only in solution from the in-

Table 20-2   Equilibrium Concentrations in Aqueous Solutions of the Halogens, 25 °C, mol L^{-1}

	Cl_2	Br_2	I_2
Total solubility	0.091	0.21	0.0013
Concentration X_2(aq), mol L^{-1}	0.061	0.21	0.0013
$[H^+] = [X^-] = [HOX]$	0.030	1.15×10^{-3}	6.4×10^{-6}

teraction of the halogen and Hg^{II} oxide:

$$2X_2 + 2HgO + H_2O \longrightarrow HgO \cdot HgX_2 + 2HOX \qquad (20\text{-}5.6)$$

The hypohalous acids are very weak acids but good oxidizing agents, especially in acid solution (see Table 20-1).

The *hypohalite ions* can be produced in principle by dissolving the halogens in base according to the general reaction

$$X_2 + 2OH^- \longrightarrow XO^- + X^- + H_2O \qquad (20\text{-}5.7)$$

and for these *rapid* reactions the equilibrium constants are all favorable: 7.5×10^{15} for Cl_2, 2×10^8 for Br_2, and 30 for I_2.

However, the hypohalite ions tend to disproportionate in basic solution to produce the *halate ions:*

$$3XO^- = 2X^- + XO_3^- \qquad (20\text{-}5.8)$$

For these reactions, the equilibrium constants are very favorable: 10^{27} for ClO^-, 10^{15} for BrO^-, and 10^{20} for IO^-. Thus the *actual* products obtained on dissolving the halogens in base depend on the rates at which the hypohalite ions initially produced undergo disproportionation. These rates vary with temperature.

The disproportionation of ClO^- is slow at and below room temperature. Thus, when Cl_2 reacts with base "in the cold," reasonably pure solutions of Cl^- and ClO^- are obtained. In hot solutions, $\sim$75 °C, the rate of disproportionation is fairly rapid and good yields of ClO_3^- can be secured.

The disproportionation of BrO^- is moderately fast even at room temperature. Solutions of BrO^- can only be made and/or kept at around 0 °C. At temperatures of 50 to 80 °C quantitative yields of BrO_3^- are obtained:

$$3Br_2 + 6OH^- \longrightarrow 5Br^- + BrO_3^- + 3H_2O \qquad (20\text{-}5.9)$$

The rate of disproportionation of IO^- is so fast that it is unknown in solution. Reaction of I_2 with base hence gives IO_3^- quantitatively according to an equation analogous to that for Br_2.

Halous Acids

The only certain acid is *chlorous acid,* $HClO_2$. This is obtained in aqueous solution by treating a suspension of barium chlorite with H_2SO_4, filtering off the $BaSO_4$. It is a relatively weak acid ($K_a \approx 10^{-2}$) and cannot be isolated. *Chlorites,* $MClO_2$, are obtained by reaction of ClO_2 with solutions of bases:

$$2ClO_2 + 2OH^- \longrightarrow ClO_2^- + ClO_3^- + H_2O \qquad (20\text{-}5.10)$$

Chlorites are used as bleaching agents. In alkaline solution ClO_2^- is quite stable even on boiling. In acid solutions, the decomposition is rapid and is catalyzed by Cl^-:

$$5HClO_2 \longrightarrow 4ClO_2 + Cl^- + H^+ + 2H_2O \qquad (20\text{-}5.11)$$

Halic Acids

Iodic acid, HIO_3, is a stable white solid obtained by oxidizing I_2 with concentrated HNO_3, H_2O_2, O_3, and so on. *Chloric* and *bromic acids* are obtained in solution by treating the barium halates with H_2SO_4.

The halic acids are strong acids and are powerful oxidizing agents. The ions, XO_3^-, are pyramidal, as is to be expected from the presence of an octet, with one unshared pair, in the halogen valence shell.

Iodates of the $+4$ ions of Ce, Zr, Hf, and Th can be precipitated from 6 M nitric acid to provide a useful means of separation.

Halates

Although disproportionation of ClO_3^- is thermodynamically very favorable,

$$4ClO_3^- = Cl^- + 3ClO_4^- \qquad K \sim 10^{29} \qquad (20\text{-}5.12)$$

the reaction occurs very slowly in solution and is not a useful preparative procedure. *Perchlorates* are prepared by electrolytic oxidation of chlorates. The properties of *perchloric acid* are discussed in Section 7-11 and perchlorates are discussed in Section 5-3.

The disproportionation of BrO_3^- to BrO_4^- and Br^- is extremely unfavorable ($K \sim 10^{-33}$). *Perbromates* can be obtained only by oxidation of BrO_3^-, preferably by F_2, in basic solution

$$BrO_3^- + F_2 + 2OH^- = BrO_4^- + 2F^- + H_2O \qquad (20\text{-}5.13)$$

Figure 20-1 Schematic representation of (*a*) the one-step and (*b*) the two-step mechanism for the aquation of IO_4^- to $IO_2(OH)_4^-$. Dotted lines represent hydrogen bonds.

They are exceedingly powerful oxidants

$$BrO_4^- + 2H^+ + 2e^- = BrO_3^- + H_2O \qquad E° = +1.76 \text{ V} \qquad (20\text{-}5.14)$$

Solutions of $HBrO_4$ up to 6 M are stable, but decompose when stronger.

Periodates resemble tellurates in their stoichiometries. The main equilibria in acid solutions are

$$H_5IO_6 = H^+ + H_4IO_6^- \qquad K = 1 \times 10^{-3} \qquad (20\text{-}5.15)$$

$$H_4IO_6^- = IO_4^- + 2H_2O \qquad K = 29 \qquad (20\text{-}5.16)$$

$$H_4IO_6^- = H^+ + H_3IO_6^{2-} \qquad K = 2 \times 10^{-7} \qquad (20\text{-}5.17)$$

In aqueous solutions at 25 °C the main ion is IO_4^-. The pH-dependent equilibria are established rapidly. Kinetic studies of the hydration of IO_4^- suggest either one-step or two-step paths (Fig. 20-1), the latter being more likely. Periodic acid and its salts are used in organic chemistry as oxidants that usually react smoothly and rapidly. They are useful analytical oxidants; for example, they oxidize Mn^{2+} to MnO_4^-.

20-6 Interhalogen Compounds

The halogens form many compounds among themselves in binary combinations that may be neutral or ionic, for example, BrCl, IF_5, Br_3^+, I_3^-. *Ternary* combinations occur only in polyhalide ions, for example, $IBrCl^-$.

· Neutral interhalogen compounds are of the type XX'_n where n is an *odd* number and X' is always the lighter halogen when $n > 1$. Because n is odd, the compounds are diamagnetic; their valence electrons are present either as bonding pairs or as unshared pairs. The principles involved in the bonding are similar to those in xenon fluorides and have been discussed in Chapter 3.

Chlorine trifluoride is a liquid (bp 11.8 °C) that is commercially available in tanks. It is made by direct combination at 200 to 300 °C. Reaction of ClF_3 with excess Cl_2 gives *chlorine monofluoride*, which is a gas (bp −100 °C).

Bromine trifluoride, a red liquid (bp 126 °C), is also made by direct interaction.

These three substances, typical of all halogen fluorides, are very reactive. They react explosively with H_2O and organic substances. They are powerful fluorinating agents for inorganic compounds, and when diluted with N_2, for organic compounds.

Interhalogen ions. There are both cations and anions. Halogen fluorides react with fluoride ion acceptors, for example,

$$2ClF + AsF_5 = FCl_2^+ AsF_6^- \qquad (20\text{-}6.1)$$

or with fluoride ion donors,

$$IF_5 + CsF = Cs^+ IF_6^- \qquad (20\text{-}6.2)$$

It is not always clear that such products contain *discrete* ions. For instance in $ClF_2^+SbF_6^-$ each Cl atom has two close and two distant (belonging to SbF_6^-) fluorine neighbors in a much distorted square.

The pale yellow *triiodide* ion is formed on dissolving I_2 in aqueous KI. There are numerous salts of I_3^-. Other ions are not usually stable in aqueous solution although they can be obtained in CH_3OH or CH_3CN and as crystalline salts of large cations such as Cs^+ or R_4N^+. For chlorine, the ion is formed only in concentrated solution:

$$Cl^-(aq) + Cl_2 \rightleftharpoons Cl_3^-(aq) \qquad K \approx 0.2 \qquad (20\text{-}6.3)$$

The electrical conductance of molten I_2 is ascribed to self-ionization

$$3I_2 \rightleftharpoons I_3^+ + I_3^- \qquad (20\text{-}6.4)$$

20-7 Organic Compounds of Fluorine

Although the halogens form innumerable organic compounds, the methods of making organic fluorine compounds and some of their unusual properties are of inorganic interest. Fluorination of other halogen compounds by treatment with metal fluorides has been discussed in Section 20-3. These methods are expensive so that alternative cheaper methods suitable for industrial procedures have been developed.

1. *Replacement of chlorine using hydrogen fluoride.* Anhydrous HF is cheap and can be used to replace Cl in chloro compounds. Catalysts such as $SbCl_5$ or CrF_4 and moderate temperature and pressure are required. Examples are

$$2CCl_4 + 3HF \longrightarrow CCl_2F_2 + CCl_3F + 3HCl \qquad (20\text{-}7.1)$$

$$CCl_3COCCl_3 \xrightarrow{\text{HF}} CF_3COCF_3 \qquad (20\text{-}7.2)$$

2. *Electrolytic replacement of hydrogen by fluorine.* One of the most important laboratory and industrial methods is the electrolysis of organic compounds in liquid HF at voltages (~ 4.5–6) below that required for the liberation of F_2. Steel cells with Ni anodes and steel cathodes are used. Fluorination occurs at the anode. Although many organic compounds give conducting solutions in liquid HF, a conductivity additive may be required. Examples of such fluorinations are

$$(C_2H_5)_2O \longrightarrow (C_2F_5)_2O \qquad (20\text{-}7.3)$$

$$C_8H_{18} \longrightarrow C_8F_{18} \qquad (20\text{-}7.4)$$

$$(CH_3)_2S \longrightarrow CF_3SF_5 + (CF_3)_2SF_4 \qquad (20\text{-}7.5)$$

$$(C_4H_9)_3N \longrightarrow (C_4F_9)_3N \qquad (20\text{-}7.6)$$

$$CH_3CO_2H \longrightarrow CF_3CO_2F \xrightarrow{\text{H}_2\text{O}} CF_3CO_2H \qquad (20\text{-}7.7)$$

3. *Direct replacement of hydrogen by fluorine.* Although most organic compounds normally inflame or explode with fluorine, direct fluorination of many compounds is possible as follows.

(a) Catalytic fluorination where the reacting compound and F_2 diluted with N_2 are mixed *in the presence* of copper gauze or a cesium fluoride catalyst. An example is shown in reaction 20-7.8:

$$C_6H_6 + 9F_2 \xrightarrow{\text{Cu, 265 °C}} C_6F_{12} + 6HF \qquad (20\text{-}7.8)$$

(b) The reaction of the substrate in the solid state, over a long period of time with F_2 (diluted with He), at low temperature. It is important to allow heat, generated in the exothermic reaction (overall for replacement of H by F, ca. 420 kJ mol^{-1}), which could lead to C—C bond breaking, to be efficiently dissipated. The replacement reaction proceeds by several steps, each less exothermic than the C—C average bond strength, so that, provided the reaction time allows separate completion of individual steps, fluorination without degradation is possible. Examples of materials that can be fluorinated in this way are polystyrene, anthracene, phthalocyanine, carboranes, and so on.

(c) Inorganic fluorides such as cobalt(III) fluoride are used for the vapor-phase fluorination of organic compounds, for example,

$$(CH_3)_3N \xrightarrow{\text{CoF}_3} (CF_3)_3N + (CF_3)_2NF + CF_3NF_2 + NF_3 \quad (20\text{-}7.9)$$

4. *Other methods for fluorination.* A useful and selective fluorinating agent for oxygen compounds is SF_4 (Section 19-4); for example, ketones $RR'CO$ may be converted to $RR'CF_2$, and carboxylate groups, —CO_2H to —CF_3.

Cesium fluoride acts as a catalyst in various fluorination reactions, for example,

$$R_FCN + F_2 \xrightarrow{\text{CsF, } -78\,°C} R_FCF_2NF_2 \qquad (R_F = \text{perfluoralkyl}) \quad (20\text{-}7.10)$$

The F^- ion is very nucleophilic toward unsaturated fluorocarbons and adds to the positive center of a polarized multiple bond. The carbanion so produced may then undergo double-bond migration or may act as a nucleophile leading to the elimination of F^- or another ion by an S_N2 mechanism. Fluoride-initiated reactions of these types have wide scope. The reactions can be carried out in DMF or diglyme by using either the sparingly soluble CsF or the more soluble Et_4NF.

An example is

$$CF_2{=}CFCF_3 \xrightarrow{F^-} (CF_3)_2CF^- \xrightarrow{I_2} (CF_3)_2CFI + I^- \quad (20\text{-}7.11)$$

Properties of Organofluorine Compounds

The C—F bond energy is very high (486 kJ mol^{-1}; cf. C—H 415, and C—Cl 332 kJ mol^{-1}), but organic fluorides are not necessarily particularly stable thermodynamically. The low reactivities of fluorine derivatives can be attributed to the impossibility of expansion of the octet of fluorine and the inability of, say, water to coordinate to fluorine or carbon as the first step in hydrolysis. With chlorine this may be possible using outer d orbitals. Because of the small size of the F atom, H can be replaced by F with least introduction of strain or distortion, as compared with replacement by other halogen atoms. The F atoms also effectively shield the C atoms from attack. Finally, since C bonded to F can be considered to be effectively oxidized (whereas in C—H it is reduced), there is no tendency for oxidation by oxygen. Fluorocarbons are attacked only by hot metals, for example, molten Na. When pyrolyzed, they split at C—C rather than C—F bonds.

The replacement of H by F leads to increased density, but less than by other halogens. Completely fluorinated (called perfluoro) derivatives, C_nF_{2n+2}, have very low boiling points for their molecular weights and low intermolecular forces; the weakness of these forces is also shown by the very low coefficient of friction for polytetrafluoroethylene, $(CF_2—CF_2)_n$.

Chlorofluorocarbons are used as nontoxic, inert refrigerants, aerosol bomb propellants, and heat transfer agents. Fluoroolefins are used as monomers for free radical initiated polymerizations to give oils, greases, and the like, and also as chemical intermediates. $CF_3CHBrCl$ is a safe anaesthetic. $CHClF_2$ is used for making tetrafluoroethylene:

$$2CHClF_2 \xrightarrow{500-1000\ °C} CF_2{=}CF_2 + 2HCl \qquad (20\text{-}7.12)$$

Tetrafluoroethylene (bp -76.6 °C) can be polymerized thermally or in aqueous emulsion; the polymer is used for coating frying pans, resistant gaskets, and the like.

Fluorinated carboxylic acids are strong acids. For example, CF_3CO_2H has $K_a = 5.9 \times 10^{-1}$, while for the parent acetic acid, CH_3CO_2H, $K_a = 1.8 \times 10^{-5}$. Many reactions of fluorocarboxylic acids leave the fluoroalkyl group intact. Consider, for example, the sequence of esterification by reaction 20-7.13:

$$C_3F_7CO_2H \xrightarrow[C_2H_5OH]{H_2SO_4} C_3F_7CO_2C_2H_5 \qquad (20\text{-}7.13)$$

ammonolysis according to Eq. 20-7.14:

$$C_3F_7CO_2C_2H_5 \xrightarrow{NH_3} C_3F_7CONH_2 \qquad (20\text{-}7.14)$$

followed either by dehydration:

$$C_3F_7CONH_2 \xrightarrow{P_2O_5} C_3F_7CN \qquad (20\text{-}7.15)$$

or by reduction:

$$C_3F_7CONH_2 \xrightarrow{LiAlH_4} C_3F_7CH_2NH_2 \qquad (20\text{-}7.16)$$

all of which leaves the fluoroalkyl group untouched.

Perfluoroalkyl halides are made by reaction 20-7.17:

$$R_FCO_2Ag + I_2 \xrightarrow{\text{Heat}} R_FI + CO_2 + AgI \qquad (20\text{-}7.17)$$

Perfluoroalkyl halides are relatively reactive, undergoing free radical reactions when heated or irradiated. Because of the very strong electron-withdrawing nature of perfluoroalkyl groups, they do not undergo most of the nucleophilic reactions typical of the alkyl halides. Trifluoromethyl iodide is readily cleaved homolytically according to Eq. 20-7.18:

$$CF_3I = CF_3\cdot + I\cdot \qquad \Delta H = 115 \text{ kJ mol}^{-1} \qquad (20\text{-}7.18)$$

and radical reactions of CF_3I give CF_3 derivatives, an example being reaction 20-7.19:

$$CF_3I + P \xrightarrow{\text{Heat}} (CF_3)_nPI_{3-n} \qquad (20\text{-}7.19)$$

STUDY GUIDE

Study Questions

A. Review

1. Where, and in what chemical form, are the halogens found in nature?
2. How are the free halogens prepared from their halide salts?
3. List the main methods for the preparations of various anhydrous compounds of chlorine.
4. Give balanced equations for preparations of the following:
   (a) $CrCl_3$ from $[Cr(H_2O)_6]Cl_3$
   (b) $FeCl_3$ from Fe
   (c) PBr_3 from red P
   (d) CuI from aqueous $CuSO_4$
   (e) $FeCl_2$ from Fe
   (f) $GdCl_3$ from Gd_2O_3
5. Why is it impossible to make iodides of elements in high oxidation states, whereas corresponding bromides and chlorides are known?
6. Which elements give chlorides that are essentially insoluble in water or dilute HNO_3?
7. How may halides act as bridging ligands?
8. Give balanced equations for the preparations of the following oxo chlorides:
   (a) ClO_2 (b) I_2O_5
   (c) $NaOCl(aq)$ (d) $NaClO_2$
   (e) $NaClO_3$ (f) $NaClO_4$
9. What are the general formulas and names of the four types of oxo acids of the halogens and their anions? In the case of iodine, there is one of unique stoichiometry. What is its formula?

10. Name one cationic, one neutral, and one anionic interhalogen compound. In those consisting of three or more atoms, state the rule that predicts which atom will be the central atom.

11. I_2 has a very low solubility in water, but dissolves readily in KI(aq). Why?

12. Describe two methods for making fluoroorganic compounds.

B. Additional Exercises

1. F_2O_2 has a very short O—O bond (1.217 Å) compared with those in H_2O_2 (1.48 Å) and O_2^{2-} (1.49 Å). F_2O_2 also has relatively long O—F bonds (1.575 Å) compared with those in OF_2. Why?

2. ClO_2 is a free radical with one unpaired electron, but it has no tendency to dimerize as does NO_2. Why?

3. Suggest a geometry for SbF_3 and $SbCl_5$. Classify each Sb atom according to the AB_xE_y scheme of Chapter 3.

4. Draw the shapes of the following molecules and ions, giving the AB_xE_y classification and the hybridization for each central atom. (a) ClF   (b) BrF_3 (c) IF_5 (d) IF_7 (e) ClF_4^- (f) I_3^- (g) BrF_4^+ (h) ICl_2^+

5. What is the order of acid strength for the following: HClO, $HClO_2$, $HClO_3$, and $HClO_4$? Why?

6. Why cannot F_2 be obtained by electrolysis of aqueous solutions of NaF?

7. Predict the details of the structures of (a) O_2F_2 (b) ClO_2 (c) BrO_3^- (d) $H_4IO_6^-$ (e) BrO_4^-

8. Write balanced equations for each of the following:
   (a) The oxidation of aqueous HCl by MnO_2.
   (b) The oxidation of aqueous HI by MnO_4^-.
   (c) Hydrolysis of SeF_6.
   (d) Reduction of $KClO_3$ by oxalic acid.
   (e) Reaction of aqueous barium chlorite with sulfuric acid.
   (f) Oxidation of Mn^{2+} to MnO_4^- by periodic acid.

9. How might you obtain CF_3NO from CF_3I?

10. An unknown metal carbonyl (1.86 g) was heated with excess iodine dissolved in pyridine, liberating carbon monoxide. The gas was passed over I_2O_5, and the resulting I_2 was extracted with CCl_4. The amount of I_2 in the CCl_4 solution was determined by reaction with sodium thiosulfate, 20.0 mL of a 1.00 M solution being required. Write balanced equations for each step in the analysis, and calculate the formula of the unknown metal carbonyl.

11. Describe the bonding in I_3^- and I_3^+.

12. Describe the three-center, four-electron bond system of the molecular halide M_2Cl_{10}, structure 20-II.

C. Problems from the Literature of Inorganic Chemistry

1. Consider the properties of the perbromate ion as reported by E. H. Appleman, *Inorg. Chem.*, **1969**, *8*, 223–227.
   (a) Perbromic acid in aqueous solution and alkali perbromates were shown to contain the same tetrahedral BrO_4^- ion. On what basis was this conclusion reached?
   (b) Periodates are rapidly hydrated to $H_4IO_6^-$. How was it demonstrated that this does not happen for perbromate?

2. The IF_4^- ion is featured in the work by K. O. Christe and D. Nauman, *Inorg. Chem.*, **1973**, *12*, 59–62.

   (a) How was the square-planar geometry of IF_4^- established?

   (b) Discuss the geometries of IF_4^- and XeF_4 in terms of VSEPR theory.

3. The BrF_4^+ cation was studied by M. D. Lind and K. O. Christe, *Inorg. Chem.*, **1972**, *11*, 608–612.

   (a) Discuss the structure in the solid state of $[BrF_4^+][Sb_2F_{11}^-]$ by taking the view that it is constructed through Lewis acid–base interactions between $[BrF_4^+]$, $[SbF_6^-]$, and SbF_5. Identify all donor–acceptor interactions in Fig. 1 of this paper.

   (b) What would be the geometries of $[BrF_4^+]$, $[SbF_6^-]$, and SbF_5 in the absence of these solid state interactions?

4. The compound ClF_3O was described in a series of papers by K. O. Christe et al., *Inorg. Chem.*, **1972**, *11*, 2189, 2192, 2196, 2201, 2205, 2209, 2212.

   (a) Write equations representing the synthesis of ClF_3O (i) from Cl_2O—note the precautions! (ii) from $NaClO_2$, and (iii) from $ClONO_2$.

   (b) Write equations for the thermal decomposition of ClF_3, ClF_5, IOF_5, $FClO_2$, and ClF_3O.

   (c) What reactions may be used in photochemical syntheses of ClF_3O?

   (d) What is the structure of ClF_3O? Classify it according to the AB_xE_y system.

   (e) List two reactions in which ClF_3O serves as a Lewis acid.

   (f) List two reactions in which ClF_3O serves as a Lewis base.

   (g) What are the structures of the ions ClF_4O^- and ClF_2O^+?

SUPPLEMENTARY READING

Banks, R. E., Ed. *Preparation, Properties, and Industrial Applications of Organofluorine Compounds*, Wiley-Horwood, Chichester, 1982.

Christe, K. O. and Schack, C. J., "Chlorine Oxyfluorides," *Adv. Inorg. Chem. Radiochem.*, **1976**, *18*, 319.

Downs, A. J. and Adams, C. J., *The Chemistry of Chlorine, Bromine, Iodine, and Astatine*, Pergamon Press, New York, 1975.

Emeleus, H. J., *The Chemistry of Fluorine and its Compounds*, Academic, New York, 1969.

Foster, R., *Organic Charge Transfer Complexes*, Academic, New York, 1969.

Gillespie, R. J. and Morton, M. J., "Halogen and Interhalogen Cations," *Q. Rev.*, **1971**, *25*, 553.

Gutmann, V., *Halogen Chemistry*, Academic, New York, 1967.

Holloway, J. H. and Laycock, D., "Preparations and Reactions of Inorganic Main-Group Oxide Fluorides," *Adv. Inorg. Chem. Radiochem.*, **1983**, *27*, 157.

Schafer, H., "Gaseous Chloride Complexes Containing Halogen Bridges," *Adv. Inorg. Chem. Radiochem.*, **1983**, *26*, 201.

Sheppard, W. A. and Sharts, C. M., *Organo Fluorine Chemistry*, Benjamin, New York, 1970.

Solymosi, F., *Structure and Stability of Salts of Halogen Oxoacids in the Solid Phase*, Wiley, New York, 1977.

Tatlow, J. C. et al., Eds., *Advances in Fluorine Chemistry*, Vols. 1–7, Butterworths, London, 1966–1973.

chapter 21

THE NOBLE GASES

21-1 Occurrence, Isolation, and Applications

The noble gases (Table 21-1) are minor constituents of the atmosphere, from which Sir William Ramsay was first able to isolate Ne, Ar, Kr, and Xe. W. F. Hillebrand had isolated helium gas from uranium minerals, and Ramsey was able to demonstrate that the gas has the same spectrum as the element identified spectroscopically in the sun by Sir J. Norman Lockyer and Sir E. Frankland in 1868.

Helium occurs in radioactive minerals, and, notably, in some natural gases in the United States. Its origin is entirely from the decay of uranium or thorium isotopes that emit α-particles. These α-particles are helium nuclei that acquire electrons from surrounding elements, and if the rock is sufficiently impermeable, the helium remains trapped. The gas radon, all of whose isotopes are radioactive with short half-lives, was characterized in the decay series from uranium and thorium.

Ne, Ar, Kr, and Xe are obtained from fractionation of liquid air. The gases were originally termed inert, and thought to have no chemical reactivity at all. They provided the key to the problem of valency, the interpretation of the periodic table, and the concept of the closed electron shell configuration. Although we now know that some of the noble gases can form compounds, they still provide a point of reference in these respects.

A main use of helium is as the liquid in cryoscopy. Argon may be used to provide an inert atmosphere in laboratory apparatus, in welding, and in gas-filled electric light bulbs. Neon is used for discharge lighting tubes, giving the familiar red glow of "neon" signs.

21-2 The Chemistry of Xenon

During studies with the very reactive gas PtF_6, N. Bartlett found that with oxygen, a crystalline solid, $[O_2^+][PtF_6^-]$, was formed. He noted that since the ionization enthalpy of Xe is almost identical with that of O_2, an analogous reaction might be expected and, indeed, in 1962 he reported the first compound containing a noble gas, a red crystalline solid first believed to be $[Xe^+][PtF_6^-]$ but now known to be more complex.

There is now an extensive chemistry of xenon with bonds to F and O; one compound with a Xe—N bond is known, but compounds with bonds to other

Table 21-1 Some Properties of the Noble Gases

Element	Outer Configuration	1st Ionization Enthalpy kJ mol^{-1}	Normal bp, K	Vol. % in atmosphere ($\times 10^4$)
He	$1s^2$	2369	4.2	5.2
Ne	$2s^2\,2p^6$	2078	27.1	18.2
Ar	$3s^2\,3p^6$	1519	87.3	9340.0
Kr	$4s^2\,4p^6$	1349	120.3	11.4
Xe	$5s^2\,5p^6$	1169	166.1	0.08
Rn	$6s^2\,6p^6$	1036	208.2	—

elements are highly unstable. A few krypton compounds exist but while there should be an extensive chemistry of Rn, the short lifetimes of the isotopes make study impossible. Xenon reacts directly only with fluorine, but oxygen compounds can be obtained from the fluorides. Certain compounds are very stable and can be made in large quantities. Table 21-2 lists some of the more important compounds and their properties.

Table 21-2 Some Xenon Compounds

Oxidation State	Compound	Form	mp, °C	Structure	Remarks
II	XeF_2	Colorless crystals	129	Linear	Hydrolyzed to $Xe + O_2$; very soluble in HF(ℓ)
IV	XeF_4	Colorless crystals	117	Square	Stable
VI	XeF_6	Colorless crystals	49.6	Complex, see text	Stable
	Cs_2XeF_8	Yellow solid		Archimedan antiprism	Stable to 400 °C
	$XeOF_4$	Colorless liquid	-46	Square pyramid	Stable
	XeO_2F_2	Colorless crystals	31	See–saw F-axial	Stable
	XeO_3	Colorless crystals		Pyramidal	Explosive, hygroscopic; stable in solution
VIII	XeO_4	Colorless gas	-35.9	Tetrahedral	Explosive
	XeO_6^{4-}	Colorless salts		Octahedral	Anions $HXeO_6^{3-}$, $H_2XeO_6^{2-}$, $H_3XeO_6^-$ also exist

Fluorides

Thermodynamic studies of reactions 21-2.1 to 21-2.3:

$$Xe + F_2 = XeF_2 \qquad\qquad (21\text{-}2.1)$$

$$XeF_2 + F_2 = XeF_4 \qquad\qquad (21\text{-}2.2)$$

$$XeF_4 + F_2 = XeF_6 \qquad\qquad (21\text{-}2.3)$$

show that only these three fluorides exist. The three equilibria are established rapidly only above 250 °C, and the synthesis of one fluoride either from the others or instead of the others must be performed above this temperature. The three fluorides are volatile substances, subliming readily at 25 °C. They can be stored in nickel vessels, but XeF_4 and XeF_6 are exceptionally readily hydrolyzed, and even traces of water must be excluded.

Xenon difluoride, XeF_2, is best made by interaction of Xe with a deficiency of F_2 at high pressures. The deficiency of F_2 insures exclusive formation of the difluoride. It dissolves in water to give solutions with a pungent odor of XeF_2. Hydrolysis is slow in acid solution, but rapid in the presence of bases, due to reaction 21-2.4:

$$XeF_2 + 2OH^- = Xe + \tfrac{1}{2}O_2 + 2F^- + H_2O \qquad (21\text{-}2.4)$$

Such aqueous solutions are strong oxidizers, converting HCl to Cl_2 and Ce^{3+} to Ce^{4+}. Xenon difluoride is also a mild fluorinating agent for organic compounds; for example, benzene forms C_6H_5F.

Xenon tetrafluoride, XeF_4, is the easiest of the three fluorides to prepare. On heating a 1:5 mixture of Xe and F_2 at 400 °C and ca. 6-atm pressure for a few hours, XeF_4 is formed quantitatively. It resembles XeF_2 except for its behavior on hydrolysis, as discussed later. XeF_4 will fluorinate aromatic rings in compounds such as toluene.

Xenon hexafluoride, XeF_6, is obtained by the interaction of XeF_4 and F_2 under pressure or directly from Xe and F_2 at temperatures above 250 °C and pressures > 50 atm. Xenon hexafluoride is extremely reactive, attacking even quartz as in Eq. 21-2.5:

$$SiO_2 + 2XeF_6 \longrightarrow 2XeOF_4 + SiF_4 \qquad (21\text{-}2.5)$$

XeF_6 is a strong acid according to the Lux–Flood definition that was discussed in Chapter 7. It accepts oxide ion from other compounds and inserts fluoride ion in its place. The order of decreasing Lux–Flood acidity is

$$XeF_6 > XeO_2F_4 > XeO_4 > XeOF_4 > XeF_4 > XeO_2F_2 > XeO_3 > XeF_2$$

Any acid reacts by accepting oxide from any base beneath it in this series, and replacing it with fluoride. This can be useful in synthesis, Eq. 21-2.6 being an example:

$$XeOF_4 + XeO_3 \longrightarrow 2XeO_2F_2 \qquad (21\text{-}2.6)$$

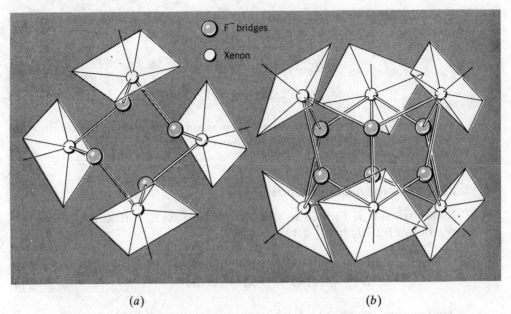

Figure 21-1 The tetrameric (*a*) and the hexameric (*b*) units that make up the crystal structure of XeF_6. Each is built up of XeF_5^+ units bridged by F^- ions. There are at least four crystalline forms of the substance, three of which are built up of tetramers and one which includes both tetramers and hexamers.

The colorless crystals of XeF_6 contain both tetramers and hexamers each made up of XeF_5^+ units linked by unsymmetrical and bent F^- bridges as shown in Fig. 21-1. Monomeric XeF_6 in liquid or the vapor has a distorted octahedral structure because of a lone pair of electrons at Xe.

Xenon Fluoride Complexes

The xenon fluorides will react with strong Lewis acids such as SbF_5 or IrF_5 to give adducts. The three types of adducts formed by XeF_2 are $XeF_2 \cdot MF_5$, $2XeF_2 \cdot MF_5$, and $XeF_2 \cdot 2MF_5$, where M = Ru, Ir, Pt, and so on. Although $XeF_2 \cdot IF_5$ has a molecular rather than ionic structure, in most cases adduct formation involves fluoride ion transfer to give structures that contain ions such as XeF^+ (formed by loss of F^- from XeF_2), $Xe_2F_3^+$ (which has a planar structure 21-I),

$$
\begin{array}{ccc}
& \overset{\displaystyle F}{\underset{\displaystyle 151°}{\frown}} \text{2.14 Å} & \\
\text{Xe} & & \text{Xe} \quad \text{1.90 Å} \\
F^{\diagup} & & {}^{\diagdown}F \\
& \text{21-I} &
\end{array}
$$

and XeF_5^+ (formed by transfer of F^- from XeF_6). Examples include $[XeF_5^+][PtF_6^-]$ and reaction 21-2.7:

$$2XeF_2 + AsF_5 \longrightarrow [Xe_2F_3^+][AsF_6^-] \qquad (21\text{-}2.7)$$

XeF_6 can act as a Lewis acid toward F^- and can be converted to heptafluoro or octafluoro xenates as in reactions 21-2.8 and 21-2.9:

$$XeF_6 + RbF \longrightarrow RbXeF_7 \qquad (21\text{-}2.8)$$

$$2RbXeF_7 \longrightarrow XeF_6 + Rb_2XeF_8 \qquad (21\text{-}2.9)$$

These rubidium octafluoro xenates are among the most stable xenon compounds known and decompose only above 400 °C.

Xenon–Oxygen Compounds

·Xenon trioxide is formed in the hydrolysis of XeF_4 and XeF_6 according to reactions 21-2.10 and 21-2.11:

$$3XeF_4 + 6H_2O \longrightarrow XeO_3 + 2Xe + \tfrac{3}{2}O_2 + 12HF \qquad (21\text{-}2.10)$$
$$XeF_6 + 3H_2O \longrightarrow XeO_3 + 6HF \qquad (21\text{-}2.11)$$

The colorless, odorless, and stable aqueous solutions of XeO_3 appear to contain XeO_3 molecules. On evaporation of water, XeO_3 is obtained as a white deliquescent solid that is dangerously explosive. In basic solution, a xenate(VI) ion, $HXeO_4^-$, is formed as in reaction 21-2.12:

$$XeO_3 + OH^- \longrightarrow HXeO_4^- \qquad (21\text{-}2.12)$$

The ion $HXeO_4^-$ slowly disproportionates to give a xenate(VIII) (or perxenate ion, XeO_6^{4-}), as in reaction 21-2.13:

$$2HXeO_4^- + 2OH^- \longrightarrow XeO_6^{4-} + Xe + O_2 + 2H_2O \qquad (21\text{-}2.13)$$

Perxenates are also formed by oxidation of $HXeO_4^-$ with ozone. The perxenate ions are yellow and are powerful and rapid oxidizing agents. Salts such as $Na_4XeO_6 \cdot 8H_2O$ are stable and sparingly soluble in water.

In alkaline solution, the main form is the ion $HXeO_6^{3-}$, and perxenates are only slowly reduced by water. However, in acid solution, reduction by water according to Eq. 21-2.14:

$$H_2XeO_6^{2-} + H^+ \longrightarrow HXeO_4^- + H_2O + \tfrac{1}{2}O_2 \qquad (21\text{-}2.14)$$

is almost instantaneous, and the hydroxyl radical is involved as an intermediate.

When barium perxenate is heated with concentrated sulfuric acid, xenon tetroxide, XeO_4, is formed as an explosive and unstable gas.

The aqueous chemistry of xenon is summarized by the potentials:

Acid solution $\qquad H_4XeO_6 \xrightarrow{\;2.36\text{ V}\;} XeO_3 \xrightarrow{\;2.12\text{ V}\;} Xe$

$$XeF_2 \xrightarrow{\;2.64\text{ V}\;} Xe$$

Alkaline solution $\qquad HXeO_6^{3-} \xrightarrow{\;0.94\text{ V}\;} HXeO_4^- \xrightarrow{\;1.26\text{ V}\;} Xe$

21-3 Other Noble Gas Chemistry

Radon might be expected to display even more chemistry than xenon, but because of the radioactivity of all radon isotopes, rather little has been learned about it. Apparently at least one radon fluoride of uncertain composition does exist.

The other noble gas atoms have higher ionization energies than the xenon atom, and they therefore are much less reactive. In a consistent manner those compounds formed by the lighter noble gases are less stable than those of xenon.

KrF_2 is obtained when an electric discharge is passed through a mixture of Kr and F_2 at -180 °C. It resembles XeF_2 in being a volatile white solid constructed of linear FKrF molecules, but differs in that it is thermodynamically unstable, as indicated by Eqs. 21-3.1 and 21-3.2:

$$KrF_2(g) = Kr(g) + F_2(g) \qquad \Delta H° = -63 \text{ kJ mol}^{-1} \qquad (21\text{-}3.1)$$

$$XeF_2(g) = Xe(g) + F_2(g) \qquad \Delta H° = 105 \text{ kJ mol}^{-1} \qquad (21\text{-}3.2)$$

STUDY GUIDE

Study Questions

A. Review

1. What is the origin of terrestrial helium?
2. Why do the boiling points of the noble gases vary systematically with atomic number? What interatomic forces account for this variation?
3. How are XeF_2, XeF_4, and XeF_6 prepared?
4. Write balanced equations for the hydrolyses of XeF_2, XeF_4, and XeF_6.
5. How are xenates and perxenates made?

B. Additional Exercises

1. Write balanced equations for
   (a) The oxidation of $HXeO_4^-$ by ozone.
   (b) The reduction of XeO_3 by I^- in acid solution to give Xe.
   (c) Oxidation by XeF_2 of HCl.
   (d) Oxidation by XeF_2 of Ce^{3+}.
   (e) Synthesis of $[XeF^+][SbF_6^-]$.
2. Show the electron-pair geometry around each atom in $Xe_2F_3^+$ and classify each atom using the AB_xE_y system.
3. Draw the Lewis diagrams and show the electron-pair geometries around each atom in
   (a) XeF_4 (b) XeO_3
   (c) XeO_6^{4-} (d) $XeOF_4$
   (e) XeF_5^+ (f) $HXeO_4^-$
   (g) XeF_8^{2-} (h) XeF_7^-

4. Prepare a MO description of the bonding in XeF_2 using only a colinear set of p orbitals.

5. Discuss the following reactions in terms of the Lux–Flood definition of acids and bases:

(a) $XeF_6 + XeO_2F_2 \longrightarrow 2XeOF_4$

(b) $XeO_3F_2 + XeO_2F_2 \longrightarrow XeOF_4 + XeO_4$

(c) $XeF_2 + Na_4XeO_6 \longrightarrow$ no reaction

C. Questions from the Literature of Inorganic Chemistry

1. Consider the work by J. L. Huston, *Inorg. Chem.*, **1982**, *21*, 685–688.

(a) Write a plausible sequence of reactions for the hydrolysis of XeF_4 in excess water.

(b) Explain reactions 1, 2, 4, 11, 12, 16, and 17 in terms of the Lux–Flood definition of acids and bases. Identify the acid and base in each reaction.

(c) Prepare an order of base strength for each of the bases featured in the reactions of (b).

2. Consider the series of papers by N. Bartlett et al., *Inorg. Chem.*, **1973**, *12*, 1713, 1717, 1722.

(a) Explain how each of the following adducts may be considered to arise from fluoride ion transfer to give ionic compounds with weak F^- bridges in the solid state: (i) $XeF_4 \cdot 2SbF_5$; (ii) $XeF_2 \cdot RuF_5$ and $XeF_4 \cdot RuF_5$; (iii) $XeF_4 \cdot SbF_5$ and $XeF_4 \cdot 2SbF_5$; and (iv) $XeOF_4 \cdot SbF_5$ and $XeOF_4 \cdot 2SbF_5$

(b) Describe the geometries (ignoring the weak F^- bridges) of the cations in the compounds of (a). Use the AB_xE_y classification, and pay close attention to the positions of the lone electron pairs.

(c) Do the oxygens in $XeOF_3^+$ and XeO_2F_2 prefer equatorial or axial positions?

SUPPLEMENTARY READING

Bartlett, N., *The Chemistry of the Noble Gases*, Elsevier, Amsterdam, 1971.

Halloway, J. H., *Noble Gas Chemistry*, Methuen, New York, 1968.

Hawkins, D. T., Falconer, W. E., and Bartlett, N., *Noble Gas Compounds, A Bibliography 1962–1976*, Plenum, New York, 1978.

Moody, G. J., "A Decade of Xenon Chemistry," *J. Chem. Educ.*, **1974**, *51*, 628.

Selig, H. and Halloway, J. H. *Topics in Current Chemistry No. 124*, F. L. Bosche, Ed., Springer-Verlag, 1984.

Seppelt, K. and Lentz, D. *Prog. Inorg. Chem.* **1982**, *29*, 168.

chapter 22

ZINC, CADMIUM, AND MERCURY

22-1 Introduction

The position of Zn, Cd, and Hg in the periodic table is discussed in Section 2-5, and some properties are given in Table 8-2. Mercury shows such unique behavior that it cannot be considered as homologous to Zn and Cd.

Although these elements characteristically form +2 cations, they do not have much in common with the Be, Mg, and Ca to Ra group except for some resemblances between Zn, Be, and Mg. Thus BeO, Be(OH)$_2$, and BeS have the same structures as ZnO, Zn(OH)$_2$, and ZnS, and there is some similarity in the solution and complex chemistry of Zn^{2+} and Mg^{2+}. The main cause of the differences between the Group IIA(2) and the Group IIB(12) ions arises because of the high polarizability of the filled d shell of the Group IIB(12) ions compared with the nonpolarizable, noble gas-like electron configurations of the Group IIA(2) ions.

22-2 Occurrence, Isolation, and Properties of the Elements

The elements have relatively low abundance in nature (of the order 10^{-6} of the earth's crust for Zn and Cd), but have long been known because they are easily obtained from their ores.

Zinc occurs widely, but the main source is *sphalerite*, (ZnFe)S, which commonly occurs with galena, PbS; cadmium minerals are scarce but, as a result of its similarity to Zn, Cd occurs by isomorphous replacement in almost all zinc ores. Methods of isolation involve flotation and roasting; Zn and Pb are recovered simultaneously by a blast furnace method. Cadmium is invariably a by-product and is usually separated from Zn by distillation or by precipitation from sulfate solutions by Zn dust:

$$Zn + Cd^{2+} = Zn^{2+} + Cd \qquad E^0 = +0.36 \text{ V} \qquad (22\text{-}2.1)$$

The only important ore of mercury is *cinnabar*, HgS; this is roasted to give the oxide which, in turn, decomposes at ca. 500 °C, the mercury vaporizing.

Zinc and cadmium are white, lustrous, but tarnishable metals. Their structures deviate but slightly from perfect hexagonal close packing. Mercury is a

419

shiny liquid at ordinary temperatures. All are remarkably volatile for heavy metals, mercury uniquely so. Mercury gives a monoatomic vapor and has an appreciable vapor pressure (1.3×10^{-3} mm) at 20 °C. It is also surprisingly soluble in both polar and nonpolar liquids: A saturated solution in water at 25 °C has 6×10^{-8} g of $Hg/g \; H_2O$. Because of its high volatility and moderate toxicity, mercury should always be kept in stoppered containers and handled in well-ventilated areas. It becomes extremely hazardous in the biosphere because there are bacteria that convert it to the exceedingly toxic CH_3Hg^+ ion. Mercury is readily lost from aqueous solutions of mercuric salts owing to reduction by traces of reducing materials and by disproportionation of Hg_2^{2+}.

Both Zn and Cd are very electropositive and react readily with nonoxidizing acids, releasing H_2 and giving the divalent ions; Hg is inert to nonoxidizing acids. Zinc also dissolves in strong bases because of its ability to form zincate ions (see Eq. 22-2.2), commonly written ZnO_2^{2-}.

$$Zn + 2OH^- \longrightarrow ZnO_2^{2-} + H_2 \qquad (22\text{-}2.2)$$

Cadmium does not dissolve in bases.

Zinc and Cd react readily when heated in O_2, to give the oxides. Although Hg and O_2 are unstable with respect to HgO at 25 °C, their rate of combination is exceedingly slow; the reaction proceeds at a useful rate at 300 to 350 °C, but above ca. 400 °C the ΔG becomes positive and HgO decomposes rapidly into the elements:

$$HgO(s) = Hg(\ell) + \tfrac{1}{2}O_2 \qquad \Delta H_{diss} = 90.4 \text{ kJ mol}^{-1} \qquad (22\text{-}2.3)$$

This ability of Hg to absorb O_2 from the air and regenerate it as O_2 was of considerable importance in the earliest studies of oxygen by A. L. Lavoisier and J. Priestley.

All three elements react with halogens and with nonmetals such as S, Se, P, and so on.

Zinc and Cd form many alloys. Some, such as brass, which is a copper–zinc alloy, are of technical importance. Mercury combines with many other metals, sometimes with difficulty but sometimes, as with Na or K, very vigorously, giving *amalgams*. Many amalgams are of continuously variable compositions, while others are compounds, such as Hg_2Na. Some of the transition metals do not form amalgams, and iron is commonly used for containers of Hg. Sodium amalgams and amalgamated Zn are frequently used as reducing agents for aqueous solutions.

22-3 The Univalent State

Zinc, Cd, and Hg form the ions M_2^{2+}. The Zn_2^{2+} and Cd_2^{2+} ions are unstable, especially Zn_2^{2+}, and are known only in melts or solids. Thus addition of Zn to fused $ZnCl_2$ gives a yellow solution and, on cooling, a yellow glass that contains Zn_2^{2+}.

The ions have a metal–metal bond, $^+M\!-\!M^+$; Raman spectra allow the estimation of force constants, and they show that the order of bond strength is $Zn_2^{2+} < Cd_2^{2+} < Hg_2^{2+}$.

The mercury(I) ion, Hg_2^{2+}, is formed on reduction of mercury(II) salts in aqueous solution. X-ray diffraction studies on many compounds such as Hg_2Cl_2, Hg_2SO_4, and $Hg_2(NO_3)_2 \cdot 2H_2O$, show that the $Hg\!-\!Hg$ distances range from 2.50 to 2.70 Å, depending on the associated anions. The shortest distances are found with the least covalently bound anions, for example, NO_3^-.

$Hg^I\!-\!Hg^{II}$ Equilibria

An understanding of the thermodynamics of these equilibria is essential to an understanding of the chemistry of the mercury(I) state. The important values are the potentials

$$Hg_2^{2+} + 2e^- = 2Hg \qquad E^0 = 0.789 \text{ V} \qquad (22\text{-}3.1)$$

$$2Hg^{2+} + 2e^- = Hg_2^{2+} \qquad E^0 = 0.920 \text{ V} \qquad (22\text{-}3.2)$$

$$Hg^{2+} + 2e^- = Hg \qquad E^0 = 0.854 \text{ V} \qquad (22\text{-}3.3)$$

For the disproportionation equilibrium

$$Hg_2^{2+} = Hg + Hg^{2+} \qquad E^0 = -0.131 \text{ V} \qquad (22\text{-}3.4)$$

from which it follows that

$$K = \frac{[Hg^{2+}]}{[Hg_2^{2+}]} = 6.0 \times 10^{-3} \qquad (22\text{-}3.5)$$

The implication of the standard potentials is clearly that only oxidizing agents with potentials in the range -0.79 to -0.85 V can oxidize mercury to Hg^I but not to Hg^{II}. Since no common oxidizing agent meets this requirement, it is found that when mercury is treated with an excess of oxidizing agent it is entirely converted into Hg^{II}. However, when mercury is in at least 50% excess, only Hg^I is obtained since, according to Eq. 22-3.4, Hg readily reduces Hg^{2+} to Hg_2^{2+}.

The equilibrium constant for reaction 22-3.4 shows that Hg_2^{2+} is stable with respect to disproportionation, but by only a small margin. Thus any reagents that reduce the activity (by precipitation or complexation) of Hg^{2+}, to a significantly greater extent than they lower the activity of Hg_2^{2+}, will cause *disproportionation* of Hg_2^{2+}. There are many such reagents, so that the number of stable Hg^I compounds is quite restricted.

Thus, when OH^- is added to a solution of Hg_2^{2+}, a dark precipitate consisting of Hg and HgO is formed; evidently mercury(I) hydroxide, if it could be isolated, would be a stronger base than HgO. Similarly, addition of sulfide ions to a solution of Hg_2^{2+} gives a mixture of Hg and the extremely insoluble HgS. Mercury(I) cyanide does not exist because $Hg(CN)_2$, although soluble, is so slightly dissociated. The reactions in these cited cases are

$$Hg_2^{2+} + 2OH^- \longrightarrow Hg + HgO(s) + H_2O \qquad (22\text{-}3.6)$$

$$Hg_2^{2+} + S^{2-} \longrightarrow Hg + HgS(s) \qquad (22\text{-}3.7)$$

$$Hg_2^{2+} + 2CN^- \longrightarrow Hg + Hg(CN)_2(aq) \qquad (22\text{-}3.8)$$

Dimercury(I) Compounds

As we indicated previously, no hydroxide, oxide, or sulfide can be obtained by addition of the appropriate anion to aqueous Hg_2^{2+}, nor have these compounds been otherwise made.

Among the best known dimercury(I) compounds are the *halides*. The fluoride is unstable toward water, being hydrolyzed to hydrofluoric acid and unisolable hydroxide (which disproportionates as shown previously). The other halides are insoluble, which thus precludes the possibilities of hydrolysis or disproportionation to give Hg^{II} halide complexes. Mercury(I) nitrate and perchlorate are soluble in water, but Hg_2SO_4 is sparingly soluble.

22-4   Divalent Zinc and Cadmium Compounds

Binary Compounds

Oxides

The *oxides*, ZnO and CdO, are formed on burning the metals in air or by pyrolysis of the carbonates or nitrates; oxide smokes can be obtained by combustion of the alkyls, cadmium oxide smokes being exceedingly toxic. Zinc oxide is normally white but turns yellow on heating. CdO varies in color from greenish yellow through brown to nearly black, depending on its thermal history. These colors are the result of various kinds of lattice defects. Both oxides sublime at very high temperatures.

The hydroxides are precipitated from solutions of salts by addition of bases. $Zn(OH)_2$ readily dissolves in an excess of alkali bases to give "zincate" ions, and solid zincates such as $NaZn(OH)_3$ and $Na_2[Zn(OH)_4]$ can be crystallized from concentrated solutions. $Cd(OH)_2$ is insoluble in bases. Both Zn and Cd hydroxide readily dissolve in an excess of strong ammonia to form the ammine complexes, for example, $[Zn(NH_3)_4]^{2+}$. The complete set of formation constants for the cadmium system was presented in Section 6-4.

Sulfides

The *sulfides* are obtained by direct interaction or by precipitation by H_2S from aqueous solutions, acidic for CdS, neutral or basic for ZnS. The sulfides, as well as the selenides and tellurides, all have the wurtzite or zinc blende structures shown in Chapter 4.

Halides

The fluorides are essentially ionic, high melting solids, whereas the other *halides* are more covalent in nature. The fluorides are sparingly soluble in water, a reflection of the high lattice energies of the ZnF_2 (rutile) and CdF_2 (fluorite) structures. The other halides are much more soluble, not only in water but in alcohols, ketones, and similar donor solvents. Aqueous solutions of cadmium halides contain all the species Cd^{2+}, CdX^+, CdX_2, and CdX_3^- in equilibrium.

Oxo Salts and Aqua Ions

Salts of oxo acids such as the nitrate, sulfate, sulfite, perchlorate, and acetate are soluble in water. The Zn^{2+} and Cd^{2+} ions are rather similar to Mg^{2+}, and many of their salts are isomorphous with magnesium salts, for example, $Zn(Mg)SO_4 \cdot 7H_2O$. The aqua ions are acidic, and aqueous solutions of salts are hydrolyzed. In perchlorate solution the only species for Zn, Cd (and Hg) below 0.1 M are the MOH^+ ions, for example,

$$Zn^{2+}(aq) + H_2O \rightleftharpoons ZnOH^+(aq) + H^+ \qquad (22\text{-}4.1)$$

For more concentrated cadmium solutions, the principal species is Cd_2OH^{3+}

$$2Cd^{2+}(aq) + H_2O \rightleftharpoons Cd_2OH^{3+}(aq) + H^+ \qquad (22\text{-}4.2)$$

In the presence of complexing anions, for example, halide, species such as $Cd(OH)Cl$ or $CdNO_3^+$ may be obtained.

Complexes

All of the halide ions except F^- form complex halogeno anions when present in excess, but for Zn^{2+} and Cd^{2+} the formation constants are many orders of magnitude smaller than those for Hg^{2+}. The same applies to complex cations with NH_3 and amines, many of which can be isolated as crystalline salts.

Zinc dithiocarbamates (Section 14-6), are industrially important as accelerators in the vulcanization of rubber by sulfur. Zinc complexes are also of great importance biologically (Section 31-9). Zinc compounds, especially $ZnCO_3$ and ZnO, are used in ointments, since zinc apparently promotes healing processes.

By contrast, cadmium compounds are extremely poisonous, possibly because of the substitution of Cd for Zn in an enzyme system, and consequently they constitute a serious environmental hazard, for example, in the neighborhood of Zn smelters.

22-5 Divalent Mercury Compounds

Binary Compounds

Red HgO is formed on gentle pyrolysis of mercury(I) or mercury(II) nitrate, by direct interaction at 300 to 350 °C, or as red crystals by heating of an alkaline solution of K_2HgI_4. Addition of OH^- to aqueous Hg^{2+} gives a yellow precipitate of HgO; the yellow form differs from the red only in particle size.

No hydroxide has been obtained, but the oxide is soluble in water (10^{-3}–10^{-4} mol L^{-1}), the exact solubility depending on particle size, to give a solution of what is commonly assumed to be the hydroxide, although there is no proof for such a species. This "hydroxide" is an extremely weak base:

$$K = \frac{[Hg^{2+}][OH^-]^2}{[Hg(OH)_2]} = 1.8 \times 10^{-22} \tag{22-5.1}$$

and is somewhat amphoteric, though more basic than acidic.

Mercury(II) sulfide, HgS, is precipitated from aqueous solutions as a black, highly insoluble compound. The solubility product is 10^{-54}, but the sulfide is somewhat more soluble than this figure would imply because of hydrolysis of Hg^{2+} and S^{2-} ions. The black sulfide is unstable with respect to a red form identical with the mineral cinnabar and changes into it when heated or digested with alkali polysulfides or mercury(I) chloride.

Mercury(II) fluoride is essentially ionic and crystallizes in the fluorite structure; it is almost completely decomposed even by cold water, as would be expected for an ionic compound that is the salt of a weak acid and an extremely weak base.

In sharp contrast to the fluoride, the other halides show marked covalent character. *Mercury(II) chloride* crystallizes in an essentially molecular lattice. Relative to ionic HgF_2, the other halides have very low melting and boiling points, for example, $HgCl_2$, mp 280 °C. They also show marked solubility in many organic solvents. In aqueous solution they exist almost exclusively (~99%) as HgX_2 molecules, but some hydrolysis occurs, the principal equilibrium being, for example,

$$HgCl_2 + H_2O \rightleftharpoons Hg(OH)Cl + H^+ + Cl^- \tag{22-5.2}$$

Mercury(II) Oxo Salts

Among the mercury(II) salts that are essentially ionic and, hence, highly dissociated in aqueous solution are the nitrate, sulfate, and perchlorate. Because of the great weakness of mercury(II) hydroxide, aqueous solutions of these salts tend to hydrolyze extensively and must be acidified to be stable.

In aqueous solutions of $Hg(NO_3)_2$ the main species are $Hg(NO_3)_2$, $HgNO_3^+$, and Hg^{2+}, but at high concentrations of NO_3^- the complex anions $[Hg(NO_3)_{3,4}]^{-,2-}$ are formed.

Mercury(II) carboxylates, especially the acetate and the trifluoroacetate, are of considerable importance because of their utility in attacking unsaturated hydrocarbons (Section 29-6). They are made by dissolving HgO in the hot acid and crystallizing. The trifluoroacetate is also soluble in benzene, acetone, and THF, which increases its utility, while the acetate is soluble in water and alcohols.

Mercury(II) ions catalyze a number of reactions of complex compounds such as the aquation of $[Cr(NH_3)_5X]^{2+}$. Bridged transition states, for example,

$$[(H_2O)_5CrCl]^{2+} + Hg^{2+} = [(H_2O)_5Cr—Cl—Hg]^{4+} \tag{22-5.3}$$

are believed to be involved.

The silver ion is similarly able to accelerate the rates of substitution of halo and other ligands. In both cases, the catalysis arises because Hg^{2+} or Ag^+ is able to enhance the breaking of the bond to the leaving group in what would otherwise be a slow, dissociative (D or I_d in the terminology of Section 6-5) mechanism.

Mercury(II) Complexes

The Hg^{2+} ion forms many strong complexes. The characteristic coordination numbers and stereochemical arrangements are two-coordinate (*linear*) and four-coordinate (*tetrahedral*). Octahedral coordination is less common; a few three- and five-coordinate complexes are also known. There appears to be considerable covalent character in the mercury–ligand bonds, especially in the two-coordinate compounds.

In addition to halide or pseudohalide complex ions, such as $[HgCl_4]^{2-}$ or $[Hg(CN)_4]^{2-}$, there are cationic species such as $[Hg(NH_3)_4]^{2+}$ and $[Hg(en)_3]^{2+}$.

There are also a number of novel compounds in which —Hg— or —HgX is bound to a transition metal. Some of these compounds may be obtained by reaction of $HgCl_2$ with carbonylate anions (Section 28-9), for example,

$$2Na^+Co(CO)_4^- + HgCl_2 = 2NaCl + (CO)_4Co—Hg—Co(CO)_4 \quad (22\text{-}5.4)$$

STUDY GUIDE

Study Questions

A. Review

1. Give the electronic structures of Zn, Cd, and Hg, and explain their position in the periodic table.
2. What are the electron configurations of the 2+ cations of Zn, Cd, and Hg?
3. Write balanced equations for the action on Zn of (a) 3 M HCl and (b) 3 M KOH.
4. Describe the interaction of Hg and O_2 and the properties of HgO.
5. What are the electron configurations of the 1+ cations?
6. What factors alter the ease of disproportionation of Hg^I?
7. Why do the hydroxide, oxide, or sulfide of Hg^I not exist?
8. Draw the structures of rutile, fluorite, and zinc blende.
9. What is the nature of $HgCl_2$ in solution and in the solid state?

B. Additional Exercises

1. Suggest the reason, in thermodynamic terms, why the sign of ΔG for the following reaction changes (from $-$ to $+$) at about 400 °C

$$Hg(\ell) + \tfrac{1}{2}O_2(g) \longrightarrow HgO(s)$$

2. Why is it that when Hg is oxidized with an excess of oxidant only Hg^{II} is formed, yet when an excess of Hg is present during the oxidation, only Hg^I is formed?

3. By what methods can it be proved that the mercurous (mercury(I)) ion is the dimer Hg_2^{2+} in solution?

4. The zinc and cadmium dithiocarbamates are dimeric $[M(S_2CNR_2)_2]_2$. Draw a plausible structure.

5. Write balanced equations for
   (a) The disproportionation of mercury(I) hydroxide.
   (b) The hydrolysis of Hg^{II} fluoride.
   (c) The hydrolysis of zinc nitrate.
   (d) Thermal decomposition of mercury(II) oxide.

6. Calculate $\Delta G°$ for reaction 22-3.4.

SUPPLEMENTARY READING

Dean, P. A. W., "The Coordination Chemistry of the Mercuric Halides," *Prog. Inorg. Chem.,* **1978,** *24,* 109.

McAuliffe, C. A., Ed., *The Chemistry of Mercury,* Macmillan, New York, 1977.

Miller, M. W. and Clarkson, T. W., Eds., *Mercury, Mercurials, and Mercaptans,* Thomas, Springfield, IL, 1973.

Roberts, H. L., "The Chemistry of Mercury," *Adv. Inorg. Chem. Radiochem.,* **1968,** *11,* 309.

part 3

TRANSITION ELEMENTS

chapter 23

INTRODUCTION TO THE TRANSITION ELEMENTS: LIGAND FIELD THEORY

23-1 Introduction

As we noted in Section 8-12, the transition elements are often defined as those which, *as elements*, have partly filled d or f shells. For practical purposes, however, we shall consider as transition elements all those that have partly filled d or f shells in any of their important compounds as well. Thus we include the coinage metals, Cu, Ag, and Au.

The transition elements are all metals, mostly hard strong ones that conduct heat and electricity well. They form many colored and paramagnetic compounds because of their partially filled shells.

In this part of the book we treat them in detail, beginning here with an account of their electronic structures, spectra, magnetic properties, and some other related matters. We then deal with the d-block elements, that is, those in which the partially filled shells are the $3d$, $4d$, or $5d$ shells. We shall then turn to the *lanthanides*, in which the $4f$ shell is partially filled, and, finally, the *actinides*, in which the $5f$ shell is partially filled.

23-2 Ligand Field Theory

The term *ligand field theory* refers to an entire body of theoretical apparatus used to understand the bonding and associated electronic (magnetic, spectroscopic, etc.) properties of complexes and other compounds formed by the transition elements.

There is nothing fundamentally different about the bonding in transition metal compounds as compared with that in compounds of the main group elements. All the usual forms of valence theory that are applied to the main group elements can be applied, successfully, to the transition elements. In general, the MO method applied to the transition metal compounds gives valid and useful results, the more so as the level of approximation is raised, just as in all other cases.

There are, however, two things that set the study of the electronic structures of transition metal compounds apart from the remaining body of valence

429

theory. One is the presence of partly filled d and f shells. This leads to experimental observations not possible in most other cases: paramagnetism, visible absorption spectra, and apparently irregular variations in thermodynamic and structural properties. The second is that there is a crude but effective approximation, called *crystal field theory*, that provides a powerful yet simple method of understanding and correlating all of those properties that arise primarily from the presence of the partly filled shells.

The crystal field theory provides a way of determining, by simple electrostatic considerations, how the energies of the metal ion orbitals will be affected by the set of surrounding atoms or ligands. It works best when the symmetry is high but, with additional effort, can be applied more generally. Crystal field theory is a *model* and not a realistic description of the forces actually at work. However, its simplicity and convenience have earned it a place in the coordination chemist's "toolbox."

In the immediately following sections the crystal field theory is described and illustrated. Then the more complete MO method is outlined. After that, the electronic properties of transition metal complexes are discussed in terms of the "orbital splittings," which the crystal field theory enables us to work out relatively easily.

Our attention will be confined entirely to the d-block elements, and will be focused primarily on those of the $3d$ series. This is where the crystal field theory works best. The splittings of f orbitals are generally so small that they are not chemically important.

23-3   The Crystal Field Approach

Let us consider a metal ion, M^{m+}, lying at the center of an octahedral set of point charges, as is shown in Fig. 23-1. Let us suppose that this metal ion has a single d electron outside of closed shells; such an ion might be Ti^{3+}, V^{4+}, and

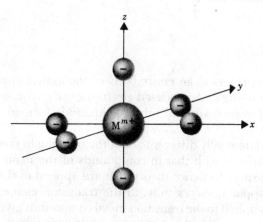

Figure 23-1   A sketch showing six negative charges arranged octahedrally around a central M^{m+} ion, with a set of Cartesian axes for reference.

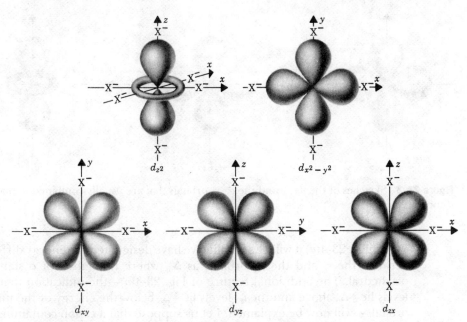

Figure 23-2 Sketches showing the distribution of electron density in the five d orbitals, and their orientation with respect to the set of six octahedrally arranged negative charges of Fig. 23-1.

so on. In the free ion, this d electron would have had equal probability of being in any one of the five d orbitals, since all are equivalent. Now, however, the d orbitals are not all equivalent. Some are concentrated in regions of space closer to the negative ions than are others, and the electron will obviously prefer to occupy the orbital(s) in which it can get as far as possible from the negative charges. Recalling the shapes of the d orbitals (Fig. 2-6) and comparing them with Fig. 23-1, we see that both the d_{z^2} and $d_{x^2-y^2}$ orbitals have lobes that are heavily concentrated in the vicinity of the charges, whereas the d_{xy}, d_{yz}, and d_{zx} orbitals have lobes that project between the charges. This is illustrated in Fig. 23-2. It can also be seen that each of the three orbitals in the latter group, namely, d_{xy}, d_{yz}, d_{zx}, is equally favorable for the electron; these three orbitals have entirely equivalent environments in the octahedral complex. The two relatively unfavorable orbitals, d_{z^2} and $d_{x^2-y^2}$, are also equivalent; this is not obvious from inspection of Fig. 23-2, but Fig. 23-3 shows why it is so. As indicated, the d_{z^2} orbital can be resolved into a linear combination of two orbitals, $d_{z^2-x^2}$ and $d_{z^2-y^2}$, each of which is obviously equivalent to the $d_{x^2-y^2}$ orbital. It is to be stressed, however, that these two orbitals do not have separate existences, and the resolution of the d_{z^2} orbital in this way is only a device to persuade the reader *pictorially* that d_{z^2} is equivalent to $d_{x^2-y^2}$ in relation to the octahedral distribution of charges.

Thus, in the octahedral environment of six negative charges, the metal ion now has two kinds of d orbitals: Three of one kind, equivalent to one another and labeled t_{2g}, and two of another kind, equivalent to each other, labeled e_g; furthermore, the e_g orbitals are of higher energy than the t_{2g} orbitals. These results may be expressed in an energy-level diagram as shown in Fig. 23-4(a).

$$d_{z^2-x^2} \qquad\qquad d_{z^2-y^2} \qquad\qquad d_{z^2}$$

Figure 23-3 Sketches of the $d_{z^2-x^2}$ and the $d_{z^2-y^2}$ orbitals that are usually combined to make the d_{z^2} orbital.

In Fig. 23-4(a) it will be seen that we have designated the energy difference between the e_g and the t_{2g} orbitals as Δ_o, where the subscript o stands for octahedral. The additional feature of Fig. 23-4(a)—the indication that the e_g levels lie $\frac{3}{5}\Delta_o$ above and the t_{2g} levels lie $\frac{2}{5}\Delta_o$ below the energy of the unsplit d orbitals—will now be explained. Let us suppose that a cation containing ten d electrons, two in each of the d orbitals, is first placed at the center of a hollow sphere whose radius is equal to the M to X internuclear distance and that charge of total quantity $6e$ is spread uniformly over the sphere. In this spherically symmetric environment the d orbitals are still fivefold degenerate. The energy of all orbitals is, of course, greatly raised when the charged sphere encloses the ion. The entire energy of the system, that is, the metal ion and the charged sphere, has a definite value. Now suppose the total charge on the sphere is caused to collect into six discrete point charges, each of magnitude

Figure 23-4 Energy-level diagrams showing the splitting of a set of d orbitals (degenerate in the uncoordinated ion at the center of the diagram) by octahedral and tetrahedral crystal fields. (a) The splitting caused by octahedral coordination of six ligands. (b) The splitting caused by tetrahedral coordination of four ligands. Brackets, } or {, designate orbitals that are degenerate.

e, and each lying at a vertex of an octahedron but still on the surface of the sphere. Merely redistributing the negative charge over the surface of the sphere in this manner cannot alter the total energy of the system when the metal ion consists entirely of spherically symmetrical electron shells, and yet we have already seen that, as a result of this redistribution, electrons in e_g orbitals now have higher energies than those in t_{2g} orbitals. It must therefore be that the total increase in energy of the four e_g electrons equals the total decrease in energy of the six t_{2g} electrons. This then implies that the rise in the energy of the e_g orbitals is 6/4 times the drop in energy of the t_{2g} orbitals, which is equivalent to the $\frac{3}{5}:\frac{2}{5}$ ratio shown.

This pattern of splitting, in which the algebraic sum of all energy shifts of all orbitals is zero, is said to "preserve the center of gravity" of the set of levels. This center of gravity rule is quite general for any splitting pattern when the forces are purely electrostatic and where the set of levels being split is well removed in energy from all other sets with which they might be able to interact.

By an analogous line of reasoning it can be shown that the electrostatic field of four charges surrounding an ion at the vertices of a tetrahedron causes the *d* shell to split up as shown in Fig. 23-4(*b*). In this case the d_{xy}, d_{yz}, and d_{zx} orbitals are less stable than the d_{z^2} and $d_{x^2-y^2}$ orbitals. This may be appreciated qualitatively if the spatial properties of the *d* orbitals are considered with regard to the tetrahedral array of four negative charges as is depicted in Fig. 23-5. If the cation, the anions, and the cation–anion distance are the same in both the octahedral and tetrahedral cases, it can be shown that

$$\Delta_t = \tfrac{4}{9}\,\Delta_o$$

Since the pure electrostatic crystal field model is not quantitatively precise, the factor four ninths need not be taken literally. Rather, the practical meaning of

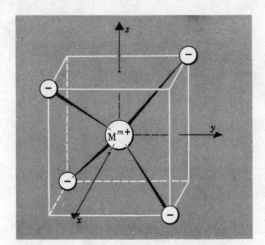

Figure 23-5 A sketch showing the tetrahedral arrangement of four negative charges around a cation, M^{m+}, with the Cartesian coordinate system oriented to identify the positions of the *d* orbitals.

the result is that, other things being about equal, the crystal field splitting in a tetrahedral complex will be about one half the magnitude of that in an octahedral complex.

These results have been derived on the assumption that ionic ligands, such as F^-, Cl^-, or CN^-, may be represented by point negative charges. Ligands that are neutral, however, are dipolar (e.g., 23-I and 23-II), and they approach

$$3^{\delta-}:N-H^{\delta+}$$

with $H^{\delta+}$ above and $H^{\delta+}$ below the central N—$H^{\delta+}$

$$2^{\delta-}:\ddot{O}$$

with $H^{\delta+}$ above and $H^{\delta+}$ below

23-I   23-II

the metal ion with their negative poles. Actually, in the field of the positive metal ion, such ligands are further polarized. Thus, in a complex such as a hexaammine, the metal ion is surrounded by six dipoles with their negative ends closest; this array has the same general effects on the d orbitals as an array of six anions, so that all of these results are valid for complexes containing neutral, dipolar ligands.

We next consider the pattern of splitting of the d orbitals in tetragonally distorted octahedral complexes and in planar complexes. We begin with an octahedral complex, MX_6, from which we slowly withdraw two trans ligands. Let these be the two on the z axis. As soon as the distance from M^{m+} to these two ligands becomes greater than the distance to the other four, new energy differences among the d orbitals arise. First, the degeneracy of the e_g orbitals is lifted, the z^2 orbital becoming more stable than the $(x^2 - y^2)$ orbital. This

Figure 23-6 An energy-level diagram showing the further splitting of the d orbitals as an octahedral array of ligands becomes distorted by progressive withdrawal of two trans ligands along the z axis. Brackets, } or {, designate orbitals that are degenerate.

$$M = Co^{II}, Ni^{II}, Cu^{II}$$

Figure 23-7 The correspondence between the energy-level diagrams of octahedral ML_6 and square-planar ML_4 complexes of some metal ions in the first transitio.. series.

happens because the ligands on the z axis exert a much more direct repulsive effect on a d_{z^2} electron than upon a $d_{x^2-y^2}$ electron. At the same time the threefold degeneracy of the t_{2g} orbitals is lifted. As the ligands on the z axis move away, the yz and zx orbitals remain equivalent to one another, but they become more stable than the xy orbital because their spatial distribution makes them more sensitive to the charges along the z axis than is the xy orbital. Thus for a small tetragonal distortion of the type considered, we may draw the energy-level diagram shown in Fig. 23-6. It should be obvious that for the opposite type of tetragonal distortion, that is, one in which two trans ligands lie closer to the metal ion than do the other four, the relative energies of the split components will be inverted.

As Fig. 23-6 shows, it is in general *possible* for the tetragonal distortion to become so large that the z^2 orbital eventually drops below the xy orbital. Whether this will actually happen for any particular case, even when the two trans ligands are completely removed so that we have the limiting case of a square, four-coordinated complex, depends on quantitative properties of the metal ion and the ligands concerned. Semiquantitative calculations with parameters appropriate for square complexes of Co^{II}, Ni^{II}, and Cu^{II} lead to the energy-level diagram shown in Fig. 23-7, in which the z^2 orbital has dropped so far below the xy orbital that it is nearly as stable as the (yz, zx) pair. As Fig. 23-6 indicates, the d_{z^2} level might even drop below the (d_{xz}, d_{yz}) levels and, in fact, experimental results suggest that in some cases (e.g., $PtCl_4^{2-}$) it does.

23-4 The Molecular Orbital Approach

The electrostatic crystal field theory is the simplest model that can account for the fact that the d orbitals split up into subsets in ligand environments. It is, of

Figure 23-8 The six metal orbitals with σ symmetry and the ligand group orbitals (Σ) that overlap properly with these metal orbitals to form σ-type molecular orbitals in an ML_6 complex. Each ligand group orbital (Σ, with subscripts to designate the matching d orbital) is shown adjacent to the metal orbital with which it overlaps. The resulting molecular orbitals are listed in Fig. 23-9. The E_g set is doubly degenerate and the T_{1u} set is triply degenerate.

course, a physically unrealistic model in certain ways, and it is also incomplete as a treatment of metal–ligand bonding, since it deals only with the d orbitals. It is possible to treat the electronic structures of complexes from a MO point of view. This is more general, more complete, and potentially more accurate. It includes the crystal field model as a special case.

Let us consider first an octahedral complex, MX_6, in which each ligand, X, has only a sigma orbital, directed toward the metal atom, and no π orbitals. The six σ orbitals of the ligands are designated σ_x and σ_{-x} (from those ligands along the x axis), σ_y and σ_{-y} (from those ligands along the y axis), and σ_z and σ_{-z} (from the ligands along the z axis). These six orbitals can be combined to make six distinct linear combinations, or ligand *group orbitals*, as shown in Fig. 23-8. Each ligand group orbital (Σ in Fig. 23-8) has a symmetry that is proper for overlap with only one of the metal s, p, or d orbitals, Each such overlap between one of the six ligand group orbitals and a metal valence orbital results

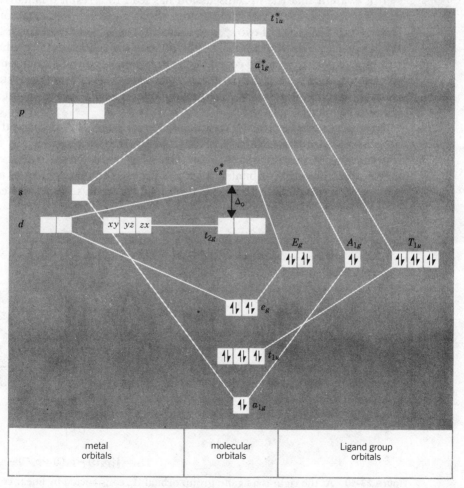

Figure 23-9 The MO energy-level diagram that arises from the σ-type molecular orbitals of Fig. 23-8. This diagram applies generally to an ML_6 complex with no π bonding.

in the formation of a bonding MO and an antibonding MO, according to the general principles of MO theory as described in Chapter 3. Figure 23-9 gives an energy-level diagram that shows the formation of these bonding and antibonding molecular orbitals. Three of the d orbitals of the metal (d_{xy}, d_{yz}, and d_{zx}) are nonbonding, having zero overlap with each of the ligand group orbitals. These triply degenerate, nonbonding d orbitals are designated the t_{2g} set in Fig. 23-9.

The three molecular orbitals (bonding or antibonding) derived from the p orbitals have the same energy (they are degenerate), and are denoted t_{1u} (or t_{1u}^*). Similarly, the two molecular orbitals derived from the d_{z^2} and $d_{x^2-y^2}$ orbitals are degenerate and are denoted e_g (or e_g^*). The s orbital forms molecular orbitals denoted a_{1g} or a_{1g}^*. If each of the ligand σ orbitals originally contained an electron pair (which is the only situation of practical interest), these six electron pairs will then be found in the six (three t_{1u}, two e_g, a_{1g}) σ-bonding orbitals of the complex, as is also shown in Fig. 23-9.

It is evident that the MO discussion has lead to a result qualitatively the same as that from the crystal field theory with regard to the metal d orbitals: They are split into a set of two e_g^*, and a set of three t_{2g}, with the former having a higher energy than the latter. The MO picture also shows explicitly how the main binding energy of the complex arises, namely, by the formation of six two-electron bonds. The main difference between the MO and the crystal field results is that the e_g^* orbitals as they are obtained in the MO treatment *are not pure metal d orbitals.*

We can generalize the MO treatment by supposing that the ligand atoms also possess π orbitals. Such π orbitals can overlap with the d_{xy}, d_{yz}, and d_{zx} orbitals, as is illustrated for the d_{zx} orbital in Fig. 23-10. Thus, instead of only one set of t_{2g} molecular orbitals, which are pure d orbitals, there will now be two sets. The positions of these sets of t_{2g} and t_{2g}^* orbitals in the MO energy-

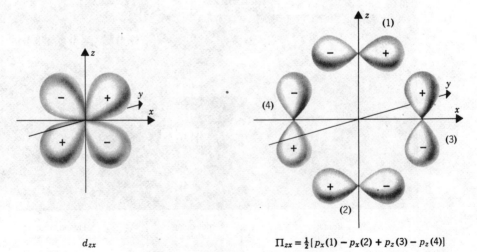

$$d_{zx} \qquad\qquad \Pi_{zx} = \tfrac{1}{2}[p_x(1) - p_x(2) + p_z(3) - p_z(4)]$$

Figure 23-10 At the right is a ligand group orbital Π_{zx} constructed by linear combination of ligand p orbitals and oriented to have optimum overlap with the metal d_{zx} orbital shown at the left. Analogous ligand group orbitals, Π_{xy} and Π_{yz}, overlap with the metal d_{xy} and d_{yz} orbitals, respectively.

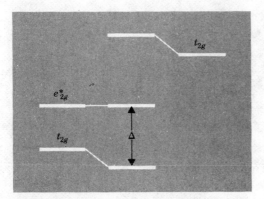

Figure 23-11 An energy-level diagram showing how π bonding such as that shown in Fig. 23-10 increases the value of Δ.

level diagram is quite variable depending on the nature of the ligand π orbitals. One case of rather general importance arises when the ligand π orbitals are empty and of higher energy than the metal d orbitals. Ligands that provide this situation include (1) phosphines, where the empty π orbitals are phosphorus $3d$ orbitals, and (2) CN^- and CO where the empty π orbitals are antibonding $p\pi^*$ orbitals.

The interaction of the high-energy ligand π orbitals with the metal t_{2g} orbitals results in depressing the latter and thus increasing the separation between the t_{2g} and e_g^* orbitals, as shown in Fig. 23-11.

From the MO point of view, we see that a number of factors influence the ligand field splitting of the metal "d orbitals" and, further, that the "d orbitals" of crystal field theory are actually not pure d orbitals. It is remarkable, however, that the simple crystal field model is nevertheless a useful, qualitative working tool. In practice we do not try to use it to make quantitative predictions; that is, we do not try to calculate Δ_o (or Δ_t or any other d orbital splitting) from theory. Instead we derive these splittings from electronic spectra and use only the qualitative features of the d-orbital splitting patterns as given by crystal field theory.

23-5 Magnetic Properties of Transition Metal Compounds

One of the most useful applications of ligand field theory—whether in the simple electrostatic (crystal field) form or in a more sophisticated form—is to understand and correlate the magnetic properties of transition metal complexes. This is important because, when properly interpreted, the magnetic properties of these compounds are very useful in identifying and characterizing them.

The most basic question to ask concerning any paramagnetic ion is: How many unpaired electrons are present? We now see how this question may be handled in terms of the orbital splittings described in the preceding sections. We have already noted (Section 2-6) that according to Hund's first rule, if a group of n or fewer electrons (say n') occupy a set of n degenerate orbitals,

$$E = E_0 + (E_0 + \Delta E) \qquad\qquad E = E_0 + E_0 + P$$
$$= 2E_0 + \Delta E \qquad\qquad\qquad = 2E_0 + P$$

(a)　　　　　　　　　　　(b)

Figure 23-12　A hypothetical two-orbital system, showing the two possible distributions of two electrons. The resulting total energies are as shown.

they will spread themselves out among the orbitals and give n' unpaired spins. This is true because pairing of electrons is an unfavorable process; energy must be expended to make it occur. If two electrons are not only to have their spins paired but also to be placed in the same orbital, there is a further unfavorable energy contribution because of the increased electrostatic repulsion between electrons that are compelled to occupy the same regions of space. Let us suppose now that in some hypothetical molecule we have two orbitals separated by an energy ΔE and that two electrons are to occupy these orbitals. By referring to Fig. 23-12, we see that when we place one electron in each orbital, their spins will remain uncoupled and their combined energy will be $(2E_0 + \Delta E)$. If we place both of them in the lower orbital, their spins will have to be coupled to satisfy the exclusion principle, and the total energy will be $(2E_0 + P)$, where P stands for the energy required to cause pairing of two electrons in the same orbital. Thus, whether this system will have distribution (a) or (b) for its ground state depends on whether ΔE is greater or less than P.

Octahedral Complexes

An argument of this type can be applied to octahedral complexes, using the d-orbital splitting diagram previously deduced. As is indicated in Fig. 23-13, we may place one, two, or three electrons in the d orbitals without any possible uncertainty about how they will occupy the orbitals. They will follow Hund's first rule and enter the more stable t_{2g} orbitals with their spins all parallel, regardless of the strength of the crystal field (as measured by the magnitude of Δ_0). Furthermore, for ions with eight, nine, and ten d electrons, there is only one possible way in which the orbitals may be occupied to give the lowest energy, as shown in Fig. 23-13. For each of the remaining configurations, d^4, d^5, d^6, and d^7, two possibilities exist, and the question of which one represents the ground state can be answered only by comparing the values of Δ_0 and P, an average pairing energy. The two configurations for each case, together with simple expressions for their energies, are set out in Fig. 23-14. The configurations with the maximum possible number of unpaired electrons are called the *high-spin* configurations, and those with the minimum number of unpaired spins are called the *low-spin* or *spin-paired* configurations. These configurations

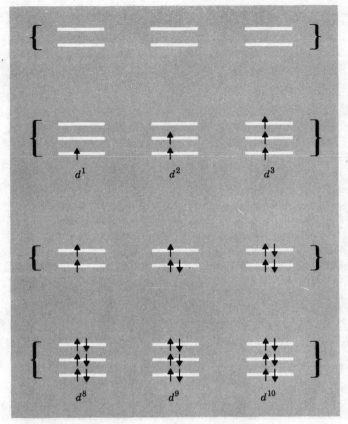

Figure 23-13 Sketches showing the unique ground-state electron configurations for d orbitals in octahedral fields with the d configurations d^1, d^2, d^3, d^8, d^9, and d^{10}.

can be written out in a notation similar to that used for electron configurations of free atoms, whereby we list each occupied orbital or set of orbitals, using a right superscript to show the number of electrons present. For example, the ground state for a d^3 ion in an octahedral field is t_{2g}^3; the two possible states for a d^5 ion in an octahedral field are t_{2g}^5 and $t_{2g}^3 e_g^2$. This notation is further illustrated in Fig. 23-14. The energies are referred to the energy of the unsplit configuration (the energy of the ion in a spherical shell of the same total charge) and are simply the sums of $-\frac{2}{5}\Delta_o$ for each t_{2g}, electron, $+\frac{3}{5}\Delta_o$ for each e_g electron, and P for every pair of electrons occupying the same orbital.

For each of the four cases where high- and low-spin states are possible, we may obtain from the equations for the energies, which are given in Fig. 23-13, the following expression for the relation between Δ_o and P at which the high- and low-spin states have equal energies.

$$\Delta_o = P$$

The relationship is the same in all cases, and means that the spin state of any ion in an octahedral electrostatic field depends simply on whether the mag-

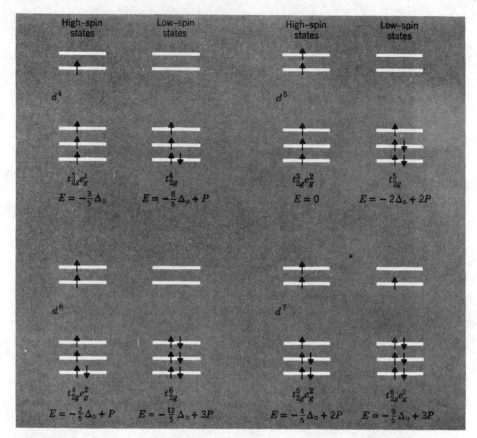

Figure 23-14 Diagrams showing the two possibilities (high spin and low spin) for the ground-state electron configurations of d^4, d^5, d^6, and d^7 ions in octahedral fields. Also shown is the notation for writing out the configurations and expressions for their energies, derived as explained in the text.

nitude of the field as measured by the splitting energy, Δ_o, is greater or less than the mean pairing energy, P, for the particular ion. For a particular ion of the d^4, d^5, d^6, or d^7 type, the stronger the crystal field, the more likely it is that the electrons will crowd as much as possible into the more stable t_{2g} orbitals, whereas in the weaker crystal fields, where $P > \Delta_o$, the electrons will remain spread out over the entire set of d orbitals as they do in the free ion. For ions of the other types, d^1, d^2, d^3, d^8, d^9, and d^{10}, the number of unpaired electrons is fixed at the same number as in the free ion irrespective of how strong the crystal field may become.

Approximate theoretical estimates of the mean pairing energies for the relevant ions of the first transition series have been made from spectroscopic data. In Table 23-1 these energies, along with Δ_o values for some complexes (derived by methods described in the next section), are listed. It is seen that this theory affords correct predictions in all cases. We note further that the mean pairing energies vary irregularly from one metal ion to another as do the values of Δ_o for a given set of ligands. Thus, as Table 23-1 shows, the d^5 systems should be exceptionally stable in their high-spin states, whereas the d^6

Table 23–1 Crystal Field Splittings, Δ_o, and Mean Electron Pairing Energies, P, for Several Transition Metal Ions (Energies in cm^{-1})

Configuration	Ion	P	Ligands	Δ_o	Spin State Predicted	Observed
d^4	Cr^{2+}	23,500	$6H_2O$	13,900	High	High
	Mn^{3+}	28,000	$6H_2O$	21,000	High	High
d^5	Mn^{2+}	25,500	$6H_2O$	7,800	High	High
	Fe^{3+}	30,000	$6H_2O$	13,700	High	High
d^6	Fe^{2+}	17,600	$6H_2O$	10,400	High	High
			$6CN^-$	33,000	Low	Low
	Co^{3+}	21,000	$6F^-$	13,000	High	High
			$6NH_3$	23,000	Low	Low
d^7	Co^{2+}	22,500	$6H_2O$	9,300	High	High

systems should be exceptionally stable in their low-spin states. These expectations are in excellent agreement with the experimental facts.

Tetrahedral Complexes

Metal ions in tetrahedral electrostatic fields may be treated by the same procedure outlined previously for the octahedral cases. For tetrahedral fields it is found that for the d^1, d^2, d^7, d^8, and d^9 cases only high-spin states are possible, whereas for d^3, d^4, d^5, and d^6 configurations both high-spin and low-spin states are in principle possible. Once again the existence of low-spin states requires that $\Delta_t > P$. Since Δ_t values are only about half as great as Δ_o values, it is to be expected that low-spin tetrahedral complexes of first transition series ions with d^3, d^4, d^5, and d^6 configurations will be extremely rare, and that is the case.

Square and Tetragonally Distorted Octahedral Complexes

The square and tetragonally distorted octahedral complexes must be considered together because, as we noted previously, they merge into one another.

Even when the strictly octahedral environment does not permit the existence of a low-spin state, as in the d^8 case, distortions of the octahedron will cause further splitting of degenerate orbitals that may become great enough to overcome pairing energies and cause electron pairing. Let us consider as an example the d^8 system in an octahedral environment that is then subjected to a tetragonal distortion. We have already seen (Fig. 23-6) how a decrease in the electrostatic field along the z axis may arise, either by moving the two z-axis ligands out to a greater distance than are their otherwise identical neighbors in the xy plane, or by having two different ligands on the z axis that make an intrinsically smaller contribution to the electrostatic potential than do the four in the xy plane. Irrespective of its origin, the result of a tetragonal distortion of an initially octahedral field is to split apart the $(x^2 - y^2)$ and z^2 orbitals. We have also seen that if the tetragonal distortion, that is, the disparity between the contributions to the electrostatic potential of the two z axis ligands and the other four, becomes sufficiently great, the z^2 orbital may fall below the xy orbital.

Figure 23-15 Energy-level diagrams showing the possible high-spin and low-spin ground states for a d^8 system (e.g., Ni^{2+}) in a tetragonally distorted octahedral field. (*a*) High-spin and low-spin possibilities for a weakly distorted system. (*b*) The low-spin result for a strongly distorted, or square complex.

In either case, the two least stable d orbitals are now no longer degenerate but are separated by some energy, Q. Now the question of whether the tetragonally distorted d^8 complex will have high- or low-spin depends on whether the pairing energy, P, is greater or less than the energy, Q. Figure 23-15(*a*) shows the situation for the case of a "weak" tetragonal distortion, that is, for one in which the second highest d orbital is still d_{z^2}.

Figure 23-15(*b*) shows a possible arrangement of levels for a strongly tetragonally distorted octahedron, or for the extreme case of a square, four-coordinate complex (compared with Fig. 23-7), and the low-spin form of occupancy of these levels for a d^8 ion. In this case, due to the large separation between the highest and second highest orbitals, the high-spin configuration is impossible to attain considering the pairing energies of the real d^8 ions, for example, Rh^I, Ir^I, Ni^{II}, Pd^{II}, Pt^{II}, and Au^{III}, which normally occur. All square complexes of these species are diamagnetic. Similarly, for a d^7 ion in a square complex, as exemplified by certain Co^{II} complexes, only the low-spin state with one unpaired electron should occur, and this is in accord with observation.

Other Forms of Magnetic Behavior

We have just indicated how the number of unpaired electrons on a transition metal ion in a complex, or other compound, can be understood in terms of the d-orbital splitting. The experimental method for determining the number of unpaired electrons has been discussed in Section 2-8; it is based on measuring the magnetic susceptibility of the substance. Here we must point out that certain additional factors must be considered in attempting to relate the magnetic moments of individual ions with the measured susceptibilities of bulk compounds.

Diamagnetism (which was briefly mentioned in Section 2-8) is a property of all forms of matter. All substances contain at least some if not all electrons in closed shells. In closed shells there is no net angular momentum since the spin momenta cancel each other and so do the orbital momenta, and no net magnetic moment can result. However, when a substance is placed in a magnetic field, the closed shells are affected in such a way that the orbitals are all tipped and a small, net magnetic moment is set up in opposition to the applied field. This is called diamagnetism, and because the small induced moment is opposed to the applied field, the substance is repelled. In a substance that has no unpaired electrons, this will be the only response to the field. The substance will tend to move away from the strongest part of the field, and it is said to be diamagnetic. The susceptibility of a diamagnetic substance is negative and is independent of field strength and of temperature.

It is important to realize that even a substance that does have unpaired electrons also has diamagnetism because of whatever closed shells of electrons are also present. Thus the positive susceptibility measured is less than that expected for the unpaired electrons alone, because the diamagnetism partially cancels the paramagnetism. This is a small effect, typically amounting to less than 10% of the true paramagnetism, but in accurate work a correction for it must be applied.

Paramagnetism has already been discussed in Section 2-8. Simple paramagnetism occurs when the individual ions having the unpaired electrons are far enough apart to behave independently of one another. Curie's law (Eq. 2-8.1) is thus followed. The magnetic moment obtained can be directly, with allowance for small contributions (positive or negative) from orbital motion, interpreted in terms of the number of unpaired electrons.

Ferromagnetism and antiferromagnetism occur in substances where the individual paramagnetic atoms or ions are close together and each one is strongly influenced by the orientation of the magnetic moments of its neighbors. In ferromagnetism (so-called because it is very conspicuous in metallic iron) the interaction is such as to cause all moments to tend to point in the same direction. This enormously enhances the magnitude of the susceptibility of the substance as compared with what it would be if all the individual moments behaved independently. Ferromagnetism is generally found in the transition metals, and also in some of their compounds.

Antiferromagnetism occurs when the nature of the interaction between neighboring paramagnetic ions is such as to favor opposite orientations of their magnetic moments, thus causing partial cancellation. Antiferromagnetic substances thus have magnetic susceptibilities less than those expected for an array of independent magnetic ions. It occurs quite often among simple salts of ions such as Mn^{2+}, Fe^{3+}, and Gd^{3+}, which have large intrinsic magnetic moments. The antiferromagnetic coupling involves interaction through the anions lying between the metal atoms in the crystal, and disappears in dilute solutions.

Ferro- or antiferromagnetic behavior causes deviations from the Curie law, as is shown in Fig. 23-16. In each case there is a temperature at which the temperature dependence of the susceptibility changes abruptly. This is the

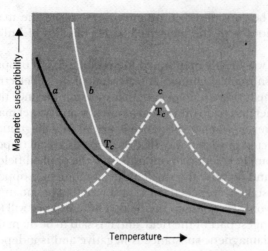

Figure 23-16 Magnetic susceptibility versus temperature plots for (*a*) a simple paramagnetic (Curie law) substance, (*b*) a ferromagnetic substance, and (*c*) an antiferromagnetic substance. T_c denotes the Curie temperatures in (*b*) and (*c*). For antiferromagnetism, the Curie point is also often called the Néel temperature.

Curie temperature, T_c, which is a characteristic property of the substance. Above T_c, the behavior is similar to that of the Curie law. Below T_c, the susceptibility either rises (ferromagnetism) or falls (antiferromagnetism) in a manner quite different from that implied by the Curie law. At the Curie temperature the effect of thermal energy in tending to randomize the individual spin orientations begins to get the upper hand over the ferro- or antiferromagnetic coupling interactions.

23-6 Electronic Absorption Spectroscopy

Ions with a Single *d* Electron

The simplest possible case of an ion with a single *d* electron is an ion with a d^1 configuration, lying at the center of an octahedral field, for example, the Ti^{III} ion in $[Ti(H_2O)_6]^{3+}$. The *d* electron will occupy a t_{2g} orbital. On irradiation with light of frequency *v*, equal to Δ_o/h, where *h* is Planck's constant and Δ_o is the energy difference between the t_{2g} and e_g orbitals, it should be possible for such an ion to capture a quantum of radiation and convert that energy into energy of excitation of the electron from the t_{2g} to the e_g orbitals. The absorption band that results from this process is found in the visible spectrum of the hexaaquotitanium(III) ion, shown in Fig. 23-17, and is responsible for its violet color. Two features of this absorption band are of importance here: its position and its intensity.

In discussing the positions of absorption bands in relation to the splittings

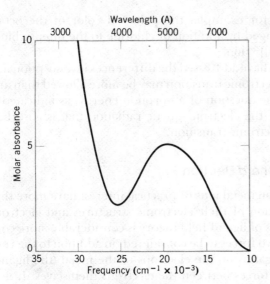

Figure 23-17 The electronic absorption spectrum of $[Ti(H_2O)_6]^{3+}$.

of the d orbitals, it is convenient and common practice to use the same unit, the reciprocal centimeter or wave number, abbreviated cm^{-1}, for both the unit of frequency in the spectra and the unit of energy for the orbitals. With this convention, we see that the spectrum of Fig. 23-17 tells us that Δ_o in $[Ti(H_2O)_6]^{3+}$ is 20,000 cm^{-1}.

We note in Fig. 23-17 that the absorption band is very weak. Its molar absorbance at the maximum is five, whereas one-electron transitions that are theoretically "allowed," usually have absorbances of 10^4–10^5. This suggests that the transition in question is not "allowed" but is instead "forbidden" according to the quantum theory. That is indeed the case, for the following reason. It is a general rule of quantum mechanics that for any electronic transition to be "allowed" in a system that has a center of symmetry, it is a necessary (though not sufficient) condition that the electron move, as a result of the transition, from an orbital that is even with respect to inversion through the center of symmetry, to an orbital that is uneven with respect to inversion (or visa versa). Since all d orbitals are even with respect to inversion, this selection rule is not satisfied for electronic transitions that move an electron from one d orbital to another. Hence d–d transitions of transition metal compounds are generally of low intensity (weakly absorbing).

These d–d absorptions are measurable, though, and this selection rule evidently is relaxed in some way. For all transition metal compounds, there are vibrations of the ligands that slightly spoil the symmetry of the coordination sphere so as to remove the center of symmetry. This relaxes the rigorous requirement mentioned previously. In the case of tetrahedral compounds, the structures lack a center of symmetry. This makes the selection rule inapplicable, and the d–d transitions become not-forbidden. It is, consequently a general observation that for tetrahedral complexes, the d–d absorption bands are considerably more intense than in octahedral complexes, often by a factor of 10 or more. This is why, for example, the **pale** red color of the octahedral $[Co(H_2O)_6]^{2+}$ ion is changed by addition of chloride to the **intense** blue color of the tetrahedral $[CoCl_4]^{2-}$ ion.

In this discussion we have addressed the differences in absorption intensity that arise because one electronic transition may be more allowed than another. We must also address the question of absorption energy, as indicated by the wave number (cm^{-1}) of the electromagnetic radiation that is absorbed as a result of a particular electronic transition.

Ions with More Than One *d* Electron

The majority of transition metal ions of practical interest have more than one *d* electron. An explanation of their electronic structures and electronic absorption spectra in terms of ligand field theory is considerably more complex, because there are now two forces to be considered; in addition to the repulsive forces exerted by the ligands on the electrons of the metal (the ligand field splitting), there are the forces between the electrons themselves. It is one of the great triumphs of modern physics that the methods for handling such complex problems in an accurate and useful way have been developed. Although it would be beyond the scope of this book to develop this methodology from first principles, it is important to provide a working sketch of how the electronic absorption spectra of coordination compounds may be interpreted. To do this, we shall first examine the case of a d^2 ion, where we shall be able to display all of the factors that are important for d^n ions in general. Once this basis is set down, it should be straightforward to apply the results to the remaining cases, namely, d^3 to d^8.

Notations for The Electronic States of d^n Atoms and Ions

In examining the case of a d^n ion in an octahedral ligand field, certain symbols and terminologies are employed. We give here the pertinent definitions.

We must first define two terms that will be used throughout the following discussion: electron configuration and electronic state. The term **electron configuration** refers to the way electrons occupy orbitals. We have frequently made use of this term, and employed throughout the text a shorthand notation for specifying electron configurations. We wrote, for example, in Chapter 2, $1s^2 2s^2 2p^5$ as the electron configuration of the fluorine atom. For the vanadium ion, V^{3+}, we can say simply that the ground electron configuration is d^2, it being understood that we are talking about the $3d$ orbitals and that all lower-energy orbitals are fully occupied. For an ion in a ligand field (i.e., a coordination compound), where the *d* orbitals are split into subsets, a very similar notation for electron configuration is used. For example, in an octahedral field, the ground electron configuration of the V^{3+} ion would be written t_{2g}^2, and the two possible excited configurations would be written $t_{2g}^1 e_g^1$ and e_g^2. For a high-spin Mn^{2+} ion the electron configuration is $t_{2g}^3 e_g^2$, and for Ni^{2+} it is $t_{2g}^6 e_g^2$.

Having briefly mentioned electron configurations, it is now necessary to define electronic states. By the term **electronic state** we shall mean an energy level that is available to an ensemble of electrons. (It is, as such, something quite distinct from an energy for, say, a one-electron orbital, because the energy of an electronic state will be governed by interactions of the electrons, as well as by the energies of the orbitals that house the electrons.) In general, from a given electron configuration, more than one electronic state can arise. The only exceptions to this statement are a closed shell configuration, and, to a good approximation, the d^1 and d^9 configurations.

All other d^n electron configurations individually give rise to more than one electronic state because there are always several different ways that the electrons of a given electron configuration can interact with one another. Each different way of interacting among the electrons in any one electron configuration gives a different net energy for the ensemble of electrons. It is this energy that characterizes the resulting electronic state of the atom, molecule, or ion.

For example, if we have a p^2 electron configuration, the electron spins can be parallel (to give an electronic state with total spin equal to $2 \times \frac{1}{2} = 1$) or the two electrons in this electron configuration may be opposed (to give an electronic state with total spin equal to 0). There is a third electronic state that arises from this p^2 electron configuration, but we do not develop the details until later. For now it is sufficient to have demonstrated that a given electron configuration may give rise to a number of different electronic states. To illustrate the importance of this, consider carbon, which has the p^2 configuration. The states just mentioned for carbon differ in energy by about 125 kJ mol^{-1}.

Before proceeding, we need to designate the symbols to be used in specifying the different electronic states that we shall encounter. Just as lower case letters are used for orbitals of various degeneracies, so are capital letters used, as follows:

(a) Singly degenerate orbitals: a or b.
    Singly degenerate states: A or B

(b) Doubly degenerate orbitals: e
    Doubly degenerate states: E

(c) Triply degenerate orbitals: t
    Triply degenerate states: T

Subscripts 1 or 2 are used to distinguish among states of like degeneracy. In addition, subscripts g or u are employed for molecules that have a center of symmetry; subscript g designates states whose wave functions are even (from the German *gerade*), and subscript u designates states whose wave functions are uneven (from the German *ungerade*) with respect to inversion through the center of symmetry. For example, in an octahedral ligand environment, the set of p orbitals is triply degenerate and each p orbital is uneven with respect to inversion (that is, the wave function changes sign upon inversion). The p orbitals in this environment are designated the t_{1u} set, and the electronic state arising from the electron configuration p^1 is designated T_{1u}. In an octahedral environment of ligands, three of the d orbitals are degenerate as well as even with respect to inversion. These three orbitals constitute the t_{2g} set in the octahedral ligand field, and the electronic state that arises from the t_{2g}^1 electron configuration is the T_{2g} state.

The symbols are further modified to designate the spin multiplicity of the electronic state, by adding a left superscript number. The left superscript, or spin multiplicity, of the electronic state is the value $(2S + 1)$, where S is the absolute value of the algebraic sum of the spins of the individual electrons. For example, for a d^1 electron configuration, $S = \frac{1}{2}$ and spin multiplicity is two. For a d^2 electron configuration in which the electron spins are parallel, $S = \frac{1}{2} + \frac{1}{2} = 1$, and spin multiplicity $(2S + 1)$ is three. In a d^5 electron configuration with four "up" spins and one "down" spin, $S = 4(\frac{1}{2}) + (-\frac{1}{2}) = \frac{3}{2}$, and spin multiplicity $(2S + 1)$ is four.

The spin multiplicity is related to the total spin quantum number, S, by the relationship given previously, namely, spin multiplicity equals $2S + 1$, for the following reason. When an ion with a total spin quantum number, S, is placed in a magnetic field, the rules of quantization allow the total electron spin vector (whose length is $[S(S + 1)]^{1/2}$) to take only those orientations relative to the magnetic field direction, **H,** that give projections in the field direction equal to $+S, S - 1, S - 2, \ldots, -S$, as shown, for example, in Fig. 23-18. In general, the number of values from $+S$ to $-S$, in integral steps, is $(2S + 1)$, and that is where the relationship between S and spin multiplicity comes from. In verbal use, the spin multiplicities are pronounced as follows: 1 (singlet), 2 (doublet), 3 (triplet), 4 (quartet), 5 (quintet), 6 (sextet).

For a d^1 ion in an octahedral field of ligands, then, we have the two possible electron configurations e_g^1 and t_{2g}^1. The two states that arise are thus ^2E_g and $^2T_{2g}$, pronounced "doublet ee gee" and "doublet tee two gee", respectively. One electronic state that arises from the t_{2g}^2 electron configuration is the $^3T_{1g}$ state, pronounced "triplet tee one gee."

It remains only to point out that the **total degeneracy of a state** is the product of its spin and orbital degeneracies. The spin degeneracy is given by the spin multiplicity. The orbital degeneracy is designated by the letter scheme listed previously. Thus, for the three states mentioned in the preceding paragraph, the total degeneracies are those given in Table 23-2.

Figure 23-18 The allowed orientations of the electron spin vector in a magnetic field. Two cases are shown. The rules of quantization allow only those orientations of the vector that give projections equal to $+\frac{1}{2}$ or $-\frac{1}{2}$ (for the case where $S = \frac{1}{2}$) or which give projections of $+1, 0,$ or -1 (for the case where $S = 1$).

Table 23-2 The Degeneracies of Three States

State	Spin Degeneracy	Orbital Degeneracy	Total Degeneracy
^2E_g	2	2	4
$^2T_{2g}$	2	3	6
$^3T_{1g}$	3	3	9

The Electronic States Arising from a d^2 System

The procedure that we shall employ to work out the electronic states of a d^2 ion in an octahedral ligand field involves our considering two limiting cases, and then correlating the two. In one limit we have a ligand field so strong that the interactions between the two electrons are negligible in comparison with the energy differences between the various electronic states that arise from the electron configuration. This is called the **strong field** case. In the other extreme, we consider a ligand field that is so weak that the interaction among the electrons overshadows the ligand field, so that the various electronic states arising from the electron configuration have energies that are determined almost solely by interaction of the two electrons in the configuration. This is termed the **weak field** case.

The Strong Field Case. If we assume that the ligand field splitting is very large, then every electronic state arising from the electron configuration t_{2g}^2 will be of lower energy than every electronic state arising from the electron configuration $t_{2g}^1 e_g^1$, and similarly, every electronic state arising from the electron configuration e_g^2 will be higher in energy than those of the first two. This means that we can deal separately with each of the three possible electron configurations (t_{2g}^2, $t_{2g}^1 e_g^1$, and e_g^2), and we do so in the following way, beginning with the electron configuration e_g^2. The student may wish to preview the right side of Fig. 23-20, as this is the result towards which we are now working.

We have available a pair of e_g orbitals, and for each electron, two possible spin quantum numbers, $+\frac{1}{2}$ or $-\frac{1}{2}$. Thus we may assign the first electron of the set to the e_g orbitals in four different ways. We represent this by drawing a set of four boxes, each of which represents a distinct combination of orbital and spin quantum numbers for the single electron. We next ask how may the second electron of the e_g^2 electron configuration be assigned to the set of four boxes. Because of the Pauli exclusion principle, each box may hold only one electron. There are, then, six distinct and nonrepetitious ways of assigning two electrons to the four boxes, as illustrated in Fig. 23-19(a). This number six could have been anticipated by noting that we are simply asking for the number of ways to choose pairs from among four equivalent objects, and this is given by the product of the number of ways to choose the first one (4) times the remaining number of ways to choose the second (3), divided by two since the order of choice for identical objects is immaterial. Thus we have for the e_g^2 electron configuration: $(4 \times 3)/2 = 6$. Each of these six distinct arrangements of electrons in the e_g^2 electron configuration is called a **microstate.**

The arrangements of electrons in the boxes as done in Fig. 23-19(a) represent the six microstates that are included in the electron configuration e_g^2.

We shall now show, but not derive rigorously, the fact that these six microstates comprise three electronic states arising from the e_g^2 electron configuration. Two of the six microstates of Fig. 23-19(a) are spin triplets, because the electrons in each of the two microstates are parallel; these are microstates labeled (a) and (b) in Fig. 23-19(a). Together with one of the others, these constitute a spin-triplet state that is, orbitally, singly degenerate: $^3A_{2g}$. The remaining microstates of the e_g^2 electron configuration are the components of two singlet electronic states, $^1A_{1g}$ and ^1E_g. Note that when the orbital $(A + A + E)$ and spin (triplet + singlet + singlet) multiplicities of these three states are summed up, they correspond to a total of six: $(3 \times 1) + (1 \times 1) + (1 \times 2) = 6$, the total degeneracy of the e_g^2 electron configuration.

We now turn our attention to Fig. 23-19(b), where we display the 15 distinct and nonrepetitious microstates that are available to the electron configuration t_{2g}^2. Of these, three [(a), (b), and (c)] have $S = +1$ and three [(d), (e), and (f)] have $S = -1$. The other 9 microstates all have $S = 0$. The 3 microstates with $S = +1$, the 3 microstates with $S = -1$, and 3 of the remaining 9 microstates together constitute a $^3T_{1g}$ electronic state of the t_{2g}^2 electron configuration. From the remaining 6 microstates with $S = 0$, we can derive (without showing the

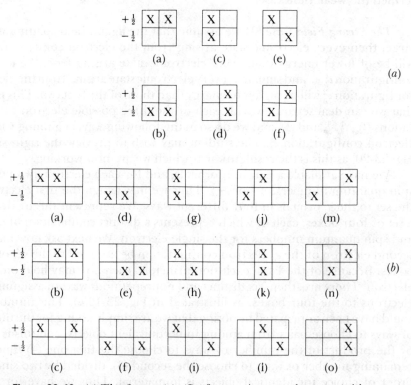

Figure 23-19 (a) The 6 ways (a)–(f) of arranging two electrons (with spin either $+\frac{1}{2}$ or $-\frac{1}{2}$) into two orbitals that are doubly degenerate. (b) The 15 ways (a)–(o) of arranging two electrons (with spin either $+\frac{1}{2}$ or $-\frac{1}{2}$) into three orbitals that are triply degenerate.

details) the spin-singlet electronic states: $^1A_{1g}$, ^1E_g, and $^1T_{2g}$. Thus for the electron configuration t_{2g}^2 we find 4 electronic states with a total degeneracy of 15:

$$^3T_{1g} \qquad\qquad ^1T_{2g} \qquad\qquad ^1E_g \qquad\qquad ^1A_{1g}$$
$$(3 \times 3) \; + \; (1 \times 3) \; + \; (1 \times 2) \; + \; (1 \times 1) = 15$$

We may say this same thing in another way; out of the electron configuration t_{2g}^2 there arise 15 microstates that are grouped into 4 different electronic states, having 4 different energies.

Last we consider the third and only remaining possibility for a d^2 ion in an octahedral ligand field: The electron configuration $t_{2g}^1 e_g^1$. One electron is free to occupy one of four boxes (the electron in the e_g orbitals), whereas the other electron is free to occupy one of six boxes (the t_{2g} electron), leading to a total of 24 different microstates. Since each electron is in a different type of orbital, the Pauli exclusion principle is never a problem, no matter what spin assignments are made. Also, we need not divide by two even though the two electrons are indistinguishable. The result is that, among the 24 distinct and nonrepetitious microstates of the $t_{2g}^1 e_g^1$ electron configuration, there arise the electronic states $^1T_{1g}$, $^1T_{2g}$, $^3T_{1g}$, and $^3T_{2g}$, whose total degeneracy is, as required, 24.

The result of our analysis of the d^2 ion in the strong field limit is shown on the right of Fig. 23-20. We imply here that the energy difference among the electronic states is small (in the limit, zero) compared to the energy differences (Δ_o) between the three electron configurations.

The Weak Field Case. In the weak field limit (shown on the left in Fig. 23-20), we are dealing with a set of electronic states for which the energies are determined only by the interactions of the d electrons with one another. This is a problem that was solved by atomic spectroscopists quite independently of any work on either metal complexes or ligand field theory, because, in the weak field limit, there is necessarily no ligand set. For the metal ions of the first transition series (where the ligand field analysis of electronic absorption spectroscopy is most useful), there is, fortunately, a relatively convenient and more or less quantitative scheme for describing the electronic states that arise from a given $3d^n$ electron configuration. This same scheme is also reasonably satisfactory for $4d^n$ systems, but it has some inadequacies (from a quantitative point of view) for the $5d^n$ ions. We shall now describe this approach, which is called the Russell–Saunders or LS coupling scheme.

In this scheme, we use for the electronic states a set of quantum numbers and state symbols that closely parallel those used for a single electron. Just as an electron in a particular orbital has a certain orbital angular momentum quantum number, ℓ {and an orbital angular momentum given by the quantity $[\ell(\ell + 1)]^{1/2}$}, so each electronic state arising from a given electron configuration, d^n, has a total angular momentum quantum number, L, and an orbital angular momentum given by the quantity $[L(L + 1)]^{1/2}$. Thus, just as we have s, p, d, f, ... orbitals, we have S, P, D, F, ... electronic states for a d^n ion. These letter designations for the electronic states correspond to total orbital angular momentum quantum numbers, $L = 0, 1, 2, \ldots$, respectively.

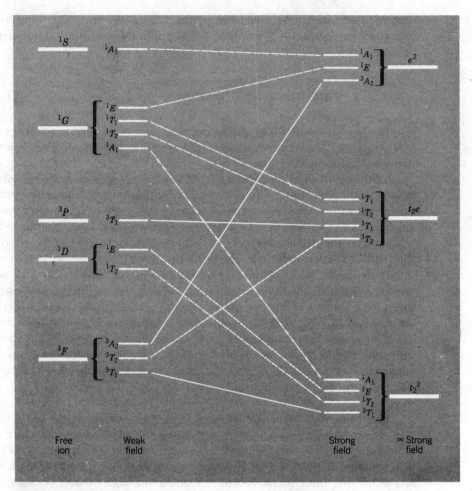

Figure 23-20   A correlation diagram for a d^2 ion in an octahedral environment. All states and orbitals are of the gerade type, and the subscript g has therefore been omitted.

Each electronic state is also characterized by its spin quantum number, S. Thus, even for a vanishing (or in the weak field limit, vanished) ligand field, ions with one, two, three, four, . . . , unpaired electrons have spin quantum numbers, $S = \frac{1}{2}, 1, \frac{3}{2}, 2, . . .$, and, then, spin multiplicities (given by $2S + 1$) of 2 (doublet), 3 (triplet), 4 (quartet), 5 (quintet), . . . , respectively.

We illustrate briefly with an ion having $L = 2$ and $S = \frac{3}{2}$. The electronic state would be designated ^4D. A few other examples are

$$L = 3, S = 1: \quad ^3F$$

$$L = 4, S = \frac{1}{2}: \quad ^2G$$

$$L = 0, S = 2: \quad ^5S$$

We note that for all d^1 ions, the electronic state must be solely ^2D, since $L = \ell = 2$.

For each electronic state that we identify using the Russell–Saunders coupling scheme, there is an orbital degeneracy as well as a spin degeneracy. The orbital degeneracies of the various electronic states are S (0), P (3), D (5), F (7), . . . , and so on. These degeneracies correspond, of course, to those of the comparable orbitals having the same ℓ values in lower case.

In summary, according to the Russell–Saunders coupling scheme, there are two quantum numbers L and S that characterize a given electronic state, just as we have ℓ and s quantum numbers that characterize a single electron. These two quantum numbers can be used to define and designate the various electronic states of a given d^n electron configuration. The Russell–Saunders scheme allows us to list all of the electronic states that arise from a d^n configuration and to estimate their energies. The scheme applies well to the $3d^n$ (and perhaps also to $4d^n$) cases involving weak field ligands. The procedures for applying the scheme demand a greater knowledge of quantum mechanics than is appropriate at this level, so we shall simply list the results of the analysis, along with some observations that will prove useful when applying the results to the interpretation of electronic absorption spectroscopy for the various coordination compounds. It is this latter purpose that remains the goal of Section 23-6.

For the d^2 case, the combinations of orbital and spin angular momenta (i.e., the couplings of quantum numbers L and S) that are consistent with the Pauli exclusion principle are represented by the following electronic state symbols:

$$^3F, \; ^1D, \; ^3P, \; ^1G, \; ^1S$$

It should be noted that a set of five d orbitals coupled with two choices for spin is equivalent to a set of 10 boxes. Thus a total of $(10 \times 9)/2 = 45$ microstates are possible in the d^2 electron configuration. Also, as expected, the sum of the degeneracies of these states will be found to be 45.

This list is given in order of increasing energy, as predicted by theory and established by experiment. Spectroscopic data are available for all of the d^2 ions that are of common occurrence, and the data provide not only the correct order of the electronic states, but also the exact value of the energy differences between the states.

The fact that the electronic state of lowest energy is the ^3F state is expected on the basis of Hund's rules. Hund's first rule, which was discussed in Chapter 2, says that for any partially filled shell, the most stable arrangement will be the one with the highest spin multiplicity, namely, the arrangement with the maximum number of parallel electron spins. The second rule says that, among states of highest spin multiplicity (in this case, spin triplets), the state with highest orbital angular momentum is preferred. In this list for the states of a d^2 ion, and among those that are triplets, the one of lower energy is, then, the F state, for which $L = 3$.

In Fig. 23-20 we have placed these five free ion electronic states of the d^2 electron configuration in the correct order, on the vertical energy scale. We must next ask what happens to each of these states as the octahedral ligand field increases in strength from zero (for the free ion) to some small value. After doing this we shall need to connect the various states on the left and right sides of the diagram in order to trace the energies of the various states as the ligand field strength increases to the strong field case.

On the left portion of the diagram of Fig. 23-20 we have shown that a state with an orbital angular momentum quantum number, L, will split in the same way as a set or orbitals characterized by the corresponding value of the quantum number, ℓ. Thus a D electronic state ($L = 2$) splits into E and T_2 states in an octahedral ligand field, just as a set of five d orbitals ($\ell = 2$) splits into the sets e_g and t_{2g} in an octahedral field. If, as here, the D electronic state is one derived from a d^n electron configuration, it and the states into which it splits will be of *gerade* character, just as the d orbitals are *gerade*. Also, weak ligand fields cannot alter the spin multiplicity of an electronic state, so that all states derived from a given free ion electronic state will retain the same spin multiplicity.

In Table 23-3 are listed the states into which the various free ion electronic states are split by the influence of an octahedral ligand field. Note that an S state, being nondegenerate, does not split, and a P state in an octahedral ligand field survives with its threefold orbital degeneracy. All the other free ion states are split to one extent or another into states by an octahedral ligand field. We say that the degeneracies of the various states are lifted, to one extent or another, by the ligand field. By employing the information of Table 23-3, we can complete the left side of Fig. 23-20 as shown for the weak field case.

We now have the two edges of a complete energy-level diagram for a d^2 ion in an octahedral ligand field. At the extreme left we see what states exist when the ligand field strength is zero and how these states are affected as a very weak field is applied. At the extreme right, we have information on what electronic states exist in the presence of a ligand field so strong that it completely overwhelms the electron–electron interactions. Our task now is to connect the two sides of this incomplete diagram so as to obtain a picture of how the electronic states of a d^2 configuration behave under realistic conditions, namely, at intermediate values of the ligand field strength.

We note first that the inventories of states on each side of Fig. 23-20 are the same; they must be if we are to be able to connect the two sides of the diagram completely. To carry this out, there are two rules that must be followed: First, only two states that are exactly alike may be connected. Second, connecting lines for states of the same type may never cross. With these rules, the connecting lines (or the state to state correlations) may be drawn in Fig.

Table 23-3   The Splitting of Free Ion Electronic
States in an Octahedral Ligand Field

Electronic States of the Free Ion	Electronic States of the Ion in an Octahedral Field
S	A_1
P	T_1
D	$E + T_2$
F	$A_2 + T_1 + T_2$
G	$A_1 + E + T_1 + T_2$
H	$E + T_1 + T_1 + T_2$

23-20 in an absolutely unambiguous way. The correlations between triplet states have been drawn using solid lines, and those between singlet states have been drawn using broken lines, so that they are easy to distinguish.

Now that we have this diagram, what does it tell us? The following are the most important things as far as spectroscopy is concerned.

1. For all ligand field strengths, the ground electronic state of a d^2 system is a spin triplet, *i.e.* the $^3T_{1g}$ state. Any d^2 ion in an octahedral field (however strong) of ligands will have two unpaired electrons in the ground state.

2. We have already pointed out that a general selection rule of quantum mechanics is that transitions between states of like parity (i.e., *gerade–gerade* or, similarly, *ungerade–ungerade*) are discouraged. Recall, then, that any absorption bands assigned to transitions from the ground state of Fig. 23-20 to other electronic states of Fig. 23-20 are greatly discouraged by this selection rule.

3. It is another general selection rule of quantum mechanics that electronic transitions between states of different spin multiplicities are forbidden. As in most cases, the rigorous selection rule is relaxed, and we conclude more realistically that such transitions, though not completely unobserved, are at least greatly discouraged, and consequently, weak in absorption intensity when measured spectroscopically. Application of this selection rule to the d^2 case brings us to the conclusion that the only spin-allowed transitions are those from the triplet ground state to triplet excited states. Thus three absorption bands for a d^2 system are predicted: those from the $^3T_{1g}$ ground state to the excited states $^3T_{2g}$, $^3A_{2g}$, and $^3T_{1g}$. The last excited electronic state originates from the ^3P free ion state.

4. Another general selection rule for electronic transitions is that two-electron transitions are much less probable than are one-electron transitions. Thus the $^3A_{2g}$ state, which in the strong field limit correlates with the e_g^2 electron configuration, is not readily reached from the $^3T_{1g}$ ground state, which is derived from the t_{2g}^2 electron configuration. This transition should then be considerably weaker in absorption intensity than the other two spin-allowed transitions.

In summary, for a d^2 system, we expect to observe three electronic absorption bands, all of which are weak in absorption intensity. Each of the absorptions is spin allowed, but one is expected to be weaker than the other two because it is a transition involving two electrons. We shall make a direct comparison of these predictions with experiment as soon as we have introduced a more quantitative form of the energy-level diagram given in Fig. 23-20.

Quantitative Interpretation of Electronic Absorption Spectra for Various d^n Systems

The energy-level diagram (actually a simple correlation diagram) that is presented in Fig. 23-20 for the d^2 octahedral case is entirely correct as far as it goes, but it lacks some features necessary for practical, quantitative use. In fact, we have available to us calculations of electronic state energies as a function of ligand field strength, and we can use these results for a quantitative fitting of observed spectra. This has been done by Tanabe and Sugano, and Tanabe–Sugano diagrams, presented in Fig. 23-21, are widely used to correlate and

Figure 23-21 Energy-level diagrams [after Tanabe and Sugano, *J. Phys. Soc. Jpn.*, **1954**, *9*, 753.] for the d^2–d^8 configurations, in octahedral symmetry.

Figure 23-21   (continued)

interpret spectra for ions of all types, from d^2 to d^8. To provide an understanding of these diagrams, we shall first take the d^2 case and compare it in detail with Fig. 23-20.

The energies of the various electronic states are given in the Tanabe–Sugano diagram on the vertical axis, and the ligand field strength increases from left to right on the horizontal axis. The symbols in the diagrams of Fig. 23-21 omit the subscript g, it being understood that all states are *gerade* states. Also, in Tanabe–Sugano diagrams, the zero of energy for any particular d^n ion is taken to be the energy of the ground state. Regardless of the ligand field strength, then, the horizontal axis represents the energy of the ground state, and the energies of the excited electronic states are plotted against the energy of the ground state.

The unit of energy in a Tanabe–Sugano diagram is the parameter B, called Racah's parameter. For different isoelectronic ions (i.e., the d^2 ions Ti^{2+} and V^{3+}, or the d^4 ions Cr^{2+}, Mn^{3+}, and Fe^{4+}), the values of B are different, as shown at the top of each diagram in Fig. 23-21. By plotting energies using the parameter B, one Tanabe–Sugano diagram may be used for all members of an isoelectronic group.

An Example of a d^2 Ion. Let us now take the V^{3+}(aq) ion as an example of an octahedral d^2 system. The well-known green color of this ion is caused by an electronic absorption spectrum that displays two weak absorption bands, one at 17,800 and one at 25,700 cm^{-1}. The absorptions are weak in intensity, and have molar absorptivities (L mol^{-1} cm^{-1}) of 3.5 and 6.6, respectively. Such low values for molar absorptivity suggest that the electronic transitions that are responsible for the absorption of electromagnetic radiation are transitions that are forbidden, as we have anticipated. Using the diagram for a d^2 ion from Fig. 23-21, we can discover only three spin allowed transitions, as we pointed out before using Fig. 23-20. Let us assign the first absorption band at 17,800 cm^{-1} to the transition $^3T_{1g} \rightarrow {}^3T_{2g}$ and the second band at 25,700 cm^{-1} to the transition $^3T_{1g} \rightarrow {}^3T_{1g}$. We shall not assign one of the two observed absorptions to the transition to the $^3A_{2g}$ state, as that represents a two electron jump, as discussed previously. We can now proceed to use the Tanabe–Sugano diagram to try to get a "fit" of the energies for these two absorptions.

We now look at the d^2 Tanabe–Sugano diagram for the value on the horizontal axis of Δ/B that gives the best fit to these experimental absorption band energies. We find that the best value of Δ/B is about 29, as this is the point where the energies of the two states are in a ratio of 1.43 (as judged by the values of both states at this value of Δ/B), agreeing with the experimental ratio of 1.44. At Δ/B of 29.0, we find transition energies (differences in energy between the ground state and each of the two excited states) of 28.5 B and 40.5 B. Using the observed energies in reciprocal centimeters, we can then calculate that the value of B for the $[V(H_2O)_6]^{3+}$ ion must be 630 cm^{-1}. This is only 73% of the value of B for the free ion that is listed in the diagram for uncomplexed V^{3+}.

An Example of a d^8 Ion. The Ni^{2+} ion, like the vanadium ion discussed previously, exists in aqueous solutions of its salts as the hexaaqua nickel ion, $[Ni(H_2O)_6]^{2+}$. Aqueous solutions of salts such as $NiSO_4$, $NiCl_2$, and so on, have a pale green color. Upon addition of aqueous NH_3 or the bidentate ethyl-

Figure 23-22 The electronic spectra of $[Ni(H_2O)_6]^{2+}$ (——) and $[Ni(en)_3]^{2+}$ (------). Also shown is the correspondence between wavelength and the colors of the visible portion of the spectrum.

enediamine, $H_2NCH_2CH_2NH_2$, the color of these aqueous solutions becomes deep blue or purple, respectively. We show in Fig. 23-22 the electronic absorption spectra of the ions $[Ni(H_2O)_6]^{2+}$ and $[Ni(en)_3]^{2+}$. The wavelengths involved cover the near UV, through the visible, to the near IR portions of the spectrum. The spectrum for each ion has three main absorption bands. For the hexaaqua ion, the lowest one is at about 8800 cm^{-1} and the uppermost one is at 24,000 cm^{-1}.

Let us turn now to the Tanabe–Sugano diagram for d^8 ions. At a value of Δ/B of ca. 11, we get good agreement between experiment and theory for the ratio of the energies of the two bands at 8800 and 24,000 cm^{-1} of the hexaaqua Ni^{2+} ion. Here we have assumed that the value of B in the complex is about 80% of that for the free ion. We are then able to predict that the middle absorption band in the spectrum, assigned to the transition $^3A_{2g} \rightarrow {}^3T_{1g}$, should be at $E/B = 18$, which becomes 16,000 cm^{-1}, if we let $B = 865$ (80% of 1080). This is in good agreement with the observed position of the middle "bands" in the spectrum of the hexaaqua ion. Similarly, for the Δ/B value of 13, and $B = 865$, we can fit all three bands in the spectrum of $[Ni(en)_3]^{2+}$.

We are now able to demonstrate that the ligand field strength of the three en ligands is greater than that of the six H_2O ligands at Ni^{2+}. In fact it is greater by the amount $\frac{13}{11} = 1.18$, as based on the values of Δ/B deduced previously. This is what causes the spectrum to shift to higher energies (and the colors of the complexes to change) when the en ligand set replaces the water ligands.

Three other observations may be made about the nickel(II) ion spectra shown in Fig. 23-22. First we note that the middle absorption band in the spectrum of the ion $[Ni(H_2O)_6]^{2+}$ is really two close bands. The reason for this is that, at a ligand field strength of 11 B, there is a ^1E_g state that is practically degenerate with the $^3T_{1g}$ state. This can be seen in the d^8 Tanabe–Sugano diagram of Fig. 23-21. Because of an effect that has not been considered in our treatment, namely, "spin-orbit coupling," when two states of different spin multiplicity become nearly equal in energy, they get "mixed together," and there is then enough triplet character in both states to make transitions from the triplet ground state to both excited states become spin allowed. In other words, the transition $^3A_{2g} \to {}^1E_g$ becomes allowed because the spin selection rule is relaxed by spin-orbit coupling between the two excited states ^1E_g and $^3T_{1g}$.

Second, it can be seen that the spectrum of the $[Ni(en)_3]^{2+}$ ion is considerably more intense than that of the hexaaqua ion. This is because the $[Ni(en)_3]^{2+}$ ion lacks a center of symmetry, and the usual selection rule forbidding d–d transitions is relaxed.

Finally, on comparing the absorption spectra with the "color map" of the visible region of the spectrum, as is done in Fig. 23-22, it can be seen that the colors of the two ions are consistent with their spectra. The green $[Ni(H_2O)_6]^{2+}$ ion absorbs both the red and the blue ends of the spectrum, but transmits the central green region. The purple $[Ni(en)_3]^{2+}$ ion, however, absorbs the middle region of the visible spectrum (and some of the red), but transmits the purple and blue regions.

Examples of d^5 Ions. We now examine the spectra of the very pale pink, high-spin d^5 ions $[Mn(H_2O)_6]^{2+}$ and $[Fe(H_2O)_6]^{3+}$. It should be noted that the latter is obtained only in very strong noncomplexing acids, because the hexaaqua ion readily dissociates a proton to give $[Fe(H_2O)_5OH]^{2+}$, which is yellow brown. The reason both of these ions have extremely pale colors is that their d–d absorption spectra are even weaker (by a factor of about 100) than those we have looked at so far. The spectrum of the $[Mn(H_2O)_6]^{2+}$ ion is shown in Fig. 23-23, where it can be seen that the molar absorptivities (L mol^{-1} cm^{-1}) are extremely low. Why should these absorption bands be so extraordinarily weak? The answer must be given in terms of one or more selection rules that discourage the electronic transitions.

Even before we look at the Tanabe–Sugano diagram, we can foresee the answer. For a high-spin d^5 configuration, each d orbital is singly occupied, and all spins are parallel. This requires the ground electronic state to be a spin

Figure 23-23 The electronic absorption spectrum of $[Mn(H_2O)_6]^{2+}$. Arrows indicate predicted band positions.

sextet, $^6A_{1g}$. There is, furthermore, no way to promote an electron from a t_{2g} orbital to an e_g orbital without reversing its spin. Thus, for the high-spin d^5 case, all possible d–d electronic transitions are spin forbidden. It is this extra degree of forbiddenness that decreases the absorption intensities by a factor of about 100 compared to the usual d–d absorption band. Apart from this intensity question, the $[Mn(H_2O)_6]^{2+}$ absorption spectrum can be explained in the usual way, and the band assignments are shown in Fig. 23-23.

Charge-Transfer Spectra

While the d–d absorption bands of many transition metal complexes are usually their most important electronic spectroscopic feature, there is another class of electronic transitions that can always occur and sometimes play a prominent role in the spectra of coordination compounds. A d–d transition involves redistribution of electrons among orbitals that are mainly (in the crystal field model, entirely) localized on the metal atom. There are also electronic transitions in which an electron moves from an essentially ligand-based orbital to an essentially metal-based orbital, or vice versa. When this happens, charge is transferred from one part of the coordination sphere to another. The resulting spectroscopic features and the electronic transitions from which they arise are called, respectively, charge-transfer (CT) bands and charge-transfer (CT) transitions.

There are two broad classes of CT transitions. When an electron passes from a ligand-based orbital to a metal-based one, we have a ligand-to-metal charge-transfer (LMCT) absorption band, or transition. When the electron moves from an orbital that is largely metal based to one that is ligand based, we have a metal-to-ligand charge-transfer (MLCT) absorption, or transition. A few illustrations can now be given.

The most familiar CT transition may be the one that is responsible for the intense red color that identifies the Fe^{3+} ion upon addition of thiocyanate ion (SCN^-) to aqueous solutions of Fe^{3+}. The reason that this color is so intense is because the LMCT transition of the complex is an allowed electronic transition in every aspect. No selection rule is violated by the transition. There is no change in spin multiplicity associated with the transition and the electron moves from a ligand orbital that is *ungerade* to a metal orbital that is *gerade*. Such a CT transition is allowed by these two important selection rules, and the absorption intensity (as measured by molar absorptivity) is about 1000 times greater than that of a typical d–d transition. These are characteristic features of many CT transitions.

It may also be noted that the yellow-brown color of the $[Fe(H_2O)_5OH]^{2+}$ ion is due to an OH to metal LMCT band in the near UV, which is so intense that its tail, or low-energy edge, absorbs significantly in the blue end of the visible spectrum.

In general, LMCT bands are found in the visible region or very near UV region, for complexes having lone-pair electrons on anionic ligands and metal atoms in high oxidation states. These are just the sorts of complexes that should favor movement of electron density from the electron-rich ligands to metals with high positive charges. Furthermore, the high-spin Fe^{3+} ion has vacancies in both its t_{2g} and its e_g orbital sets, and both types of LMCT transition, that is to either the metal e_g or t_{2g} orbitals, occur.

The other type of CT transition, namely, metal–ligand or MLCT transitions, are less common. They are likely to occur in the visible region of the spectrum. MLCT absorptions are expected only in systems containing metals in low oxidation states and ligands with empty π^* orbitals. Organometallic compounds that we shall discuss in later chapters fall into this category. Thus, the Group VIA(6) metal hexacarbonyl molecules, $M(CO)_6$ (M = Cr, Mo, W), all have a MLCT band around 35,000 cm^{-1}, which involves the transfer of a metal t_{2g} electron to the π^* orbitals of the CO ligands. These absorptions have molar absorptivities of ca. 15,000 L mol^{-1} cm^{-1}, as compared to values on the order of 1–100 for typical d–d absorption bands.

23-7 Some Generalizations Concerning Ligand Field Splittings and Spectra

Certain generalizations may be made about the dependence of the magnitudes of Δ values on the valence and atomic number of the metal ion, the symmetry of the coordination shell, and the nature of the ligands. For octahedral complexes containing high-spin metal ions, it may be inferred from the accumulated data for a large number of systems that:

1. Δ_o values for complexes of the first transition series are 7500–12,500 cm^{-1} for divalent ions and 14,000–25,000 cm^{-1} for trivalent ions.

2. Δ_o values for corresponding complexes of metal ions in the same group and with the same valence increase by 30 to 50% on going from the first transition series to the second and by about this amount again from the second to the third. This is well illustrated by the Δ_o values for the complexes $[Co(NH_3)_6]^{3+}$, $[Rh(NH_3)_6]^{3+}$, and $[Ir(NH_3)_6]^{3+}$, which are, respectively, 23,000, 34,000, and 41,000 cm^{-1}.

3. Δ_t values are about 40 to 50% of Δ_o values for complexes differing as little as possible except in the geometry of the coordination shell, in agreement with theoretical expectation.

4. The dependence of Δ values on the identity of the ligands follows a regular order known as the spectrochemical series, which will now be explained.

The Spectrochemical Series

It has been found by experimental study of the spectra of a large number of complexes containing various metal ions and various ligands, that ligands may be arranged in a series according to their capacity to cause d-orbital splittings. This series, for the more common ligands, is I$^-$ < Br$^-$ < Cl$^-$ < F$^-$ < OH$^-$ < $C_2O_4^{2-}$ < H_2O < —NCS$^-$ < py < NH_3 < en < bipy < o-phen < NO_2^- < CN$^-$. The idea of this series is that the d-orbital splittings and, hence, the relative frequencies of visible absorption bands for two complexes containing the same metal ion but different ligands can be predicted from this series whatever the particular metal may be. We have already seen a typical illustration of the relative positions of en and H_2O in the spectrochemical series when we examined the d–d spectra of the $[Ni(H_2O)_6]^{2+}$ and $[Ni(en)_3]^{2+}$ ions. Naturally, one cannot expect such a simple rule to be universally applicable. The following qualifications must be remembered in applying it.

1. The series is based on data for metal ions in common oxidation states. Because the nature of the metal–ligand interaction in an unusually high or unusually low oxidation state of the metal may be in certain respects qualitatively different from that for the metal in a normal oxidation state, striking violations of the order shown may occur for complexes in unusual oxidation states.

2. Even for metal ions in their normal oxidation states inversions of the order of adjacent or nearly adjacent members of the series are sometimes found.

23-8   Structural and Thermodynamic Effects of *d*-Orbital Splittings

Regardless of what type or level of theory is used to account for the existence of the *d*-orbital splittings, the fact that they do exist is of major importance. Their existence affects both structural and thermodynamic properties of the ions and their complexes.

Ionic Radii

Figure 23-24 shows a plot of the octahedral radii of the divalent ions of the first transition series. The points for Cr^{2+} and Cu^{2+} are indicated with open circles because the Jahn–Teller effect, to be discussed later, makes it difficult to obtain these ions in truly octahedral environments, thus rendering the assessment of their "octahedral" radii somewhat uncertain. A smooth curve has also been drawn through the points for Ca^{2+}, Mn^{2+}, and Zn^{2+} ions, which have the electron configurations $t_{2g}^0 e_g^0$, $t_{2g}^3 e_g^2$, and $t_{2g}^6 e_g^4$, respectively. In these three cases the distribution of *d*-electron density around the metal ion is spherical because all *d* orbitals are either unoccupied or equally occupied. Because the

Ca^{2+} Sc^{2+} Ti^{2+} V^{2+} Cr^{2+} Mn^{2+} Fe^{2+} Co^{2+} Ni^{2+} Cu^{2+} Zn^{2+}

Figure 23-24 The relative ionic radii of divalent ions of the first transition series. The white line is a theoretical curve as explained in the text.

shielding of one d electron by another from the nuclear charge is imperfect, there is a steady contraction in these three ionic radii. It is seen that the radii of the other ions are all below the values expected from the curve passing through Ca^{2+}, Mn^{2+}, and Zn^{2+}. This is because the d electrons in these ions are not distributed uniformly (i.e., spherically) about the nuclei as we shall now explain.

The Ti^{2+} ion has the configuration t_{2g}^2. This means that the negative charge of two d electrons is concentrated in those regions of space away from the metal–ligand bond axes. Thus, compared with the effect that they would have if distributed spherically around the metal nucleus, these two electrons provide abnormally little shielding between the positive metal ion and the negative ligands; therefore, the ligand atoms are drawn in closer than they would be if the d electrons were spherically distributed. Thus, in effect, the radius of the metal ion is smaller than that for the hypothetical, isoelectronic spherical ion. In V^{2+} this same effect is found in even greater degree because there are now three t_{2g} electrons providing much less shielding between metal ion and ligands than would three spherically distributed d electrons. For Cr^{2+} and Mn^{2+}, however, we have the configurations $t_{2g}^3 e_g^1$ and $t_{2g}^3 e_g^2$, in which the electrons added to the t_{2g}^3 configuration of V^{2+} go into orbitals that concentrate them mainly between the metal ion and the ligands. These e_g electrons thus provide a great deal more screening than would be provided by spherically distributed electrons, and indeed the effect is so great that the radii actually increase. The same sequence of events is repeated in the second half of the series. The first three electrons added to the spherical $t_{2g}^3 e_g^2$ configuration of Mn^{2+} go into the t_{2g} orbitals where the screening power is abnormally low, and the radii therefore decrease abnormally rapidly. On going from Ni^{2+}, with the configuration $t_{2g}^6 e_g^2$, to Cu^{2+} and Zn^{2+}, electrons are added to the e_g orbitals where their screening power is abnormally high, and the radii again cease to decrease and actually show small increases. Similar effects are found with trivalent ions, with ions of other transition series, and in tetrahedral complexes.

The Jahn–Teller Effect

In 1937 Jahn and Teller showed that in general no nonlinear molecule can be stable in a degenerate electronic state. The molecule must become distorted in such a way as to break down the degeneracy. It develops that one of the most important areas of application of this Jahn–Teller theorem is the stereochemistry of the complexes of certain transition metal ions.

To illustrate, we consider an octahedrally coordinated Cu^{2+} ion. There is one vacancy in the e_g orbitals, in either the $d_{x^2-y^2}$ or the d_{z^2} orbital. If the coordination is strictly octahedral, the two configurations $d_{x^2-y^2}^2 d_{z^2}^1$ and $d_{x^2-y^2}^1 d_{z^2}^2$, are of equal energy. This is the sense in which the electronic state of the Cu^{2+} ion is doubly degenerate. However, this is a state which, according to the Jahn–Teller theorem, cannot be stable, and the octahedron must distort so that the two configurations just mentioned are no longer of equal energy.

Actually, it is easy to see why this will happen. Suppose the actual configuration in the e_g orbitals is $d_{x^2-y^2}^1 d_{z^2}^2$. The ligands along the z axis are much more screened from the charge of the Cu^{2+} ion than are the four ligands along the x and y axes. The z-axis ligands will therefore tend to move further away. As

	Cu—X	Cu—X'
X = Cl	2.30	2.95
X = Br	2.40	3.18
X = F	1.93	2.27

Figure 23-25 The distorted six coordination found in the Cu(II) halides, distances in angstroms. This elongation of the axial Cu—X' bonds constitutes an example of the Jahn–Teller effect.

they do so, however, the d_{z^2} orbital will become more stable than the $d_{x^2-y^2}$ orbital, thus removing the degeneracy, as is shown in Fig. 23-6. Of course, if we begin with a $d_{x^2-y^2}^2 d_{z^2}^1$ configuration, a distortion of the opposite kind would be expected. The question of which situation will actually occur is very difficult to predict, and there are, in fact, still other possibilities. However, it is the former type of distortion, the elongation on one axis, which is actually observed in a large number of Cu^{2+} complexes.

This is well illustrated by the copper(II) halides. In each case the Cu^{2+} ion has a coordination number of six, with four near neighbors in a plane and two more remote ones. The actual distances are shown in Fig. 23-25.

It is not difficult to see that the reasoning involved in the Cu^{2+} case will apply in all cases where an odd number (1 or 3) of electrons would occupy the e_g orbitals in an octahedral complex. In the case of a single electron, either the $d_{x^2-y^2}$ or the d_{z^2} orbital could be occupied, and the occupied orbital should "push away" the ligands toward which it is directed. The important cases in which this may be expected are

$$t_{2g}^3 e_g^1 \quad \text{high-spin } Cr^{2+} \text{ and } Mn^{3+}$$

$$t_{2g}^6 e_g^1 \quad \text{low-spin } Co^{2+} \text{ and } Ni^{3+}$$

Distortions similar to those for Cu^{2+} are, indeed, found for the "octahedral" complexes of these ions.

Ligand Field Stabilization Energies

We learned in Section 23-2 that the d orbitals of an ion in an octahedral field are split so that three of them become more stable (by $2\Delta_0/5$) and two of them less stable (by $3\Delta_0/5$) than they would be in the absence of the splitting. Thus, for example, a d^2 ion will have each of its two d electrons stabilized by $2\Delta_0/5$, giving a total stabilization of $4\Delta_0/5$. Recalling from Section 23-7 that Δ_0 values run about 10,000 and 20,000 cm^{-1} for di- and trivalent ions of the first transition series, we can see that these "extra" stabilization energies—extra in the sense that they would not exist if the d shells of the metal ions were symmetrical as are the other electron shells of the ions—will amount to ~ 100 and ~ 200 kJ mol^{-1}, respectively, for di- and trivalent d^2 ions. These *ligand field stabilization energies,* LFSEs, are of course of the same order of magnitude as the energies of most chemical changes, and they will therefore play an important role in the thermodynamic properties of transition metal compounds.

Let us first consider high-spin octahedral complexes. Every t_{2g} electron represents a stability increase (i.e., energy lowering) of $2\Delta_o/5$, whereas every e_g electron represents a stability decrease of $3\Delta_o/5$. Thus, for any configuration $t_{2g}^p e_g^q$, the net stabilization will be given by $(2p/5 - 3q/5)\Delta_o$.

The results obtained for all of the ions, that is, d^0 to d^{10}, using this formula are collected in Table 23-4. Since the magnitude of Δ_o for any particular complex can be obtained from the spectrum, it is possible to determine the magnitudes of these crystal field stabilization energies independently of thermodynamic measurements and, thus, to determine what part they play in the thermodynamics of the transition metal compounds.

The enthalpies of hydration of the divalent ions of the first transition series are the energies of the processes:

$$M^{2+}(gas) + \infty H_2O = [M(H_2O)_6]^{2+}(aq) \qquad (23\text{-}8.1)$$

They can be estimated by using thermodynamic cycles. The energies calculated are shown by the filled circles in Fig. 23-26. It will be seen that a smooth curve, which is nearly a straight line passes through the points for the three ions, $Ca^{2+}(d^0)$, $Mn^{2+}(d^5)$, and $Zn^{2+}(d^{10})$, which have no LFSE, while the points for all other ions lie above this line. If we subtract the LFSE from each of the actual hydration energies, the values shown by open circles are obtained, and these fall on the smooth curve. It may be noted that, alternatively, LFSEs could have been estimated from Fig. 23-20 and used to calculate Δ_o values. Either way, the agreement between the spectrally and thermodynamically assessed Δ_o values provides evidence for the fundamental correctness of the idea of *d*-orbital splitting.

Another important example of the thermodynamic consequences of ligand field splittings is shown in Fig. 23-27 where the lattice energies of the di-chlorides of the metals from calcium to zinc are plotted versus atomic number. Once again they define a curve with two maxima, and a minimum at Mn^{2+}. As previously, the energies for all the ions having LFSEs lie above the curve passing

Table 23-4 Ligand Field Stabilization Energies, LFSEs, for Octahedrally and Tetrahedrally Coordinated High-Spin Ions

| Number of *d* Electrons | Stabilization Energies | | Difference, Octahedral–Tetrahedral[b] |
	Octahedral	Tetrahedral	
1, 6	$2\Delta_o/5$	$3\Delta_t/5$	$\Delta_o/10$
2, 7[a]	$4\Delta_o/5$	$6\Delta_t/5$	$2\Delta_o/10$
3, 8	$6\Delta_o/5$	$4\Delta_t/5$	$8\Delta_o/10$
4, 9	$3\Delta_o/5$	$2\Delta_t/5$	$4\Delta_o/10$
0, 5, 10	0	0	0

[a]For the d^2 and d^7 ions, the figure obtained in this way and given above is not exactly correct because of the effect of configuration interaction.

[b]Assuming $\Delta_o = 2\Delta_t$.

Figure 23-26 Hydration energies of some divalent ions of the first transition series. Solid circles are the experimentally obtained hydration energies. Open circles are energies corrected for LFSE.

through the energies of the three ions that do not have ligand field stabilization energy. Similar plots are obtained for the lattice energies of other halides and of the chalconides of di- and trivalent metals.

It is important to note that the LFSEs, critical as they may be in explaining the *difference* in energies between various ions in the series, make up only a small fraction, 5–10%, of the *total* energies of combination of the metal ions with the ligands. In other words, the LFSEs though crucially important in many ways, are not by any means major sources of the binding energies in complexes.

Figure 23-27 The lattice energies of the dichlorides of the elements from Ca to Zn.

Stability of Coordination Compounds

It is a fairly general observation that the equilibrium constants for the formation of analogous complexes of the divalent metal ions of Mn to Zn with ligands that contain nitrogen as the donor atom fall in the following order of the metal ions $Mn^{2+} < Fe^{2+} < Co^{2+} < Ni^{2+} < Cu^{2+} > Zn^{2+}$. LFSEs are responsible for this general trend. If it is assumed that $\Delta S°$ values in the formation of a particular complex by the different metal ions will be essentially constant, then this order of formation constants is also the order of $-\Delta H°$ values for complex formation. Figure 23-26 shows that this order is the same as the order of hydration energies of gaseous ions. When an aqueous aqua ion, $[M(H_2O)_6]^{2+}$, reacts with a set of ligands to form a complex, LFSE in the complex is usually greater than that in the aqua ion. In each case, it will be greater by about the same fraction, say 20%. Thus, in each case, the replacement of water molecules by the new ligands will have a $-\Delta H°$ value that is proportional to the LFSE and the magnitudes of these $-\Delta H°$ values are in the same order as the LFSEs themselves.

STUDY GUIDE

Scope and Purpose

We have continued the discussion of coordination compounds that was begun in Chapter 6. The various theoretical treatments that have been presented are the electrostatic or crystal field model and the delocalized MO model. Each has its advantages, and the student should become comfortable with the language and the approach of both theories. The section on electronic absorption spectroscopy is certainly optional, but it does provide a concise sketch of a very important area of research into coordination compounds. The approaches to bonding theory that are presented here will be of great importance to the discussions in subsequent chapters.

Study Questions

A. Review

1. What is a practical definition of a transition element? What fraction of the ca. 109 known elements are of this type?
2. List some of the important characteristics of the transition elements.
3. Make drawings of the d orbitals, and state which fall into the e_g and which fall into the t_{2g} set in an octahedral ligand field.
4. What is the "center of gravity" rule and how does it apply to the splitting of the d orbitals in octahedral and in tetrahedral ligand fields.
5. Prepare a diagram that traces how the d orbital splitting pattern changes as an octahedral complex is altered via a tetragonal distortion that is first weak and then reaches the extreme case where a square, four-coordinate complex is obtained.
6. According to the crystal field theory, the e_g and t_{2g} orbitals are purely metal d orbitals. How is this different from the approach of MO theory?

7. By using orbital splitting diagrams, show which d^n electron configurations are capable of giving both low-spin and high-spin configurations in an octahedral ligand field.

8. Calculate the spin-only magnetic moments that are expected in each case from Problem 7.

9. Why are d–d electronic transitions weakly absorbing? Why are the absorptions observable at all, if they are forbidden?

10. Use the Tanabe–Sugano diagrams to show which d^n configurations that are high spin in the presence of a weak ligand field can become low spin at high values of the ligand field strength.

11. What is the spectrochemical series, and what limitations must be remembered in using it?

12. Which electronic transitions for a d^5 ion are spin allowed?

13. How does Δ_o change on going from one octahedral complex to another with the same ligand set, but (a) M^{3+} in place of M^{2+} or (b) a second series transition element in place of a first transition series element?

14. Explain the correlation between ion size and the number of d electrons.

15. Use Cr^{2+} to illustrate the influence of the Jahn–Teller effect on the ground-state structures of certain transition metal complexes.

16. Calculate, in units of Δ_o, the LFSEs of the following high-spin ions in their octahedral complexes Fe^{2+}, Mn^{2+}, Mn^{3+}, Co^{2+}.

B. Additional Exercises

1. How should the d orbital splitting pattern for a tetrahedral complex be modified if the tetrahedron is flattened? Elongated?

2. What d-orbital splitting pattern would you expect for (a) a linear L—M—L complex, (b) a planar and triangular ML_3 complex, (c) a pyramidal ML_3 complex, (d) a trigonal-bipyramidal ML_5 complex, (e) a square-pyramidal ML_5 complex?

3. What d-orbital splitting pattern would you expect for an ML_8 complex with the eight ligands situated at the corners of a cube?

4. The complex $[NiCl_4]^{2-}$ is paramagnetic with two unpaired electrons, while $[Ni(CN)_4]^{2-}$ is diamagnetic. Deduce the structures of these two complexes and explain the observations in terms of ligand field theory.

5. Predict the relative positions of the absorption maximum in the spectra of $[Ti(CN)_6]^{3-}$, $[TiCl_6]^{3-}$, and $[Ti(H_2O)_6]^{3+}$.

6. What geometry do you expect for four-coordinate complexes of Zn^{2+}? Explain in terms of LFSEs.

7. Predict the magnetic properties and the LFSE for each of the following:

   (a) $[Fe(CN)_6]^{3-}$ (b) $[Ru(NH_3)_6]^{2+}$

   (c) $[Co(NH_3)_6]^{3+}$ (d) $[CoCl_4]^{2-}$

   (e) $[Fe(H_2O)_6]^{2+}$ (f) $[Mn(H_2O)_6]^{2+}$

   (g) $[CoF_6]^{3-}$ (h) $[Cr(H_2O)_6]^{2+}$

8. Why are tetrahedral complexes usually not low spin?

9. Prepare a drawing that shows the π-bond system that is responsible for the high position of CO in the spectrochemical series. Clearly show the donor orbital of the metal and the acceptor orbital of the CO ligand.

10. Consider the data of Fig. 23-24. For which ion is the effective nuclear charge highest? Why?

11. Use the appropriate Tanabe–Sugano diagram to estimate the positions of the three absorption bands for $[Ni(en)_3]^{2+}$.

12. Give the electronic state symbol for the ground electronic state arising from each of the octahedral d^n electron configurations, including high-spin and low-spin possibilities where appropriate.

SUPPLEMENTARY READING

Ballhausen, C. J. and Gray, H. B., "Electronic Structures of Metal Complexes," in *Coordination Chemistry*, A. E. Martell, Ed., Van Nostrand-Reinhold, New York, 1971.

Cotton, F. A., *Chemical Applications of Group Theory*, Wiley, New York, 1971.

Fackler, J. P., *Symmetry in Coordination Chemistry*, Academic, New York, 1971.

Figgis, B. N., *Introduction to Ligand Fields*, Wiley, New York, 1966.

Jørgensen, C. K., *Modern Aspects of Ligand Field Theory*, North-Holland, Amsterdam, 1971.

König, E. and Kremer, S., *Ligand Field Energy Level Diagrams*, Plenum, New York, 1977.

Lever, A. B. P., *Inorganic Electronic Spectroscopy*, Elsevier, Amsterdam, 2nd Ed., 1984.

Mabbs, F. E. and Machin, D. J., *Magnetism and Transition Metal Complexes*, Wiley-Halsted, New York, 1973.

McClure, D. S. and Stephens, P. J., "Electronic Spectra of Coordination Compounds," in *Coordination Chemistry*, A. E. Martell, Ed., Van Nostrand-Reinhold, New York, 1971.

Schläfer, H. L. and Glieman, G., *Basic Principles of Ligand Field Theory*, Wiley, New York, 1969.

chapter 24

THE ELEMENTS OF THE FIRST TRANSITION SERIES

As we have seen from their position in the periodic table (Section 2-5), these metals show variable valency. In this chapter we first discuss some of their common features and then consider the chemistry of individual elements.

24-1 The Metals

The metals are hard, refractory, electropositive, and good conductors of heat and electricity. The exception is copper, a soft and ductile metal, relatively noble, but second only to Ag as a conductor of heat and electricity. Some properties are given in Table 24-1. Manganese and iron are attacked fairly readily but the others are generally unreactive at room temperature. All react on heating with halogens, sulfur, and other nonmetals. The carbides, nitrides, and borides are commonly nonstoichiometric, interstitial, hard, and refractory.

24-2 The Lower Oxidation States

The oxidation states are given in Table 24-2, the most common and important (especially in aqueous chemistry) are in bold type. Table 24-2 also gives the d electron configurations. The chemistries can be classified on this basis; for example, the d^6 series is V^{-1}, Cr^0, Mn^I, Fe^{II}, Co^{III}, Ni^{IV}. Comparisons of this kind can occasionally emphasize similarities in spectra and magnetic properties. However, the differences in properties of the d^n species due to differences in the nature of the metal, its energy levels, and especially the charge on the ion, often exceed the similarities.

1. *The oxidation states less than II.* With the exception of copper, where copper(I) binary compounds and complexes, and the Cu^+ ion are known, the chemistry of the I, 0, $-$I, and $-$II formal oxidation states is entirely concerned with:

    (a) π-acid ligands such as CO, NO, PR_3, CN^-, 2,2'-bipyridine, and so on.

    (b) organometallic chemistry in which olefins, acetylenes, or aromatic systems such as benzene are bound to the metal.

473

Table 24-1 Some Properties of the First Transition Series Metals

	Ti	V	Cr	Mn	Fe	Co	Ni	Cu
mp °C	1668	1890	1875	1244	1537	1493	1453	1083
Properties	Hard, corrosion resistant	Hard, corrosion resistant	Brittle, corrosion resistant	White, brittle, reactive	Lustrous, reactive	Hard, bluish color	Quite corrosion resistant	Soft and ductile, reddish color
Density, g cm^{-3}	4.51	6.11	7.19	7.18	7.87	8.90	8.91	8.94
E^0, V^a	—^{b}	−1.19	−0.91	−1.18	−0.44	−0.28	−0.24	+0.34
Solubility in acids	Hot HCl, HF	HNO$_3$, HF concentrated H$_2$SO$_4$	dilute HCl, H$_2$SO$_4$	dilute HCl, H$_2$SO$_4$ and so on	dilute HCl, H$_2$SO$_4$ and so on	Slowly in dilute HCl and so on	dilute HCl, H$_2$SO$_4$	HNO$_3$; hot concentrated H$_2$SO$_4$

^{a}For $M^{2+}_{aq} + 2e^- = M(s)$.

^{b}No +2 ion in aqueous solution.

Table 24-2 Oxidation States of First Series Transition Elements[a]

Ti		V		Cr		Mn		Fe		Co		Ni		Cu	
		0	d^5	0	d^6	0	d^7	0	d^8	0	d^9	**0**	d^{10}		
		1	d^4	1	d^5	**1**	d^6			1	d^8	1	d^9	1	d^{10}
2	d^2	2	d^3	2	d^4	2	d^5	2	d^6	2	d^7	2	d^8	2	d^9
3	d^1	3	d^2	3	d^3	3	d^4	3	d^5	3	d^6	3	d^7	3	d^8
4	d^0	4	d^1	4	d^2	4	d^3	4	d^4	4	d^5	4	d^6		
		5	d^0	5	d^1	5	d^2			5	d^4				
				6	d^0	6	d^1	6	d^2						
						7	d^0								

[a]Formal negative oxidation states are known in compounds of π-acid ligands, for example, Fe^{-II} in $[Fe(CO)_4]^{2-}$, Mn^{-I} in $[Mn(CO)_5]^-$, and so on.

There is an extensive chemistry of mixed compounds such as $(\eta^6\text{-}C_6H_6)Cr(CO)_3$ or $(\eta^4\text{-}C_4H_6)Fe(CO)_3$. These topics are described in Chapters 28 and 29. Some organometallic compounds in higher oxidation states are known, however, mainly for the cyclopentadienyl ligand as in $(\eta^5\text{-}C_5H_5)_2Ti^{IV}Cl_2$, $(\eta^5\text{-}C_5H_5)_2Fe^{II}$, and $[(\eta^5\text{-}C_5H_5)_2Co^{III}]^+$. With π-acid or organic ligands, transition metals also form many compounds with bonds to hydrogen, for example, $H_2Fe(PF_3)_4$. Compounds with M—H bonds are very important in certain catalytic reactions (Chapter 30).

2. *The II oxidation state.* The binary compounds in this state are usually ionic. The metal oxides are basic; they have the NaCl structure but are often nonstoichiometric, particularly for Ti, V, and Fe. The *aqua ions*, $[M(H_2O)_6]^{2+}$, except for the unknown Ti^{2+} ion, are well characterized in solution and in crystalline solids. The potentials and colors are given in Table 24-3. Note that the V^{2+}, Cr^{2+}, and Fe^{2+} ions are oxidized by air in acidic solution.

The aqua ions may be obtained by dissolution of the metals, oxides, carbonates, and so on, in acids and by electrolytic reduction of M^{3+} salts. Hydrated salts with noncomplexing anions usually contain $[M(H_2O)_6]^{2+}$; typical ones are

$$Cr(ClO_4)_2\cdot6H_2O \qquad Mn(ClO_4)_2\cdot6H_2O \qquad FeF_2\cdot8H_2O \qquad FeSO_4\cdot7H_2O$$

However, certain *halide hydrates* do *not* contain the aqua ion. Thus $VCl_2\cdot4H_2O$ is *trans*-$VCl_2(H_2O)_4$, $MnCl_2\cdot4H_2O$ is a polymer with *cis*-$MnCl_2(H_2O)_4$ units; the diaqua species of Mn, Fe, Co, Ni, and Cu have a linear polymeric edge-shared chain structure with *trans*-$[MCl_4(H_2O)_2]$ octahedra. $FeCl_2\cdot6H_2O$ contains *trans*-$FeCl_2(H_2O)_4$ units.

The water molecules of $[M(H_2O)_6]^{2+}$ can be displaced by ligands such as NH_3, en, $EDTA^{4-}$, CN^-, acac, and so on. The resulting complexes may be cationic, neutral, or anionic depending on the charge of the ligands. For Mn^{2+} complexes, the formation constants in aqueous solution are low compared with those of the other ions, because of the absence of ligand field stabilization energy in the d^5 ion (Section 23-8). In complexes the ions are normally *octahedral*, but for the Cu^{2+} and Cr^{2+} ions two H_2O molecules in trans positions are much further from the metal than the other four equatorial ones, because

Table 24-3 Standard Potentials^a (Volts, Acid Solution) and Colors for $[M(H_2O)_6]^{2+}$ and $[M(H_2O)_6]^{3+}$

	Ti	V	Cr	Mn	Fe	Co	Ni	Cu^b
$M^{2+} + 2e^- = M$	—	−1.19	−0.91	−1.18	−0.44	−0.28	−0.24	+0.34
$M^{3+} + e^- = M^{2+}$	−0.37	−0.25	−0.41	+1.59	+0.77	+1.84	—	—
Color M^{2+}(aq)	—	Violet	Sky blue	Pale pink	Pale green	Pink	Green	Blue green
Color M^{3+}(aq)	Violet	Blue	Violet	Brown	v. Pale purple	Blue	—	—

^{a}Some potentials depend on acidity and complexing anions, for example, for Fe^{3+}—Fe^{2+} in 1 M acids: HCl, +0.70; HClO₄, +0.75; H₃PO₄, +0.44; 0.5 M H₂SO₄, +0.68 V.

^{b}Cu²⁺ + e^- = Cu⁺; E_0 = +0.15 V; Cu⁺ + e^- = Cu; E_0 = +0.52 V.

of the Jahn–Teller effect (Section 23-8). For Mn, the complex [Mn(EDTA)H₂O] is seven-coordinate. With halide ions, SCN⁻ and some other ligands, *tetrahedral* species MX_4^{2-} and MX_2L_2, may be formed, the tendency being greatest for Co, Ni, and Cu.

Addition of OH⁻ to the M²⁺ solutions gives *hydroxides*, some of which can be obtained as crystals. $Fe(OH)_2$ and $Ni(OH)_2$ have the brucite, $Mg(OH)_2$, structure. On addition of HCO_3^- the carbonates of Mn, Fe, Co, Ni, and Cu are precipitated.

24-3 The III Oxidation State

All of the elements form at least some compounds in this state but for Cu only a few complexes, not stable toward water, are known.

The fluorides (MF_3) and oxides (M_2O_3) are generally ionic but the chlorides, bromides, and iodides (where known) as well as sulfides and similar compounds may have considerable covalent character.

The elements Ti to Co form octahedral *ions*, $[M(H_2O)_6]^{3+}$. The Co³⁺ and Mn³⁺ ions are very readily reduced by water (Table 24-3). The Ti³⁺ and V³⁺ ions are oxidized by air. In aqueous solution high acidities are required to prevent hydrolysis, for example,

$$[Ti(H_2O)_6]^{3+} = [Ti(H_2O)_5OH]^{2+} + H^+ \qquad K = 1.3 \times 10^{-4} \qquad (24\text{-}3.1)$$

Addition of OH⁻ to the solutions gives *hydrous oxides* rather than true hydroxides. In fairly concentrated halide solutions, complexes of the type $[MCl(H_2O)_5]^{2+}$, $[MCl_2(H_2O)_4]^+$, and so on, are commonly formed, and crystalline chlorides of V, Fe, and Cr are of the type *trans*-$[VCl_2(H_2O)_4]^+Cl^-\cdot 2H_2O$. The alums, such as $CsTi(SO_4)_2\cdot 12H_2O$, or $KV(SO_4)_2\cdot 12H_2O$ contain the hexaaqua ion as do certain hydrates like $Fe(ClO_4)_3\cdot 10H_2O$.

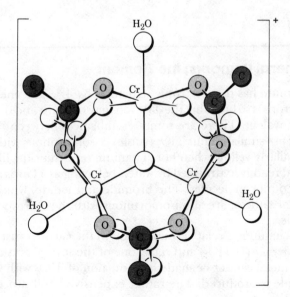

24-I

There are many M^{III} complexes, anionic, cationic, or neutral, mostly *octahedral*. For Cr^{III} and Co^{III} especially, hundreds of octahedral complexes that are substitutionally inert are known. Representative octahedral complexes are $[TiF_6]^{3-}$, $[V(CN)_6]^{3-}$, $Cr(acac)_3$, and $[Co(NH_3)_6]^{3+}$.

The halides, MX_3, act as Lewis acids and form adducts such as $VX_3(NMe_3)_2$, and $CrCl_3(THF)_3$, as well as the ionic species $[VCl_4]^-$, $[CrCl_4]^-$, and so on.

A special feature of the M^{3+} ions is the formation of basic carboxylates in which an O atom is in the center of a triangle of metal atoms (structure 24-I). The latter are linked by carboxylate bridge groups, and the sixth coordination position is occupied by a water molecule or other ligand. This oxo-centered unit has been proved for carboxylates of V, Cr, Mn, Fe, Co, Ru, Rh, and Ir.

24-4 The IV and Higher Oxidation States

The IV state is the most important state for Ti where the main chemistry is that of TiO_2 and $TiCl_4$ and derivatives. Although there are compounds like VCl_4, the main V^{IV} chemistry is that of the oxovanadium(IV) or vanadyl ion VO^{2+}. This ion can behave like an M^{2+} ion, and it forms many complexes that may be cationic, neutral, or anionic, depending on the ligand.

For the remaining elements, the IV oxidation state is not very common or well established except in fluorides, fluorocomplex ions, oxo anions, and a few complexes. Some tetrahedral compounds with —OR, —NR$_2$, or —CR$_3$ groups are known for a few elements, notably Cr; examples are $Cr(OCMe_3)_4$ and $Cr(1\text{-norbornyl})_4$.

The oxidation states V and above are known for V, Cr, Mn, and Fe in fluorides, fluorocomplexes or oxo anions, for example, CrF_5, $KMnO_4$, and K_2FeO_4. All are powerful oxidizing agents.

TITANIUM

24-5 General Remarks; the Element

Titanium has the electronic structure, $3d^2 4s^2$. The energy of removal of four electrons is so high that the Ti^{4+} ion may not exist and titanium(IV) compounds are covalent. There are some resemblances between Ti^{IV} and Sn^{IV} and their radii are similar. Thus TiO_2 (rutile) is isomorphous with SnO_2 (cassiterite) and is similarly yellow when hot. Titanium tetrachloride, like $SnCl_4$, is a distillable liquid readily hydrolyzed by water, behaving as a Lewis acid and giving adducts with donor molecules. The bromide and iodide, which form crystalline molecular lattices, are also isomorphous with the corresponding Group IVB(14) halides.

Titanium is relatively abundant in the earth's crust (0.6%). The main ores are *ilmenite* (FeTiO$_3$) and *rutile*, one of the several crystalline varieties of TiO_2. The metal cannot be made by reduction of TiO_2 with C because a very stable carbide is produced. The rather expensive Kroll process is used. Ilmenite or rutile is treated at red heat with C and Cl_2 to give $TiCl_4$, which is fractionated to free it from impurities such as $FeCl_3$. The $TiCl_4$ is then reduced with molten Mg at ~800 °C in an atmosphere of argon. This gives Ti as a spongy mass from which the excess of Mg and $MgCl_2$ is removed by volatilization at 1000 °C. The sponge may then be fused in an electric arc and cast into ingots; an atmosphere of Ar or He must be used as titanium readily reacts with N_2 and O_2 when hot.

Titanium is lighter than other metals of similar mechanical and thermal properties and is unusually resistant to corrosion. It is used in turbine engines and industrial chemical, aircraft, and marine equipment. It is unattacked by dilute acids and bases. It dissolves in hot HCl giving Ti^{III} chloro complexes and in HF or HNO_3 + HF to give fluoro complexes. Hot HNO_3 gives a hydrous oxide.

TITANIUM COMPOUNDS

The most important stereochemistries in titanium compounds are the following:

Ti^{II}	Octahedral $\rbrace$	in most compounds and in solution
Ti^{III}	Octahedral	
Ti^{IV}	Tetrahedral	in $TiCl_4$, $Ti(CH_2Ph)_4$, and so on
	Octahedral	in TiO_2 and Ti^{IV} complexes

24-6 Binary Compounds of Titanium

Titanium tetrachloride, a colorless liquid (bp 136 °C), has a pungent odor, fumes strongly in moist air, and is vigorously, though not violently, hydrolyzed by water:

$$TiCl_4 + 2H_2O = TiO_2 + 4HCl \qquad (24-6.1)$$

With a deficit of water or on addition of $TiCl_4$ to aqueous HCl, partially hydrolyzed species are formed.

Titanium oxide has three crystal forms—rutile (see Fig. 4-1), anatase, and brookite—all of which occur in nature. The dioxide that is used in large quantities as a white pigment in paints is made by vapor phase oxidation of $TiCl_4$ with oxygen. The precipitates obtained by addition of OH^- to Ti^{IV} solutions are best regarded as hydrous TiO_2, not a true hydroxide. This material is amphoteric and dissolves in concentrated NaOH.

Materials called "titanates" are of technical importance, for example, as ferroelectrics. Nearly all of them have one of the three major mixed metal oxide structures (Section 4-8). Indeed, the names of two of the structures are those of the titanium compounds that were the first found to possess them, namely, $FeTiO_3$ (*ilmenite*) and $CaTiO_3$ (*perovskite*).

24-7   Titanium(IV) Complexes

Aqueous Chemistry; Oxo Salts

There is no firm evidence for the Ti^{4+} aqua ion. In aqueous solutions of Ti^{IV} there are only oxo species; basic oxo salts or hydrated oxides may be precipitated. These oxo salts have formulas such as $TiOSO_4 \cdot H_2O$ and $(NH_4)_2TiO(C_2O_4)_2 \cdot H_2O$, and have chains or rings, $(Ti\!-\!O\!-\!Ti\!-\!O\!-\!)_x$. There is spectroscopic evidence for TiO^{2+} only in 2M $HClO_4$ solution, but some compounds with a $Ti\!=\!O$ group have been characterized.

Anionic Complexes

The solutions obtained by dissolving the metal or hydrous oxide in aqueous HF contain fluoro complex ions, mainly $[TiF_6]^{2-}$, which can be isolated as crystalline salts. In aqueous HCl, $TiCl_4$ gives yellow oxo complex anions but from solutions saturated with gaseous HCl, salts of the $[TiCl_6]^{2-}$ ion may be obtained.

Adducts of TiX_4

The halides form adducts, TiX_4L or TiX_4L_2, which are crystalline solids often soluble in organic solvents. These adducts are invariably *octahedral*. Thus $[TiCl_4(OPCl_3)]_2$ and $[TiCl_4(MeCOOEt)]_2$ are dimeric, with two chlorine bridges, while $TiCl_4(OPCl_3)_2$ has octahedral coordination with the *cis*-$OPCl_3$ groups.

Peroxo Complexes

One of the most characteristic reactions of aqueous Ti solutions is the development of an intense orange color on addition of H_2O_2. This reaction can be used for the colorimetric determination of either Ti or of H_2O_2. Below pH 1, the main species is $[Ti(O_2)(OH)(aq)]^+$.

Solvolytic Reactions of $TiCl_4$; Alkoxides and Related Compounds

Titanium tetrachloride reacts with compounds containing active hydrogen atoms with loss of HCl. The replacement of chloride is usually incomplete in the absence of an HCl acceptor such as an amine or alkoxide ion. The *alkoxides* are typical of other transition metal alkoxides, which we shall not discuss. They can be obtained by reactions such as

$$TiCl_4 + 4ROH + 4R'NH_2 \longrightarrow Ti(OR)_4 + 4R'NH_3Cl \quad (24\text{-}7.1)$$

The alkoxides are liquids or solids that can be distilled or sublimed. They are soluble in organic solvents such as benzene, but are exceedingly readily hydrolyzed by even traces of water, to give polymeric species with —OH— or —O— bridges. The initial hydrolytic step probably involves coordination of water to the metal; a proton on H_2O could then interact with the oxygen of an OR group through hydrogen bonding, leading to hydrolysis:

$$
\begin{array}{c}
H \\
\diagdown \\
O\!-\!M(OR)_x \\
\diagup \\
H
\end{array}
\longrightarrow
\begin{array}{c}
H \\
\diagdown \\
O\!-\!M(OR)_{x-1} \\
\diagup \quad | \\
H\text{------}:O \\
\diagup \\
R
\end{array}
$$

$$M(OH)(OR)_{x-1} + ROH \qquad (24\text{-}7.2)$$

Although monomeric species can exist, for example, when made from secondary and tertiary alcohols, and in dilute solution, alkoxides are usually polymers. Solid $Ti(OC_2H_5)_4$ is a tetramer, with the structure shown in Fig. 24-1. The alkoxides are often referred to as "alkyltitanates" and under this name they are used in heat-resisting paints, where eventual hydrolysis to TiO_2 occurs.

Another class of titanium compounds, the *dialkylamides*, are also representative of similar compounds of other transition metals. These are liquids or volatile solids readily hydrolyzed by water. Unlike the alkoxides they are not polymeric. They are made by reaction of the metal halide with lithium dialkylamides

$$TiCl_4 + 4LiNEt_2 = Ti(NEt_2)_4 + 4LiCl \qquad (24\text{-}7.3)$$

Such amides can undergo a wide range of "insertion" reactions (Section 30-3); thus with CS_2, the dithiocarbamates are obtained

$$Ti(NEt_2)_4 + 4CS_2 = Ti(S_2CNEt_2)_4 \qquad (24\text{-}7.4)$$

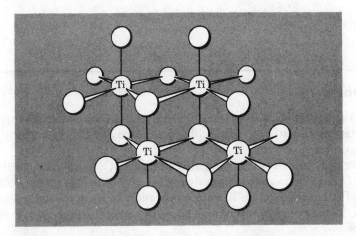

Figure 24-1 The tetrameric structure of $Ti(OC_2H_5)_4$. Only Ti and O atoms are shown. Each Ti is octahedrally coordinated.

24-8 The Chemistry of Titanium(III), d^1, and Titanium(II), d^2

Binary Compounds

Titanium trichloride, (TiCl$_3$) has several crystalline forms. The violet α form is made by H$_2$ reduction of TiCl$_4$ vapor at 500 to 1200 °C. The reduction of TiCl$_4$ by aluminum alkyls (Section 30-10) in inert solvents gives a brown β form that is converted into the α form at 250 to 300 °C. The α form has a layer lattice containing TiCl$_6$ groups. β-TiCl$_3$ is fibrous with single chains of TiCl$_6$ octahedra sharing edges. This structure is of particular importance for the stereospecific polymerization of propene using TiCl$_3$ as catalyst (Ziegler–Natta process) (Section 30-9).

The *dichloride* is obtained by high temperature syntheses:

$$TiCl_4 + Ti = 2TiCl_2 \qquad (24\text{-}8.1)$$

or

$$2TiCl_3 = TiCl_2 + TiCl_4 \qquad (24.8.2)$$

Aqueous Chemistry and Complexes

Aqueous solutions of the $[Ti(H_2O)_6]^{3+}$ ion are obtained by reducing aqueous Ti^{IV} either electrolytically or with zinc. The violet solutions reduce O$_2$ and, hence, must be handled in a N$_2$ or H$_2$ atmosphere:

$$\text{``}TiO^{2+}(aq)\text{''} + 2H^+ + e^- = Ti^{3+} + H_2O \qquad E° = \text{ca. } 0.1 \text{ V} \quad (24\text{-}8.3)$$

The Ti^{3+} solutions are used as fairly rapid, mild reducing agents in volumetric analysis. In HCl solutions the main species is $[TiCl(H_2O)_5]^{2+}$.

There is no aqueous chemistry of Ti^{II} because of its ready oxidation, but a few Ti^{II} complexes such as $[TiCl_4]^{2-}$ can be made in nonaqueous media.

VANADIUM

24-9 The Element

Vanadium is widely distributed but there are few concentrated deposits. It occurs in petroleum from Venzuela, and is recovered as V$_2$O$_5$ from flue dusts after combustion.

Very pure vanadium is rare because, like titanium, it is quite reactive toward O$_2$, N$_2$, and C at the elevated temperatures used in metallurgical processes. Since its chief commercial use is in alloy steels and cast iron, to which it lends ductility and shock resistance, commercial production is mainly as an iron alloy, *ferrovanadium.*

Vanadium metal is not attacked by air, alkalis, or nonoxidizing acids other than HF at room temperature. It dissolves in HNO$_3$, concentrated H$_2$SO$_4$, and aqua regia.

VANADIUM COMPOUNDS

The stereochemistries for the most important classes of vanadium compounds are the following:

$\left.\begin{array}{l} V^{II} \\ V^{III} \end{array}\right\}$ Octahedral as in $[V(H_2O)_6]^{2+}$
           $VF_3(s)$ or $[V(ox)_3]^{3-}$

V^{IV} $\left\{\begin{array}{l} \text{Tetrahedral as in } VCl_4 \text{ or } V(CH_2SiMe_3)_4 \\ \text{Square pyramidal in } O{=}V(acac)_2 \\ \text{Octahedral in } VO_2, K_2VCl_6, O{=}V(acac)_2py, \text{ and so on} \end{array}\right.$

V^V Octahedral as in $[VO_2(ox)_2]^{3-}$, $VF_5(s)$

24-10 Binary Compounds

Halides

In the highest oxidation state only VF_5 is known. The colorless liquid (bp 48 °C), has a high viscosity (cf. SbF_5, Section 17-4) and has chains of VF_6 octahedra linked by cis-V—F—V bridges; it is monomeric in the vapor.

The *tetrachloride* is obtained from V + Cl_2 or from CCl_4 on red-hot V_2O_5. It is a dark red oil (bp 154 °C), which is violently hydrolyzed by water to give solutions of oxovanadium(IV) chloride. It has a high dissociation pressure and loses chlorine slowly when kept, but rapidly on boiling, leaving violet VCl_3. The latter may be decomposed to pale green VCl_2, which is then stable:

$$2VCl_3(s) \longrightarrow VCl_2(s) + VCl_4(g) \qquad (24\text{-}10.1)$$

$$VCl_3(s) \longrightarrow VCl_2(s) + \tfrac{1}{2}Cl_2(g) \qquad (24\text{-}10.2)$$

Vanadium(V) Oxide

Addition of dilute H_2SO_4 to solutions of ammonium vanadate gives a brick-red precipitate of V_2O_5. This oxide is acidic and dissolves in NaOH to give colorless solutions containing the *vanadate* ion, $[VO_4]^{3-}$. On acidification, a complicated series of reactions occurs involving the formation of hydroxo anions and polyanions (cf. Section 5-4). In very strong acid solutions, the *dioxovanadium(V) ion* (VO_2^+) is formed.

24-11 Oxovanadium Ions and Complexes

The two oxo anions, VO_2^+ and VO^{2+}, have an extensive chemistry and form numerous complex compounds. All of the compounds show IR and Raman bands that are characteristic for M=O groups. The VO_2^+ group is angular. Examples of complexes are cis-$[VO_2Cl_4]^{3-}$, cis-$[VO_2EDTA]^{3-}$, and cis-$[VO_2(ox)_2]^{3-}$. The cis arrangement for dioxo compounds of metals with no d electrons is preferred over the trans arrangement that is found in some other metal dioxo systems, for example, $[RuO_2]^{2+}$, because the strongly π-donating O ligands then have exclusive use of one $d\pi$ orbital each (d_{xz}, d_{yz}) and share a third one

(d_{xy}), whereas in the trans configuration they would have to share two $d\pi$ orbitals and leave one unused.

The oxovanadium(IV) or vanadyl compounds are among the most stable and important of vanadium species, and the VO unit persists through a variety of chemical reactions. Solutions of V^{3+} are oxidized in air, while V^V is readily reduced by mild reducing agents to form the blue oxovanadium(IV) ion, $[VO(H_2O)_5]^{2+}$:

$$VO^{2+} + 2H^+ + e^- = V^{3+} + H_2O \qquad E° = 0.34 \text{ V} \qquad (24\text{-}11.1)$$

$$VO_2^+ + 2H^+ + e^- = VO^{2+} + H_2O \qquad E° = 1.0 \text{ V} \qquad (24\text{-}11.2)$$

Addition of base to $[VO(H_2O)_5]^{2+}$ gives the yellow hydrous oxide $VO(OH)_2$, which redissolves in acids giving the cation.

Oxovanadium(IV) compounds are usually blue green. They may be either five-coordinate square pyramidal (structure 24-II) or six-coordinate with a distorted octahedron. Examples are $[VO(bipy)_2Cl]^+$, $VO(acac)_2$, and $[VO(NCS)_4]^{2-}$. The VO bond is short (1.56–1.59 Å), so that VO bonds can properly be regarded as multiple ones, the π component arising from electron flow $O(p\pi) \rightarrow V(d\pi)$. Even in VO_2, which has a distorted rutile structure, one bond (1.76 Å) is conspicuously shorter than the others in the VO_6 unit (note that in TiO_2 all Ti—O bonds are substantially equal).

All of the five-coordinate complexes such as 24-II take up a sixth ligand quite readily, becoming octahedral.

24-II

24-12 The Vanadium(III) Aqua-Ion and Complexes

The electrolytic or chemical reduction of acid solutions of vanadates or V^{IV} solutions gives solutions of V^{III} that are quite readily reoxidized to VO^{2+}. Crystalline salts can be obtained. Addition of OH^- precipitates the hydrous oxide V_2O_3.

24-13 Vanadium(II)

When V^{III} solutions are reduced by Zn in acid, violet air-sensitive solutions of $[V(H_2O)_6]^{2+}$ are obtained. These are oxidized by water with evolution of hydrogen despite the fact that the V^{3+}/V^{2+} potential (Table 24-3) suggests otherwise. Vanadium(II) solutions are often used to remove traces of O_2 from inert gases.

The salt $VSO_4 \cdot 6H_2O$ is obtained as violet crystals on addition of ethanol to reduced sulfate solutions. Because of its d^3 configuration the $[V(H_2O)_6]^{2+}$ ion like $[Cr(H_2O)_6]^{3+}$ is kinetically inert, and its substitution reactions are relatively slow.

CHROMIUM

24-14 The Element Chromium

Apart from stoichiometric similarities, chromium resembles the Group VIB(16) elements of the sulfur group only in the acidity of CrO_3 and the covalent nature and ready hydrolysis of CrO_2Cl_2 (cf. SO_3, SO_2Cl_2).

The chief ore is *chromite*, $FeCr_2O_4$, which is a spinel with Cr^{III} on octahedral sites and Fe^{II} on the tetrahedral ones. It is reduced by C to the carbon-containing alloy ferrochromium:

$$FeCr_2O_4 + 4C \xrightarrow{\text{Heat}} Fe \cdot 2Cr + 4CO \qquad (24\text{-}14.1)$$

When pure Cr is required, the chromite is first treated with molten NaOH and O_2 to convert the Cr^{III} to CrO_4^{2-}. The melt is dissolved in water and sodium dichromate precipitated. This is then reduced:

$$Na_2Cr_2O_7 + 2C \xrightarrow{\text{Heat}} Cr_2O_3 + Na_2CO_3 + CO \qquad (24\text{-}14.2)$$

The oxide is then reduced:

$$Cr_2O_3 + 2Al \xrightarrow{\text{Heat}} Al_2O_3 + 2Cr \qquad (24\text{-}14.3)$$

Chromium is resistant to corrosion, hence its use as an electroplated protective coating. It dissolves fairly readily in HCl, H_2SO_4, and $HClO_4$, but it is passivated by HNO_3.

CHROMIUM COMPOUNDS

The most common stereochemistries for chromium compounds are the following:

$$\left.\begin{array}{l} Cr^{II} \\ Cr^{III} \end{array}\right\} \quad \text{Octahedral as in } [Cr(H_2O)_6]^{2+} \text{ or } [Cr(NH_3)_6]^{3+}$$

$$Cr^{IV} \quad \text{Tetrahedral as in } Cr(O\text{-}t\text{-Bu})_4$$

$$\left.\begin{array}{l} Cr^{V} \\ Cr^{VI} \end{array}\right\} \quad \text{Tetrahedral as in } [CrO_4]^{3-}, [CrO_4]^{2-}, CrO_3$$

24-15 Binary Compounds

Halides

The anhydrous Cr^{II} halides are obtained by action of HCl, HBr, or I_2 on the metal at 600 to 700 °C or by reduction of the trihalides with H_2 at 500 to 600 °C. $CrCl_2$ dissolves in water to give a blue solution of Cr^{2+} ion.

The red-violet trichloride, $CrCl_3$, is made by the action of $SOCl_2$ on the hydrated chloride. The flaky form of $CrCl_3$ is due to its layer structure.

Chromium(III) chloride forms adducts with donor ligands. The violet tetrahydrofuranate, *fac*-$CrCl_3(THF)_3$, which crystallizes from solutions formed by the action of a little zinc on $CrCl_3$ in THF, is a particularly useful material for the preparation of other chromium compounds such as carbonyls or organometallic compounds.

Oxides

The green α-Cr_2O_3 (corundum structure) is formed on burning Cr in O_2, on thermal decomposition of CrO_3, or on roasting the hydrous oxide, $Cr_2O_3 \cdot nH_2O$. The latter, commonly called "chromic hydroxide," although its water content is variable, is precipitated on addition of OH^- to solutions of Cr^{III} salts. The hydrous oxide is amphoteric, dissolving readily in acid to give $[Cr(H_2O)_6]^{3+}$, and in concentrated alkali to form "chromites."

Chromium oxide and chromium supported on other oxides such as Al_2O_3 are important catalysts for a wide variety of reactions.

Chromium(VI)oxide, CrO_3, is obtained as an orange-red precipitate on adding sulfuric acid to solutions of $Na_2Cr_2O_7$. It is thermally unstable above its melting point (197 °C), losing O_2 to give Cr_2O_3. The structure consists of infinite chains of CrO_4 tetrahedra sharing corners. It is soluble in water and highly poisonous.

Interaction of CrO_3 and organic substances is vigorous and may be explosive, but CrO_3 is used in organic chemistry as an oxidant, usually in acetic acid as solvent.

24-16 The Chemistry of Chromium(II), d^4

Aqueous solutions of the blue *chromium(II) ion* are best prepared by dissolving electrolytic Cr metal in dilute mineral acids. The solutions must be protected from air (Table 24-3)—even then, they decompose at rates varying with the acidity and the anions present, by reducing water with liberation of H_2.

The mechanisms of reductions of other ions by Cr^{2+} have been extensively studied, since the resulting Cr^{3+} complex ions are substitution inert. Much information regarding ligand-bridged transition states (Section 6-5) has been obtained in this way.

Chromium(II) *acetate*, $Cr_2(O_2CCH_3)_4(H_2O)_2$, is precipitated as a red solid when a Cr^{2+} solution is added to a solution of sodium acetate. Its structure is typical of carboxylate-bridged complexes with water end groups, structure 24-X. The short Cr—Cr bond (2.36 Å) and diamagnetism are accounted for by the existence of a quadruple Cr—Cr bond, consisting of a σ, two π, and a δ

component. This was the first compound containing a quadruple bond to be discovered (1844).

24-17 The Chemistry of Chromium(III), d^3

Chromium(III) Complexes

There are thousands of chromium(III) complexes which, with a few exceptions, are all six-coordinate. The principal characteristic is their relative kinetic inertness in aqueous solutions. It is because of this that so many complex species can be isolated, and why much of the classical complex chemistry studied by early workers, notably S. M. Jørgensen and A. Werner, involved chromium. They persist in solution, even where they are thermodynamically unstable.

The hexaaqua ion, $[Cr(H_2O)_6]^{3+}$, occurs in numerous salts such as the violet hydrate, $[Cr(H_2O)_6]Cl_3$, and alums, $M^ICr(SO_4)_2 \cdot 12H_2O$. The chloride has three isomers, the others being the dark green *trans*-$[CrCl_2(H_2O)_4]Cl \cdot 2H_2O$, which is the usual form, and pale green $[CrCl(H_2O)_5]Cl_2 \cdot H_2O$. The ion is acidic and the hydroxo ion condenses to give a dimeric hydroxo bridged species:

$$[Cr(H_2O)_6]^{3+} \underset{H^+}{\overset{-H^+}{\rightleftharpoons}} [Cr(H_2O)_5OH]^{2+} \rightleftharpoons \left[(H_2O)_4Cr \underset{\underset{H}{O}}{\overset{\overset{H}{O}}{<>}} Cr(H_2O)_4 \right]^{4+}$$

$$(24\text{-}17.1)$$

On addition of further base, soluble polymeric species of high molecular weight and eventually dark green gels of the hydrous oxide are formed.

The most numerous complexes are those of amine ligands. These provide examples of virtually all the kinds of isomerism possible in octahedral complexes. In addition to the mononuclear species, for example, $[Cr(NH_3)_5Cl]^{2+}$, there are many polynuclear complexes in which two or sometimes more metal atoms are bridged by hydroxo groups or, less commonly, oxygen in a linear Cr—O—Cr group. A representative example is $[(NH_3)_5Cr(OH)Cr(NH_3)_5]^{5+}$.

24-18 The Chemistry of Chromium(IV), d^2, and Chromium(V), d^1

The most readily accessible of these rare oxidation states are those with bonds to C, N, and O. A representative synthesis is

$$CrCl_3(THF)_3 + 4LiCH_2SiMe_3 \overset{Ether}{\rightleftharpoons} Li^+[Cr^{III}(CH_2SiMe_3)_4]^- + 3LiCl$$

$$(24\text{-}18.1)$$

$$[Cr(CH_2SiMe_3)_4]^- \rightleftharpoons Cr(CH_2SiMe_3)_4 + e^- \qquad (24\text{-}18.2)$$

The oxidation of the green Cr^{III} anion to the purple, petroleum-soluble Cr^{IV} compound can be made by air. The alkoxides and dialkylamides are similarly made from *fac*-$CrCl_3(THF)_3$; one example is the dark blue $Cr(OCMe_3)_4$.

For Cr^V some chromites containing CrO_4^{3-} are known. Reduction of CrO_3 with concentrated HCl in the presence of alkali ions at 0 °C gives salts $M_2[Cr^VOCl_5]$.

24-19 The Chemistry of Chromium(VI), d^0

Chromate and Dichromate Ions

In basic solutions above pH 6, CrO_3 forms the tetrahedral yellow *chromate* ion, CrO_4^{2-}. Between pH 2 and 6, $HCrO_4^-$ and the orange-red *dichromate* ion, $Cr_2O_7^{2-}$, are in equilibrium. At pH's below 1 the main species is H_2CrO_4. The equilibria are

$$HCrO_4^- \rightleftharpoons CrO_4^{2-} + H^+ \qquad K = 10^{-5.9} \qquad (24\text{-}19.1)$$

$$H_2CrO_4 \rightleftharpoons HCrO_4^- + H^+ \qquad K = 4.1 \qquad (24\text{-}19.2)$$

$$Cr_2O_7^{2-} + H_2O \rightleftharpoons 2HCrO_4^- \qquad K = 10^{-2.2} \qquad (24\text{-}19.3)$$

In addition there are the base-hydrolysis equilibria:

$$Cr_2O_7^{2-} + OH^- \rightleftharpoons HCrO_4^- + CrO_4^{2-} \qquad (24\text{-}19.4)$$

$$HCrO_4^- + OH^- \rightleftharpoons CrO_4^{2-} + H_2O \qquad (24\text{-}19.5)$$

The CrO_4^{2-} ion is tetrahedral; $Cr_2O_7^{2-}$ has the structure shown in Fig. 24-2.

The pH-dependent equilibria are quite labile and on addition of cations that form insoluble chromates, for example, Ba^{2+}, Pb^{2+}, Ag^+, the chromates and not the dichromates are precipitated. Only for HNO_3 and $HClO_4$ are the equilibria as given previously. When HCl is used, there is essentially quantitative conversion into the *chlorochromate* ion, while with sulfuric acid a sulfato complex results:

$$CrO_3(OH)^- + H^+ + Cl^- \longrightarrow CrO_3Cl^- + H_2O \qquad (24\text{-}19.6)$$

$$CrO_3(OH)^- + HSO_4^- \longrightarrow CrO_3(OSO_3)^{2-} + H_2O \qquad (24\text{-}19.7)$$

Acid solutions of dichromate are strong oxidants:

$$Cr_2O_7^{2-} + 14H^+ + 6e^- = 2Cr^{3+} + 7H_2O \qquad E° = 1.33 \text{ V} \qquad (24\text{-}19.8)$$

Figure 24-2 The structure of the dichromate ion as found in $Na_2Cr_2O_7$.

In alkaline solution, the chromate ion is much less oxidizing

$$CrO_4^{2-} + 4H_2O + 3e^- = Cr(OH)_3(s) + 5OH^- \quad E° = 0.13 \text{ V} \quad (24\text{-}19.9)$$

Chromium(VI) does not give rise to the extensive and complex series of poly-acids and polyanions characteristic of the somewhat less acidic oxides of V^V, Mo^{VI}, and W^{VI}. The reason for this is perhaps the greater extent of multiple bonding, $Cr=O$, for the smaller chromium ion.

   Chromyl chloride, CrO_2Cl_2, a deep-red liquid is formed by the action of HCl on chromium(VI) oxide:

$$CrO_3 + 2HCl \longrightarrow CrO_2Cl_2 + H_2O \qquad (24\text{-}19.10)$$

or on warming dichromate with an alkali metal chloride in concentrated sulfuric acid:

$$K_2Cr_2O_7 + 4KCl + 3H_2SO_4 \longrightarrow 2CrO_2Cl_2 + 3K_2SO_4 + 3H_2O$$
$$(24\text{-}19.11)$$

It is photosensitive but otherwise rather stable, vigorously oxidizes organic matter, and is hydrolyzed by water to CrO_4^{2-} and HCl.

24-20 Peroxo Complexes of Chromium(IV), (V), and (VI)

Like other transition metals, notably Ti, V, Nb, Ta, Mo, and W, chromium forms peroxo compounds in the higher oxidation states. They are all more or less unstable both in and out of solution, decomposing slowly with the evolution of O_2. Some are explosive or flammable in air.

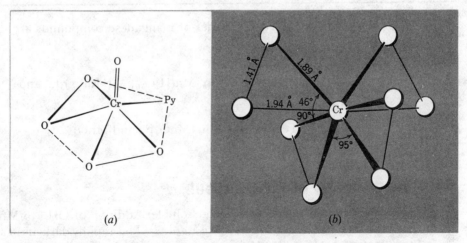

Figure 24-3 (a) The structure of $CrO(O_2)_2py$. The coordination polyhedron is approximately a pentagonal pyramid with the oxide ligand at the apex. (b) The dodecahedral structure of the CrO_8^{3-} ion, a tetraperoxide complex.

When acid dichromate solutions are treated with H_2O_2, a deep blue color rapidly appears:

$$HCrO_4^- + 2H_2O_2 + H^+ \longrightarrow CrO(O_2)_2 + 3H_2O \qquad (24\text{-}20.1)$$

The blue species decomposes fairly readily, giving Cr^{3+}, but it may be extracted into ether where it is more stable. On addition of pyridine to the ether solution, the compound $(py)CrO_5$ is obtained. The pyridine complex has the bisperoxo structure shown in Fig. 24-3(*a*).

Treatment of alkaline chromate solutions with 30% H_2O_2 gives the red-brown peroxochromates, $M_3^I CrO_8$ [Fig. 24-3(*b*)]. They are paramagnetic with one unpaired electron.

MANGANESE

24-21 The Element

The highest oxidation state of manganese corresponds to the total number of $3d$ and $4s$ electrons, but it occurs only in the oxo compounds MnO_4^-, Mn_2O_7, and MnO_3F. These compounds show some similarity to corresponding compounds of the halogens.

Manganese is relatively abundant, and occurs in substantial deposits, mainly oxides, hydrous oxides, or the carbonate. From them, or the Mn_3O_4 obtained by roasting them, the metal can be obtained by reduction with Al.

Manganese is quite electropositive, and readily dissolves in dilute, non-oxidizing acids.

MANGANESE COMPOUNDS

The most common stereochemistries of manganese compounds are the following:

$$\left.\begin{array}{l} Mn^{II} \\ Mn^{III} \\ Mn^{IV} \end{array}\right\} \text{ Octahedral as in } [Mn(H_2O)_6]^{2+}, [Mn(ox)_3]^{3-} \text{ and } [MnCl_6]^{2-}$$

$$\left.\begin{array}{l} Mn^{VI} \\ Mn^{VII} \end{array}\right\} \text{ Tetrahedral as in } [MnO_4]^{2-} \text{ and } MnO_4^-$$

24-22 The Chemistry of Manganese(II), d^5

Manganese(II) salts are mostly water soluble. Addition of OH^- to Mn^{2+} solutions produces the gelatinous white *hydroxide*. This rapidly darkens in air due to oxidation, as shown by the base potentials

$$MnO_2 \xrightarrow{-0.1\ V} Mn_2O_3 \xrightarrow{-0.2\ V} Mn(OH)_2 \qquad (24\text{-}22.1)$$

Addition of SH^- gives hydrous MnS, which also oxidizes becoming brown in air; on boiling in the absence of air the salmon pink material changes into green crystalline MnS. The sulfate, $MnSO_4$, is very stable and may be used for Mn analysis as it can be obtained on fuming down sulfuric acid solutions to dryness. The phosphate and carbonate are sparingly soluble. The equilibrium constants for the formation of manganese(II) complexes are relatively low as the Mn^{2+} ion has no ligand field stabilization energy (Section 23-8). However, chelating ligands such as en, ox, or $EDTA^{4-}$ form complexes isolable from aqueous solution.

In aqueous solution the formation constants for halogeno complexes are very low, for example,

$$[Mn_{(aq)}]^{2+} + Cl^- \rightleftharpoons MnCl^+_{(aq)} \qquad K \approx 4 \qquad (24\text{-}22.2)$$

but in ethanol or acetic acid, salts of complex anions of varying types may be isolated, such as

MnX_3^-	Octahedral with perovskite structure
$[MnX_4]^{2-}$	Tetrahedral (green yellow) or polymeric octahedral with halide bridges (pink)
$[MnCl_6]^{4-}$	Only Na and K salts known; octahedral

Mn^{2+} ions may occupy tetrahedral holes in certain glasses and substitute for Zn^{II} in ZnO. Tetrahedral Mn^{II} has a green-yellow color, far more intense than the pink of the octahedrally coordinated ion, and it very often exhibits intense yellow-green fluorescence. Most commercial phosphors are manganese-activated zinc compounds, wherein Mn^{II} ions are substituted for some of the Zn^{II} ions in tetrahedral surroundings as, for example, in Zn_2SiO_4.

Only the very strong ligand fields give rise to spin pairing as in the ions $[Mn(CN)_6]^{4-}$ and $[Mn(CNR)_6]^{2+}$, which have only one unpaired electron.

24-23 The Chemistry of Manganese(III), d^4

Oxides

When any manganese oxide or hydroxide is heated at 1000 °C, black crystals of Mn_3O_4 (*haussmannite*) are formed. This is a spinel, $Mn^{II}Mn_2^{III}O_4$. When $Mn(OH)_2$ is allowed to oxidize in air, a hydrous oxide is formed that gives $MnO(OH)$ on drying.

Manganese(III) Aqua Ion

The manganese(III) ion can be obtained by electrolytic or peroxodisulfate oxidation of Mn^{2+} solutions or by reduction of MnO_4^-. It cannot be obtained in high concentrations as it is reduced by water (Table 24-3). It also has a strong tendency to hydrolyze and to disproportionate in weakly acid solution:

$$2Mn^{3+} + 2H_2O = Mn^{2+} + MnO_2(s) + 4H^+ \qquad K \approx 10^9 \qquad (24\text{-}23.1)$$

The dark brown crystalline *acetylacetonate*, $Mn(acac)_3$ is readily obtained by oxidation of basic solutions of Mn^{2+} by O_2 or Cl_2 in the presence of acetylacetone.

The basic-oxo centered acetate (structure 24-I), which is obtained by the action of $KMnO_4$ on Mn^{II} acetate in acetic acid, will oxidize olefins to lactones. It is used industrially for oxidation of toluene to phenol.

Manganese(III) and manganese(IV) complexes are probably important in photosynthesis, where oxygen evolution depends on manganese.

24-24 The Chemistry of Manganese(IV), d^3 and Manganese(V), d^2

The most common compound of Mn^{IV} is *manganese dioxide*, a grey to black solid found in nature as *pyrolusite*. When made by the action of oxygen on manganese at a high temperature it has the rutile structure found for many other oxides, MO_2, for example, those of Ru, Mo, W, Re, Os, Ir, and Rh. However, as normally made, for example, by heating $Mn(NO_3)_2 \cdot 6H_2O$ in air, it is nonstoichiometric. A hydrated form is obtained by reduction of aqueous $KMnO_4$ in basic solution.

Manganese dioxide is inert to most acids except when heated, but it does not dissolve to give Mn^{IV} in solution; instead, it functions as an oxidizing agent, the exact manner of this depending on the acid. With HCl, chlorine is evolved:

$$MnO_2(s) + 4H^+ + 4Cl^- = Mn^{2+} + 2Cl^- + Cl_2 + 2H_2O \quad (24\text{-}24.1)$$

With sulfuric acid at 110 °C, oxygen is evolved and an Mn^{III} acid sulfate is formed. Hydrated manganese dioxide is used in organic chemistry for the oxidation of alcohols and other compounds.

Mn^V is little known except in bright blue "hypomanganates" that are formed by reduction of permanganate with an excess of sulfite.

24-25 The Chemistry of Manganese(VI), d^1, and Manganese(VII), d^0

Manganese(VI) is known only as the deep green *manganate* ion, $[MnO_4]^{2-}$. This is formed on oxidizing MnO_2 in fused KOH with KNO_3 or air.

The manganate ion is stable only in very basic solutions. In acid, neutral, or slightly basic solutions it readily disproportionates according to the equation

$$3MnO_4^{2-} + 4H^+ = 2MnO_4^- + MnO_2(s) + 2H_2O \quad K \approx 10^{58} \quad (24\text{-}25.1)$$

Manganese(VII) is best known in the form of salts of the *permanganate ion*. $KMnO_4$ is manufactured by electrolytic oxidation of a basic solution of K_2MnO_4. Aqueous solutions of MnO_4^- may be prepared by oxidation of solutions of the Mn^{II} ion with very powerful oxidizing agents such as PbO_2 or $NaBiO_3$. The ion has an intense purple color, and crystalline salts appear almost black.

Solutions of permanganate are intrinsically unstable, decomposing slowly but observably in acid solution:

$$4MnO_4^- + 4H^+ \longrightarrow 3O_2(g) + 2H_2O + 4MnO_2(s) \quad (24\text{-}25.2)$$

In neutral or slightly alkaline solutions in the dark, decomposition is immeasurably slow. It is catalyzed by light so that standard permanganate solutions should be stored in dark bottles.

In *basic* solution, permanganate is a powerful oxidant:

$$MnO_4^- + 2H_2O + 3e^- = MnO_2(s) + 4OH^- \quad E° = +1.23 \text{ V} \quad (24\text{-}25.3)$$

In very strong base and with an excess of MnO_4^-, however, manganate ion is produced:

$$MnO_4^- + e^- = MnO_4^{2-} \quad E° = +0.56 \text{ V} \quad (24\text{-}25.4)$$

In *acid* solution permanganate is reduced to Mn^{2+} by an excess of reducing agent:

$$MnO_4^- + 8H^+ + 5e^- = Mn^{2+} + 4H_2O \quad E° = +1.51 \text{ V} \quad (24\text{-}25.5)$$

but because MnO_4^- oxidizes Mn^{2+}

$$2MnO_4^- + 3Mn^{2+} + 2H_2O = 5MnO_2(s) + 4H^+ \quad E° = +0.46 \text{ V} \quad (24\text{-}25.6)$$

the product in the presence of an excess of permanganate is MnO_2. The addition of amounts of $KMnO_4$ to concentrated H_2SO_4 gives stoichiometrically

$$2KMnO_4 + 3H_2SO_4 \rightleftharpoons 2K^+ + Mn_2O_7 + H_3O^+ + 3HSO_4^- \quad (24\text{-}25.7)$$

the dangerous explosive oil, Mn_2O_7. This can be extracted into CCl_4 or chlorofluorocarbons in which it is reasonably stable and safe.

IRON

24-26 The Element Iron

Beginning with this element, there is no oxidation state equal to the total number of valence-shell electrons, which in this case is eight. The highest oxidation state is VI, and it is rare. Even the trivalent state, which rose to a peak of importance at chromium, now loses ground to the divalent state.

Iron is the second most abundant metal, after Al, and the fourth most abundant element in the earth's crust. The core of the earth is believed to consist mainly of Fe and Ni. The major ores are Fe_2O_3 (*hematite*), Fe_3O_4 (*magnetite*), FeO(OH) (*limonite*), and $FeCO_3$ (*siderite*).

Pure iron is quite reactive. In moist air it is rather rapidly oxidized to give a hydrous iron(III) oxide (rust) that affords no protection, since it flakes off, exposing fresh metal surfaces. Finely divided iron is pyrophoric.

The metal dissolves readily in dilute mineral acids. With nonoxidizing acids and in the absence of air, Fe^{II} is obtained. With air present or when warm dilute HNO_3 is used, some of the iron goes to Fe^{III}. Very strongly oxidizing media such as concentrated HNO_3 or acids containing dichromate passivate iron. Air-free water and dilute air-free solutions of OH^- have little effect, but iron is attacked by hot concentrated NaOH (see the following section).

IRON COMPOUNDS

The main stereochemistries of iron compounds are as follows:

Fe^{II}　Octahedral as in $Fe(OH)_2$, $[Fe(H_2O)_6]^{2+}$, and $[Fe(CN)_6]^{4-}$
Fe^{III}　Octahedral as in $[Fe(H_2O)_6]^{3+}$ and $Fe(acac)_3$

24-27 Binary Compounds

Oxides and Hydroxides

The addition of OH^- to Fe^{2+} solutions gives the pale green *hydroxide*, which is very readily oxidized by air to give red-brown hydrous iron(III) oxide.

$Fe(OH)_2$, a true hydroxide with the $Mg(OH)_2$ structure, is somewhat amphoteric. Like Fe, it dissolves in hot concentrated NaOH, from which solutions blue crystals of $Na_4[Fe^{II}(OH)_6]$ can be obtained.

The *oxide*, FeO, may be obtained as a black pyrophoric powder by ignition of Fe^{II} oxalate: It is usually nonstoichiometric $Fe_{0.95}O$, which means that some Fe^{III} is present. The addition of OH^- to iron(III) solutions gives a red-brown gelatinous mass commonly called iron(III) hydroxide, but it is best described as a *hydrous oxide*, $Fe_2O_3 \cdot nH_2O$. This has several forms; one, FeO(OH), occurs in the mineral *lepidocrocite* and can be made by high temperature hydrolysis of iron(III) chloride. On heating at 200 °C the hydrous oxides form red-brown α-Fe_2O_3, which occurs as the mineral *hematite*. This has the corundum structure with an hcp array of O and Fe^{3+} in the octahedral interstices.

The black crystalline oxide, Fe_3O_4, a mixed Fe^{II}–Fe^{III} oxide, occurs in nature as *magnetite*. It can be made by ignition of Fe_2O_3 above 1400 °C. It has the inverse spinel structure (Section 4-8).

Chlorides are used as source material for the synthesis of other iron compounds. Anhydrous *iron(II) chloride* can be made by passing HCl gas over heated iron powder, by reducing $FeCl_3$ with Fe(s) in THF or by refluxing $FeCl_3$ in chlorobenzene. It is a very pale green, almost white, solid.

Iron(III) chloride is obtained by the action of chlorine on heated iron as almost black, red-brown crystals. Although in the gas phase there are dimers, Fe_2Cl_6, in the crystal the structure is nonmolecular and there are Fe^{III} ions occupying two thirds of the octahedral holes in alternate layers of Cl^- ions.

Iron(III) chloride quite readily hydrolyzes in moist air. It is soluble in ethers and other polar solvents.

Ferrites such as $M^{II}Fe_2O_4$ are important mixed oxide materials used in magnetic tapes for recording purposes.

24-28 Chemistry of Iron(II), d^6

The iron(II) ion, $[Fe(H_2O)_6]^{2+}$, gives many crystalline salts. Mohr's salt, $(NH_4)_2 \cdot [Fe(H_2O)_6] \cdot 2SO_4$, is reasonably stable toward air and loss of water, and is commonly used to prepare standard solutions of Fe^{2+} for volumetric analysis and as a calibration substance in magnetic measurements. By contrast, $FeSO_4 \cdot 7H_2O$ slowly effloresces and turns brown-yellow when kept in air.

Addition of HCO_3^- or SH^- to aqueous solutions of Fe^{2+} precipitates $FeCO_3$ and FeS, respectively. The Fe^{2+} ion is oxidized in acid solution by air to Fe^{3+}. With ligands other than water present, substantial changes in the potentials may occur, and the Fe^{II}–Fe^{III} system provides an excellent example of the effect of ligands on the relative stabilities of oxidation states:

$$[Fe(CN)_6]^{3-} + e^- = [Fe(CN)_6]^{4-} \qquad E° = 0.36 \text{ V} \qquad (24\text{-}28.1)$$

$$[Fe(H_2O)_6]^{3+} + e^- = [Fe(H_2O)_6]^{2+} \qquad E° = 0.77 \text{ V} \qquad (24\text{-}28.2)$$

$$[Fe(phen)_3]^{3+} + e^- = [Fe(phen)_3]^{2+} \qquad E° = 1.12 \text{ V} \qquad (24\text{-}28.3)$$

Complexes

Octahedral complexes are generally paramagnetic, and quite strong ligand fields are required to cause spin pairing. Diamagnetic complex ions are $[Fe(CN)_6]^{4-}$ and $[Fe(dipy)_3]^{2+}$. Formation of the red 2,2'-bipyridine and 1,10-phenanthroline complexes is used as a test for Fe^{2+}.

Some tetrahedral complexes like $[FeCl_4]^{2-}$ are known. Among the most important complexes are those involved in biological systems (Chapter 31) or models for them. An important iron(II) compound is ferrocene (Section 29-14).

24-29 The Chemistry of Iron(III), d^5

Iron(III) occurs in crystalline salts with most anions other than those such as iodide that are incompatible because of their reducing properties:

$$Fe^{3+} + I^- = Fe^{2+} + \tfrac{1}{2}I_2 \qquad (24\text{-}29.1)$$

Salts containing the ion $[Fe(H_2O)_6]^{3+}$, such as $Fe(ClO_4)_3 \cdot 10H_2O$, are pale pink to nearly white and the aquo ion is pale purple. Unless Fe^{3+} solutions are quite strongly acid, hydrolysis occurs and the solutions are commonly yellow because of the formation of hydroxo species that have charge-transfer bands in the ultraviolet region tailing into the visible region.

The initial hydrolysis equilibria are

$$[Fe(H_2O)_6]^{3+} = [Fe(H_2O)_5(OH)]^{2+} + H^+ \qquad (24\text{-}29.2)$$
$$K = 10^{-3.05}$$

$$[Fe(H_2O)_5(OH)]^{2+} = [Fe(H_2O)_4(OH)_2]^+ + H^+ \qquad (24\text{-}29.3)$$
$$K = 10^{-3.26}$$

$$2[Fe(H_2O)_6]^{3+} = [Fe(H_2O)_4(OH)_2Fe(H_2O)_4]^{4+} + 2H^+ \qquad (24\text{-}29.4)$$
$$K = 10^{-2.91}$$

The binuclear species in Eq. (24-29.4) probably has the structure 24-III.

$$\left[\begin{array}{c} \text{H}_2\text{O} \quad \text{H} \quad \text{OH}_2 \\ \text{H}_2\text{O} \diagdown \ \mid \diagup \text{O} \diagdown \ \mid \diagup \text{OH}_2 \\ \text{Fe} \qquad \text{Fe} \\ \text{H}_2\text{O} \diagup \ \mid \diagdown \text{O} \diagup \ \mid \diagdown \text{OH}_2 \\ \text{H}_2\text{O} \quad \text{H} \quad \text{OH}_2 \end{array}\right]^{4+}$$

24-III

From the constants it is clear that, even at pH's 2–3, hydrolysis is extensive. In order to have solutions containing, ~99% $[\text{Fe}(\text{H}_2\text{O})_6]^{3+}$ the pH must be around zero. As the pH is raised to about 2–3, more highly condensed species than the dinuclear one are formed, attainment of equilibrium becomes sluggish, and soon colloidal gels are formed. Ultimately, hydrous Fe_2O_3 is precipitated.

Iron(III) ion has a strong affinity for F^-

$$\text{Fe}^{3+} + \text{F}^- = \text{FeF}^{2+} \qquad K_1 \approx 10^5 \qquad (24\text{-}29.5)$$

$$\text{FeF}^{2+} + \text{F}^- = \text{FeF}_2^+ \qquad K_2 \approx 10^5 \qquad (24\text{-}29.6)$$

$$\text{FeF}_2^+ + \text{F}^- = \text{FeF}_3 \qquad K_3 \approx 10^3 \qquad (24\text{-}29.7)$$

The corresponding constants for chloro complexes are only ~10, ~3, and ~0.1, respectively. In very concentrated HCl the tetrahedral FeCl_4^- ion is formed, and its salts with large cations may be isolated. Complexes with SCN^- are an intense red, and this serves as a sensitive qualitative and quantitative test for ferric ion; $\text{Fe}(\text{SCN})_3$ and/or $\text{Fe}(\text{SCN})_4^-$ may be extracted into ether. Fluoride ion, however, will discharge this color. In the solid state, $[\text{FeF}_6]^{3-}$ ions are known but in solutions only species with fewer F atoms occur.

The hexacyanoferrate ion, $[\text{Fe}(\text{CN})_6]^{3-}$, in contrast to $[\text{Fe}(\text{CN})_6]^{4-}$, is quite poisonous because the CN^- ions rapidly dissociate, whereas $[\text{Fe}(\text{CN})_6]^{4-}$ is not labile.

The affinity of Fe^{III} for NH_3 and amines is low except for chelates such as EDTA^{4-}; 2,2'-bipyridine and 1,10-phenanthroline produce ligand fields strong enough to cause spin pairing (cf. Fe^{II}) and form quite stable ions that can be isolated with large anions.

A number of hydroxo- and oxygen-bridged species, one of which has been mentioned previously, are of interest in that they may show unusual magnetic properties due to coupling between the iron atoms via the bridges. One example is the complex bis(salicylaldehyde)ethylenediiminato, $[\text{Fe}(\text{salen})]_2\text{O}$, which

has a nonlinear $\text{Fe} \overset{\displaystyle \text{O}}{\diagup \diagdown} \text{Fe}$ group, while $\text{Fe}(\text{salen})\text{Cl}$ can form both mononuclear and binuclear complexes (structure 24-IV). The latter has marked antiferromagnetic coupling between the Fe atoms.

24-IV

24-30 The Chemistry of Iron(IV) and (VI)

There are only a few complexes such as $[Fe(S_2CNR_2)_3]^+$ and $[Fe(diars)_2Cl_2]^{2+}$ for Fe^{IV}, and the unusual hydrocarbon soluble alkyl, $Fe(1\text{-norbornyl})_4$ (Section 29-11). No stable Fe^V compounds are known.

The best known compound of iron(VI) is the oxo anion, $[FeO_4]^{2-}$, obtained by chlorine oxidation of suspensions of $Fe_2O_3 \cdot nH_2O$ in concentrated NaOH or by fusing Fe powder with KNO_3. The red-purple ion is paramagnetic with two unpaired electrons. The Na and K salts are quite soluble but the Ba salt can be precipitated. The ion is relatively stable in basic solution but decomposes in neutral or acid solution according to the equation

$$2[FeO_4]^{2-} + 10H^+ = 2Fe^{3+} + \tfrac{3}{2}O_2 + 5H_2O \qquad (24\text{-}30.1)$$

It is an even stronger oxidizing agent than MnO_4^- and can oxidize NH_3 to N_2, Cr^{II} to CrO_4^{2-}, and also primary amines and alcohols to aldehydes.

COBALT

24-31 The Element Cobalt

The trends toward decreased stability of the very high oxidation states and the increased stability of the II state relative to the III state, which occur through the series Ti, V, Cr, Mn, and Fe, persist with Co. The highest oxidation state is now IV, and only a few such compounds are known. Cobalt(III) is relatively unstable in simple compounds, but the low-spin complexes are exceedingly numerous and stable, especially where the donor atoms (usually N) make strong contributions to the ligand field. There are also numerous complexes of Co^I. This oxidation state is better known for cobalt than for any other element of the first transition series except copper. All Co^I complexes have π-acid ligands (Chapter 28).

Cobalt always occurs in association with Ni and usually also with As. The chief sources of cobalt are "speisses," which are residues in the smelting of arsenical ores of Ni, Cu, and Pb.

Cobalt is relatively unreactive, although it dissolves slowly in dilute mineral acids.

COBALT COMPOUNDS

The main stereochemistries found in cobalt compounds are the following:

Co^{II} { Tetrahedral as in $[CoCl_4]^{2-}$ and $CoCl_2(PEt_3)_2$
Octahedral as in $[Co(H_2O)_6]^{2+}$

Co^{III} Octahedral as in $[Co(NH_3)_6]^{3+}$

24-32 Chemistry of Cobalt(II), d^7

The dissolution of Co, or the hydroxide or carbonate, in dilute acids gives the pink aqua ion, $[Co(H_2O)_6]^{2+}$, which forms many hydrated salts.

Addition of OH^- to Co^{2+} gives the *hydroxide*, which may be blue or pink depending on the conditions; it is weakly amphoteric dissolving in very concentrated OH^- to give a blue solution containing the $[Co(OH)_4]^{2-}$ ion.

Complexes

The most common Co^{II} complexes may be either octahedral or tetrahedral. There is only a small difference in stability and both types, with the same ligand, may be in equilibrium. Thus for water there is a very small but finite concentration of the tetrahedral ion

$$[Co(H_2O)_6]^{2+} \rightleftharpoons [Co(H_2O)_4]^{2+} + 2H_2O \qquad (24\text{-}32.1)$$

Addition of excess Cl^- to pink solutions of the aqua ion readily gives the blue tetrahedral species

$$[Co(H_2O)_6]^{2+} + 4Cl^- = [CoCl_4]^{2-} + 6H_2O \qquad (24\text{-}32.2)$$

Tetrahedral complexes, $[CoX_4]^{2-}$, are formed by halide, pseudohalide, and OH^- ions. Cobalt(II) forms tetrahedral complexes more readily than any other transition metal ion. Co^{2+} is the only d^7 ion of common occurrence. For a d^7 ion, ligand field stabilization energies disfavor the tetrahedral configuration relative to the octahedral one to a smaller extent (see Table 23-4) than for any other $d^n(1 \leq n \leq 9)$ configuration. This argument is valid only in comparing the behavior of one metal ion with another and not for assessing the absolute stabilities of the configurations for any particular ion.

24-33 The Chemistry of Cobalt(III), d^6

In the absence of complexing agents, the oxidation of $[Co(H_2O)_6]^{2+}$ is very unfavorable (Table 24-3) and Co^{3+} is reduced by water. However, electrolytic or O_3 oxidation of cold acidic solutions of $Co(ClO_4)_2$ gives the aqua ion, $[Co(H_2O)_6]^{3+}$, in equilibrium with $[Co(OH)(H_2O)_5]^{2+}$. At 0 °C, the half-life of these diamagnetic ions is about a month. In the presence of complexing agents, such as NH_3, the stability of Co^{III} is greatly improved:

$$[Co(NH_3)_6]^{3+} + e^- = [Co(NH_3)_6]^{2+} \qquad E^0 = 0.1 \text{ V} \qquad (24\text{-}33.1)$$

In the presence of OH^- ion, cobalt(II) hydroxide is readily oxidized by air to a black hydrous oxide:

$$CoO(OH)(s) + H_2O + e^- = Co(OH)_2(s) + OH^- \qquad E^0 = 0.17 \text{ V}$$
$$(24\text{-}33.2)$$

The Co^{3+} ion shows a particular affinity for N donors such as NH_3, en, EDTA, NCS^-, and so on, and complexes are exceedingly numerous. They generally undergo ligand-exchange reactions relatively slowly, like Cr^{3+} and Rh^{3+}. Hence, from the days of Werner and Jørgensen, they have been extensively studied. A large part of our knowledge of the isomerism, modes of reaction, and general properties of octahedral complexes as a class is based on studies of Co^{III} complexes. All known Co^{III} complexes are octahedral.

Cobalt(III) complexes are synthesized by oxidation of Co^{2+} in solution in the presence of the ligands. Oxygen or hydrogen peroxide and a catalyst, such as activated charcoal, are used. For example,

$$4Co^{2+} + 4NH_4^+ + 20NH_3 + O_2 \longrightarrow 4[Co(NH_3)_6]^{3+} + 2H_2O$$
$$(24\text{-}33.3)$$

$$4Co^{2+} + 8(en) + 4(en)\cdot H^+ + O_2 = 4[Co(en)_3]^{3+} + 2H_2O \qquad (24\text{-}33.4)$$

From a reaction similar to Eq. 24-33.4 in the presence of HCl the green salt, trans-$[Co(en)_2Cl_2][H_5O_2]Cl_2$, is obtained. This may be isomerized to the purple racemic cis-isomer on evaporation of a neutral aqueous solution at 90 to 100 °C. Both the cis and the trans isomer are aquated when heated in water:

$$[Co(en)_2Cl_2]^+ + H_2O \longrightarrow [Co(en)_2Cl(H_2O)]^{2+} + Cl^- \qquad (24\text{-}33.5)$$

$$[Co(en)_2Cl(H_2O)]^{2+} + H_2O \longrightarrow [Co(en)_2(H_2O)_2]^{3+} + Cl^- \qquad (24\text{-}33.6)$$

and on treatment with solutions of other anions are converted into other $[Co(en)_2X_2]^+$ species, for example,

$$[Co(en)_2Cl_2]^+ + 2NCS^- \longrightarrow [Co(en)_2(NCS)_2]^+ + 2Cl^- \qquad (24\text{-}33.7)$$

The initial reaction of Co^{II} with oxygen may involve oxidative–addition (Section 30-2) of O_2 to Co^{II} to give a transient Co^{IV} species that then reacts with another Co^{II} to produce a binuclear *peroxo-bridged* species:

$$\left[L_nCo\right]^{2+} + O_2 \longrightarrow \left[L_nCo^{IV}\underset{O}{\overset{O}{\diagdown\;\diagup}}\right]^{2+} \tag{24-33.8}$$

$$\left[L_nCo^{IV}\underset{O}{\overset{O}{\diagdown\;\diagup}}\right]^{2+} + \left[L_nCo\right]^{2+} \longrightarrow \left[L_nCo\diagdown^{O}\diagdown_{O}\diagup CoL_n\right]^{4+} \tag{24-33.9}$$

Complexes such as $[(NH_3)_5CoOOCo(NH_3)_5]^{4+}$ or $[(NC)_5CoOOCo(CN)_5]^{6-}$ have been isolated, although these ions decompose fairly readily in water or acids. The open-chain species $[(NH_3)_5CoOOCo(NH_3)_5]^{4+}$ can be cyclized in the presence of base to

$$\left[(NH_3)_4Co\underset{\underset{H_2}{N}}{\overset{O-O}{\diagup\;\diagdown}}Co(NH_3)_4\right]^{3+}$$

Such peroxo species, open chain or cyclic, contain low-spin Co^{III} and bridging peroxide (O_2^{2-}) ions.

The O_2-bridged binuclear complexes can often be oxidized in a one-electron step. The resulting ions were first prepared by Werner, who formulated them as peroxo-bridged complexes of Co^{III} and Co^{IV}. However, esr data have shown that the single unpaired electron is distributed equally over *both* cobalt ions, and is best regarded as belonging formally to a superoxide, O_2^-, ion but delocalized over the planar Co^{III}—O—O—Co^{III} group. The structures (Fig. 24-4) show that the O—O distance is close to that for the O_2^- ion (1.28 Å) and much shorter than the distance (1.47 Å) in the peroxo complexes.

Although no cobalt-containing complex is known to be involved in oxygen metabolism, there are several that provide models for metal-to-oxygen binding in biological systems. Of greatest interest are those that undergo *reversible* oxygenation and deoxygenation in solution. The Schiff base complexes such as Co(acacen) (structure 24-V) in DMF or pyridine take up O_2 reversibly below 0 °C, for example.

$$\text{(structure 24-V)} \quad + \text{DMF} + O_2 \longrightarrow Co(acacen)(DMF)O_2$$
$$K = 2.1 \text{ at } -10\text{ °C}$$

24-V

$$\tag{24-33.10}$$

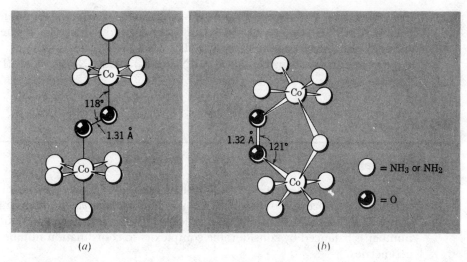

Figure 24-4 The structures of (a) $[(NH_3)_5CoO_2Co(NH_3)_5]^{5+}$, and

$$(b) \quad \left[(NH_3)_4Co \underset{\underset{H_2}{N}}{\overset{O_2}{\diagdown}} Co(NH_3)_4 \right]^{4+}$$

There is octahedral coordination about each cobalt ion and the angles and distances shown are consistent with the assumption that there are bridging superoxo groups. The five-membered ring in (b) is essentially planar.

The initial complex has one unpaired electron, and so also do the oxygen adducts, but esr data indicate that in the latter the electron is heavily localized on the oxygen atoms. There is also an IR absorption band due to an O—O stretching vibration. The adducts can be formulated as octahedral, low-spin Co^{III} complexes containing a coordinated superoxide (O_2^-) ion. The Co—O—O chain is bent. A second type of complex involves the reversible formation of oxygen bridges, Co—O—O—Co, which are similar to those discussed previously.

Finally, we note in connection with oxidation that in acid solutions, cobalt(III) carboxylates catalyze not only the oxidation of alkyl side chains in aromatic hydrocarbons, but even alkanes. A cobalt catalyzed process is used commercially for oxidation of toluene to phenol. The actual nature of "cobaltic acetate," a green material made by ozone oxidation of Co^{2+} acetate in acetic acid is uncertain; it can, however, be converted by pyridine to an oxo centered species similar to those known for other M^{III} carboxylates (structure 24-I).

24-34 Complexes of Cobalt(I), d^8

With the exception of reduced vitamin B_{12} and models for this system (Section 31-8), which appear to be Co^I species, all Co^I compounds involve ligands of the π-acid type (Chapter 28). The coordination is trigonal bipyramidal or tetrahedral. The compounds are usually made by reducing $CoCl_2$ in the presence of the ligand by agents such as N_2H_4, Zn, $S_2O_4^{2-}$, or Al alkyls.

Representative examples are $CoH(N_2)(PPh_3)_3$, $[Co(CNR)_5]^+$, $CoCl(PR_3)_3$.

NICKEL

24-35 The Element

The trend toward decreased stability of higher oxidation states continues, so that only Ni^{II} normally occurs with a few compounds *formally* containing Ni^{III} and Ni^{IV}. The relative simplicity of nickel chemistry in terms of oxidation number is balanced by considerable complexity in coordination numbers and geometries.

Nickel occurs in combination with arsenic, antimony, and sulfur as in *millerite* (NiS) and in *garnierite*, a magnesium–nickel silicate of variable composition. Nickel is also found alloyed with iron in meteors; the interior of the earth is believed to contain considerable quantities. In general, the ore is roasted in air to give NiO, which is reduced to Ni with C. Nickel is usually purified by electrodeposition but some high purity nickel is still made by the carbonyl process. Carbon monoxide reacts with impure nickel at 50 °C and ordinary pressure or with nickel–copper matte under more strenuous conditions, giving volatile $Ni(CO)_4$, from which metal of 99.90 to 99.99% purity is obtained on thermal decomposition at 200 °C.

Nickel is quite resistant to attack by air or water at ordinary temperatures when compact and is, therefore, often electroplated as a protective coating. It dissolves readily in dilute mineral acids. The metal or high Ni alloys are used to handle F_2 and other corrosive fluorides. The finely divided metal is reactive to air and may be pyrophoric. Nickel absorbs considerable amounts of hydrogen when finely divided and special forms of Ni, for example, Raney nickel, are used for catalytic reductions.

NICKEL COMPOUNDS

24-36 The Chemistry of Nickel(II), d^8

The binary compounds such as NiO, $NiCl_2$, and so on, need no special comment.

Nickel(II) forms a large number of *complexes* with coordination numbers six, five, and four having all the main structural types, namely, octahedral, trigonal bipyramidal, square pyramidal, tetrahedral, and square. It is characteristic that complicated equilibria, which are generally temperature dependent and sometimes concentration dependent, often exist between these structural types.

Six-Coordinate Complexes

The commonest six-coordinate complex is the green aqua ion, $[Ni(H_2O)_6]^{2+}$, that is formed on dissolution of Ni, $NiCO_3$, and so on, in acids and gives salts like $NiSO_4 \cdot 7H_2O$.

The water molecules in the aqua ion can be readily displaced especially by amines to give complexes such as *trans*-$[Ni(H_2O)_2(NH_3)_4]^{2+}$, $[Ni(NH_3)_6]^{2+}$, or $[Ni(en)_3]^{2+}$. These amine complexes are usually blue or purple because of shifts in absorption bands when H_2O is replaced by a stronger field ligand (Section 23-6).

Four-Coordinate Complexes

Most of the four-coordinate complexes are square. This is a consequence of the d^8 configuration, since the planar ligand set causes one of the d orbitals $(d_{x^2-y^2})$ to be uniquely high in energy, and the eight electrons can occupy the other four d orbitals but leave this strongly antibonding one vacant. In tetrahedral coordination, on the other hand, occupation of antibonding orbitals is unavoidable. With the congeneric d^8 systems Pd^{II} and Pt^{II} this factor becomes so important that no tetrahedral complex is formed.

Planar complexes of Ni^{II} are thus invariably diamagnetic. They are frequently red, yellow, or brown owing to the presence of an absorption band of medium intensity ($\epsilon \approx 60$) in the range 450–600 nm.

Probably the best known example is the red *bis(dimethylglyoximato)nickel(II)*, $Ni(dmgH)_2$, which is used for the gravimetric determination of nickel; it is precipitated on addition of ethanolic $dmgH_2$ to ammoniacal nickel(II) solutions. It has the structure (24-VI) where the H-bond is symmetrical, but these units are *stacked* one on top of the other in the crystal. Here, and in similar square compounds of Pd^{II} and Pt^{II} (Section 25-28), there is evidence of metal to metal interaction, even though the distance in the stack is too long for true bonding.

24-VI   24-VII

Similar square complexes are given by certain β-ketoenolates, for example, (structure 24-VII) as well as by unidentate π-acid ligands, for example, $NiBr_2(PEt_3)_2$, and by CN^- and SCN^-. The cyano complex, $[Ni(CN)_4]^{2-}$, is readily formed on addition of CN^- to $Ni^{2+}(aq)$. The green $Ni(CN)_2$ first precipitated redissolves to give the yellow ion, which can be isolated as, for example, $Na_2[Ni(CN)_4] \cdot 3H_2O$. On addition of an excess of CN^- the red ion, $[Ni(CN)_5]^{3-}$, is formed, which can be precipitated only by use of large cations.

Tetrahedral Complexes

Tetrahedral complexes are less common than planar complexes, and are all paramagnetic. They are of the types $[NiX_4]^{2-}$, NiX_3L^-, NiL_2X_2, and $Ni(L—L)_2$ where X is halogen, L is a neutral ligand such as R_3P or R_3PO, and L—L is a bidentate uninegative ligand; $[NiL_4]^{2+}$ is known where L = hexamethylphosphoramide.

Five-Coordinate Complexes

Five-coordinate complexes usually have trigonal-bipyramidal geometry but some are square pyramidal. Many contain the tetradentate "tripod" ligands such as $N[CH_2CH_2NMe_2]_3$ (see structures 6-XVa and 6-XVb).

24-37 Conformational Properties of Nickel(II) Complexes

The main structural and conformational changes that nickel(II) complexes undergo are the following:

1. *Formation of five- and six-coordinate complexes results from the addition of ligands to square complexes.* For *any* square complex, NiL_4, the following equilibria with additional ligands, L′, must in principle exist:

$$ML_4 + L' = ML_4L' \tag{24-37.1}$$

$$ML_4 + 2L' = ML_4L_2' \tag{24-37.2}$$

Where L = L′ = CN^-, only the five-coordinate species is formed, but in most systems in which L′ is a good donor such as pyridine, H_2O, C_2H_5OH, and so on, the equilibria lie far in favor of the six-coordinate species. These have a trans structure and a high-spin electron configuration; many may be isolated as pure compounds. Thus, the β-diketone complex (structure 24-VII) is normally prepared in the presence of water and/or alcohol and is first isolated as the green, paramagnetic dihydrate or dialcoholate, from which the red, square complex is then obtained by heating to drive off the solvent.

Another type of square complex that picks up H_2O, anions, or solvent is shown in structure 24-VIII.

$$
\left[
\begin{array}{c}
\text{PhHC—N} \overset{H_2}{} \quad \overset{H_2}{} \text{N—CHPh} \\
| \quad \quad Ni \quad \quad | \\
\text{PhHC—N} \underset{H_2}{} \quad \underset{H_2}{} \text{N—CHPh}
\end{array}
\right]^{2+}
$$

24-VIII

2. *Monomer–polymer equilibria* can occur. Four-coordinate complexes may associate or polymerize, to give five- or six-coordinate species. In some cases, the association is very strong and the four-coordinate monomers are observed only at high temperatures. In others the position of the equilibrium is such that both red, diamagnetic monomers and green or blue, paramagnetic poly-

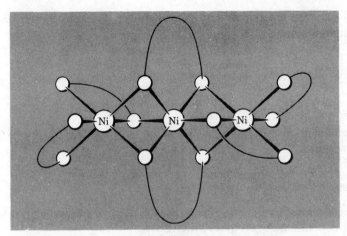

Figure 24-5 Sketch indicating the trimeric structure of nickel acetylacetonate. The unlabeled circles represent oxygen atoms, and the curved lines connecting them in pairs represent the remaining portions of the acetylacetonate rings. (Reproduced by permission from J. C. Bullen, R. Mason, and P. Pauling, *Inorg. Chem.*, **1965**, *4*, 456. Copyright © American Chemical Society.)

mers are present in a temperature- and concentration-dependent equilibrium around room temperature. A clear example of this situation is provided by the *acetylacetonate* (Fig. 24-5). As a result of the sharing of some oxygen atoms, each nickel atom achieves octahedral coordination. This trimer is very stable, and detectable quantities of monomer appear only at temperatures around 200 °C in a noncoordinating solvent. It is, however, readily cleaved by donors such as H_2O or pyridine, to give six-coordinate monomers. When the methyl groups of the acetylacetonate ligand are replaced by the very bulky $C(CH_3)_3$ groups, trimerization is completely prevented and the planar monomer (structure 24-VII) results. When groups sterically intermediate between CH_3 and $C(CH_3)_3$ are used, temperature- and concentration-dependent monomer–trimer equilibria are observed in noncoordinating solvents.

  3. *Square–tetrahedral equilibria and isomerism* can occur. Complexes such as NiL_2X_2 where L represents a mixed alkylarylphosphine exist in solution in an equilibrium distribution between the tetrahedral and square forms. In some cases it is possible to isolate two crystalline forms of the compound, one yellow–red and diamagnetic, the other green or blue with two unpaired electrons. There is even a case, $Ni[(C_6H_5CH_2)(C_6H_5)_2P]_2Br_2$, in which *both* tetrahedral and square complexes are found together in the same crystalline substance.

24-38 Higher Oxidation States of Nickel

Oxides and Hydroxides

The action of Br_2 on alkaline solutions of Ni^{2+} gives a black hydrous oxide, $NiO(OH)$. Other black substances can be obtained by electrolytic oxidation; some of them contain alkali metal ions.

The Edison or nickel–iron battery, which uses KOH as the electrolyte, is based on the reaction

$$Fe + 2NiO(OH) + 2H_2O \underset{\text{Charge}}{\overset{\text{Discharge}}{\rightleftharpoons}}$$
$$Fe(OH)_2 + 2Ni(OH)_2 \quad (\sim 1.3 \text{ V}) \quad (24\text{-}38.1)$$

but the mechanism and the true nature of the oxidized nickel species are not fully understood.

Complexes

There are several authentic complexes of *nickel(III)*. Oxidation of $NiX_2(PR_3)_2$ with the appropriate halogen gives $NiX_3(PR_3)_2$.

Nickel(IV) complexes are even rarer, and the dithiolene complexes (Section 28-18), which could formally be regarded as containing Ni^{4+} and $S_2CR_2^{2-}$ ligands, are best regarded as Ni^{II} complexes.

COPPER

24-39 The Element

Copper has a single *s* electron outside the filled $3d$ shell. It has little in common with the alkalis except formal stoichiometries in the $+I$ oxidation state. The filled *d* shell is much less effective than is a noble-gas shell in shielding the *s* electron from the nuclear charge, so that the first ionization potential of Cu is higher than those of the alkalis. Since the electrons of the *d* shell are also involved in metallic bonding, the heat of sublimation and the melting point of copper are also much higher than those of the alkalis. These factors are responsible for the more noble character of copper. The effect is to make compounds more covalent and to give them higher lattice energies, which are not offset by the somewhat smaller radius of Cu^+, 0.93 Å compared with Na^+, 0.95; and K^+, 1.33 Å.

The second and third ionization potentials of Cu are very much lower than those of the alkalis and account in part for the transition metal character.

Copper is not abundant (55 ppm) but is widely distributed as a metal, in sulfides, arsenides, chlorides, and carbonates. The commonest mineral is chalcopyrite, $CuFeS_2$. Copper is extracted by oxidative roasting and smelting, or by microbial-assisted leaching, followed by electrodeposition from sulfate solutions.

Copper is used in alloys such as brass and is completely miscible with gold. It is very slowly superficially oxidized in moist air, sometimes giving a green coating of hydroxo carbonate and hydroxo sulfate (from SO_2 in the atmosphere).

Copper readily dissolves in nitric acid and in sulfuric acid in the presence of oxygen. It is also soluble in KCN or ammonia solutions in the presence of oxygen, as indicated by the potentials

$$Cu(s) + 2NH_3 \xrightarrow{-0.12\text{ V}} [Cu(NH_3)_2]^+ \xrightarrow{-0.01\text{ V}} [Cu(NH_3)_4]^{2+} \quad (24\text{-}39.1)$$

COPPER COMPOUNDS

The stereochemistry of the more important copper compounds is as follows:

Cu^I Tetrahedral as in $CuI(s)$ or $[Cu(CN)_4]^{3-}$

Cu^{II} $\begin{cases} \text{Square as in } CuO(s), [Cu(py)_4]^{2+}, \text{ or } [CuCl_4]^{2-} \\ \text{Distorted octahedral with two longer trans bonds, for example,} \\ [Cu(H_2O)_6]^{2+}, CuCl_2(s) \end{cases}$

24-40 The Chemistry of Copper(I), d^{10}

Copper(I) compounds are diamagnetic and, except where color results from the anion or charge-transfer bands, are colorless.

The relative stabilities of the Cu^I and Cu^{II} states are indicated by the potentials

$$Cu^+ + e^- = Cu(s) \qquad E^0 = 0.52 \text{ V} \qquad (24\text{-}40.1)$$

$$Cu^{2+} + e^- = Cu^+ \qquad E^0 = 0.153 \text{ V} \qquad (24\text{-}40.2)$$

From these we have

$$Cu(s) + Cu^{2+} = 2Cu^+ \qquad E^0 = -0.37 \text{ V} \qquad (24\text{-}40.3)$$

$$\frac{1}{K} = \frac{[Cu^{2+}]}{[Cu^+]^2} = \sim 10^6$$

The relative stabilities depend very strongly on the nature of anions or other ligands present, and vary considerably with solvent or the nature of neighboring atoms in a crystal.

In *aqueous* solution only low equilibrium concentrations of Cu^+ ($<10^{-2}M$) can exist (see the following section). The only copper(I) compounds that are stable to water are the highly insoluble ones such as $CuCl$ or $CuCN$. This instability toward water is due partly to the greater lattice and solvation energies and higher formation constants for complexes of the Cu^{2+} ion so that ionic Cu^I derivatives are unstable.

The equilibrium $2\,Cu^I \rightleftharpoons Cu + Cu^{II}$ can readily be displaced in either direction. Thus, with CN^-, I^-, and Me_2S, Cu^{II} reacts to give the Cu^I compound. The Cu^{II} state is favored by anions that cannot give covalent bonds or bridging groups, for example, ClO_4^- and SO_4^{2-}, or by complexing agents that have their greater affinity for Cu^{II}. Thus ethylenediamine reacts with copper(I) chloride in aqueous potassium chloride solution:

$$2CuCl + 2(en) = [Cu(en)_2]^{2+} + 2Cl^- + Cu^0 \qquad (24\text{-}40.4)$$

The latter reaction also depends on the chelate nature of the ligand. Thus for ethylenediamine, K is $\sim 10^7$, for pentamethylenediamine (which does not chelate) 3×10^{-2}, and for ammonia 2×10^{-2}. Hence, in the last case the reaction is

$$[Cu(NH_3)_4]^{2+} + Cu^0 = 2[Cu(NH_3)_2]^+ \qquad (24\text{-}40.5)$$

The lifetime of the Cu^+ ion in water is usually very short (<1 s), but dilute solutions from reduction of Cu^{2+} with V^{2+} or Cr^{2+} may last for several hours in the absence of air.

An excellent illustration of how the stability of the Cu^I ion relative to that of the Cu^{II} ion may be affected by the solvent is the case of acetonitrile. Cu^I is very effectively solvated by CH_3CN, and the halides have relatively high solubilities (e.g., CuI, 35 g/kg CH_3CN) versus negligible solubilities in H_2O. Cu^I is more stable than Cu^{II} in CH_3CN, and Cu^{II} acts as a comparatively powerful oxidizing agent.

Copper(I) Binary Compounds

The *oxide* and *sulfide* are more stable than the corresponding Cu^{II} compounds at high temperatures. Cu_2O is made as a yellow powder by controlled reduction of an alkaline solution of a copper(II) salt with hydrazine or, as red crystals, by thermal decomposition of CuO. Copper(I) sulfite (Cu_2S) is a black crystalline solid prepared by heating copper and sulfur in the absence of air; it is, however, markedly nonstoichiometric.

Copper(I) chloride and *bromide* are made by boiling an acidic solution of the copper(II) salt with an excess of copper; on dilution, white CuCl or pale yellow CuBr is precipitated. Addition of I^- to a solution of Cu^{2+} forms a precipitate that rapidly and quantitatively decomposes to CuI and iodine. CuF is unknown. The halides have the zinc blende structure (tetrahedrally coordinated Cu^+). They are insoluble in water, but the solubility is enhanced by an excess of halide ions owing to formation of, for example, $[CuCl_2]^-$, $[CuCl_3]^{2-}$, and $[CuCl_4]^{3-}$.

Copper(I) Complexes

The most common types of Cu^I complexes are those of simple halide or amine ligands that are usually *tetrahedral*. Even those with stoichiometries such as K_2CuCl_3 still have tetrahedral coordination as there are chains sharing halide ions.

Copper(I) also forms several kinds of polynuclear complexes in which four Cu atoms lie at the vertices of a tetrahedron. In $Cu_4I_4L_4$ (L $= R_3P$, R_3As) species, there is a triply bridging I atom on each face of the Cu_4 tetrahedron and one ligand, L, is coordinated to a Cu atom at each vertex (structure 24-IX).

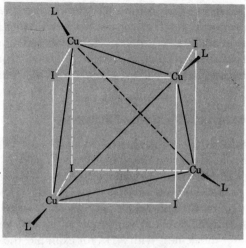

(24-IX)

24-41 The Chemistry of Copper(II), d^9

Most Cu^I compounds are fairly readily oxidized to Cu^{II}, but further oxidation to Cu^{III} is difficult. There is a well-defined aqueous chemistry of Cu^{2+}, and a large number of salts of various anions, many of which are water soluble, exist in addition to a wealth of complexes.

Before we discuss copper(II) chemistry, it is pertinent to note the stereo-chemical consequences of the d^9 configuration of Cu^{II}. This makes Cu^{II} subject to distortions (Section 23-8) if placed in an environment of cubic (i.e., regular octahedral or tetrahedral) symmetry. The result is that Cu^{II} is nearly always found in environments appreciably distorted from these regular symmetries. The characteristic distortion of the octahedron is such that there are *four short* Cu—L *bonds in the plane and two trans long ones*. In the limit, this elongation leads to a situation indistinguishable from square coordination as found in CuO and many discrete complexes of Cu^{II}. Thus the cases of tetragonally distorted "octahedral" coordination and square coordination cannot be sharply differentiated.

Some distorted tetrahedral complexes, such as $M_2^ICuX_4$, are also known provided M is large like cesium. $(NH_4)_2CuCl_4$ has a planar anion.

Binary Compounds

Black crystalline CuO is obtained by pyrolysis of the nitrate or other oxo salts; above 800 °C it decomposes to Cu_2O. The *hydroxide* is obtained as a blue bulky precipitate on addition of NaOH to Cu^{2+} solutions; warming an aqueous slurry dehydrates this to the oxide. The hydroxide is readily soluble in strong acids and also in concentrated NaOH, to give deep blue anions, probably of the type $[Cu_n(OH)_{2n-2}]^{2+}$. In ammoniacal solutions the deep blue tetraammine complex is formed.

The common *halides* are the yellow chloride and the almost black bromide, having structures with infinite parallel bands of square CuX_4 units sharing edges. The bands are arranged so that a tetragonally elongated octahedron is completed about each copper atom by halogen atoms of neighboring chains. $CuCl_2$ and $CuBr_2$ are readily soluble in water, from which hydrates may be crystallized, and also in donor solvents such as acetone, alcohol, and pyridine.

The Aqua Ion and Aqueous Chemistry

Dissolution of copper, the hydroxide, carbonate, and so on, in acids gives the blue-green aqua ion that may be written $[Cu(H_2O)_6]^{2+}$. Two of the H_2O molecules are further from the metal than the other four. Of the numerous crystalline hydrates the blue sulfate, $CuSO_4 \cdot 5H_2O$, is best known. It may be dehydrated to the virtually white anhydrous substance. Addition of ligands to aqueous solutions leads to the formation of complexes by successive displacement of water molecules. With NH_3, for example, the species $[Cu(NH_3)(H_2O)_5]^{2+}$ $\cdots [Cu(NH_3)_4(H_2O)_2]^{2+}$ are formed in the normal way, but addition of the fifth and sixth molecules of NH_3 is difficult. The sixth can be added only in liquid ammonia. The reason for this unusual behavior is connected with the Jahn–Teller effect. Because of it, the Cu^{II} ion does not bind the fifth and sixth ligands strongly (even the H_2O). When this intrinsic weak binding of the fifth and sixth ligands is added to the normally expected decrease in the stepwise formation constants (Section 6-4), the formation constants, K_5 and K_6, are very small indeed. Similarly, it is found with ethylenediamine that $[Cu(en)(H_2O)_4]^{2+}$ and $[Cu(en)_2(H_2O)_2]^{2+}$ form readily, but $[Cu(en)_3]^{2+}$ is formed only at extremely high concentrations of en.

Multidentate ligands that coordinate through O or N, such as amino acids, form copper(II) complexes of considerable stability. The blue solutions formed by addition of tartrate to Cu^{2+} solutions (known as *Fehling's solution* when basic and when *meso*-tartrate is used) may contain monomeric, dimeric, or polymeric species at different pH values. The dimer, $Na_2[Cu\{(\pm)C_4O_6H_2\}] \cdot 5H_2O$, has square Cu^{II} coordination, two tartrate bridges, and a Cu—Cu distance of 2.99 Å.

Polynuclear Compounds with Magnetic Anomalies

Copper forms many compounds in which the Cu—Cu distances are short enough to indicate significant M–M interaction, but in no case is there an actual bond. Particular examples are the bridged *carboxylates* and the related 1,3-triazinidol complexes (structures 24-X and 24-XI). Although in other cases of carboxylates with the same structure (Cr_2^{II}, Mo_2^{II}, Rh_2^{II}, $Ru_2^{II,III}$) there is a definite M—M bond, this is *not* so for Cu. However, there is weak coupling of the unpaired electrons, one on each Cu^{II} ion, giving rise to a singlet ground state with a triplet state lying only a few kilojoules per mole above it; the latter state is thus appreciably populated at normal temperatures and the compounds are paramagnetic. At 25 °C μ_{eff} is typically about 1.4 BM/Cu atom and the temperature dependence is very pronounced. The interaction involves either the $d_{x^2-y^2}$ orbitals of the two metal atoms directly or transmission through the π orbitals of the bridge group, or both.

24-X

24-XI

Catalytic Properties of Copper Compounds

Copper compounds catalyze an exceedingly varied array of reactions, heterogeneously, homogeneously, in the vapor phase, in organic solvents, and in aqueous solutions. Many of these reactions, particularly if in aqueous solutions, involve oxidation–reduction systems and a Cu^I–Cu^{II} redox cycle. Molecular oxygen can often be utilized as oxidant, for example, in copper-catalyzed oxidations of ascorbic acid and in the Wacker process (Section 30-11).

The oxidation probably involves an initial oxidative–addition reaction (Section 30-2):

$$Cu^+ + O_2 = CuO_2^+ \tag{24-41.1}$$

$$CuO_2^+ + H^+ = Cu^{2+} + HO_2 \tag{24-41.2}$$

$$Cu^+ + HO_2 = Cu^{2+} + HO_2^- \tag{24-41.3}$$

$$H^+ + HO_2^- = H_2O_2 \tag{24-41.4}$$

Copper compounds have many uses in organic chemistry for oxidations, for example, of phenols by Cu^{2+}–amine complexes, halogenations, coupling reactions, and the like. Copper(II) has considerable biochemical importance (see Chapter 31).

STUDY GUIDE

Scope and Purpose

We have presented a rather large amount of information in a somewhat traditional and descriptive fashion, namely, a steady "march" through the metals of the first transition series and their compounds. For each element we have presented the important or interesting properties of the element and its inorganic compounds. The student should find it satisfying that the descriptions of the compounds and their reactivities are readily set down in the same "language" and using the same theories as those developed earlier in the text.

For each metal we have organized the presentation in terms of important oxidation states, coordination numbers, geometries, number of d electrons, and types of compounds. We also mention, where appropriate, the various thermodynamic stabilities of the derivatives of a particular metal ion, as well as the kinetic and mechanistic aspects of the reactions. The principal inorganic binary compounds are given first for most elements, followed by the more complex derivatives of an essentially inorganic nature, organized by the important oxidation states of the element. We anticipate covering the metalloorganic compounds in later chapters.

Study Questions

A. Review

1. Write down the ground-state electron configurations for the ions and atoms Ti^{4+}, V^{2+}, Cr^{5+}, Mn^{6+}, Fe^0, Co^{1+}, Ni^{2+}, Cu^{3+}, and Ti^{3+}.

2. Which of the ions in Question 1 typically form octahedral complexes, tetrahedral complexes, or five-coordinate complexes?

3. Which of the complexes of Question 2 would you expect to show Jahn–Teller distortions?

4. What is the chief structural difference between $TiOSO_4 \cdot H_2O$ and $VOSO_4 \cdot 5H_2O$?

5. List two examples each where the transition metal compounds MCl_4 and MCl_3 behave as Lewis acids.

6. Give two examples of disproportionation reactions that were presented in this chapter.

7. Explain why the V—O stretching frequency changes when bis(acetylacetonato)oxovanadium(IV) is dissolved in pyridine.

8. What happens when a solution of $K_2Cr_2O_7$ is added to solutions of (a) F^- (b) Cl^- (c) Br^- (d) I^- (e) OH^- (f) NO_2^- (g) SO_4^{2-} (h) H_2O_2.

9. Give two examples each of the spinels, perovskites, and alums.

10. Explain why the trivalent ions give acid solutions in water. Write balanced equations to illustrate your answer.

11. Draw the structures of $Cr_2(CO_2Me)_4(H_2O)_2$ and $Cr_3O(CO_2Me)_6(H_2O)_3Cl$. Classify each atom in these structures according to the AB_xE_y scheme of Chapter 3, and choose a hybridization for each nonmetal, nonterminal atom.

12. What are the structures of $[Ni(acac)_2]_3$, $CrCl_3(THF)_3$, and CrO_5py?

13. Why is it that the freshly prepared hydroxide (a) of Mn^{2+} is white, but turns dark brown in air, (b) of Co^{2+} is blue, but turns pink on warming, and (c) of Cu^{2+} is blue, but turns black on warming?

14. What is the number of unpaired electrons in complexes of (a) spin-paired Mn^{2+}, (b) tetrahedral Cr^{4+}, (c) tetrahedral Co^{2+}, (d) octahedral V^{3+}, (e) octahedral Co^{3+}, (f) low-spin Fe^{2+}, and (g) high-spin Mn^{2+}?

15. Give an example of a complex representing each case in Problem 14.

16. How is oxygen bound in the complexes (a) $Cs_3[TiO_2F_5]$, (b) $K_3[CrO_8]$, and (c) $[Co_2O_2(NH_3)_{10}](SO_4)_2$?

17. Enumerate the possible isomers of $[Co(en)_2(SCN)_2]^+$, and name each one according to proper nomenclature.

B. Additional Exercises

1. Draw the structures of each reactant and product found in Eqs. 24-7.4, 24-14.2, 24-18.1, 24-25.7, and 24-33.7.

2. Most M—O—M bonds are angular but some are linear, namely, that in $[(NH_3)_5Cr—O—Cr(NH_3)_5]^{4+}$. Why?

3. The densities of the metals Ca, Sc, and Zn are, respectively, 1.54, 3.00, and 7.13 g cm^{-3}. Make a plot of these data along with those given in Table 24-1 for the first transition series, and explain the various features and trends that arise.

4. Dimethyl sulfoxide (DMSO) reacts with $Co(ClO_4)_2$ in absolute ethanol to form a pink product that is a 1:2 electrolyte, and that has a magnetic moment of 4.9 BM. $CoCl_2$, however, reacts with DMSO to form a dark blue product with a magnetic moment (per Co) of 4.6 BM. The latter is a 1:1 electrolyte that has an empirical formula of $Co(DMSO)_3Cl_2$. Suggest a formula and a structure for each compound.

5. Mn(acac)$_3$ has axial Mn—O bond lengths (ca. 1.94 Å) that are shorter than the *equatorial* ones (ca. 2.00 Å). Explain.

6. Write balanced chemical equations for

   (a) Reaction of the aqua ion of Co^{2+} with the disodium salt of EDTA.

   (b) Addition of sodium bicarbonate to aqueous Fe^{2+}.

   (c) Reduction of Mn^{3+} by water.

   (d) Air oxidation of $Fe^{2+}(aq)$.

   (e) Hydrolysis of $TiCl_4$.

   (f) Oxidation of Ti^{3+} by H_2O_2.

   (g) Dissolution of the acidic V_2O_5 into aqueous NaOH.

   (h) Dissolution of the hydrous oxide $VO(OH)_2$ in aqueous HNO_3.

   (i) Burning of Cr in air.

   (j) A preparation of CrO_3.

   (k) Hydrolysis of CrO_2Cl_2.

   (l) Oxidation of aqueous Mn^{2+} with PbO_2.

   (m) A preparation of $[Co(NH_3)_6]^{3+}$.

   (n) Addition of I^- to aqueous Cu^{2+}.

   (o) Reaction of aqueous Cu^{2+} with cyanide.

7. How is the preferred tetrahedral coordination obtained in complexes with an apparent nontetrahedral stoichiometry, such as K_2CuCl_3?

8. Predict the number of unpaired electrons in $[Fe(H_2O)_6]^{2+}$ and $[Fe(CN)_6]^{4-}$. Explain your reasoning.

9. Draw the structures of the *cis*-$[VO_2Cl_4]^{3-}$ and *cis*-$[VO_2(ox)_2]^{3-}$.

10. Draw the structures of $[TiCl_4(OPCl_3)]_2$, $[TiCl_4(MeCO_2Et)]_2$, and $TiCl_4(OPCl_3)_2$. Classify each atom in the structures as AB_xE_y, and choose a hybridization for each nonterminal, nonmetal atom.

C. Problems from the Literature of Inorganic Chemistry

1. Consider the five-coordinate nickel(II) complex studied by K. N. Raymond, P. W. R. Corfield, and J. A. Ibers, *Inorg. Chem.*, **1968,** 7, 1362–1372.

   (a) What geometries are reported for the $[Ni(CN)_5]^{3-}$ ion?

   (b) What hybridization should be chosen for each Ni^{II} ion? What crystal field diagrams should be drawn for each?

(c) How big an energy difference is there, apparently, between these two coordination geometries?

(d) What minimum sequence of atomic motions would be required to convert one geometry into the other?

(e) Write balanced equations for the synthesis of this compound from cobalt(II) chloride, ethylenediamine, $[Ni(CN)_4]^{2-}$ (aq), and KCN.

2. Titanium(IV) compounds are discussed in the article by T. J. Kistenmacher and G. D. Stucky, *Inorg. Chem.*, **1971**, *10*, 122–132.

(a) Write balanced equations for the syntheses of $[PCl_4]_2[Ti_2Cl_{10}]$ and $[PCl_4][Ti_2Cl_9]$, as performed in this work.

(b) Discuss the tendency for Ti^{IV} to be octahedrally coordinated, as illustrated by these two compounds.

(c) Explain the two reactions from the viewpoint of chloride ion transfer.

(d) How and why does the solvent (here either $SOCl_2$ or $POCl_3$) influence the formation of $[Ti_2Cl_{10}]^{2-}$ instead of $[Ti_2Cl_9]^-$?

3. Pentacoordinated copper(II) ions were reported by K. N. Raymond, D. W. Meek, and J. A. Ibers, *Inorg. Chem.*, **1968**, *7*, 1111–1117.

(a) What geometry is reported for $[CuCl_5]^{3-}$ in this compound?

(b) Compare the geometries and the crystal field diagrams of $[Ni(CN)_5]^{3-}$, $[CuCl_5]^{3-}$, and $[MnCl_5]^{2-}$.

(c) Why are the axial Cu—Cl bond lengths in this complex shorter than the equatorial ones?

4. Consider isomerism among nickel complexes as reported by R. G. Hayter and F. S. Humiec, *Inorg. Chem.*, **1965**, *4*, 1701–1706.

(a) For the complexes $NiX_2(PRPh_2)_2$, state the trend that is observed for isomer preference when $X = Cl^-$, Br^-, or I^-. When does the system prefer square planar or tetrahedral geometry?

(b) Which geometry should lead to paramagnetism and which should lead to diamagnetism? Explain with crystal field diagrams.

(c) How is isomer preference related to ligand field strength in the series of complexes with ligands PEt_3, PEt_2Ph, $PEtPh_2$, and PPh_3 and for the series of complexes with ligands SCN^-, Cl^-, Br^-, and I^-?

5. Consider the adduct of oxovanadium(IV) dichloride as reported by J. E. Drake, J. Vekris, and J. S. Wood, *J. Chem. Soc. (A)*, **1968**, 1000–1005.

(a) Write an equation for the synthesis in ammonia of the title compound.

(b) What is the significance of the magnetic susceptibility ($\mu_{eff} = 1.74$ BM) found for this compound?

(c) Describe the V—O multiple bond by showing orbital-overlap diagrams.

(d) How strong is the V—O π bond as judged by the V—O distance?

(e) Why, according to the authors, is the coordination geometry around this oxovanadium(IV) compound a trigonal bipyramid and not the usual square pyramid?

6. Consider the redox reactions reported by A. J. Miralles, R. E. Armstrong, and A. Haim, *J. Am. Chem. Soc.*, **1977**, *99*, 1416–1420.

(a) Prepare crystal field diagrams (with electrons properly configured) for $[Ru(NH_3)_5py]^{3+}$, $[Co(NH_3)_5py]^{3+}$, $[Fe(CN)_6]^{4-}$, $[Fe(CN)_6]^{3-}$, and $[Ru(NH_3)_6]^{2+}$.

(b) How were these reactions shown to proceed via outer-sphere electron transfer mechanisms?

7. Consider the anation reactions studied by W. R. Muir and C. H. Langford, *Inorg. Chem.*, **1968**, *7*, 1032–1043.

(a) Why should exchange of DMSO–ligand with DMSO–solvent be more rapid than anation? Explain by drawing the solvated activated complex along an I_d reaction pathway, and consider the probability of solvent versus anion entry into the first-coordination sphere.

(b) What evidence favoring an I_d mechanism for anation do the authors report?

(c) What evidence is cited in opposition to an associative mechanism?

SUPPLEMENTARY READING

Basolo, F., Bunnett, J. F., and Halpern, J. Eds., *Collected Accounts of Transition Metal Chemistry*, American Chemical Society, 1973.

Clark, R. J. H., *The Chemistry of Titanium and Vanadium*, Elsevier, Amsterdam, 1968.

Colton, R. and Canterford, J. H., *Halides of the First Row Transition Metals*, Wiley, New York, 1969.

Cotton, F. A. and Wilkinson, G., *Advanced Inorganic Chemistry*, Wiley, New York, 1980.

Cotton, S. A., "Some Aspects of the Coordination Chemistry of Iron(III)," *Coord. Chem. Rev.*, **1972**, *8*, 185.

Hatfield, W. E. and Whyman, R., "Coordination Chemistry of Copper," in *Transition Metal Chemistry*, **1969**, *5*, 47.

Hathaway, B. J. and Billing, D. E., "The Electronic Properties and Stereochemistry of Mono-nuclear Complexes of the Copper(II) Ion," *Coord. Chem. Rev.*, **1970**, *5*, 143.

Jardine, F. H., "Copper(I) Complexes," *Adv. Inorg. Chem. Radiochem.*, **1975**, *17*, 115.

Kepert, D. L., *The Early Transition Metals*, Academic, New York, 1972.

Levason, W. and McAuliffe, C. A., "Higher Oxidation State Chemistry of Iron, Cobalt, and Nickel," *Coord. Chem. Rev.*, **1974**, *12*, 151.

Levason, W. and McAuliffe, C. A., "Higher Oxidation State Chemistry of Manganese," *Coord. Chem. Rev.*, **1972**, *7*, 353.

Parish, R. V., *The Metallic Elements*, Longman, London, 1977.

Smith, D. W., "Chlorocuprates(II)," *Coord. Chem. Rev.*, **1976**, *21*, 93.

Toth, L. E., *Transition Metal Carbides and Nitrides*, Academic, New York, 1971.

Wells, A. F., *Structural Inorganic Chemistry*, 5th Ed. Clarendon, Oxford, 1984.

Zordan, T. A. and Hepler, L. G., "Thermochemistry and Oxidation Potentials of Manganese and its Compounds," *Chem. Rev.*, **1968**, *68*, 737.

chapter 25

THE ELEMENTS OF THE SECOND AND THIRD TRANSITION SERIES

25-1 General Remarks

Some important features of these elements compared with those of the first series are as follows:

Radii. The *radii* of the heavier metals and ions are larger than those of the first series. Because of the lanthanide contraction (Section 8-12 and Table 26-1) the radii of the third series show little difference from those of the second series, despite the increased atomic number and total number of electrons.

Oxidation States.

(a) The higher oxidation states are significantly more stable than those of the first series. The oxo anions $[MO_4]^{n-}$ of Mo, W, Tc, Re, Ru, and Os are less readily reduced than those of Cr, Mn, and Fe. Some compounds such as WCl_6, ReF_7, RuO_4, and PtF_6 have no analogs in the first series. The elements in Groups IVA(4) to VIA(6) prefer their highest oxidation state.

(b) The II oxidation state is of relatively little importance except for Ru, Pd, and Pt. For molybdenum it is important, but is quite different (Mo_2^{4+}) from chromium (Cr^{2+}). Similarly the III oxidation state is relatively unimportant except for Rh, Ir, Ru, and Re.

Metal–Metal Bonding. For the first-row elements, M—M bonding occurs only in metal carbonyls and related compounds (Chapter 28) and in binuclear complexes of chromium(II), for example, $Cr_2(O_2CMe)_4(H_2O)_2$. The heavier elements are more prone to metal to metal bonding.

(a) There are binuclear species such as $M_2(O_2CMe)_4$, M = Mo, Rh, and Ru similar to that of Cr. However, there are also binuclear halides of Mo, Tc, Re, and Os, for example, $[Re_2Cl_8]^{2-}$, that have strong multiple M—M bonds.

(b) There are halides of Nb, Ta, Mo, W, and Re that are cluster compounds, for example, $[Ta_6Cl_{12}]^{2+}$ and $[Re_3Cl_{12}]^{3-}$. Some $[Au_{11}]^{3+}$ clusters are also known.

Magnetic Properties. The heavier elements tend to give *low-spin* compounds. Ions with an even number of electrons are often diamagnetic. Even where there is an odd number of d electrons, there is frequently only one unpaired electron. The simple interpretation of magnetic moments that is usually possible for first-row paramagnetic species can seldom be made because of complications due to spin-orbit coupling. The spin-pairing can be attributed to the greater spatial extension of the $4d$ and $5d$ orbitals. Double occupancy of an orbital produces less interelectronic repulsion than in the smaller $3d$ orbitals. The electronic absorption spectra are also more difficult to interpret in general. A given set of ligands produces splittings in the order $5d > 4d > 3d$.

Stereochemistries. For the early members of the second and third rows especially, higher coordination numbers of seven and eight are more common than in the first-row elements. However, for the platinum group metals, the maximum coordination number, with few exceptions, is six.

ZIRCONIUM AND HAFNIUM

25-2 General Remarks: The Elements

The atomic and ionic radii of Zr and Hf are virtually identical. Their chemistry is hence remarkably similar. There are usually only small differences, for example, in solubilities or volatilities of compounds.

The significant differences from Ti are

1. There are few compounds in oxidation states below IV.

2. The $+4$ ions have a high charge, there is no partly filled d shell that might give stereochemical preferences, and they are relatively large (0.74, 0.75 Å). Thus they usually have coordination numbers in compounds and complexes of seven and eight rather than six, and various coordination polyhedra are formed, especially with O and F ligands. For example, we have:

ZrF_6^{2-}	Octahedron in Li_2ZrF_6 and $CuZrF_6 \cdot 4H_2O$
ZrF_7^{3-}	Pentagonal bipyramid, in Na_3ZrF_7
ZrF_7^{3-}	Capped trigonal prism in $(NH_4)_3ZrF_7$
$Zr_2F_{12}^{4-}$	Pentagonal bipyramids sharing an edge in $K_2CuZr_2F_{12} \cdot 6H_2O$
ZrF_8^{4-}	Square antiprism, in $Cu_2ZrF_8 \cdot 12H_2O$
$Zr_2F_{14}^{6-}$	Square antiprisms sharing an edge in $Cu_3Zr_2F_{14} \cdot 16H_2O$

3. Though there are a few compounds, particularly the halides, of Zr^{III}, this is not nearly so important an oxidation state as for titanium.

Zirconium occurs as *baddeleyite*, a form of ZrO_2, and *zircon*, $ZrSiO_4$. Hafnium always accompanies Zr to the extent of fractions of the percentage of Zr. Separations are difficult, but solvent extraction or ion-exchange procedures are effective. The metals are made by the Kroll process (Section 24-5). They are similar to Ti both physically (being hard, resistant, and stainless steel-like in appearance) and chemically (being readily attacked only by HF, to give fluoro complexes).

COMPOUNDS OF ZIRCONIUM(IV), d^0

Since the chemistries are so similar we shall refer only to zirconium. All the compounds are white unless the anion is colored.

25-3 Binary Compounds

The *oxide* ZrO_2, is made by heating the *hydrous oxide*, which is precipitated on addition of OH^- to Zr^{IV} solutions. ZrO_2 is very refractory (mp 2700 °C) and exceptionally resistant to attack. It is used for crucibles and furnace linings and so on.

The *tetrachloride* is made by direct interaction or by action of Cl_2 on a mixture of ZrO_2 and C. It is tetrahedral in the vapor phase but in crystalline form there are chains of $ZrCl_6$ octahedra.

Like $TiCl_4$, $ZrCl_4$ is a Lewis acid and forms adducts with donors such as Cl^-, $POCl_3$, ethers, and the like. It is only partially hydrolyzed by water at room temperature to give the stable oxide chloride, $ZrOCl_2$.

25-4 Aqueous Chemistry and Complexes

ZrO_2 is more basic than TiO_2 and is virtually insoluble in an excess of base. There is a more extensive aqueous chemistry of zirconium because of a lower tendency toward complete hydrolysis. Nevertheless, it is doubtful whether Zr^{4+} aqua ions exist even in strongly acid solutions. The hydrolyzed ion is often referred to as the "zirconyl" ion, ZrO^{2+}, but $Zr{=}O$ bonds do *not* exist. The complex, $ZrOCl_2 \cdot 8H_2O$, which crystallizes from dilute HCl solutions, contains the ion, $[Zr_4(OH)_8(H_2O)_{16}]^{8+}$. Here the Zr atoms lie in a distorted square, linked by pairs of hydroxo bridges, and also bound to four H_2O molecules so that the Zr atom is coordinated by eight oxygen atoms in a distorted dodecahedron.

Like Ce^{4+} and other $+4$ ions, Zr has an *iodate* insoluble in 6 M HNO_3. In fairly concentrated HF solutions, *only* $[ZrF_6]^{2-}$ is present in solution. The salts that crystallize *from* these solutions may contain $[ZrF_7]^{3-}$, $[ZrF_8]^{4-}$, and binu-clear anions as listed in Section 25-2.

Other eight-coordinate complexes are the carboxylate, $Zr(O_2CR)_4$, the ace-tylacetonate, $Zr(acac)_4$, the oxalate, $Na_4[Zr(ox)_4]$, and the nitrate, $Zr(NO_3)_4$.

NIOBIUM AND TANTALUM

25-5 The Elements

Niobium and Ta, though metallic, have chemistries in the V oxidation state that are similar to those of typical nonmetals. They have virtually no cationic chemistry but form numerous anionic complexes most of which have coordination numbers of seven and eight. In their lower oxidation states they form many metal–atom cluster compounds. Only niobium forms lower states in aqueous solution.

Niobium is 10–12 times more abundant than Ta. The *columbite–tantalite* series of minerals have the general composition $(Fe/Mn)(Nb/Ta)_2O_6$, with variable ratios of (Fe/Mn) and (Nb/Ta). Niobium is also obtained from *pyrochlore*, a mixed calcium–sodium niobate. Separation and production of the metals is complex. Both metals are bright, high melting, and resistant to acids. They dissolve with vigor in an HNO_3-HF mixture, and very slowly, in fused NaOH.

NIOBIUM AND TANTALUM COMPOUNDS

25-6 The Chemistry of Niobium and Tantalum (V), d^0

Binary Compounds

The *oxides*, M_2O_5, are dense white powders, commonly made by ignition of other Nb or Ta compounds in air. Addition of OH^- to halide solutions gives the gelatinous hydrous oxides. The oxides are scarcely attacked by acids other than HF but are dissolved by fused $NaHSO_4$ or NaOH. Alkali fusion gives oxo anions that are stable in aqueous solution only at high pH.

Halides and Their Complexes

The pentafluorides are volatile white solids obtained by direct interaction. They have a tetrameric structure [Fig. 25-1(a)] that is characteristic for other pentafluorides. The *pentachlorides* are yellow solids obtained by direct interaction. They are hydrolyzed to the hydrous oxide. In the crystalline form and in solvents like CCl_4 they are dimeric [Fig. 25-1(b)]. Both halides abstract oxygen from donors like Me_2SO or ether on heating to give oxochlorides, $MOCl_3$.

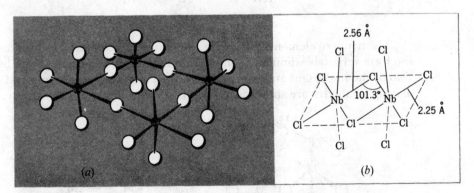

Figure 25-1 (a) The tetrameric structures of NbF_5 and TaF_5 (also MoF_5 and, with slight distortion, RuF_5 and OsF_5). Nb—F bond lengths: 2.06 Å (bridging), 1.77 Å (nonbridging). (Adapted by permission from A. J. Edwards, *J. Chem. Soc.*, **1964**, 3714.) (b) The dinuclear structure of crystalline Nb_2Cl_{10}. The octahedra are distorted.

Niobium pentachloride, Nb_2Cl_{10} is reduced by amines to give Nb^{IV} complexes, for example. $NbCl_4(py)_2$.

The halides are Lewis acids and give adducts with neutral donors and complex anions with halide ions.

The *fluoride solutions* contain $[NbOF_5]^{2-}$, $[NbF_6]^-$, and $[TaF_6]^-$ plus $[TaF_7]^{2-}$. However, from these solutions salts of different stoichiometry can be obtained: $[NbOF_6]^{3-}$, $[NbF_7]^{2-}$, and $[TaF_8]^{3-}$.

25-7 Lower Oxidation States of Niobium and Tantalum

The tetrahalides of niobium and tantalum are well known and readily form adducts, often with high coordination numbers. For example, with phosphines, the following types of complexes are known:

25-I

25-II

25-III

Coordination numbers of six (structures 25-I and 25-II), seven (structure 25-III), and eight (structure 25-IV) occur frequently in complexes of Nb^{IV} and Ta^{IV}.

25-IV

The trivalent elements form some mononuclear octahedral complexes, but also form very stable dinuclear complexes containing metal–metal double bonds. Two of the important and typical ones, which involve edge-sharing and face-sharing octahedra are shown in structures 25-V and 25-VI, respectively:

25-V

25-VI

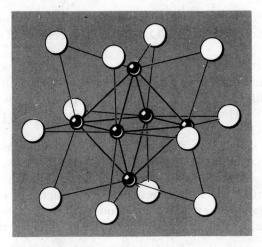

Figure 25-2 The structure of the $[M_6X_{12}]^{n+}$ units found in many halogen compounds of lower-valent niobium and tantalum. [Reproduced by permission from L. Pauling. *The Nature of the Chemical Bond*, 3rd ed., Cornell University Press, Ithaca, NY, 1960. Used by permission of the publisher.]

There are also cluster halides that have stoichiometries $MX_{2.33}$ or $MX_{2.5}$. They contain the $[M_6X_{12}]^{n+}$ unit shown in Fig. 25-2. This has an octahedron of metal atoms with halogen bridges. In aqueous solution, redox reactions occur:

$$[M_6Cl_{12}]^{2+} \underset{}{\overset{-e^-}{\rightleftharpoons}} [M_6Cl_{12}]^{3+} \underset{}{\overset{-e^-}{\rightleftharpoons}} [M_6Cl_{12}]^{4+} \qquad (25\text{-}7.1)$$

Diamagnetic · 1 Unpaired electron · Diamagnetic

Salts of these cations can be isolated.

MOLYBDENUM AND TUNGSTEN

25-8 The Elements

Molybdenum and W do not resemble Cr except in compounds with π-acid ligands. Thus the $+2$ state is not well known except in compounds with quadruply bonded Mo_2^{4+} units. The high stability of Cr^{III} in complexes has no counterpart in Mo or W chemistry. For Mo and W, the higher oxidation states are more common and more stable against reduction.

Both Mo and W have a great range of stereochemistries in addition to the variety of oxidation states, and their chemistry is among the most complex of the transition elements.

Molybdenum occurs chiefly as molybdenite, MoS_2. Tungsten is found almost exclusively in tungstates such as $CaWO_4$ (*scheelite*), or $Fe(Mn)WO_4$ (*wolframite*).

Molybdenum is roasted to the oxide, MoO_3. Tungsten is recovered after alkaline fusion and dissolution in water by precipitation of WO_3 with acids. The oxides are reduced with H_2 to give the metals as grey powders. These are readily attacked only by HF—HNO_3 mixtures or by oxidizing alkaline fusions with Na_2O_2 or KNO_3—NaOH.

The chief use of both metals is in alloy steels; even small amounts cause tremendous increases in hardness and strength. "High-speed" steels, which are used to make cutting tools that remain hard even at red heat, contain W and Cr. Tungsten is also used for lamp filaments. The elements give hard, refractory, and chemically inert interstitial compounds with B, C, N, or Si on direct reaction at high temperatures. Tungsten carbide is used for tipping cutting tools, and the like.

Molybdenum is used in oxide and other systems as a catalyst for a variety of reactions, one example being the "ammonoxidation" synthesis of acrylonitrile

$$CH_2{=}CHCH_3 + NH_3 + \tfrac{3}{2}O_2 \longrightarrow CH_2{=}CHCN + 3H_2O \quad (25\text{-}8.1)$$

Molybdenum is present in some enzymes, notably those that reduce N_2.

MOLYBDENUM AND TUNGSTEN COMPOUNDS

25-9 Oxides and Oxoanions

The *trioxides* are obtained on heating the metal or other compounds in air. MoO_3 is white and WO_3 is yellow. They are not attacked by acids other than HF but dissolve in bases to form molybdates or tungstates. Alkali metal or NH_4^+ salts that are water soluble contain the tetrahedral ions MoO_4^{2-} and WO_4^{2-}. Most other cations give insoluble salts; $PbMoO_4$ can be used for the gravimetric determination of Mo.

When solutions of molybdates or tungstates are made weakly acid, condensation occurs giving complicated polyanions. In more strongly acid solutions the *hydrated oxides*, $MoO_3 \cdot 2H_2O$ (yellow) and $WO_3 \cdot 2H_2O$ (white), are formed. These contain MO_6 octahedra sharing corners.

Unlike chromates which are powerful oxidants (Section 24-19), the Mo and W anions are weak oxidants.

25-10 Halides

Interaction of Mo or W with F_2 gives the colorless *hexafluorides*, MoF_6 (bp 35 °C) and WF_6 (bp 17 °C). Both are readily hydrolyzed.

Chlorination of hot Mo gives only the dimeric pentachloride, Mo_2Cl_{10}, which is a dark red solid with a structure in the crystal very similar to that of Nb_2Cl_{10} [Fig. 25-1(*b*)].

$$MoCl_3 \xleftarrow[400\ °C]{H_2} Mo_2Cl_{10} \xrightarrow[benzene]{Reflux} MoCl_4 \xleftarrow[250\ °C]{CCl_4} MoO_2$$

aq. HCl $\Bigg/$ $Cl_2 \Big\uparrow 500\ °C$ $\underset{600\ °C}{Mo} \Big\Vert \underset{CCl_4,\ 250\ °C}{Cl_2\ in}$

$[MoOCl_5]^{2-}$ $\swarrow$ $Mo \xrightarrow[750\ °C]{COCl_2} Mo_6Cl_{12} \longrightarrow [Mo_6Cl_8]^{4+}$ salts

Figure 25-3 The various preparations of molybdenum chlorides.

Mo_2Cl_{10} is soluble in benzene and in polar organic solvents. It is monomeric in solution and is presumably solvated. It readily abstracts oxygen from oxygenated solvents to give the oxo species and is rapidly hydrolyzed by water. The preparation of other Mo chlorides is shown in Fig. 25-3.

Chlorination of hot W gives the dark blue-black monomeric *hexachloride*, WCl_6. It is soluble in CS_2, CCl_4, alcohol, and ether. It reacts slowly with cold water, rapidly with hot, to give tungstic acid. Mo_2Cl_{10} and WCl_6 are the usual starting materials for synthesis of a variety of compounds such as dialkylamides, alkoxides, organometallics, and carbonyls.

The so-called "dihalides," M_6Cl_{12}, contain $[M_6Cl_8]^{4+}$ clusters (Fig. 25-4) similar to those of Nb and Ta, but with 8 face-bridging rather than 12 edge-bridging chlorine atoms. The Mo clusters differ in that they do not undergo reversible oxidation, but W_6Cl_{12} can be oxidized by Cl_2 at high temperatures. The $(M_6X_8)^{4+}$ units can coordinate six electron-pair donors, one to each metal atom along a four-fold axis of the octahedron. Thus, in molybdenum dichloride, the $(Mo_6Cl_8)^{4+}$ units are connected by bridging Cl atoms (four per unit) and there are nonbridging Cl atoms in the remaining two coordination positions.

The bridging groups in the $[M_6X_8]^{4+}$ units can undergo replacement reaction only slowly, whereas the six outer ligands are labile. Thus mixed halides

Figure 25-4 The structural unit $M_6X_8^{4+}$, as found frequently in halide cluster compounds.

such as $Mo_6Cl_8Br_4$ and complexes such as $[Mo_6Cl_8(Me_2SO)_6]^{4+}$ and $Mo_6Cl_8Cl_4(PPh_3)_2$ can be made.

In aqueous solution $[M_6X_8]^{4+}$ units are unstable to strongly nucleophilic groups such as OH^-, CN^-, or SH^-.

25-11 Complexes of Molybdenum and Tungsten

There are very many complexes of all types in oxidation states from II to VI.

Mo^{II} Species with Mo—Mo Quadruple Bonds

Interaction of $Mo(CO)_6$ (Section 28-8) with carboxylic acids gives dimers, $Mo_2(CO_2R)_4$, that have the same tetrabridged structure as $Cr_2(O_2CR)_4$, Section 24-16. Although $Cr_2(O_2CMe)_4$ with HCl gives only Cr^{2+}, the Mo—Mo bond is *much* stronger and persists giving chloro complexes with quadruple Mo—Mo bonds

$$Mo_2^{II}(O_2CMe)_4 \xrightarrow{\text{HCl(aq)}} [Mo_2^{II}Cl_8]^{4-} \xrightarrow{4L} Mo_2Cl_4L_4 \qquad (25\text{-}11.1)$$

where L is almost any neutral ligand.

Oxo Complexes

The most accessible complex used for the synthesis of other complexes is the emerald green pentachlorooxomolybdate(V) ion, $[MoOCl_5]^{2-}$. This is obtained by reduction of $[MoO_4]^{2-}$ in HCl solutions or by dissolving Mo_2Cl_{10} in concentrated aqueous HCl. Paramagnetic salts such as $K_2[MoOCl_5]$ can be isolated. On addition of NaOH to acid solutions, equilibria involving dimeric species occur:

$$(25\text{-}11.2)$$

The red-brown species represents a common type of Mo^V oxo species. These have an Mo_2O_3 unit with either a linear or a bent Mo—O—Mo bridge. Other types have dioxo or disulfur bridges.

In view of the interest in models for enzyme systems such as xanthine oxidase and sulfide oxidase, complexes with amino acids, and organosulfur ligands have been studied. Two examples are the xanthate $Mo^V_2O_3(S_2COEt)_4$ (structure 25-VII) and the histidine complex, $[Mo^V_2O_4(\text{L-histidine})_2]\cdot 3H_2O$ (structure 25-VIII).

25-VII   25-VIII   25-IX

Molybdenum(VI) commonly forms *dioxo* species in which the two Mo=O bonds are cis. Thus MoO_3 in 12 M HCl gives $[MoO_2Cl_4]^{2-}$ (structure 25-IX).

Tungsten does not form a comparable variety of oxo complexes, although a few are known.

TECHNETIUM AND RHENIUM

25-12 The Elements

Technetium and rhenium differ considerably from Mn the first-row element.

1. There is no analog of Mn^{2+}(aq) and only a very few complexes are known in the II oxidation state.
2. There is little cationic chemistry in any oxidation state even in complexes.
3. Both elements have an extensive chemistry in the IV and V oxidation states, and especially as oxo compounds in the V oxidation state.
4. The oxo anions MO_4^- are much weaker oxidants than permanganate.
5. The formation of clusters and metal to metal bonds is a feature of the chemistry in the II to IV oxidation states.

Rhenium is recovered from the flue dusts in the roasting of MoS_2 ores and from residues in the smelting of some Cu ores. It is usually left in solutions as the perrhenate ion, ReO_4^-. After concentration, the addition of KCl precipitates the sparingly soluble salt, $KReO_4$.

All isotopes of technetium are radioactive. ^{99}Tc (2.12×10^5 yr) is recovered in kilogram quantities from fission product wastes. There may be more ^{99}Tc in existence on the earth than Re.

The metals are obtained by H_2 reduction of the oxides or the $(NH_4)MO_4$ compounds. They are very high-melting and unreactive at room temperature. They burn in O_2 at 400 °C to give the volatile oxides, M_2O_7. They dissolve to give the oxo acid in warm aqueous Br_2 or hot HNO_3. Re dissolves in 30% H_2O_2.

Rhenium is used mainly in a Pt—Re alloy supported on alumina for catalytic reforming of petroleums. Technetium because of its radioactivity is used for radiographic scanning of the liver, the heart, and other organs.

RHENIUM COMPOUNDS

For present purposes, technetium compounds can be assumed to be similar to those of Re.

25-13 Binary Compounds

The yellow volatile oxide, Re_2O_7, is very hygroscopic and dissolves in water, from which the oxide hydrate, $O_3ReOReO_3(H_2O)_2$, can be obtained by evaporation. In NaOH, the perrhenate ion, ReO_4^-, is formed.

Saturation of HCl or H_2SO_4 solutions of ReO_4^- with H_2S gives the black *sulfide*, Re_2S_7. This procedure is used for recovery of Re from residues.

The only *halides* in the VI- and VII-oxidation states are the volatile ReF_6 and ReF_7. Chlorination of Re at ca. 550 °C gives dark red-brown Re_2Cl_{10}. It is a dimer like Mo_2Cl_{10} or Ta_2Cl_{10}. On heating, the liquid decomposes to give the *trichloride*. This is a cluster compound whose structure is shown in Fig. 25-5. The Re_3Cl_9 units are linked into a polymer by sharing of Cl atoms. This unit is extremely stable, persists in the vapor at 600 °C and forms the structural basis for much of Re^{III} chemistry.

Figure 25-5   The cluster structure of Re_3Cl_9.

25-14 Oxo Compounds and Complexes

As with Mo and W, oxo compounds are important especially in the V and VII oxidation states.

The salts of the *perrhenate* ion, ReO_4^-, have solubilities similar to perchlorates, but salts of TcO_4^- are more soluble than either. An insoluble perrhenate suitable for gravimetric analysis is given by the tetraphenylarsonium ion, $Ph_4As^+Mo_4^-$.

The ions are stable in water. They are weak oxidants. In HCl solution ReO_4^- is reduced by hypophosphite, partially to the chloro complex ion, $[Re^{IV}Cl_6]^{2-}$, which forms stable salts such as K_2ReCl_6, and partially to the $[Re_2Cl_8]^{2-}$ ion, which is isoelectronic with the $[Mo_2Cl_8]^{4-}$ ion and contains a quadruple bond between the metal atoms.

Oxo Complexes

The oxo complexes are numerous, as with molybdenum. Re_2Cl_{10} dissolves in aqueous strong HCl to give $[ReOCl_5]^{2-}$. Oxo species may have the groups $Re=O$, $Re-O-Re$ and *trans* $O=Re=O$ (Mo^{VI} has cis dioxo groups) and linear $O=Re-O-Re=O$.

There is an extensive chemistry of oxorhenium(V) compounds containing phosphine ligands. The complexes $ReOCl_3(PR_3)_2$ are obtained by interaction of ReO_4^- with PR_3 in ethanol containing HCl. The halide ion (or other ligand) opposite to the $Re=O$ bond is labile; in ethanol, for example, it is rapidly replaced, giving $ReOCl_2(OEt)(PR_3)_2$.

THE PLATINUM METALS

25-15 General Remarks

Ruthenium, osmium, rhodium, iridium, palladium, and platinum are the six heaviest members of those in Groups VIIIA(8), VIIIA(9), and VIIIA(10), commonly known as the platinum metals. They are rare elements, platinum being the commonest with an abundance of about $10^{-6}\%$, whereas the others have abundances on the order of $10^{-7}\%$. They occur as metals, often as alloys such as osmiridium, and in arsenide, sulfide, and other ores. The elements are usually associated not only with one another but also with nickel, copper, silver, and gold.

The compositions of the ores and the extraction methods vary considerably. An important source is South African Ni–Cu sulfide. The ore is concentrated by gravitation and flotation, after which it is smelted with lime, coke, and sand and is bessemerized in a convertor. The resulting Ni–Cu sulfide "matte" is cast into anodes. On electrolysis in sulfuric acid solution, Cu is deposited at the cathode, and Ni remains in solution, from which it is subsequently recovered by electrodeposition, while the platinum metals, silver, and gold collect in the anode slimes. The subsequent procedures for separation of the elements are very complicated. Although most of the separations used to involve classical precipitations or crystallizations, ion-exchange and solvent-extraction procedures are now used.

The metals are greyish white and are obtained initially as powders by ignition of salts such as $(NH_4)_2PtCl_6$. Almost all compounds of these elements give the metal when heated. However, Os is readily oxidized by air to the very volatile oxide, OsO_4, and Ru gives RuO_2 so that reduction by hydrogen is necessary, in order to recover the metals.

The metals can also be thrown out from acid solutions by the action of Zn—a common recovery procedure known as "footing."

The metals are chemically inert especially when massive. Ru and Os are best attacked by an alkaline oxidizing fusion, Rh and Ir by $HCl + NaClO_3$ at 125 to 150 °C, and Pd and Pt by concentrated $HCl + Cl_2$ or aqua regia.

The metals, as gauze or foil and especially on supports such as alumina or charcoal, on to which the metal salts are absorbed and reduced *in situ*, are extensively used as catalysts in industry. One of the biggest uses of Pt is as Pt–Re or Pt–Ge on alumina catalysts in the reforming or "platforming" of crude petroleum. Pd and Rh compounds are used in homogeneous catalytic syntheses (Chapter 30). The catalytic "after burners" in use on automobile exhausts use a platinum metal catalyst.

Platinum or its alloys are used in electrical contacts.

Both Pd and Pt are capable of absorbing large volumes of molecular hydrogen, and Pd is used for the purification of H_2 by diffusion since Pd metal is uniquely permeable to hydrogen.

25-16 General Remarks on the Chemistry of the Platinum Metals

The chemistries of these elements have some common features, but there are wide variations depending on differing stabilities of oxidation states, stereochemistries, and the like. There is little similarity to Fe, Co, and Ni except in some compounds of π-acid ligands such as CO and in stoichiometries of compounds. The important oxidation states are listed in Table 25-1. Some general points are as follows.

Binary Compounds. The halides, oxides, sulfides, and phosphides are not of great importance.

Aqueous Chemistry. This is almost exclusively that of complex compounds. Aqua ions of Ru^{II}, Ru^{III}, Rh^{III}, Ir^{III}, Pd^{II} and Pt^{II} exist in solutions of noncomplexing anions, namely, ClO_4^-, BF_4^-, $CF_3SO_3^-$ or p-toluenesulfonate, but are not ordinarily of importance.

A vast array of complex ions, predominantly with halide or nitrogen donor ligands, are water soluble. Exchange and kinetic studies have been made with many of these because of interest in (a) trans effects, especially with square Pt^{II}, (b) differences in substitution mechanisms between the ions of the three transition metal series, and (c) the unusually rapid electron transfer processes with heavy metal complex ions.

Table 25-1   Oxidation States of Platinum Metals (Bold Type Shows Main States)

	Ru	Os	Rh	Ir	Pd	Pt
	0	**0**	0	0	**0**	**0**
	1	—	**1**	**1**	—	—
	2	2	2	2	**2**	**2**
	3	3	**3**	**3**	—	3[c]
	4	**4**	**4**	**4**	4	**4**
	5[a,b]	5[a,b]	5[a]	5[a]	5[a]	5[a]
	6[a,b]	6[a,b]	6[a]	6[a]	6[a]	6[a]
	7[a,b]	7[a,b]				
	8[a,b]	**8**[a,b]				

[a]In fluorides or fluoro complexes.
[b]In oxides or oxo anions.
[c]Usually in binuclear compounds with M—M bonds.

Compounds with π-Acid Ligands.

(a)   Binary carbonyls are formed by all but Pd and Pt, the majority of them polynuclear. Substituted polynuclear carbonyls are known for Pd and Pt, and all six elements give carbonyl halides and a variety of carbonyl complexes containing other ligands.

(b)   For Ru, nitrosyl (NO) complexes are a common feature of the chemistry especially in solutions containing nitric acid.

(c)   There is an extensive chemistry of complexes with tertiary phosphines and phosphites, and to a lesser extent with R_3As and R_2S. Some of these are useful homogeneous catalysts (Chapter 30).

Mixed complexes of PR_3 with CO, alkenes, halides, and hydride ligands in at least one oxidation state are common for all of the elements.

(d)   All the elements have a strong tendency to form bonds to carbon, especially with alkenes and alkynes; Pt^{II}, Pt^{IV}, and to a lesser extent Pd^{II} have a strong tendency to form σ bonds, while Pd^{II} very readily forms π-allyl species (Section 29-16).

(e)   A characteristic feature is the formation of complexes with M—H bonds when the metal halides in higher oxidation states are reduced, expecially in the presence of tertiary phosphines or other ligands. Hydrogen abstraction from reaction media such as alcohols or DMF is common.

Oxidation States.   The main *oxidation states* are given in Table 25-1.

Stereochemistry.   In only a few compounds does the coordination number exceed six, for example, $OsH_4(PR_3)_3$ and $IrH_5(Pr_3)_2$. Most complexes in the +3 and +4 oxidation states are octahedral. The d^8 species Rh^I, Ir^I, Pd^{II}, and Pt^{II} normally are square or five coordinate complexes.

The +2 oxidation states for Ru and Os are five or six coordinate complexes.

RUTHENIUM AND OSMIUM

25-17 Oxo Compounds of Ruthenium and Osmium

One of the most characteristic features of the chemistry of Ru and Os is the oxidation by aqueous oxidizing agents to give the volatile *tetraoxides*.

Orange-yellow RuO_4 (mp 25 °C) is formed when acid solutions containing Ru are oxidized by MnO_4^-, Cl_2, or hot $HClO_4$. It can be distilled from the solutions or swept out by a gas stream.

Colorless OsO_4 (mp 40 °C) is more easily obtained and HNO_3 is a sufficiently powerful oxidant. The distillation first of OsO_4 and then of RuO_4 is used in their separation from other platinum metals. The RuO_4 is collected in strong HCl solutions where it is reduced to a mixture of Ru^{III} and Ru^{IV} chloro complexes. The evaporated product is sold as $RuCl_3 \cdot 3H_2O$, the commonest starting material for syntheses of Ru compounds.

The tetraoxides consist of tetrahedral molecules. They are extracted from aqueous solutions by CCl_4. Both are powerful oxidants. OsO_4 is used in organic chemistry as it oxidizes olefins to cis-diols. It is also used for biological staining as organic matter reduces it. It presents an especial hazard to the eyes and must be handled carefully. RuO_4 is much more reactive and can react vigorously with organic matter; it is very toxic.

Dissolution of OsO_4 in base gives a colorless *oxo anion*

$$OsO_4 + 2OH^- = [OsO_4(OH)_2]^{2-} \qquad (25\text{-}17.1)$$

which can be reduced to $[OsO_2(OH)_4]^{2-}$.

A much less stable orange oxo ruthenate, $[RuO_4]^{2-}$, is obtained by fusing Ru compounds with Na_2O_2 and dissolving the melt in water. The difference in stoichiometry may be due to the greater ability of the $5d$ anion to increase its coordination shell.

Reduction of RuO_4 by HCl in the presence of KCl gives $K_4[Ru_2OCl_{10}]$ as red crystals. This oxo species of $Ru^{IV}(d^4)$ is diamagnetic because the electrons become paired in a MO extending over the *linear* Ru—O—Ru bridge.

25-18 Ruthenium Chloro Complexes and Aquo Ions

The commercial product, $RuCl_3 \cdot 3H_2O$, on evaporation with HCl, is reduced to ruthenium(III) chloro complexes. With high concentrations of Cl^-, the ion $[RuCl_6]^{3-}$ may be obtained. The rate of replacement of Cl^- by H_2O decreases as the number of Cl^- ions decreases so that while the aquation of $[RuCl_6]^{3-}$ to $[RuCl_5(H_2O)]^{2-}$ occurs within seconds in water, the half-reaction time for conversion of $[RuCl(H_2O)_5]^{2-}$ to $[Ru(H_2O)_6]^{3+}$ is about 1 yr. Intermediate species such as *trans*-$[RuCl_2(H_2O)_4]^+$ can be isolated by ion exchange procedures.

The Cl^- can be removed by $AgBF_4$ and the $+3$ ion electrolytically reduced to the easily oxidized $+2$ aquo ion.

$$[Ru(H_2O)_6]^{3+} + e^- = [Ru(H_2O)_6]^{2+} \qquad E° = 0.23 \text{ V} \qquad (25\text{-}18.1)$$

$$[Ru(NH_3)_5CO]^{2+}$$

$$\uparrow CO$$

$$RuCl_3(aq) \xrightarrow{N_2H_4} [Ru(NH_3)_5(N_2)]^{2+} \underset{N_2}{\overset{H_2O}{\rightleftharpoons}} [Ru(NH_3)_5(H_2O)]^{2+}$$

$$\begin{array}{c} Zn \\ NH_4OH \\ NH_4Cl \end{array} \Bigg\downarrow boil \qquad\qquad \Bigg\downarrow \begin{array}{c} NH_4OH \\ Cl_2,\ 25 \end{array}$$

$$[Ru(NH_3)_6]^{2+} \xrightarrow[oxidize]{Air} [Ru(NH_3)_6]^{3+} \xrightarrow{Cl_2} [Ru(NH_3)_5Cl]^{2+}$$

$$\Bigg\downarrow NH_4OH$$

$$[Ru(NH_3)_5(H_2O)]^{3+}$$

Figure 25-6 Some reactions of ruthenium ammines.

25-19 Ruthenium Amine Complexes

There is an extensive chemistry of Ru with nitrogen ligands. Some of the chemistry is summarized in Fig. 25-6. The $[Ru(NH_3)_5]^{2+}$ group has remarkable π-bonding properties. It forms complexes with CO, RNC, N_2O, SO_2, and its dinitrogen complex was the first N_2 complex to be made.

25-20 Nitric Oxide Complexes

Both ruthenium and osmium form octahedral complexes, ML_5NO, that have an M—NO group. Depending on the nature of L, they may be cationic, anionic, or neutral. The MNO group can survive many chemical transformations of such complexes.

Ruthenium solutions that have at any time been treated with HNO_3 can,

$$RuH_2(N_2)(PPh_3)_3 \xleftarrow[AlEt_3]{N_2} RuClH(PPh_3)_3 \xrightarrow{CO} RuClH(CO)(PPh_3)_3$$

$$\Bigg\updownarrow N_2 \qquad\qquad \Bigg\uparrow \begin{array}{c} H_2,\ NEt_3 \\ benzene \end{array}$$

$$RuH_2(PPh_3)_4 \xleftarrow[\substack{NaBH_4 \\ benzene}]{PPh_3} RuCl_2(PPh_3)_3 \xrightarrow{acacH} Ru(acac)_2(PPh_3)_2$$

$$\Bigg\uparrow \begin{array}{c} PPh_3 \\ EtOH \end{array}$$

$$mer\text{-}RuCl_3(PPhEt_2)_3 \xleftarrow[EtOH]{PPhEt_2} \text{``RuCl}_3\cdot3H_2O\text{''}$$

$$\begin{array}{c} MeOCH_2CH_2OH \\ boil \end{array} \Bigg\downarrow PPhEt_2$$

$$[Ru_2Cl_3(PPhEt_2)_6]Cl$$

Figure 25-7 Some reactions of tertiary phosphine complexes of ruthenium. Note that the use of different phosphines may lead to different products.

and usually do contain nitrosyl species that are then difficult to remove. They are readily detected by their IR absorption in the region 1930–1845 cm^{-1} (Section 28-14).

25-21 Tertiary Phosphine Complexes

Both ruthenium and osmium have an extensive chemistry with these π-acid ligands. Some representative reactions are shown for Ru in Fig. 25-7. The $RuHCl(PPh_3)_3$ and $RuH_2(PPh_3)_3$ complexes are of interest in that they are highly active catalysts for the selective homogeneous hydrogenation of alk-l-enes (Section 30-7).

RHODIUM AND IRIDIUM

25-22 Complexes of Rhodium(III) and Iridium(III), d^6

There are many diamagnetic, kinetically inert octahedral complexes similar to those of Co^{III}. They differ from Co^{III}, first, in that octahedral halogeno complexes are readily formed, for example, $[RhCl_5(H_2O)]^{2-}$ and $[IrCl_6]^{3-}$. Second, on reduction of the trivalent complexes the divalent complex is not obtained, except under special circumstances for Rh. When the ligands are halogens, amines, or water, reduction gives the metal, or under controlled conditions, a *hydride* complex like $[Rh(NH_3)_5H]SO_4$; when π-acid ligands are present, reduction to Rh^I or Ir^I, or to iridium(III) hydrido complexes occurs.

Chlororhodates; The Rh^{III} Aqua Ion

Fusion of Rh with NaCl in Cl$_2$ followed by dissolution in water and crystallization gives Na$_3[RhCl_6]$. Addition of OH$^-$ to this pink ion gives the *hydrous*

Figure 25-8 Some reactions of rhodium trichloride.

oxide, Rh_2O_3. Dissolution of this in dilute $HClO_4$ gives $[Rh(H_2O)_6]^{3+}$, yellow salts of which can be crystallized.

When Rh_2O_3 is dissolved in HCl and the solutions are evaporated, a dark red deliquescent material, $RhCl_3 \cdot nH_2O$, is obtained. This is the usual starting material for synthesis of Rh compounds. It is soluble in alcohols as well as water. Fresh solutions do not give AgCl with Ag^+ ion, but on boiling, the red-brown solutions do turn to the yellow of $[Rh(H_2O)_6]^{3+}$. Some of its reactions are shown in Fig. 25-8.

25-23 Complexes of Rhodium(IV) and Iridium(IV), d^5

It is very difficult to oxidize Rh^{III} and only a few unstable compounds of Rh^{IV} are known. Octahedral complexes of Ir^{IV} are stable; they have an unpaired electron (t_{2g}^5).

Hexachloroiridates

Hexachloroiridates are made by heating $Ir + NaCl$ in Cl_2. The black salt Na_2IrCl_6 is very soluble in water; the so-called "chloroiridic acid" (cf. chloroplatinic acid Section 25-29) is an oxonium salt $(H_3O)_2IrCl_6 \cdot 4H_2O$. These materials are used to prepare other Ir complexes.

The dark red-brown $[Ir^{IV}Cl_6]^{2-}$ ion is rapidly and quantitatively reduced in strong OH^- solution to give yellow-green $[Ir^{III}Cl_6]^{3-}$

$$2[IrCl_6]^{2-} + 2OH^- \rightleftharpoons 2[IrCl_6]^{3-} + \tfrac{1}{2}O_2 + H_2O \qquad (25\text{-}23.1)$$

The $[IrCl_6]^{2-}$ ion will oxidize many organic compounds, and it is also quantitatively reduced by KI and $[C_2O_4]^{2-}$.

In *acid* solution we have

$$2[IrCl_6]^{2-} + H_2O = 2[IrCl_6]^{3-} + \tfrac{1}{2}O_2 + 2H^+ \qquad (25\text{-}23.2)$$
$$K = 7 \times 10^{-8} \text{ atm}^{1/2} \text{ mol}^3 \text{ L}^{-2} \text{ (25 °C)}$$

so that in 12 M HCl, oxidation of $[Ir^{III}Cl_6]^{3-}$ occurs partially at 25 °C and completely on boiling.

25-24 Complexes of Rhodium(II), d^7

Only a few of these are known, the major ones being the diamagnetic binuclear *carboxylates* that have the common tetrabridged structure. The end positions may be occupied by solvent molecules; with oxygen donors the complexes are green or blue, but with π acids, such as PPh_3, they are orange red. The carboxylates are made by boiling $RhCl_3(aq)$ with NaO_2CR in methanol. Action of very strong noncomplexing acids gives the Rh_2^{4+} aqua ion that also has a Rh—Rh bond.

25-25 Complexes of Rhodium(I) and Iridium(I), d^8

These square or five-coordinate diamagnetic complexes all have π-acid ligands. They are formed by reduction of Rh^{III} or Ir^{III} in the presence of the ligand. There have been many studies on these complexes because they provide the best systems for the study of the oxidative–addition reaction (Section 30-2) that is a characteristic feature of square d^8 complexes. For *trans*-$IrX(CO)(PR_3)_2$ the equilibria for example,

$$\text{\textit{trans}-}Ir^I Cl(CO)(PPh_3)_2 + HCl \rightleftharpoons Ir^{III}Cl_2H(CO)(PPh_3)_2 \quad (25\text{-}25.1)$$

lie well to the Ir^{III} side and the Ir^{III} complexes can be readily characterized. For Rh, the Rh^{III} complexes are much less stable.

The two yellow compounds, *trans-chlorocarbonylbis(triphenylphosphine)-rhodium* or *-iridium, trans*-$MCl(CO)(PPh_3)_2$, are obtained by reducing the halides in alcohols containing PPh_3 by HCHO, which acts as a reductant and source of CO.

Bis[(dicarbonyl)chlororhodium], $[Rh(CO)_2Cl]_2$, is obtained by passing CO saturated with ethanol over $RhCl_3 \cdot 3H_2O$ at ca. 100 °C, when it sublimes as red needles. It has the structure shown in Fig. 25-9 where the coordination around each Rh atom is planar, and there are bridging chlorides with a marked dihedral angle, along the Cl—Cl line. There appears to be some direct interaction between electrons in rhodium orbitals perpendicular to the planes of coordination.

This carbonyl chloride is a useful source of other **rhodium**(I) species, and it is cleaved by donor ligands to give cis-dicarbonyl complexes, for example.

$$[Rh(CO)_2Cl]_2 + 2L \longrightarrow 2RhCl(CO)_2L \quad (25\text{-}25.2)$$

$$[Rh(CO)_2Cl]_2 + 2Cl^- \longrightarrow 2[Rh(CO)_2Cl_2]^- \quad (25\text{-}25.3)$$

$$[Rh(CO)_2Cl]_2 + 2(acac)^- \longrightarrow 2Rh(CO)_2(acac) + 2Cl^- \quad (25\text{-}25.4)$$

Hydridocarbonyltris(triphenylphosphine)rhodium, is a yellow crystalline solid with a trigonal bipyramidal structure with equatorial phosphine groups. It is prepared by the reaction

$$\text{\textit{trans}-}RhCl(CO)(PPh_3)_2 + PPh_3 \xrightarrow[\text{EtOH}]{NaBH_4} RhH(CO)(PPh_3)_3 \quad (25\text{-}25.5)$$

Figure 25-9   The structure of crystalline $[Rh(CO)_2Cl]_2$. The chloride bridges are readily cleaved by nucleophiles.

but it is also formed by the action of $CO + H_2$ under pressure with virtually any rhodium compound in the presence of an excess of PPh_3. Its main importance is as a hydroformylation catalyst for alkenes (Section 30-9).

Chlorotris(triphenylphosphine)rhodium, $RhCl(PPh_3)_3$. This red-violet crystalline solid is formed by reduction of ethanolic solutions of $RhCl_3 \cdot 3H_2O$ with an excess of PPh_3. It is a catalyst for hydrogenation of olefins and other unsaturated substances (Section 30-7). It undergoes many oxidative–addition reactions (Section 30-2), and it abstracts CO readily from metal carbonyl complexes and from organic compounds such as acyl chlorides and aldehydes, often at room temperature to give $RhCl(CO)(PPh_3)_2$.

PALLADIUM AND PLATINUM

25-26 Chlorides

Palladous chloride, $PdCl_2$, is obtained by chlorination of Pd. Above 550 °C an unstable α form is produced, while below 550 °C it is in a β form. There are α and β forms also of $PtCl_2$. The β forms have a molecular structure with M_6Cl_{12} units (structure 25-X); the stabilization is due to halogen bridges rather than metal–metal bonds. Although the structure of α-$PtCl_2$ is not certain, it differs from that of α-$PdCl_2$, which has a flat chain (structure 25-XI). In both structures, the metal has the square coordination characteristic of Pd^{II} and Pt^{II}.

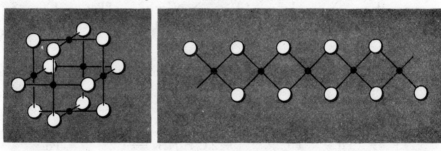

25-X   25-XI

Platinum(IV) chloride, $PtCl_4$, is obtained as red-brown crystals by heating chloroplatinic acid, $(H_3O)_2PtCl_6$, in chlorine. It is soluble in water and in HCl. The analogous chloride of Pd^{IV} does not exist.

25-27 Complexes of Palladium(II) and Platinum(II), d^8

The palladium(II) ion, Pd^{2+}, occurs in PdF_2 and is paramagnetic. However the *aqua ion*, $[Pd(H_2O)_4]^{2+}$, is spin paired and all Pd and Pt complexes are diamagnetic. Brown deliquescent salts like $[Pd(H_2O)_4](ClO_4)_2$ can be obtained when Pd is dissolved in HNO_3 or PdO in $HClO_4$.

Palladium(II) acetate is obtained as brown crystals when Pd sponge is dissolved in acetic acid containing HNO_3. It is a trimer, $[Pd(CO_2Me)_2]_3$. The metal atoms form a triangle with bridging acetate groups. The acetate acts like Pb^{IV}

and Hg^{II} acetates (Section 15-6) in attacking aromatic hydrocarbons; such "palladation" reactions are involved in many catalytic processes (cf. Chapter 30).

Palladium(II) and platinum(II) complexes are square or five-coordinate with the formulas ML_4^{2+}, ML_5^{2+}, ML_3X^+, *cis-* and *trans-*ML_2X_2, MX_4^-, and ML_3X_2, where L is a neutral ligand and X a uninegative ion. The palladium complexes are thermodynamically and kinetically less stable than their Pt^{II} analogs. Otherwise the two series of complexes are similar. The kinetic inertness of the Pt^{II} (and also Pt^{IV}) complexes has allowed them to play a very important role in the development of coordination chemistry. Many studies of geometrical isomerism and reaction mechanisms using platinum complexes have had a profound influence on our understanding of complex chemistry (cf. also Cr^{III}, Co^{III}, Rh^{III}).

There is a preference for amine ligands, halogens, CN^-, tertiary phosphines, and sulfides, R_2S, but little affinity for oxygen ligands and F^-. The concepts of hard and soft acids and bases, or class A and class B metals, are clearly shown here (Section 7-9). The strong binding of heavy donor atoms such as P is due in part to π bonding.

Many complexes have halide or other bridges, for example,

25-XII   25-XIII   25-XIV

Bridged complexes can be cleaved by donors to give mononuclear species, for example,

$$\left[\begin{matrix} Bu_3P & Cl & Cl \\ & Pd & Pd \\ Cl & Cl & PBu_3 \end{matrix}\right] + 2\ C_6H_5NH_2 \longrightarrow 2 \left[\begin{matrix} Bu_3P & Cl \\ & Pd & \\ Cl & NH_2C_6H_5 \end{matrix}\right]$$

(25-27.1)

Salts of the *halogeno anions*, $[MCl_4]^{2-}$, are common source materials. The yellowish $[PdCl_4]^{2-}$ ion is obtained when $PdCl_2$ is dissolved in HCl. The red $[PtCl_4]^{2-}$ ion is made by reduction of $[PtCl_6]^{2-}$ with oxalic acid or N_2H_5Cl.

25-28 Metal–Metal Interactions in Square Complexes

In crystals the square complexes are often stacked one above the other. Even though the metal to metal distances may be too long for true bonding, weak interactions can occur between d orbitals on adjacent metal atoms. An example is $Pt(en)Cl_2$ shown in Fig. 25-10(a); others are Ni and Pd dimethylglyoximates.

$Pt^{II}\ldots Br(chain) = \sim 3.1$ Å

Figure 25-10 (a) Linear stacks of planar Pt(en)Cl$_2$ molecules. (b) Chains of alternating Pt^{II} and Pt^{IV} atoms, with bridging bromide ions, in Pt(NH$_3$)$_2$Br$_3$.

Salts such as [Pt(NH$_3$)$_4$][PtCl$_4$], [Pd(NH$_3$)$_4$][Pd(SCN)$_4$], or [Cu(NH$_3$)$_4$][PtCl$_4$] also have stacked cations and anions so that there are chains of metal atoms. When *both* metal atoms are Pt^{II}, the crystal is green, although the constituent cations are colorless or pale yellow and the anions red. There is also (a) marked dichroism with high absorption of light polarized in the direction of the metal chains and (b) increased electrical conductivity along the chain. If steric hindrance is too large as in [Pt(EtNH$_2$)$_4$][PtCl$_4$] the structure is different and the crystal has a pink color, the sum of the colors of the constitutents.

A related class of compounds with chainlike structures differ in that the metals are linked by halide bridges [Fig. 25-10(*b*)]. Again there is high electrical conductivity along the —X—M^{II}—X—M^{IV}—X— chain.

Five-coordinate complexes are important in substitution and isomerization of square Pd^{II} and Pt^{II} complexes which proceed by an associative pathway. Some stable complexes have multifunctional ligands such as (QAS), tris[*o*-(diphenylarsino)phenylarsine], which gives salts, for example, [Pd(QAS)I]$^+$. Platinum gives the salts (R$_4$N)$_3$[Pt(SnCl$_3$)$_5$].

25-29 Complexes of Platinum(IV), d^6

There are few complexes of Pd^{IV}, a nitrato complex being formed when Pd is dissolved in concentrated HNO$_3$. However, platinum(IV) forms many thermally stable and kinetically inert octahedral complexes, ranging from cationic such as [Pt(NH$_3$)$_6$]Cl$_4$ to anionic like K$_2$[PtCl$_6$].

The most important are the sodium or potassium *hexachloroplatinates*, which are starting materials for synthesis of other compounds. The *acid* called "chloroplatinic acid" is an oxonium salt, (H$_3$O)$_2$PtCl$_6$. It is formed as orange crystals when the solution of Pt in aqua regia or in HCl saturated with chlorine is evaporated.

25-30 Complexes of Palladium(0) and Platinum(0), d^{10}

All of these involve π-acid ligands, mainly tertiary phosphines. The complex $M(PPh_3)_4$ is obtained when K_2PdCl_4 or K_2PtCl_4 is reduced by N_2H_4 in ethanol containing PPh_3. These complexes readily undergo oxidative–addition reactions (Section 30-2) in which two PPh_3 molecules are lost, for example,

$$Pt(PPh_3)_4 + CH_3I = PtI(CH_3)(PPh_3)_2 + 2PPh_3 \qquad (25\text{-}30.1)$$

They also give complexes with O_2, alkenes, and alkynes (Chapter 29).

SILVER AND GOLD

25-31 General Remarks

In spite of the similarity in electronic structures, with an s electron outside a completed d shell and high ionization potentials, there are only limited resemblances between Ag, Au, and Cu. These are as follows:

1. The metals crystallize with the same face-centered cubic (ccp) lattice.
2. Cu_2O and Ag_2O have the same body-centered cubic (bcc) structure where the metal atom has two close O neighbors and every O is tetrahedrally surrounded by four metal atoms.
3. Although the stability constant sequence for halogeno complexes of many metals is $F > Cl > Br > I$, Cu^I, and Ag^I belong to the group of ions of the more noble metals for which it is the reverse.
4. Cu^I and Ag^I (and to a lesser extent Au^I) form similar types of complexes, such as $[MCl_2]^-$, $[Et_3AsMI]_4$, and K_2MCl_3.
5. Certain complexes of Cu^{II} and Ag^{II} are isomorphous, and Ag^{III}, Au^{III}, and Cu^{III} also give similar complexes.

The only stable cation, apart from complex ions, is Ag^+. The Au^+ ion is exceedingly unstable with respect to the disproportionation

$$3Au^+(aq) = Au^{3+}(aq) + 2Au(s) \qquad K \approx 10^{10} \qquad (25\text{-}31.1)$$

Gold(III) is *invariably* complexed in all solutions, usually as anionic species such as $[AuCl_3OH]^-$. The other oxidation states, Ag^{II}, Ag^{III}, and Au^I, are either unstable to water or exist only in insoluble compounds or complex species. Intercomparisons of the standard potentials are of limited utility, particularly since these strongly depend on the nature of the anion; some useful ones are

$$Ag^{2+} \xrightarrow{\ 2.0\ V\ } Ag^+ \xrightarrow{\ 0.799\ V\ } Ag \qquad (25\text{-}31.2)$$

$$Ag(CN)_2^- \xrightarrow{\ -0.31\ V\ } Ag + 2CN^- \qquad (25\text{-}31.3)$$

$$AuCl_4^- \xrightarrow{\ 1.00\ V\ } Au + 4Cl^- \qquad (25\text{-}31.4)$$

$$Au(CN)_2^- \xrightarrow{\ -0.6\ V\ } Au + 2CN^- \qquad (25\text{-}31.5)$$

25-32 The Elements

The elements are widely distributed as metals, in sulfides and arsenides, and as AgCl. Silver is usually recovered from the work-up of other ores, for example, of lead, the platinum metals and particularly, copper. The elements are extracted by treatment with cyanide solutions in the presence of air, whereby the cyano complexes, $[M(CN)_2]^-$, are formed, and are recovered from them by addition of zinc. They are purified by electrodeposition.

Silver is white, lustrous, soft, and malleable (mp 961 °C) with the highest known electrical and thermal conductivities. It is less reactive than copper, except toward sulfur and hydrogen sulfide, which rapidly blacken silver surfaces. Silver dissolves in oxidizing acids and in cyanide solutions in the presence of oxygen or peroxide.

Gold is soft and yellow (mp 1063 °C) with the highest ductility and malleability of any element. It is unreactive and is not attacked by oxygen or sulfur but reacts readily with halogens or with solutions containing or generating chlorine such as aqua regia. It dissolves in cyanide solutions in the presence of air or hydrogen peroxide to form $[Au(CN)_2]^-$.

Both silver and gold form many useful alloys.

SILVER AND GOLD COMPOUNDS

25-33 Silver(I), d^{10}, Compounds

The silver(I) ion, Ag^+, is evidently solvated in aqueous solution but an aqua ion does *not* occur in salts, practically all of which are anhydrous. $AgNO_3$, $AgClO_3$, and $AgClO_4$ are water soluble but Ag_2SO_4 and AgO_2CCH_3 are sparingly so. The salts of oxo anions are ionic. Although the water-insoluble halides AgCl and AgBr have the NaCl structure, there appears to be appreciable covalent character in the $Ag \cdots X$ interactions. The addition of NaOH to Ag^+ solutions produces a dark brown *oxide* that is difficult to free from alkali ions. It is basic, and its aqueous suspensions are alkaline:

$$\tfrac{1}{2}Ag_2O(s) + \tfrac{1}{2}H_2O = Ag^+ + OH^- \qquad \log K = -7.42 \qquad (25\text{-}33.1)$$

$$\tfrac{1}{2}Ag_2O(s) + \tfrac{1}{2}H_2O = AgOH \qquad \log K = -5.75 \qquad (25\text{-}33.2)$$

They absorb CO_2 from the air to give Ag_2CO_3. The oxide decomposes above ~160 °C and is reduced to the metal by hydrogen. The treatment of water-soluble halides with a suspension of silver oxide is a useful way of preparing hydroxides, since the silver halides are insoluble.

The action of hydrogen sulfide on Ag^+ solutions gives the black sulfide Ag_2S. The coating often found on silver articles is Ag_2S; this can be readily reduced by contact with aluminum in dilute Na_2CO_3 solution.

Silver fluoride is unique in forming hydrates such as $AgF\cdot 4H_2O$. The other halides are precipitated by the additon of X^- to Ag^+ solutions; the color and insolubility in water increase Cl < Br < I. *Silver chloride* can be obtained as rather tough sheets that are transparent over much of the IR region and have been used for cell materials. Silver chloride and bromide are light sensitive and have been intensively studied because of their importance in photography.

For monodentate ligands, the *complex ions*, AgL^+, AgL_2^+, AgL_3^+, and AgL_4^+ exist. The constants K_1 and K_2 are usually high, whereas K_3 and K_4 are relatively small. The main species are, hence, AgL_2^+, which are linear. Because of this, chelating ligands cannot form simple ions, and they give polynuclear complexes instead. The commonest complexes are those such as $[Ag(NH_3)_2]^+$ formed by dissolving silver chloride in NH_3, $[Ag(CN)_2]^-$, and $[Ag(S_2O_3)_2]^{3-}$. Silver halides also dissolve in solutions with excess halide ion and excess Ag^+, for example,

$$AgI + nI^- \rightleftharpoons [AgI_{n+1}]^{n-} \qquad (25\text{-}33.3)$$

$$AgI + nAg^+ \rightleftharpoons Ag_{n+1}I^{n+} \qquad (25\text{-}33.4)$$

25-34 Silver(II), d^9 and Silver(III), d^8 Compounds

Silver(II)fluoride, is a brown solid formed on heating Ag in F_2; it is a useful fluorinating agent. A black oxide obtained by oxidation of Ag_2O in alkaline solution is $Ag^IAg^{III}O_2$.

Both Ag^{II} and Ag^{III} occur in complexes with appropriate ligands; the usual procedure is to oxidize Ag^+ in the presence of the ligand. Thus oxidation by $S_2O_8^{2-}$ in the presence of pyridine gives the red ion $[Ag(py)_4]^{2+}$ while in alkaline periodate solution the ion $[Ag(IO_6)_2]^{7-}$ is obtained.

25-35 Gold Compounds

The *oxide*, Au_2O_3, decomposes to Au and O_2 at about 150 °C. Chlorination of gold at 200 °C gives *gold(III) chloride*, Au_2Cl_6, as red crystals; on heating at 160 °C this in turn gives *gold(I) chloride*, AuCl.

Complexes

The *dicyanoaurate ion*, $[Au(CN)_2]^-$, is readily formed by dissolving gold in cyanide solutions in the presence of air or H_2O_2.

The interaction of Au_2Cl_6 in ether with tertiary phosphines gives gold(I) complexes, R_3PAuCl; Cl^- can be replaced by I^- or SCN^-. On reduction with $NaBH_4$, these complexes give *gold cluster compounds* with a stoichiometry, $Au_{11}X_3(PR_3)_7$. The cluster is an incomplete icosahedron with a central Au atom.

Gold alkylsulfides, $[Au(SR)]_n$, and similar compounds made from sulfurized terpenes are very soluble in organic solvents and are also probably cluster compounds. They are used as "liquid gold" for decorating ceramic and glass articles, which are then fired leaving a gold film.

Gold(III) d^8 is isoelectronic with Pt^{II}, and its compounds are hence *square*. Dissolution of Au in aqua regia or of Au_2Cl_6 in HCl gives a solution that on evaporation deposits yellow crystals of $[H_3O][AuCl_4] \cdot 3H_2O$. The tetrachloroaurate(III) ion quite readily hydrolyzes to $[AuCl_3OH]^-$.

From dilute HCl solutions Au^{III} can be extracted with a very high partition coefficient into ethyl acetate or diethylether. The yellow species in the organic layer is probably $[H_3O][AuCl_3OH]$.

STUDY GUIDE

Scope and Purpose

The scope and purpose in this chapter are the same as those for Chapter 24. The student should note the differences that arise between transition elements of the first and subsequent transition series.

Study Questions

A. Review

1. State the chief differences between the second- and third-row transition elements on the one hand and those of the first series on the other with respect to (a) atomic and ionic radii, (b) oxidation states, (c) formation of metal to metal bonds, (d) stereochemistry, and (e) magnetic properties.

2. Why are the chemical and physical properties of hafnium and zirconium compounds so similar?

3. What elements characteristically form cluster compounds in their lower oxidation states? Give examples of the three major types, two of which have six metal atoms, and the other three.

4. Draw the structures of the following $Mo_2(O_2CCF_3)_4$, $[Re_2Cl_8]^{2-}$, $TaCl_5$, NbF_5, $Mo_2O_3(S_2COEt)_4$, and $Rh_2Cl_2(CO)_4$.

5. Describe the chemical and physical properties of RuO_4 and OsO_4, including preparations and toxicology.

6. List all the elements in the group called the "platinum metals" and show how and where they are arranged in the periodic table. Indicate the relative importance of oxidation states I–VI for each.

7. What is the true nature of the so-called "dihalides" of molybdenum and tungsten?

8. Discuss the terrestrial abundance and commercial availability of technetium.

9. What evidence is there for metal to metal interactions in compounds containing square complexes of Ni^{II}, Pd^{II}, and Pt^{II} stacked so the metal atoms form chains perpendicular to the parallel planes of the complexes?

10. Show with sketches the structures of the α and β forms of $PdCl_2$. What role is direct metal–metal bonding thought to play in each?

11. What is the structure of Pd^{II} acetate?

12. How is $Pt(Ph_3P)_4$ prepared? What product is formed when it reacts with methyl iodide?

13. Contrast the chemistry of Cu with that of Ag and Au. First mention the important similarities and then several important differences.

14. Compare the chemistries of Ag^I and Au^I.

15. Write balanced equations for the following processes: (a) leaching of metallic gold by CN^- in the presence of oxygen. (b) The reaction of AgI with a solution of thiosulfate (photographer's "hypo"). (c) The reaction of aqueous $AgNO_3$ with $S_2O_8^{2-}$ in the presence of excess pyridine.

16. Name the most important silver salts that are (a) soluble in water, and (b) insoluble in water.

17. Starting with a Ni—Cu sulfide ore containing significant amounts of the platinum metals, what are the main steps by which the latter, as a group, are isolated?

B. Additional Exercises

1. What is the lanthanide contraction and what effect does it have on the chemistry of the heavier elements?

2. How would you most easily (a) dissolve tantalum metal, (b) precipitate zirconium from aqueous solution in the presence of aluminum, (c) prepare molybdenum(V) chloride from MoO_3, (d) prepare rhenium(III) chloride, (e) dissolve WO_3, (f) prepare $Rh(CO)H(PPh_3)_3$, (g) make $K_2[MoOCl_5]$ from MoO_3?

3. A number of different ions can be precipitated from solutions of $[ZrF_6]^{2-}$. These include $[ZrF_6]^{2-}$, $[ZrF_7]^{3-}$, $[Zr_2F_{12}]^{4-}$, $[ZrF_8]^{4-}$, and $[Zr_2F_{14}]^{6-}$, as discussed in Sections 25-2 and 25-4. Make careful drawings of each of these ions (from the information provided in Section 25-2).

4. How would you dissolve an alloy of Au and Ag and obtain the metals separately?

5. Give two examples of "bridge cleaving reactions" of either Rh or Pt complexes.

6. How is commercial $RuCl_3 \cdot 3H_2O$ made? What is its actual composition and structure? Suggest products when it is (a) dissolved in conc. HCl and evaporated carefully to dryness, (b) heated with aqueous hydrazine, (c) boiled in aqueous NH_4Cl/NH_4OH with zinc powder, and (d) heated with triphenylphosphine in ethanol.

7. How is commercial $RhCl_3 \cdot 3H_2O$ prepared and what is its composition and structure? What happens when it is (a) boiled with aqueous HCl, (b) warmed with excess triphenylphosphine in ethanol, (c) heated with ammonia in ethanol, or (d) boiled with sodium acetate in ethanol?

8. Suggest explanations for the following:

   (a) The aqua nickel(II) ion is paramagnetic, but the aqua palladium(II) ion is diamagnetic.

   (b) The contrast noted in (a) is not observed when NiF_2 and PdF_2 are compared; the latter are isostructural and both are paramagnetic.

   (c) There is important metal–metal bonding in the $[M_6Cl_{12}]^{n+}$ systems when M = Nb or Ta, but not when M = Pd or Pt.

9. Write balanced chemical equations representing

   (a) Preparation of ZrO_2 from aqueous Zr^{IV} solutions using hydroxide.

   (b) Hydrolysis of zirconium tetrachloride.

   (c) Reaction of molybdenum(II) chloride with chlorine.

   (d) Oxidation of Mo with Cl_2.

   (e) Three different preparations of $MoCl_4$.

   (f) Reaction of $Cr_2(O_2CMe)_4$ with HCl.

   (g) Reaction of $Mo_2(O_2CMe)_4$ with HCl.

   (h) A preparation of $[MoOCl_5]^{2-}$.

   (i) Treatment of MoO_3 with 12 M HCl.

   (j) Recovery of Re as the sulfide.

   (k) Dissolution of Re_2Cl_{10} in aqueous HCl.

   (l) A preparation of $ReOCl_2(OEt)(PPh_3)_2$.

   (m) Reduction of RuO_4 in aqueous HCl.

   (n) Reduction of $[IrCl_6]^{2-}$ by KI.

   (o) Preparation of the hexaaquarhodium(III) ion beginning with Rh metal.

   (p) Cleavage of the $[Rh(CO)_2Cl]_2$ dimer by pyridine.

   (q) Dissolution of $PdCl_2$ in HCl.

10. One would expect an octahedral complex of Ru^{IV} to be paramagnetic. Explain this with a crystal field diagram. *Octahedral* Ru^{IV} in the linear, oxo-bridged dimer $[Ru_2OCl_{10}]^{4-}$ is, however, diamagnetic. Show the orbital overlap that takes place in this system to allow spin pairing, as discussed in Seciton 25-17.

11. Draw the structure of $Mo_2(O_2CMe)_4$.

12. Draw the structure of $Zr(acac)_4$.

13. Draw the structure of Mo_2Cl_{10}.

14. Draw the structure of *trans*-$RhCl(CO)(PPh_3)_2$.

15. Determine the oxidation state of the metal in each compound of Problems 11–14.

16. Draw the structure of each reactant and product in Eq. 25-30.1. Explain why the reaction is called an "oxidative–addition." What gets oxidized? What gets reduced?

17. Describe the π-bond system in (a) $[Ru(NH_3)_5(N_2)]^{2+}$, (b) $[Ru_2OCl_{10}]^{4-}$, and (c) $RuCl(H)(CO)(PPh_3)_3$.

C. Questions from the Literature of Inorganic Chemistry

1. Consider $NbCl_4$ as reported by D. R. Taylor, J. C. Calabrese, and E. M. Larsen, *Inorg. Chem.*, **1977**, *16*, 721–722.

    (a) Write a balanced chemical equation for the synthesis as reported here of $NbCl_4$.

    (b) What structural features suggest metal–metal bonding?

    (c) What magnetic feature indicates a metal–metal interaction in this (formally) d^1 system.

    (d) There is no metal–metal bonding in the dimeric $[NbCl_5]_2$. Account for this difference.

    (e) Draw the structure of $[NbCl_5]_2$.

2. Rh complexes are reported in the article by M. J. Bennett and P. B. Donaldson, *Inorg. Chem.*, **1977**, *16*, 655–660.

    (a) What is the geometry about Rh in the complexes $Rh(PPh_3)_3Cl$ as reported here? What is the oxidation state of Rh?

    (b) Show orbital overlap diagrams of the metal to ligand π back-bond that is involved in the "π acidity" of the unique phosphine ligand.

    (c) Why is metal to ligand π back-bonding strongest in the bond to the PPh_3 ligand that is uniquely trans to Cl^-?

3. Consider the paper by A. J. Edwards, *J. Chem. Soc. Dalton Trans.*, **1972**, 582–584.

    (a) $WOCl_4$ has an oxygen-bridged infinite chain structure, with a melting point of 209 °C. What does the melting point of $ReOCl_4$ (30 °C) suggest about its structure?

    (b) Draw the structure of the $ReOCl_4$ dimers reported here. How strong is the bridging Re$\cdots$Cl interaction? How do you know?

    (c) What does the author suggest is the geometry in that vapor state of (i) $MoCl_5$, (ii) $WOCl_4$, (iii) $WSCl_4$, and (iv) $ReOCl_4$? Explain these geometries.

4. Consider the work by K. G. Caulton and F. A. Cotton, *J. Am. Chem. Soc.*, **1969**, *91*, 6517–6518.

    (a) What evidence do the authors present for the presence of a Rh—Rh single bond?

    (b) Show the orbital overlap that is responsible for the formation of this Rh—Rh bond.

    (c) Should the molecule be paramagnetic or diamagnetic? Explain your reasoning.

SUPPLEMENTARY READING

Bottomley, F., "Nitrosyl Complexes of Ruthenium," *Coord. Chem. Rev.,* **1978,** *26,* 7.

Burgmayer, S. J. N. and Stiefel, E. I., "Molybdenum Enzymes, Cofactors, and Model Systems," *J. Chem. Educ.,* **1985,** *62,* 943.

Canterford, J. H. and Colton, R., *Halides of the Second and Third Transition Series,* Wiley-Interscience, New York, 1968.

Colton, R., *The Chemistry of Rhenium and Technetium,* Wiley, New York, 1965.

Cotton, F. A., "Compounds with Multiple Metal to Metal Bonds," *Chem. Soc. Rev.,* **1975,** *4,* 27.

Dellien, I., Hall, F. M., and Hepler, L. G., "Chromium, Molybdenum, and Tungsten: Thermodynamic Properties, Chemical Equilibria, and Standard Potentials," *Chem. Rev.,* **1976,** *76,* 283.

Fairbrother, F., *The Chemistry of Niobium and Tantalum,* Elsevier, Amsterdam, 1967.

Griffith, W. P., *The Chemistry of the Rarer Platinum Metals,* Wiley-Interscience, New York, 1967.

Hartley, F. R., *The Chemistry of Palladium and Platinum,* Wiley, New York, 1973.

Hill, J. O., Worsley, I. G., and Hepler, L. G., "Thermochemistry and Oxidation Potentials of Vanadium, Niobium, and Tantalum," *Chem. Rev.,* **1971,** *71,* 127.

Larsen, E. M., "Zirconium and Hafnium Chemistry," *Adv. Inorg. Chem. Radiochem.,* **1970,** *13,* 1.

MacDermott, T. E., "The Structural Chemistry of Zirconium Compounds," *Coord. Chem. Rev.,* **1973,** *11,* 1.

Miller, D. A. and Bereman, R. D., "The Chemistry of the d^1 Complexes of Niobium, Tantalum, Zirconium, and Hafnium," *Coord. Chem. Rev.,* **1973,** *9,* 107.

Mitchell, P. C. H., Ed., "The Chemistry and Uses of Molybdenum," *J. Less-Common Met.,* **1974,** *36.*

Puddephat, R. J., *The Chemistry of Gold,* Elsevier, Amsterdam, 1978.

Rard, J. A. "Inorganic Aspects of Ruthenium Chemistry," in *Chem. Rev.,* **1985,** 81, 1.

Rouschias, G., "Recent Advances in the Chemistry of Rhenium," *Chem. Rev.,* **1974,** *74,* 531.

Seddon, E. A. and Seddon, K. R. *The Chemistry of Ruthenium,* Elsevier, Amsterdam, 1984.

Stiefel, E. I., "The Coordination and Bioinorganic Chemistry of Molybdenum," *Prog. Inorg. Chem.,* **1977,** *22,* 1.

Walton, R. A., "Halides and Oxyhalides of the Early Transition Series and Their Stability and Reactivity in Nonaqueous Media," *Prog. Inorg. Chem.,* **1972,** *16,* 1.

chapter 26

SCANDIUM, YTTRIUM, LANTHANUM, AND THE LANTHANIDES

26-1 General Features

The position of these elements in the periodic table is discussed in Section 2-5. Note that actinium, although the first member of the actinide elements (Chapter 27), is a true member of the Group IIIA(3) series, Sc, Y, La, Ac. Except for some similarities in the chemistries of Sc and Al, little resemblance exists between these elements and the Group IIIB(13) elements, Al to Tl.

The elements and some of their properties are given in Table 26-1. Strictly speaking, the lanthanide elements are the 14 that follow La and in which the $4f$ electrons are successively added to the La configuration. However, the term lanthanide is usually taken to include lanthanum itself, as indeed, this element is the prototype for the succeeding 14. The progressive decrease in the radii of the atoms and ions of these elements, which when summed is called the *lanthanide contraction,* has been discussed, Section 8-12.

The elements are all highly electropositive with the M^{3+}/M potential varying from -2.25 V (Lu) to -2.52 V (La). The chemistry is predominantly ionic and of the M^{3+} ions.

Yttrium, which lies above La in Group IIIA(3) has a similar $+3$ ion with a noble gas core; because of the effect of the lanthanide contraction, the Y^{3+} radius is close to the values for Tb^{3+} and Dy^{3+}. Consequently, Y occurs in lanthanide minerals. The lighter element in Group IIIA(3), *scandium,* is also considered here, although it has a smaller ionic radius and shows chemical behavior intermediate between that of Al and that of Y and the lanthanides.

Variable Valency

Certain lanthanides (Table 26-1) form $+2$ or $+4$ ions. The $+2$ ions are readily oxidized and the $+4$ ions are readily reduced to the $+3$ ion. A simplified explanation for the occurrence of these valences is that empty, half-filled or filled f shells are especially stable. A similar phenomenon has been noted concerning the ionization enthalpies of the elements of the first transition series (Section 2-7), and half-filling of the $3d$ shell accounts for the stability of manganese(II). For the lanthanides, the oxidation state IV for cerium gives Ce^{4+}

Table 26-1   Some Properties of Scandium, Yttrium, and the Lanthanides

Z	Name	Symbol	Electron Configuration	Valences	M^{3+} Radius Å	M^{3+} Color
21	Scandium	Sc	[Ar] $3d^14s^2$	3	0.68	Colorless
39	Yttrium	Y	[Kr] $4d^15s^2$	3	0.88	Colorless
57	Lanthanum	La	[Xe] $5d^16s^2$	3	1.06	Colorless
58	Cerium	Ce	[Xe] $4f^15d^16s^2$	3, 4	1.03	Colorless
59	Praseodymium	Pr	[Xe] $4f^36s^2$	3, 4	1.01	Green
60	Neodymium	Nd	[Xe] $4f^46s^2$	3	0.99	Lilac
61	Promethium	Pm	[Xe] $4f^56s^2$	3	0.98	Pink
62	Samarium	Sm	[Xe] $4f^66s^2$	2, 3	0.96	Yellow
63	Europium	Eu	[Xe] $4f^76s^2$	2, 3	0.95	Pale pink
64	Gadolinium	Gd	[Xe] $4f^75d6s^2$	3	0.94	Colorless
65	Terbium	Tb	[Xe] $4f^96s^2$	3, 4	0.92	Pale pink
66	Dysprosium	Dy	[Xe] $4f^{10}6s^2$	3	0.91	Yellow
67	Holmium	Ho	[Xe] $4f^{11}6s^2$	3	0.89	Yellow
68	Erbium	Er	[Xe] $4f^{12}6s^2$	3	0.88	Lilac
69	Thulium	Tm	[Xe] $4f^{13}6s^2$	3	0.87	Green
70	Ytterbium	Yb	[Xe] $4f^{14}6s^2$	2, 3	0.86	Colorless
71	Lutetium	Lu	[Xe] $4f^{14}5d6s^2$	3	0.85	Colorless

with the empty f shell configuration of La^{3+}. Similarly the formation of Yb^{2+} gives this ion an f^{14} configuration. The half-filled f^7 configuration of Gd^{3+} is formed by reduction to give Eu^{2+} or oxidation to give Tb^{4+}. That other factors are involved, however, is shown by the existence of many $+2$ ions stabilized in CaF_2 lattices and of Pr^{4+} and Nd^{4+} fluoride complexes.

Magnetic and Spectral Properties

The lanthanide ions that have unpaired electrons are colored and are paramagnetic. There is a fundamental difference from the d-block elements in that the $4f$ electrons are inner electrons and are very effectively shielded from the influence of external forces by the overlying $5s^2$ and $5p^6$ shells. Hence, there are essentially only very weak effects of ligand fields. As a result, electronic transitions between f orbitals give rise to extremely narrow absorption bands, quite unlike the broad bands resulting from d–d transitions, and the magnetic properties of the ions are little affected by their chemical surroundings.

Coordination Numbers and Stereochemistry

It is characteristic of the M^{3+} ions that *coordination numbers exceeding 6 are common.* Very few 6-coordinate species are known but coordination numbers of 7, 8, and 9 are important. In the ion $[Ce(NO_3)_6]^{2-}$, the Ce is surrounded by 12 oxygen atoms of chelate NO_3 groups.

The decrease in radii from La to Lu also has the effect that different crystal structures and coordination numbers may occur for different parts of the lanthanide group. For example, the metal atoms in the trichlorides La to Gd are 9-coordinate, whereas the chlorides of Tb to Lu have an $AlCl_3$ type structure with the metal being octahedrally coordinated. Similar differences in coordination numbers occur for ions in solution.

26-2 Occurrence and Isolation

Scandium is quite a common element being as abundant as As and twice as abundant as B. However, it is not readily available, partly owing to a lack of rich ores, and partly due to the difficulty of separation. It may be separated from Y and the lanthanides, which may be associated with Sc minerals, by cation exchange procedures using oxalic acid as elutant.

The lanthanide elements, including La and Y, were originally known as the rare earths—from their occurrence in oxide (or in old usage, earth) mixtures. They are *not* rare elements and their absolute abundances are relatively high. Thus even the scarcest, Tm, is as common as Bi and more common than As, Cd, Hg, or Se. The major source is *monazite,* a heavy dark sand of variable composition. Monazite is essentially a lanthanide orthophosphate, but may contain up to 30% thorium. La, Ce, Pr, and Nd usually account for ca. 90% of the lanthanide content of minerals, with Y and the heavier elements accounting for the rest. Minerals carrying lanthanides in the $+3$ oxidation state are usually poor in Eu which, because of its tendency to give the $+2$ state, is often concentrated in minerals of the Ca group.

Promethium occurs only in traces in U ores as a spontaneous fission fragment of ^{238}U. Milligram quantities of pink $^{147}Pm^{3+}$ salts can be isolated by ion exchange methods from fission products in spent fuel of nuclear reactors where $^{147}Pm(\beta^-, 2.64 \text{ yr})$ is formed.

The lanthanides are separated from most other elements by precipitation of oxalates or fluorides from HNO_3 solution, and from each other by ion exchange on resins. Cerium and europium are normally first removed. Cerium is oxidized to Ce^{IV} and is then precipitated from $6 M HNO_3$ as Ce^{IV} iodate or separated by solvent extraction. Europium is reduced to Eu^{2+} and is removed by precipitation as $EuSO_4$.

The ion-exchange behavior depends primarily on the hydrated ionic radius. As with the alkalis, the smallest ion crystallographically (Lu) has the largest hydrated radius, while La has the smallest hydrated radius. Hence, La is the most tightly bound and Lu is the least, and the elution order is Lu → La (Fig. 27-3). This trend is accentuated by use of complexing agents at an appropriate pH; the ion of smallest radius also forms the strongest complexes and, hence, the preference for the aqueous phase is enhanced. Typical complexing ligands are α-hydroxyisobutyric acid, $(CH_3)_2CH(OH)CO_2H$, $EDTAH_4$, and other hydroxo or amino carboxylic acids. From the eluates the M^{3+} ions are recovered by acidification with dilute HNO_3 and addition of oxalate ion, which precipitates the oxalates essentially quantitatively. These are then ignited to the oxides.

Cerium(IV) (also Zr^{IV}, Th^{IV}, and Pu^{IV}) is readily extracted from HNO_3 solutions by tributyl phosphate dissolved in kerosene or other inert solvent and can be separated from the $+3$ lanthanide ions. The $+3$ lanthanide nitrates can also be extracted under suitable conditions with various phosphate esters or acids. Extractability under given conditions increases with increasing atomic number; it is higher in strong acid or high NO_3^- concentrations.

The Metals

The lighter metals (La to Gd) are obtained by reduction of the trichlorides with Ca at 1000 °C or more. For Tb, Dy, Ho, Er, Tm, and also Y the trifluorides are used because the chlorides are too volatile. Promethium is made by reduction of PmF_3 with lithium. Eu, Sm, and Yb trichlorides are reduced only to the dihalides by Ca. Reduction of the $+3$ oxides with La at high temperatures gives the metals.

The metals are silvery white and highly electropositive. They react with water, slowly in the cold, rapidly on heating, to liberate hydrogen. They tarnish in air and burn easily to give the oxides M_2O_3; cerium is the exception giving CeO_2. Lighter "flints" are mixed metals containing mostly cerium. Yttrium is resistant to air even up to 1000 °C owing to formation of a protective oxide coating. The metals react with H_2, C, N_2, Si, P, S, halogens, and other nonmetals at elevated temperatures.

Many physical properties of the metals change smoothly along the series, except for Eu and Yb and occasionally Sm and Tm (cf. Fig. 26-1). The deviations occur with those lanthanides that have the greatest tendency to exist in the $+2$ state; presumably these elements tend to donate only two electrons to the conduction bands of the metal, thus leaving larger cores and affording lower binding forces. Note, too, that Eu and Yb dissolve in ammonia (Section 10-3).

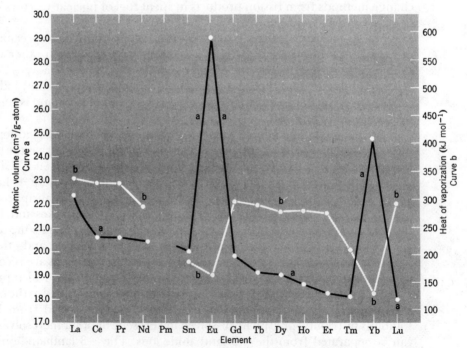

Figure 26-1 The atomic volumes (curve a) and heats of vaporization (curve b) of the lanthanide metals.

LANTHANIDE COMPOUNDS

26-3 The Trivalent State

Oxides and Hydroxides

The oxide Sc_2O_3 is less basic than the other oxides and closely resembles Al_2O_3; it is similarly amphoteric, dissolving in NaOH to give a "scandate" ion, $[Sc(OH)_6]^{3-}$.

The oxides of the remaining elements resemble CaO and absorb CO_2 and H_2O from the air to form carbonates and hydroxides, respectively. The *hydroxides*, $M(OH)_3$, are true compounds whose basicities decrease with increasing Z, as would be expected from the decrease in ionic radius. They are precipitated from aqueous solutions by bases as gelatinous masses. They are not amphoteric.

Halides

Scandium is again exceptional. Its fluoride resembles AlF_3, being soluble in excess HF to give the $[ScF_6]^{3-}$ ion; Na_3ScF_6 is like cryolite (Figure 13-2). However, $ScCl_3$ is not a Friedel–Crafts catalyst like $AlCl_3$ and does not behave as a Lewis acid; its structure is like that of $FeCl_3$, Section 24-27.

Lanthanide fluorides are of importance because of their insolubility. Addition of HF or F^- precipitates MF_3 from solutions even 3 M in HNO_3 and is a characteristic test for lanthanide ions. The fluorides of the heavier lanthanides are slightly soluble in an excess of HF owing to complex formation. Fluorides may be redissolved in 3 M HNO_3 saturated with H_3BO_3, which removes F^- as BF_4^-.

The *chlorides* are soluble in water, from which they crystallize as hydrates. The anhydrous chlorides are best made by the reaction

$$M_2O_3 + 6NH_4Cl \xrightarrow{\sim 300\,°C} 2MCl_3 + 3H_2O + 6NH_3 \qquad (26\text{-}3.1)$$

Aqua Ions, Oxo Salts, and Complexes

Scandium forms a hexaaqua ion $[Sc(H_2O)_6]^{3+}$ that is readily hydrolyzed. Scandium β-diketonates are also octahedral like those of Al and unlike those of the lanthanides.

For the lanthanides and yttrium, the aqua ions, $[M(H_2O)_n]^{3+}$, have coordination numbers exceeding six as in $[Nd(H_2O)_9]^{3+}$. These are hydrolyzed in water:

$$[M(H_2O)_n]^{3+} + H_2O \rightleftharpoons [M(OH)(H_2O)_{n-1}]^{2+} + H_3O^+ \qquad (26\text{-}3.2)$$

The tendency to hydrolyze increases from La to Lu, which is consistent with the decrease in the ionic radii. Yttrium also gives predominantly $Y(OH)^{2+}$. For Ce^{3+}, however, only about 1% of the metal ion is hydrolyzed without forming a precipitate, and the main equilibrium appears to be

$$3Ce^{3+} + 5H_2O \rightleftharpoons [Ce_3(OH)_5]^{4+} + 5H^+ \qquad (26\text{-}3.3)$$

In aqueous solutions, rather weak *fluoride* complexes, MF_{aq}^{2+} are formed. Complex anions are *not* formed, a feature that distinguishes the $+3$ lanthanides as a group from the $+3$ actinide elements that *do* form anionic complexes in strong HCl solutions.

The most stable and common complexes are those with *chelating oxygen ligands*. The formation of water-soluble complexes by citric and other hydroxo acids is utilized in ion-exchange separations, as we noted previously. The complexes usually have coordination numbers >6.

β-diketone (β-dik) ligands such as acetylacetone are especially important, since some of the fluorinated β-diketones give complexes that are volatile and suitable for gas-chromatographic separation. The preparation of β-diketonates by conventional methods invariably gives hydrated or solvated species such as $M(acac)_3 \cdot C_2H_5OH \cdot 3H_2O$ that have coordination numbers >6. Prolonged drying over $MgClO_4$ gives the very hygroscopic $M(\beta\text{-dik})_3$.

An important use of Eu and Pr β-diketonate complexes that are soluble in organic solvents, such as those derived from 1,1,1,2,2,3,3-heptafluoro-7,7-dimethyl-4,6-octanedione, is as shift reagents in nmr spectrometry. The paramagnetic complex deshields the protons of complicated molecules, and vastly improved separation of the resonance lines may be obtained.

Other uses for lanthanide compounds depend on their spectroscopic properties. Y and Eu in oxide or silicate lattices have fluorescent or luminescent behavior and the phosphors are used in color television tubes. In CaF_2 lattices the $+2$ ions show laser activity as do salts of $[Eu(\beta\text{-dik})_4]^-$.

26-4   The Tetravalent State

Cerium(IV)

This is the only $+4$ lanthanide that exists in aqueous solution as well as in solids. The dioxide, CeO_2, is obtained by heating $Ce(OH)_3$ or oxo salts in air. It is unreactive and is dissolved by acids only in the presence of reducing agents (H_2O_2, Sn^{II}, etc.) to give Ce^{3+} solutions. Hydrous cerium(IV) oxide, $CeO_2 \cdot nH_2O$, is a yellow, gelatinous precipitate obtained on treating Ce^{IV} solutions with OH^-; it redissolves in acids.

The *cerium(IV) ion* in solution is obtained by oxidation of Ce^{3+} in HNO_3 or H_2SO_4 with $S_2O_8^{2-}$ or bismuthate. Its chemistry is similar to that of Zr^{4+} and $+4$ actinides. Thus Ce^{4+} gives phosphates insoluble in $4 M$ HNO_3 and iodates insoluble in $6 M$ HNO_3, as well as an insoluble oxalate. The phosphate and iodate precipitations can be used to separate Ce^{4+} from the trivalent lanthanides.

The yellow-orange hydrated ion, $[Ce(H_2O)_n]^{4+}$, is a fairly strong acid, hydrolyzes readily, and probably exists only in strong $HClO_4$ solution. In other acids complex formation accounts for the acid dependence of the potential:

$$Ce^{IV} + e^- = Ce^{III} \qquad E° = + 1.28 \text{ V } (2\ M \text{ HCl})$$
$$+ 1.44 \text{ V } (1\ M\ H_2SO_4)$$
$$+ 1.61 \text{ V } (1\ M\ HNO_3)$$
$$+ 1.70 \text{ V } (1\ M\ HClO_4)$$

(26-4.1)

Comparison of the potential in H_2SO_4, where at high $SO_4{}^{2-}$ concentrations the major species is $[Ce(SO_4)_3]^{2-}$, with that for the oxidation of water:

$$O_2 + 4H^+ + 4e^- = 2H_2O \qquad E° = +1.229 \text{ V}$$

(26-4.2)

shows that the acid Ce^{IV} solutions commonly used in analysis are metastable.

Cerium(IV) is used as an oxidant in analysis and in organic chemistry, where it is commonly used in acetic acid. The solutions oxidize aldehydes and ketones at the α-carbon atom. Benzaldehyde yields benzoin.

Complex anions are formed quite readily. The analytical standard "ceric ammonium nitrate," which can be crystallized from HNO_3, contains the hexanitratocerate anion, $[Ce(NO_3)_6]^{2-}$.

Praseodymium(IV) and Terbium(IV)

These exist only in oxides and fluorides. The oxide systems are very complex and nonstoichiometric. The potential Pr^{IV}/Pr^{III} is estimated to be $+2.9$ V so that it is not surprising that Pr^{IV} does not exist in aqueous solution.

26-5 The Divalent State

The $+2$ state is known in both solutions and solid compounds of Sm, Eu, and Yb (Table 26-2). Less well established are Tm^{2+} and Nd^{2+}, but the $+2$ ions of all the lanthanides can be prepared and stabilized in CaF_2 or BaF_2 lattices by reduction of, for example, MF_3 in CaF_2 with Ca.

The *europium(II)* ion can be made by reducing aqueous Eu^{3+} solutions with Zn or Mg. The other ions require the use of Na amalgam. All three can be prepared by electrolytic reduction in aqueous solution or in halide melts.

Table 26-2 Properties of the Lanthanide $+2$ Ions

Ion	Color	$E°$, V[a]	Crystal Radius, Å[b]
Sm^{2+}	Blood red	-1.55	1.11
Eu^{2+}	Colorless	-0.43	1.10
Yb^{2+}	Yellow	-1.15	0.93

[a]For $M^{3+} + e^- = M^{2+}$.
[b]Pauling radii, Ca^{2+}, 0.99, Sr^{2+}, 1.13, Ba^{2+}, 1.35.

The ions Sm^{2+} and Yb^{2+} are quite rapidly oxidized by water. Eu^{2+} is oxidized by air.

The Eu^{2+} ion resembles Ba^{2+}. Thus the sulfate and carbonate are insoluble, whereas the hydroxide is soluble. The stability of the Eu^{2+} complex with $EDTA^{4-}$ is intermediate between those of Ca^{2+} and Sr^{2+}.

Crystalline compounds of Sm, Eu, and Yb are usually isostructural with the Sr^{2+} or Ba^{2+} analogs.

STUDY GUIDE

Study Questions

A. Review

1. Name the lanthanide elements and give their electron configurations.
2. Explain the position of the lanthanides in the periodic table and their relation to the Al, Ga, In, and Tl group.
3. What is the "lanthanide contraction"? What effect does it have on the chemistry of later elements?
4. Compare the main features of the chemistry of ions of highly electropositive elements with charges $+1$, $+2$, and $+3$.
5. Why are scandium and yttrium usually considered along with the lanthanide elements?
6. Which lanthanide elements show departure from the usual $+3$ oxidation state? Give the electron configurations of these ions.
7. What is characteristic about the coordination numbers of lanthanide ions? Give examples.
8. How are the lanthanide ions separated from each other?
9. What are the characteristic precipitation reactions of lanthanide $+2$, $+3$, and $+4$ ions?
10. How are anhydrous lanthanide chlorides made?
11. What are the interesting features of lanthanide β-diketonates?

B. Additional Exercises

1. Work out the number of unpaired electrons in the ions (a) Pr^{3+}, (b) Pm^{3+}, (c) Sm^{2+}, (d) Gd^{3+}, (e) Tb^{4+}, (f) Tm^{3+}, and (g) Lu^{2+}.
2. Why do the electronic absorption spectra of lanthanide ions have sharp bands unlike the broad bands in the spectra of the $3d$ elements?
3. Write balanced chemical equations representing
    (a) Preparation of anhydrous $PrCl_3$.
    (b) Reduction of CeO_2 in aqueous solution by Sn^{2+}.
    (c) Dissolution of $CeO_2 \cdot nH_2O$ in aqueous HCl.
    (d) Oxidation of Ce^{3+} in aqueous HNO_3 by $S_2O_8^{2-}$.
    (e) Reduction of aqueous Eu^{3+} with Zn.
4. Discuss the pH and anion dependence of the Ce^{III}–Ce^{IV} couple.

5. Why is Pr^{IV} not stable in aqueous solution? Write a balanced equation for its reaction with water. What is $E°$ for this reaction?

6. Explain the increase in hydrolysis that takes place from La to Lu, as the size of the ions M^{3+} decreases through the lanthanide contraction.

C.   Questions from the Literature of Inorganic Chemistry

1. Consider the Nd complex reported by R. A. Anderson, D. H. Templeton, and A. Zalkin, *Inorg. Chem.*, **1978**, *17*, 1962–1965.

   (a) Write balanced chemical equations for the synthesis (two steps) of the title compound.

   (b) Calculate the percentage yield.

   (c) Prepare diagrams of each class of oxygen as found in this structure: (i) terminal, (ii) edge bridging, and (iii) trigonal face bridging.

   (d) What geometry is defined by the Nd_6 group?

   (e) Based on the reported magnetic susceptibility data, what is the number of unpaired electrons per Nd atom? What is the formal charge on each Nd? What is the ground-state electron configuration for each Nd?

2. Two types of lanthanide compounds are described by D. C. Bradley, J. S. Ghotra, F. A. Hart, M. B. Hursthouse, and P. R. Raithby, *J. Chem. Soc. Dalton Trans.*, **1977**, 1166–1172.

   (a) Write balanced chemical equations for the preparations, as reported here, of the adducts $[M\{N(SiMe_3)_2\}_3(PPh_3O)]$, where M = La, Eu, or Lu. What is the oxidation state of the metal in these complexes?

   (b) These complexes contain the monoanionic bis(trimethylsilyl)amido ligands, $[N(SiMe_3)_2]^-$, and the neutral triphenylphosphine oxide ligand (Ph_3PO). Draw a Lewis diagram for each of these ligands, and classify each nonhydrogen atom in these ligands according to the AB_xE_y system. What hybridization is appropriate for each nonterminal atom in these ligands?

   (c) What is the coordination geometry about La in the complex from (a)?

   (d) Write balanced chemical equations for the syntheses, as reported here, of the μ-peroxo dimers $[M_2\{N(SiMe_3)_2\}_4(O_2)(Ph_3PO)_2]$, where M = La, Pr, Sm, or Eu.

   (e) What is unusual about the peroxo bridge that is reported here? (Compare the O—O distance with those found in Table 18-2.) Should this be considered to be an O_2^{2-} ligand?

SUPPLEMENTARY READING

Asprey, L. B. and Cunningham, B. B., "Unusual Oxidation States of Some Actinide and Lanthanide Elements," *Prog. Inorg. Chem.*, **1960**, *2*, 267.

Bagnall, K. W., Ed., *Lanthanides and Actinides,* Butterworths, London, 1972.

Brown, D., *Halides of the Lanthanides and Actinides,* Wiley-Interscience, New York, 1968.

Bunzli, J. G. and Wessner, D., "Rare Earth Complexes with Neutral Macrocyclic Ligands," *Coord. Chem. Rev.*, **1984,** *60*, 191.

Callow, R. J., *The Industrial Chemistry of Lanthanons, Yttrium, Thorium, and Uranium,* Pergamon Press, New York, 1967.

Cotton, S. A. and Hart, F. A., *The Heavy Transition Elements,* MacMillan, New York, 1975.

Horowitz, C. T., *Scandium,* Academic, New York, 1975.

Koppikar, D. K., Sivapullaiah, P. V., Ramakrishnan, L., and Soundararajan, S., "Complexes of the Lanthanides with Neutral Oxygen Donor Ligands," *Struct. Bonding,* **1978,** *34,* 135.

Melson, G. A. and Stotz, R. W., "The Coordination Chemistry of Scandium," *Coord. Chem. Rev.,* **1971,** 7, 133.

Morss, L. R., "Thermochemical Properties of Yttrium, Lanthanum, and the Lanthanide Elements and Ions," *Chem. Rev.,* **1974,** *74,* 827.

Sinha, S. P., *Europium,* Springer-Verlag, Berlin, 1968.

Topp, N. E., *The Chemistry of the Rare Earth Elements,* Elsevier, Amsterdam, 1965.

chapter 27

THE ACTINIDE ELEMENTS

27-1 General Features

The actinide elements and the electronic structures of the atoms are given in Table 27-1. Their position in the periodic table and their relation to the lanthanide elements are discussed in Chapter 8. It will be evident in the following pages that the term *actinides* is not as apt for these elements as is the term lanthanides for elements 59–72. The elements immediately following Ac, which is similar to La and has only the +3 state, do not resemble it very closely at all. Thorium, protactinium and, to a lesser extent, uranium are homologous with their vertical groups in the periodic table, that is, Hf, Ta, and W. However, beginning with americium, there is pronounced lanthanide-like behavior. This, coupled with the existence of the +3 state for all the elements, justifies the term actinide.

The atomic spectra of these heavy elements are very complex, and it is difficult to identify levels in terms of quantum numbers and configurations. The energies of the $5f$, $6d$, $7s$, and $7p$ levels are comparable, and the energies involved in an electron moving from one level to another may lie within the range of chemical binding energies. Thus the electronic structure of an ion in a given oxidation state may be different in different compounds, and in solution may be dependent on the nature of the ligands. It is thus often impossible to say which orbitals are being used in bonding or to decide whether the bonding is covalent or ionic.

A difference from the $4f$ group is that the $5f$ orbitals have a greater spatial extension relative to the $7s$ and $7p$ orbitals than the $4f$ orbitals have relative to the $6s$ and $6p$. Thus $5f$ orbitals can, and do, participate in bonding to a far greater extent than the $4f$ orbitals. A reflection of this potential for covalent bonding is shown by the formation of organometallic compounds similar to those formed by the d-block elements. Examples are di-η^8-cyclooctatetraenyl uranium, $(\eta^8\text{-}C_8H_5)_2U$, and tri-$\eta^5$-cyclopentadienyl uranium benzyl, $(\eta^5\text{-}C_5H_5)_3UCH_2C_6H_5$.

Ionic Radii

The ionic radii of actinide and lanthanide ions are compared in Fig. 27-1. Notice that there is an "actinide contraction" similar to the lanthanide contraction.

Table 27-1   The Actinide Elements and Some of Their Properties

Z	Name	Symbol	Electronic Structure[a] of Atom	Radii, Å M^{3+}	M^{4+}
89	Actinium	Ac	$6d\,7s^2$	1.11	—
90	Thorium	Th	$6d^2 7s^2$	—	0.90
91	Protactinium	Pa	$5f^2 6d 7s^2$ or $5f^1 6d^2 7s^2$	—	0.96
92	Uranium	U	$5f^3 6d 7s^2$	1.03	0.93
93	Neptunium	Np	$5f^5 7s^2$	1.01	0.92
94	Plutonium	Pu	$5f^6 7s^2$	1.00	0.90
95	Americium	Am	$5f^7 7s^2$	0.99	0.89
96	Curium	Cm	$5f^7 6d 7s^2$	0.985	0.88
97	Berkelium	Bk	$5f^8 6d 7s^2$ or $5f^9 7s^2$	0.98	
98	Californium	Cf	$5f^{10} 7s^2$	0.977	
99	Einsteinium	Es	$5f^{11} 7s^2$		
100	Fermium	Fm	$5f^{12} 7s^2$		
101	Mendelevium	Md	$5f^{13} 7s^2$		
102	Nobelium	No	$5f^{14} 7s^2$		
103	Lawrencium	Lr	$5f^{14} 6d 7s^2$		
104	Rutherfordium	Rf			

[a]Outside Rn structure.

Magnetic and Spectroscopic Properties

The magnetic properties of the actinide ions are complicated and difficult to interpret. The electronic absorption spectra that result from f–f transitions consist, like those of the lanthanides, of quite narrow bands.

Oxidation States

There is a far greater range of oxidation states compared with the lanthanides, which is in part attributable to the fact that the $5f$, $6d$, and $7s$ levels are of comparable energies. The known states are given in Table 27-2.

27-2   Occurrence and Properties of the Elements

All of the elements are radioactive. The terrestrial occurrence of U and Th is due to the half-lives of ^{235}U, ^{238}U, and ^{232}Th, which are sufficiently long to have enabled them to persist since genesis. These isotopes are the ones formed in the radioactive series and found in uranium and thorium minerals. The half-lives of even the most stable of the elements following uranium are so short that any amounts formed at genesis would have disappeared quite quickly.

The first new elements, neptunium and plutonium, named like uranium after the planets, were made in 1940 by E. M. McMillan and P. Abelson and by G. T. Seaborg, E. M. McMillan, J. W. Kennedy, and A. Wahl, respectively, by bombardments of uranium using particles from the cyclotron in Berkeley. Both are now obtained from spent uranium fuel elements of nuclear reactors

Figure 27-1 Radii of actinide and lanthanide ions. (Reproduced by permission from D. Brown, *Halides of Lanthanides and Actinides*, Wiley-Interscience Publishers, New York, 1968.)

where they are formed by capture of neutrons produced in the fission of ^{235}U fuel.

$$^{238}\text{U} \xrightarrow{n\gamma} \,^{239}\text{U} \xrightarrow[23.5m]{\beta^-} \,^{239}\text{Np} \xrightarrow[2.35d]{\beta^-} \,^{239}\text{Pu(24,360 yr)} \quad (27\text{-}2.1)$$

$$\begin{array}{c}^{235}\text{U} \xrightarrow{2n\gamma} \\ \xrightarrow{n,\,2n} \\ ^{238}\text{U}\end{array} \,^{237}\text{U} \xrightarrow[6.75d]{\beta^-} \,^{237}\text{Np} \,(2.2 \times 10^6 \text{ yr}) \quad (27\text{-}2.2)$$

Only Pu is normally recovered since ^{239}Pu has fission properties similar to ^{235}U and can be used as a fuel or in nuclear weapons. Some ^{237}Np is used to prepare ^{238}Pu (86.4 yr), which is used as a power source for satellites.

Isotopes of elements following Pu are made by successive neutron capture

Table 27-2 Oxidation States of Actinides with Corresponding Members of Lanthanides

Ac	Th	Pa	U	Np	Pu	Am	Cm	Bk	Cf	Es	Fm	Md	No	Lr
					2				2	2	2	2	2	
3	3	3	3	3	3	**3**	**3**	**3**	**3**	**3**	**3**	**3**	3	3
	4	4	4	4	4	4	4							
		5	5	**5**	5	5		5?						
			6	6	6	6								
				7	7									

La	Ce	Pr	Nd	Pm	Sm	Eu	Gd	Tb	Dy	Ho	Er	Tm	Yb	Lu
f^0							f^7							f^{14}

in ^{239}Pu in nuclear reactors. Examples are

$$^{239}\text{Pu} \xrightarrow{n\gamma} {}^{240}\text{Pu} \xrightarrow{n\gamma} {}^{241}\text{Pu} \xrightarrow[13.2 \text{ yr}]{\beta^-} {}^{241}\text{Am}(433 \text{ yr}) \quad (27\text{-}2.3)$$

$$^{239}\text{Pu} \xrightarrow{4n\gamma} {}^{243}\text{Pu} \xrightarrow[5 \text{ hr}]{\beta^-} {}^{243}\text{Am} \xrightarrow{n\gamma} {}^{244}\text{Am}$$

$$26 \text{ min} \downarrow \beta^- \qquad\qquad\qquad (27\text{-}2.4)$$

$$^{244}\text{Cm}(7.6 \text{ yr})$$

The elements 100–104 are made by bombardment of Pu, Am, or Cm with accelerated ions of B, C, or N.

The isotopes ^{237}Np and ^{239}Pu can be obtained in multikilograms, Am and Cm in >100-g amounts, Bk, Cf, and Es in milligrams, and Fm in 10^{-6} g quantities. The isotopes of elements above Fm are short-lived and only tracer quantities are yet accessible. The metals are all chemically very reactive. The intense radiation from the elements with short half-lives can cause rapid decomposition of compounds. Ac and Cm glow in the dark.

27-3 General Chemistry of the Actinides

The chemistry of the actinides is very complicated, especially in solutions. It has been studied in great detail because of its relevance to nuclear energy, and the chemistry of plutonium is better known than that of many natural elements.

The principal features of the actinides, all of which are electropositive metals, are the following:

1. *Actinium* has only the +3 state and is entirely lanthanide-like.

2. *Thorium* and *protactinium* show limited resemblance to the other elements. They can perhaps best be regarded as the heaviest members of the Ti, Zr, Hf and V, Nb, and Ta groups, respectively.

3. *Uranium, Np, Pu, and Am* are all quite similar differing mainly in the relative stabilities of their oxidation states, which range from +3 to +6.

4. *Curium* is lanthanide-like and corresponds to gadolinium in that at Cm the 5*f* shell is half-full. It differs from Gd in having +4 compounds. By comparison with the lanthanides the previous element *americium* should show the +2 state, like Eu, and the succeeding element, berkelium the +4 state, like Tb. This is the case.

5. The elements Cm and Lr are lanthanide-like. *Lawrencium*, like Lu, has a filled *f* shell so that element 104 should and, as far as is yet known does, have hafnium-like behavior. The elements from 104 onward should be analogs of Hf, Ta, W, and so on. For example, element 112, for which an unsubstantiated claim was made, should resemble Hg. It is uncertain how many more elements can be synthesized. The observation of element 109 was recently claimed (*cf.* Chapter 8).

6. A characteristic feature of the compounds and complexes of actinides, like the lanthanides, is the occurrence of *high coordination numbers* up to

12 as in $[\text{Th}(\text{NO}_3)_6]^{2-}$. Coordination geometries in solids are especially complicated.

7. The various cations of U, Np, Pu, and Am have a very complex solution chemistry. The free energies of various oxidation states differ little, and for Pu the $+3$, $+4$, $+5$, and $+6$ states can actually coexist. The chemistry is complicated by hydrolysis, polymerization, complexing, and disproportionation reactions. Also, for the most radioactive species, chemical reactions are induced by the intense radiation.

The Metals

The metals are prepared by the reduction of anhydrous fluorides, chlorides, or oxides by Li, Mg, or Ca at 1100 to 1400 °C. They are silvery white and reactive, tarnishing in air, and pyrophoric when finely divided. They are soluble in common acids; HNO_3 or HCl are the best solvents.

Uranium normally has a black oxidized film. When enriched in ^{235}U, the metal can initiate a nuclear explosion above a certain critical mass, and this is true also for plutonium. The metals U, Np, and Pu are similar and are the densest of metals.

Americium and Cm are much lighter metals with higher melting points than U, Np, and Pu and resemble the lanthanides. The metallic radius of *californium* indicates that it is divalent like Eu and Yb.

Oxidation States

The oxidation states have been summarized in Table 27-2.

The $+3$ state is the one common to all actinides except for Th and Pa. It is the preferred state for Ac, Am, and all the elements following Am. The most readily oxidized $+3$ ion is U^{3+}, which is oxidized by air or more slowly by water.

The chemistry is similar to that of the lanthanides. For example, the fluorides are precipitated from dilute HNO_3 solutions. Since the ionic sizes of both series are comparable, there is considerable similarity in the formation of complex ions, such as citrates, and in the magnitude of the formation constants. The separation of $+3$ lanthanides and actinides into groups and from each other requires ion-exchange methods (Section 26-2).

The $+4$ state is the principal state for thorium. For Pa, U, Np, Pu, and Bk, $+4$ cations are known in solution, but for Am and Cm in solution there are only complex fluoroanions. All form solid $+4$ compounds. Element 104 has been found only in the $+4$ state.

The $+4$ cations in acid solution can be precipitated by iodate, oxalate, phosphate, and fluoride. The *dioxides*, MO_2, from Th to Bk have the fluorite structure. The tetrafluorides, MF_4, for both actinides and lanthanides are isostructural.

The $+5$ state, for Pa, is the preferred state, in which it resembles Ta. For U to Am only a few solid compounds are known. For these elements the *dioxo ions*, $[\text{MO}_2]^+(\text{aq})$, are of importance (discussed shortly).

In the $+6$ state the only simple compounds are the hexafluorides, MF_6, of

U, Np, and Pu. The principal chemistry is that of the *dioxo ions,* $[MO_2]^{2+}$, of U, Np, Pu, and Am (discussed shortly).

The +2 and +7 states are quite rare. The +2 state is confined to Am (the 5*f* analog of Eu) where the +2 ion can occur in CaF_2 lattices, and to Cf, Es, Fm, Md, and No, which have +2 ions in solution. These are chemically similar to Ba^{2+}. The Md^{2+} ion is less readily oxidized than Eu^{2+} ($E° = -0.15$ vs -0.43 V).

The +7 state is known only in oxoanions of Np and Pu when alkaline solutions are oxidized by O_3 or PuO_2 and Li_2O are heated in oxygen. Representative oxo anions, are $[NpO_4(OH)_2]^{3-}$ and $[PuO_6]^{5-}$.

The dioxo ions $[MO_2]^+$ and $[MO_2]^{2+}$ are both formed. The stabilities of the $[MO_2]^+$ ions are determined by the ease of disproportionation, for example,

$$2UO_2^+ + 4H^+ = U^{4+} + UO_2^{2+} + 2H_2O \qquad (27\text{-}3.1)$$

The stability order is Np > Am > Pu > U but, of course, there is dependence on the acid concentration. The UO_2^+ ion has only a transient existence in solution but is most stable in the pH range 2–4.

The $[MO_2]^{2+}$ ions are quite stable; $[AmO_2]^{2+}$ is most easily reduced, the stability order being U > Pu > Np > Am.

The $[AmO_2]^+$ and $[AmO_2]^{2+}$ ions undergo reduction at a few percent per hour by the products of their own α-radiation.

The linear dioxo ions can persist through a variety of chemical changes. They also appear as structural units in crystalline higher oxides. The ions are normally coordinated by solvent molecules or anions with four, or most often, five or six ligand atoms in or near the equatorial plane of the linear O—M—O group. These equatorial ligands are often not exactly coplanar. An example is the anion in sodium uranyl acetate shown in Fig. 27-2. Similar structures occur in $UO_2(NO_3)_2(H_2O)_2$, $Rb[UO_2(NO_3)_3]$, and so on.

• U
○ O
○ C
○ H

U—O(UO₂) = 1.71 Å
U—O(acetate) = 2.49 Å

Figure 27-2   The structure of the anion in $Na[UO_2(O_2CMe)_3]$ viewed along the linear UO_2 group. The carboxylate groups are bidentate and equivalent. The U—O distance in UO_2 is much shorter than the U—O distance in the equatorial plane.

27-4 Actinium

Actinium occurs in traces in U minerals but now can be made on a milligram scale by the neutron reaction

$$^{226}Ra(n\gamma)\ ^{227}Ra \xrightarrow{\ \beta^-\ } \ ^{227}Ac(\alpha,\ 21.7\ yr) \tag{27-4.1}$$

It is lanthanum-like in its chemistry, which is difficult to study because of the intense radiation of the decay products.

27-5 Thorium

Thorium is widely distributed, but the chief mineral is *monazite* sand, a complex phosphate that also contains lanthanides. The sand is digested with sodium hydroxide and the insoluble hydroxides are dissolved in hydrochloric acid. When the pH of the solution is adjusted to 5.8, the thorium, uranium, and about 3% of the lanthanides are precipitated as hydroxides. The thorium is recovered by extraction from >6 M hydrochloric acid solution by tributyl phosphate in kerosene.

The commonest thorium compound is the *nitrate*, $Th(NO_3)_4 \cdot 5H_2O$. This is soluble in water and alcohols, ketones, and esters. In aqueous solution the Th^{4+} ion is hydrolyzed at a pH higher than ~3. It forms complex salts such as $K_4[Th(ox)_4] \cdot 4H_2O$ and $M^{II}[Th(NO_3)_6]$. On heating, the nitrate gives the white refractory dioxide ThO_2. Action of CCl_4 on this at 600 °C gives the white crystalline $ThCl_4$, which acts as a Lewis acid.

27-6 Protactinium

Protactinium can be isolated from residues after the extraction of uranium from pitchblende. It is exceedingly difficult to handle, except in fluoride solutions where it complexes (cf., Ta). In most other acid solutions it hydrolyzes to give polymeric species and colloids that are adsorbed on vessels and precipitates. Only a few compounds, some of Pa^{IV} but mostly Pa^V, are known; they generally resemble those of Ta. For example, the chloride is Pa_2Cl_{10}, the oxide is Pa_2O_5, and the fluoroanions $[PaF_6]^-$, $[PaF_7]^{2-}$, and $[PaF_8]^{3-}$ are formed.

27-7 Uranium

Until the discovery of nuclear fission by Lise Meitner, Otto Hahn, and Fritz Strassman in 1939, uranium was used only for coloring glass and ceramics, and the main reason for working its ores was to recover radium for use in cancer therapy. The isotope ^{235}U(0.72% abundance) is the prime nuclear fuel; although natural uranium can be used in nuclear reactors moderated by D_2O, most reactors and nuclear weapons use enriched uranium. Large-scale separation of ^{235}U employs gaseous diffusion of UF_6, but a gas centrifuge method now appears more economical.

Uranium is widely distributed and is more abundant than Ag, Hg, Cd, or Bi. It has few economic ores, the main one being *uraninite* (one form is *pitchblende*) an oxide of approximate composition, UO_2. Uranium is recovered from nitric acid solutions by

1. Extraction of uranyl nitrate into diethyl ether or isobutylmethylketone; a salt such as NH_4^+, Ca^{2+}, or Al^{3+} nitrate is added as a "salting-out" agent to increase the extraction ratio to technically usable values. If tributyl phosphate in kerosene is used, no salting-out agent is necessary.
2. Removal from the organic solvent by washing with dilute HNO_3.
3. Recovery as U_3O_8 or UO_3 (see next section) by precipitation with ammonia.

Oxides

The U–O system is extremely complex. The main oxides are orange-yellow UO_3, black U_3O_8, and brown UO_2. Uranium trioxide, UO_3, is made by heating the hydrous oxide, mainly $UO_2(OH)_2 \cdot H_2O$, obtained by adding NH_4OH to $[UO_2]^{2+}$ solutions. The other oxides are obtained by the reactions

$$3UO_3 \xrightarrow{700\,°C} U_3O_8 + \tfrac{1}{2}O_2 \tag{27-7.1}$$

$$UO_3 + CO \xrightarrow{350\,°C} UO_2 + CO_2 \tag{27-7.2}$$

All oxides dissolve in HNO_3 to give uranyl nitrate, $UO_2(NO_3)_2 \cdot nH_2O$.

Halides

The *hexafluoride*, UF_6, is obtained as colorless volatile crystals, (mp 64 °C) by fluorination at 400 °C of UF_3 or UF_4. It is a very powerful oxidizing and fluorinating agent and is vigorously hydrolyzed by water.

The green *tetrachloride* is obtained on refluxing UO_3 with hexachloropropene. It is soluble in polar organic solvents and in water. The action of Cl_2 on UCl_4 gives U_2Cl_{10} and, under controlled conditions, the rather unstable UCl_6.

Hydride

Uranium reacts with hydrogen even at 25 °C to give a pyrophoric black powder:

$$U + \tfrac{3}{2}H_2 \underset{\text{heat}}{\overset{250\,°C}{\rightleftharpoons}} UH_3 \tag{27-7.3}$$

This hydride is often more suitable for the preparation of uranium compounds than is the massive metal. Some typical reactions are

$$
UH_3 + \left\{ \begin{array}{ll} H_2O & 350\ °C \\ Cl_2 & 200\ °C \\ H_2S & 450\ °C \\ HF & 400\ °C \\ HCl & 250\ °C \end{array} \right\} = \left\{ \begin{array}{ll} UO_2 & (27\text{-}7.4) \\ UCl_4 & (27\text{-}7.5) \\ US_2 & (27\text{-}7.6) \\ UF_4 & (27\text{-}7.7) \\ UCl_3 & (27\text{-}7.8) \end{array} \right.
$$

Dioxouranium(VI) or Uranyl Salts

The most common uranium salt is the yellow uranyl nitrate, which may have 2, 3, or 6 molecules of water depending on whether it is crystallized from fuming, concentrated, or dilute nitric acid. When extracted from aqueous solution into organic solvents uranyl nitrate is accompanied by four H_2O molecules and the NO_3^- ions and water are coordinated in the equatorial plane.

On addition of an excess of sodium acetate to UO_2^{2+} solutions in dilute acetic acid, the insoluble salt $Na[UO_2(O_2CMe)_3]$ is precipitated. The uranyl ion is reduced to red-brown U^{3+} by Na/Hg or zinc, and U^{3+} is oxidizable by air to green U^{4+}. The potentials (1 M $HClO_4$) are

$$
UO_2^{2+} \xrightarrow{\ 0.06\ V\ } UO_2^+ \xrightarrow{\ 0.58\ V\ } U^{4+} \xrightarrow{\ -0.63\ V\ } U^{3+} \xrightarrow{\ -1.8\ V\ } U
$$

$$
\underset{0.32\ V}{\underbrace{\hspace{3cm}}}
$$

27-8 Neptunium, Plutonium, and Americium

The extraction of plutonium from uranium fuel elements involves (a) removal of the highly radioactive fission products that are produced simultaneously in comparable amounts, (b) recovery of the uranium for reprocessing, (c) remote control of all the chemical operations because of the radiation hazard. An additional hazard is the extreme toxicity of Pu, 10^{-6} g of which is potentially lethal; a particle of $^{239}PuO_2$ only 1-μm diameter can give a very high dose of radiation, enough to be strongly carcinogenic.

The separation methods of Np, Pu, and Am from U are based on the following chemistry.

1. *Stabilities of oxidation states.* The stabilities of the major ions involved are $UO_2^{2+} > NpO_2^{2+} > PuO_2^{2+} > AmO_2^{2+}$; $Am^{3+} > Pu^{3+} \gg Np^{3+}$, U^{4+}. It is thus possible by choice of suitable oxidizing or reducing agents to obtain a solution containing the elements in different oxidation states; they can then be separated by precipitation or solvent extraction. For example, Pu can be oxidized to PuO_2^{2+} while Am remains as Am^{3+}. The former can then be removed by solvent extraction or the latter by precipitation of AmF_3.

2. *Extractability into organic solvents.* The MO_2^{2+} ions are extracted from nitrate solutions into ethers. The M^{4+} ions are extracted into tributyl phosphate in kerosene from 6 M nitric acid solutions; the M^{3+} ions are

similarly extracted from 10 to 16 M nitric acid, and neighboring actinides can be separated by a choice of conditions.

3. *Precipitation reactions.* Only M^{3+} and M^{4+} give insoluble fluorides or phosphates from acid solutions. The higher oxidation states give either no precipitate or can be prevented from precipitation by complex formation with sulfate or other ions.

4. *Ion exchange methods.* These are used mainly for small amounts of material as in the separation of Am and the following elements, as discussed later.

The following are examples of the separation of Pu from a nitric acid solution of the uranium fuel (plus its aluminum or other protective jacket).

The combination of oxidation–reduction cycles coupled with solvent extraction and/or precipitation methods removes the bulk of fission products (FP's). Certain elements—notably Ru, which forms cationic, neutral, and anionic nitrosyl complexes—may require special elimination steps. The initial uranyl nitrate solution contains Pu^{4+}, since nitric acid cannot oxidize this to Pu^{V} or Pu^{VI}.

Lanthanum Fluoride Cycle

This classical procedure was first developed by McMillan and Abelson for the isolation of neptunium, and is still of great utility. For the U to Pu separation, the cycle in Scheme 27-1 is repeated, with progressively smaller amounts of

UO_2^{2+}
Pu^{4+} $\xrightarrow{\text{Solvent extract}}$ Solvent UO_2^{2+}
FP's

Aqueous Pu^{4+}, FP's, some UO_2^{2+}

Add La^{3+} and HF(aq)

Filtrate: UO_2^{2+} Precipitate LaF_3, PuF_3 $\xrightarrow[\substack{\text{dissolve} \\ \text{hydroxide} \\ \text{in HNO}_3}]{\text{Boil with NaOH then}}$ M^{3+}, M^{4+} $\xrightarrow[\text{or } S_2O_8^{2-} + Ag^+]{BrO_3^- \text{ at } 95°C}$ La^{3+} PuO_2^{2+}

HF(aq)

Repeat cycle $\xleftarrow[\text{La}^{3+}]{\text{Add}}$ Pu^{4+} $\xleftarrow{SO_2}$ Filtrate PuO_2^{2+} Precipitate LaF_3 + most of FP's

Scheme 27-1

lanthanum carrier and smaller volumes of solution, until plutonium becomes the bulk phase.

Tributyl Phosphate Solvent Extraction Cycle

The extraction coefficients from 6 N nitric acid solutions into 30% tributyl phosphate (TBP) in kerosene are $Pu^{4+} > PuO_2^{2+}$; $Np^{4+} \sim NpO_2^+ \gg Pu^{3+}$; $UO_2^{2+} > NpO_2^+ > PuO_2^{2+}$. The M^{3+} ions have very low extraction coefficients in 6 M acid, but from 12 M hydrochloric acid or 16 M nitric acid the extraction increases and the order is Np < Pu < Am < Cm < Bk.

Thus in the U to Pu separation, after addition of NO_2^- to adjust all of the plutonium to Pu^{4+}, we have Scheme 27-2.

$$
\begin{array}{c}
\text{Aqueous}\quad\text{FP's} \\
\uparrow \\
\left.\begin{array}{c} UO_2^{2+} \\ Pu^{4+} \\ FP's \end{array}\right\} \xrightarrow[\text{TBP}]{\text{Extract}} \\
\downarrow \\
\text{Solvent}\quad UO_2^{2+},\ Pu^{4+}
\end{array}
$$

$$
\begin{array}{c}
\xrightarrow[NH_2OH]{SO_2\ \text{or}} \\
\end{array}
$$

$$
\text{Aqueous uranium} \xleftarrow[H_2O]{\text{Strip}} \text{Solvent:}\ UO_2^{2+}\ \text{or}\ U^{4+} \qquad \text{Aqueous:}\ Pu^{3+} \xrightarrow{\text{Oxidize}} Pu^{4+} \\
\downarrow \\
\text{Repeat extraction}
$$

Scheme 27-2

The extraction of ^{237}Np involves similar principles of adjustment of oxidation state and solvent extraction; Pu is reduced by iron(II) sulfamate plus hydrazine to unextractable Pu^{III}, while Np^{IV} remains in the solvent from which it is differentially stripped by water to separate it from U.

The chemistries of U, Np, Pu, and Am are quite similar and solid compounds are usually isomorphous. The main differences are in stabilities of oxidation states in solution.

For Np, the oxidation states are well separated, but by contrast to UO_2^+, NpO_2^+ is reasonably stable. Plutonium chemistry is complicated because the potentials are not well separated and, indeed, in 1 M HClO$_4$ all four oxidation states can coexist.

For Am, the normal state is Am^{3+} and powerful oxidants are required to reach the higher states.

The cations all tend to hydrolyze in water, the ease of hydrolysis being Am > Pu > Np > U and $M^{4+} > MO_2^{2+} > M^{3+} > MO_2^+$. The tendency to complexing also decreases Am > Pu > Np > U.

27-9 The Elements Following Americium

The isotope ^{242}Cm was first isolated among the products of α bombardment of ^{239}Pu, and its discovery actually preceded that of americium. Isotopes of the other elements were first identified in products from the first hydrogen bomb explosion (1952) or in cyclotron bombardments.

Ion-exchange methods have been indispensible in the separation of the elements following americium (often called the trans-americium elements) and also for tracer quantities of Np, Pu, and Am. By comparison with the elution of lanthanide ions, where La is eluted first and Lu last (Section 26-2), and by extrapolating data for Np^{3+} and Pu^{3+} the order of elution of the ions can be predicted accurately. Even a few *atoms* of an element can be identified because of the characteristic nuclear radiation.

The actinides as a group may be separated from lanthanides (always present as fission products from irradiations that produce the actinides) by use of concentrated HCl or 10 *M* LiCl. This occurs because the actinide ions more readily form chloro complex anions than lanthanides. Hence, actinides can be removed from cation exchange resins, or conversely, adsorbed on anion exchange resins. There is also, in addition to the group separation, some separation of Pu, Am, Cm, Bk, and Cf to Es.

The actinide ions are usually separated from each other by elution with citrate or similar elutant; some typical elution curves in which the relative positions of the corresponding lanthanides are also given are shown in Fig. 27-3. Observe that a striking similarity occurs in the spacings of corresponding elements in the two series. There is a distinct break between Gd and Tb and between Cm and Bk, which can be attributed to the small change in ionic radius occasioned by the half-filling of the 4*f* and 5*f* shells, respectively. The elution order is not always as regular as that in Fig. 27-3.

After separation by ion exchange, macro amounts of the actinides can be precipitated by F^- or oxalate; tracer quantities can be collected by using a La^{3+} carrier.

Solid compounds of Cm, Bk, Cf, and Es, mainly oxides and halides, have been characterized.

Figure 27-3   Elution of lanthanide +3 ions (left) and actinide +3 ions (right) from Dowex 50 cation-exchange resin. Buffered ammonium 2-hydroxybutyrate was the elutant. The predicted positions of elements 102 and 103 (unobserved here) are also shown. (Reproduced by permission from J. J. Katz and G. T. Seaborg, *The Chemistry of the Actinide Elements*, Methuen, London, 1957.)

STUDY GUIDE

Study Questions

A. Review

1. Name the actinide elements and list their electron configurations.
2. List the oxidation states for actinide elements.
3. Which actinide isotopes can be obtained in macroscopic amounts?
4. What are characteristic reactions of actinide +3 and +4 ions?
5. Which +3 ion has its $5f$ shell half-full? What oxidation states do the preceding and succeeding elements show?
6. Which actinide element corresponds to Lu?
7. How are actinide metals made? What are their main features?
8. What is the structure of the dioxo ions MO_2^{2+} in, for example, uranyl nitrate hydrate?
9. How is actinium isolated? Which element does it most resemble?
10. What are the main sources of (a) thorium, and (b) uranium?
11. Uranium is usually recovered as uranyl nitrate. How is this converted to the metal?
12. What are the properties and main use of UF_6 ?
13. How is uranium hydride obtained? What are its uses?
14. What elements would the unknown elements 105, 107, 112, and 118 be expected to resemble?

B. Additional Exercises

1. What are the main principles upon which the separations of Np, Pu, and Am from U are made?
2. Describe the lanthanum fluoride cycle for separation of Np or Pu from U.
3. Describe the tributyl phosphate extraction separation of Np and Pu from U.
4. How are the elements Am to Lr usually separated? Why is it first necessary to separate lanthanides as a group from the actinides as a group and how is this done?
5. Compare and contrast the chemistries of the dioxo ions of U, Np, Pu, and Am.

C. Questions from the Literature of Inorganic Chemistry

1. An actinide metallocarborane is described by F. R. Fronczek, G. W. Halstead, and K. N. Raymond, *J. Am. Chem. Soc.*, **1977**, *99*, 1769–1775.
    (a) What reasons do the authors offer (in the introductory paragraphs of this paper) for anticipating that the complex reported here should be stable?
    (b) What is the coordination geometry of the Li^+ counterion for this complex? What are the ligands?
    (c) What is the oxidation state of the uranium in this dicarbollide complex?
    (d) Why can actinide ions (namely, the uranium ion in this complex) accommodate more ligands than typical d-block elements?
    (e) What is the coordination number of U in this dicarbollide complex? Is this to be considered a coordinatively saturated system?

2. A protactinium—oxygen bond was examined by D. Brown, C. T. Reynolds, and P. T. Moseley, *J. Chem. Soc. Dalton Trans.*, **1972**, 857–859.

   (a) What evidence(s) have the authors given to suggest the presence of a Pa=O double bond?

   (b) With what other mono–oxo or dioxo–halogeno complexes does this Pa—O distance compare?

3. Consider the work by R. T. Paine, R. R. Ryan, and L. B. Asprey, *Inorg. Chem.*, **1975**, *14*, 1113–1117.

   (a) Write balanced chemical equations for the hydrolytic preparations reported here of UOF_4 and UO_2F_2.

   (b) How is water slowly obtained in the stoichiometric amounts necessary for limited hydrolysis of UF_6?

   (c) How is the controlled hydrolysis reported here different from total hydrolysis in the presence of excess water?

   (d) What evidence do the authors cite for an oxygen in a "terminal, axial position"? For what other MOF_4 systems is terminal–axial placement of oxygen found?

   (e) How many different coordination environments are realized by F^- groups in this structure?

SUPPLEMENTARY READING

Bagnall, K. W., Ed., *Lanthanides and Actinides*, Butterworths, London, 1972.

Bagnall, K. W., *The Actinide Elements*, Elsevier, Amsterdam, 1972.

Brown, D., "Some Recent Preparative Chemistry of Protactinium," *Adv. Inorg. Chem. Radiochem.*, **1969**, *12*, 1.

Casellato, U., Vigato, P. A., and Vidali, M., "Actinide Complexes with Carboxylic Acids," *Coord. Chem. Rev.*, **1978**, *26*, 85.

Cleveland, J. M., *The Chemistry of Plutonium*, Gordon and Breach, New York, 1970.

Cordfunke, E. H. P., *The Chemistry of Uranium*, Elsevier, Amsterdam, 1969.

Edelstein, M. M., Ed., *Actinides in Perspective*, Pergamon Press, New York, 1982.

Fields, P. R. and Moeller, T., "Lanthanide/Actinide Chemistry," *Advances in Chemistry Series, ACS Monograph No. 71*, American Chemical Society, 1971.

Katz, J. J., Seaborg, G. T., and Morss, L. R., *The Chemistry of the Actininde Elements*, Second Edition, Chapmann and Hall, New York, 1986.

Lodhi, M. A. K., *Superheavy Elements*, Pergamon Press, New York, 1978.

Seaborg, G. T., *Man-Made Transuranium Elements*, Prentice-Hall, New York, 1963.

Seaborg, G. T., *Transuranium Elements, Products of Modern Alchemy*, Academic, New York, 1978.

Taube, M., *Plutonium: A General Survey*, Verlag Chemie, Weinheim, 1974.

Taylor, J. C., "Systematic Features in the Structural Chemistry of the Uranium Halides, Oxyhalides, and Related Transition Metal and Lanthanide Halides," *Coord. Chem. Rev.*, **1976**, *20*, 197.

part 4

SOME SPECIAL TOPICS

chapter 28

METAL CARBONYLS AND OTHER TRANSITION METAL COMPLEXES WITH π-ACCEPTOR (π-ACID) LIGANDS

28-1 Introduction

A characteristic feature of the *d*-group transition metal atoms is their ability to form complexes with a variety of neutral molecules such as carbon monoxide, isocyanides, substituted phosphines, arsines and stibines, nitric oxide, and various molecules with delocalized π orbitals, such as pyridine, 2,2′-bipyridine, and 1,10-phenanthroline (phen). Very diverse types of complexes exist, ranging from binary molecular compounds such as $Cr(CO)_6$ or $Ni(PF_3)_4$ to complex ions such as $[Fe(CN)_5CO]^{3-}$, $[Mo(CO)_5I]^-$, $[Mn(CNR)_6]^+$, and $[V(phen)_3]^+$.

In many of these complexes, the metal atoms are in low-positive, zero, or even negative *formal* oxidation states. It is a characteristic of the ligands now under discussion that they can stabilize low oxidation states. This property is associated with the fact that these ligands have vacant π orbitals in addition to lone pairs. These vacant orbitals accept electron density from filled metal orbitals to form a type of π bonding that supplements the σ bonding arising from lone-pair donation. High electron density on the metal atom—of necessity in low oxidation states—can thus be *delocalized onto the ligands*. The ability of ligands to accept electron density into low-lying empty π orbitals is called π acidity. The word acidity is used in the Lewis sense.

The stoichiometries of most complexes of π-acid ligands can be predicted by use of the noble gas formalism. This requires that the number of valence electrons possessed by the metal atom plus the number of pairs of σ electrons contributed by the ligands be equal to the number of electrons in the succeeding noble gas atom. The basis for this rule is the tendency of the metal atom to use its valence orbitals, nd, $(n + 1)s$, and $(n + 1)p$, as fully as possible, in forming bonds to ligands. Although it is of considerable utility in the design of new compounds, particularly of metal carbonyls, nitrosyls and isocyanides, and their substitution products, it is by no means infallible. It fails altogether for the bipyridine and dithiolene type of ligand, and there are significant exceptions even among carbonyls, such as $V(CO)_6$ and $[Mo(CO)_2(diphos)_2]^+$, where diphos = 1,2-bis(diphenylphosphino)ethane.

CARBON MONOXIDE COMPLEXES

The most important π-acceptor ligand is carbon monoxide. Many carbonyl complexes are of considerable structural interest as well as of importance industrially and in catalytic and other reactions. Carbonyl derivatives of at least one type are known for all of the transition metals. The first metal carbonyls, $Ni(CO)_4$ and $Fe(CO)_5$, were discovered by A. Mond in 1890 and 1891; he developed an industrial process for the isolation of pure nickel based on the formation and subsequent thermal decomposition of the volatile $Ni(CO)_4$.

28-2 Mononuclear Metal Carbonyls

The simplest carbonyls are of the type $M(CO)_x$ (Table 28-1A). The compounds are all hydrophobic, volatile, and soluble to varying degrees in nonpolar solvents. Of the *d*-block metals, the ones that form stable mononuclear carbonyls are principally those that require an integral number of carbonyl ligands to attain the number of valence electrons in the succeeding noble gas atom. The only important exception is vanadium, which forms the $V(CO)_6$ molecule. Since the number of valence electrons for the noble gases is 18, the noble gas formalism may be simplified to the *18-electron rule*—stable metal complexes will be those which, in acquiring electrons from ligands, attain a total of 18 electrons (metal valence electrons + donated ligand electrons) in their valence shell. It obviously becomes necessary to know how to count ligand electrons properly in applying this formalism.

Although there are exceptions, for the majority of simpler transition metal organometallics, and especially for the mononuclear and binuclear metal carbonyls and their derivatives, the 18-electron formalism is useful. We start with the mononuclear binary carbonyls of Table 28-1.

The 18-Electron Rule as Applied to Mononuclear Metal Carbonyls

Group VIA(6) Metals

The stable binary carbonyls are the hexacarbonyls, $M(CO)_6$, because the valence electrons of the metal (six valence electrons for Cr, Mo, or W) plus 12 electrons from the ligands (each of the six CO ligands is considered to be a 2-electron donor) brings the total to 18. Stable derivatives of the mononuclear carbonyls include those where one or more CO groups have been replaced by an equal number of 2-electron donors, so that the total number of electrons provided by ligands remains 12. Two examples are shown in reactions 28-2.1 and 28-2.2:

$$W(CO)_6 + Cl^- \longrightarrow W(CO)_5Cl^- + CO \qquad (28\text{-}2.1)$$

$$Cr(CO)_6 + R_2S \longrightarrow Cr(CO)_5SR_2 + CO \qquad (28\text{-}2.2)$$

Table 28-1 Some Representative Metal Carbonyls and Carbonyl Hydrides

Compound	Color and Form	Structure	Comments
A. Mononuclear Carbonyls			
$V(CO)_6$	Black crystals; decomposes 70 °C; sublimes in vacuum	Octahedral	Yellow orange in solution; paramagnetic $(1e^-)$
$Cr(CO)_6$ $Mo(CO)_6$ $W(CO)_6$	Colorless crystals; all sublime in vacuum	Octahedral	Stable to air; decompose 180–200 °C
$Fe(CO)_5$	Yellow liquid; mp −20 °C bp 103 °C	tbp	Action of UV gives $Fe_2(CO)_9$
$Ru(CO)_5$	Colorless liquid; mp −22 °C	tbp (by IR)	Very volatile and difficult to prepare
$Ni(CO)_4$	Colorless liquid; mp −25 °C bp 43 °C	Tetrahedral	Very toxic; musty smell; flammable; decomposes readily to metal
B. Polynuclear Carbonyls			
$Mn_2(CO)_{10}$[a]	Yellow solid mp 151 °C sublimes 50 °C $(10^{-2}$ mm)	See Fig. 28-2	The Mn—Mn bond is long (2.93 Å) and $Mn_2(CO)_{10}$ is reactive
$Fe_2(CO)_9$	Gold solid mp 100 °C decomposes	See Fig. 28-2	Very insoluble and nonvolatile
$Fe_3(CO)_{12}$	Green-black solid mp 140–150 °C decomposes	See Fig. 28-2	Moderately soluble
$Rh_4(CO)_{12}$	Brick red solid mp 150 °C decomposes sublimes 65 °C $(10^{-2}$ mm)	See Fig. 28-2	Useful reagent for many carbonyl rhodium compounds
C. Carbonyl Hydrides[b]			
$HMn(CO)_5$[a]	Colorless liquid mp −25 °C	Octahedral	Stable at 25 °C, weak acid $\delta = -7.5$ ppm[b]
$H_2Fe(CO)_4$	Yellow liquid, colorless gas mp −70 °C	v. distorted octahedron	Decomposes −10 °C Weak acid $\delta = -10.1$ ppm[b]
$H_2Fe_3(CO)_{11}$	Dark red liquid	Uncertain	
$HCo(CO)_4$	Yellow liquid, colorless gas, mp −20 °C	Distorted tbp	Decomposes above mp, strong acid $\delta = -10$ ppm[b]

[a]Very similar Tc and Re analogs are known.

[b]δ value is position of high-resolution proton magnetic resonance line in parts per million referred to tetramethylsilane reference as 0.0 ppm. Negative values to high field.

where the chloride anion or the thioether are considered to be 2-electron σ donors. Substitution reactions of the Group VIA(6) hexacarbonyls proceed by dissociative mechanisms because loss of a carbonyl ligand to give a 16-electron intermediate is more favorable than gain of an extra ligand (associative mechanism).

Fe(CO)₅

Here it is the pentacarbonyl that is favored. Eight valence electrons from the metal plus 10 from the five CO groups give the stable 18-electron configuration. This occurs similarly for the other members of the group, Ru and Os, although the monomers are unstable towards formation of the polynuclear systems discussed shortly. Replacement of a CO ligand by another 2-electron donor is a common reaction of the iron pentacarbonyl:

$$Fe(CO)_5 + py \longrightarrow Fe(CO)_4py + CO \qquad (28\text{-}2.3)$$

Again, reactions such as Eq. 28-2.3 proceed by dissociative mechanisms because of the greater likelihood of dissociation of a CO group to give a 16-electron intermediate (or transition state) than of ligand gain (associative mechanism), which would exceed the 18-electron configuration. The 18-electron rule requires that 2-electron reduction of $Fe(CO)_5$ as in Eq. 28-2.4:

$$Fe(CO)_5 + 2Na \longrightarrow Na_2[Fe(CO)_4] + CO \qquad (28\text{-}2.4)$$

be accompanied by loss of one CO ligand. Accordingly, the product of reaction 28-2.4 is the tetracarbonyl dianion. Here we consider that 8 electrons from the four CO ligands, 8 from the Fe atom, and 2 electrons that are added to provide the 2 − charge give the stable 18-electron total.

Ni(CO)₄

This nickel compound achieves the 18-electron total by coordination of four CO ligands to the 10-electron nickel center.

28-3 Polynuclear Metal Carbonyls

In each of the mononuclear metal carbonyls mentioned in Section 28-2, an even number of metal valence electrons allowed the 18-electron formalism to be satisfied by coordination from an integral number of 2-electron donor ligands. Where the metal brings an odd number of valence electrons to the structure (Mn, Tc, Re; Co, Rh, or Ir) or where condensation to polynuclear metal carbonyls is thermodynamically favorable (Fe, Ru, or Os), an understanding of how the 18-electron configuration is achieved requires consideration of metal to metal bonds.

There are numerous polynuclear carbonyls that may be homonuclear, for example, $Fe_3(CO)_{12}$, or heteronuclear, for example, $MnRe(CO)_{10}$. In these compounds there are not only linear M—C—O groups but also either M—M bonds alone or M—M bonds plus *bridging carbonyl* groups. The two principal types of bridging group are depicted in Fig. 28-1. The doubly bridging type

Figure 28-1 The two main types of bridging CO groups (a) doubly bridging and (b) triply bridging.

occurs fairly frequently and practically always in conjunction with an M—M bond.

Some important polynuclear carbonyls are listed in Table 28-1B and their structures and those of others are shown in Fig. 28-2.

Bridging CO groups very often occur in pairs, as in structure 28-Ia. Any pair of bridging CO groups can only be regarded as an alternative to a nonbridged arrangement with two terminal groups, as in (structure 28-Ib):

$$\underset{\text{28-Ia}}{\text{M}-\text{M}} \qquad \text{versus} \qquad \underset{\text{28-Ib}}{\text{M}-\text{M}}$$

The relative stabilities of the alternatives appear to depend markedly on the size of the metal atoms. The larger the metal atoms the greater is the preference for a nonbridged structure. Thus, in any group the relative stability of nonbridged structures increases as the group is descended. For example, $Fe_3(CO)_{12}$ has two bridging CO groups while $Ru_3(CO)_{12}$ and $Os_3(CO)_{12}$ have none. The generalization concerning metal atom size also covers the trend horizontally in the periodic table. Thus, the large Mn atoms form only the nonbridged $(OC)_5Mn—Mn(CO)_5$ molecule, whereas the dinuclear cobalt carbonyl, $Co_2(CO)_8$, exists as an equilibrium mixture of the bridged and nonbridged structures.

Carbonyl groups less commonly bridge triangular arrays of three metal atoms [Fig. 28-1(b)] as in $Rh_6(CO)_{16}$ (Fig. 28-2).

The presence of bridging CO groups can often be recognized from the IR spectra of the compounds (see the next section).

The 18-Electron Rule as Applied to Binuclear Metal Carbonyls

The counting of electrons in binuclear metal carbonyls should obey the following conventions:

1. Electrons in metal–metal bonds should be assigned homolytically (divided evenly) among the two metals.

Figure 28-2 The structures of some polynuclear metal carbonyls.

2. Terminal CO groups are considered to be 2-electron donors, as usual; doubly bridging CO groups contribute 1 electron to each metal.

3. Where two isomers arise because of terminal-bridging tautomerism of CO groups, the total number of valence electrons, in either case, should be found to be 18, because the number of valence electrons is unaffected by tautomerism. (Compare structures 28-Ia and 28-Ib, where in each one, each metal atom receives 2 electrons from CO ligands.)

The counting of electrons at each metal develops as follows:

$Mn_2(CO)_{10}$:

Mn	7 valence electrons
Terminal CO groups	$2 \times 5 =$ 10 electrons
Mn—Mn bond	1 electron
Total	18 electrons

$Fe_2(CO)_9$:

Fe	8 valence electrons
Terminal CO groups	$2 \times 3 =$ 6 electrons
Bridging CO groups	$1 \times 3 =$ 3 electrons
Fe—Fe bond	1 electron
Total	18 electrons

$Os_2(CO)_9$:

Os	8 valence electrons (exclusive of f electrons)
Terminal CO groups	$2 \times 4 =$ 8 electrons
Bridging CO group	$1 \times 1 =$ 1 electron
Os—Os bond	1 electron
Total	18 electrons

$Co_2(CO)_8$, the nonbridged isomer:

Co	9 valence electrons
Terminal CO groups	$2 \times 4 =$ 8 electrons
Co—Co bond	1 electron
Total	18 electrons

$Co_2(CO)_8$, the bridged isomer:

Co	9 valence electrons
Terminal CO groups	$2 \times 3 =$ 6 electrons
Bridging CO groups	$1 \times 2 =$ 2 electrons
Co—Co bond	1 electron
Total	18 electrons

The counting of electrons in clusters containing three or more metals is not always such a straightforward affair. Many clusters are found to be "formally" unsaturated, and we shall not pursue the topic here in detail. We may, however, mention two cases where the procedure for a given metal atom is quite easy:

$Ru_3(CO)_{12}$:

Ru		8 valence electrons
Terminal CO groups	$2 \times 4 =$	8 electrons
Two Ru—Ru bonds	$1 \times 2 =$	2 electrons
Total		18 electrons

$Ir_4(CO)_{12}$:

Ir		9 valence electrons
Terminal CO groups	$2 \times 3 =$	6 electrons
Three Ir—Ir bonds	$1 \times 3 =$	3 electrons
Total		18 electrons

28-4 Stereochemical Nonrigidity in Carbonyls

It is very common for bi- and polynuclear metal carbonyls to undergo rapid intramolecular rearrangements in which CO ligands are scrambled over the two or more metal atoms. These scrambling processes are observed and studied by nmr spectroscopy.

In many binuclear compounds the mechanism of scrambling has as its key steps the opening and closing of pairs of bridges, as is illustrated in the following two cases, where Cp represents the C_5H_5 group, which we discuss in detail in Chapter 29. For now, it is sufficient to note that CO groups that are labeled with *, a, or b are scrambled by the processes shown here.

(28-4.1)

(28-4.2)

A more elaborate example is presented by $Rh_4(CO)_{12}$ in which the 12 CO ligands move rapidly over the entire tetrahedral skeleton in a series of steps, each involving the concerted opening or closing of a set of three bridges, as shown here:

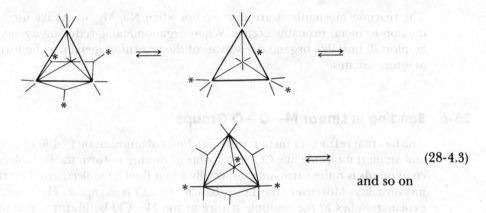

$$(28-4.3)$$

and so on

The ease with which these processes proceed in nearly all cases is attributable to the fact that in most polynuclear carbonyls the bridged and non-bridged structures differ very little in energy and, thus, whichever one is the ground state [cf. the $Cp_2Fe_2(CO)_4$ and $Cp_2Mo_2(CO)_6$ cases] the other provides an energetically accessible intermediate for the scrambling. In the examples cited, the rates at which the individual steps occur at room temperature are in the range of 10 to 10^3 times per second. Thus, in the course of any ordinary chemical reaction, complete scrambling will occur—many times over.

28-5 Preparation of Metal Carbonyls

Although many metals, when prepared in a highly dispersed form, will react with CO, only $Ni(CO)_4$ and $Fe(CO)_5$ are normally made this way. Finely divided nickel will react at room temperature; an appreciable rate of reaction with iron requires elevated temperatures and pressures.

In general, carbonyls are formed when metal compounds are reduced in the presence of CO. Usually high pressures (200–300 atm) of CO are required. In some cases, CO itself serves as the only necessary reducing agent, for example,

$$Re_2O_7 + 17CO \longrightarrow Re_2(CO)_{10} + 7CO_2 \qquad (28-5.1)$$

but usually an additional reducing agent is needed, typical ones being H_2, metals such as Na, Al, Mg, Cu, or compounds such as a trialkylaluminum or $Ph_2CO^-Na^+$

$$2CoCO_3 + 2H_2 + 8CO \xrightarrow[120-150\ °C]{250-300\ atm}$$

$$Co_2(CO)_8 + 2CO_2 + 2H_2O \qquad (28-5.2)$$

$$2Mn(acac)_2 + 10CO \xrightarrow{(C_2H_5)_3Al} Mn_2(CO)_{10} \tag{28-5.3}$$

$$CrCl_3 + 6CO \xrightarrow{C_6H_5MgBr} Cr(CO)_6 \tag{28-5.4}$$

The reaction mechanisms are obscure but when Na, Mg, or Al are used, reduction to metal probably occurs. When organometallic reducing agents are employed, unstable organo derivatives of the transition metal may be formed as intermediates.

28-6   Bonding in Linear M—C—O Groups

The fact that refractory metals, with high heats of atomization ($\sim$400 kJ mol^{-1}), and an inert molecule like CO are capable of uniting to form stable, molecular compounds is quite surprising, especially when the CO molecules retain their individuality. Moreover, the Lewis basicity of CO is *negligible*. However, the explanation lies in the multiple nature of the M—CO bond, for which there is much evidence, some of it semiquantitative.

Although we can formulate the bonding in terms of a resonance hybrid of structures 28-IIa and 28-IIb, a MO formulation is more detailed and ac-

$$\bar{M}\!-\!\overset{+}{C}\!\!\equiv\!\!O\!: \longleftrightarrow M\!\!=\!\!C\!\!=\!\!\ddot{O}\!:$$
28-IIa   28-IIb

curate. First, there is a dative overlap of the filled carbon σ orbital [Fig. 28-3(*a*)] and, second, a dative overlap of a filled *d*π or hybrid *dp*π metal orbital with an empty antibonding *p*π orbital of the carbon monoxide [Fig. 28-3(*b*)]. This bonding mechanism is synergic, since the drift of metal electrons into CO orbitals will tend to make the CO as a whole negative and, hence, to increase

(*a*)

(*b*)

Figure 28-3   (*a*) The formation of the metal←CO σ bond using a lone electron pair (most likely in an *sp* hybrid) on carbon. (*b*) The formation of the metal→CO π back-bond. Ther orbitals on the CO ligand are omitted for clarity.

its basicity via the σ orbital of carbon; also the drift of electrons to the metal in the σ bond tends to make the CO positive, thus enhancing the acceptor strength of the π orbitals. Thus, the effects of σ-bond formation strengthen the π bonding and vice versa.

The main lines of physical evidence showing the multiple nature of the M—CO bonds are bond lengths and vibrational spectra. According to the preceding description of the bonding, as the extent of back-donation from M to CO increases, the M—C bond becomes stronger and the C≡O bond becomes weaker. Thus the multiple bonding should be evidenced by shorter M—C and longer C—O bonds as compared with M—C single bonds and C≡O triple bonds, respectively. Although C—O bond lengths are rather insensitive to bond order, for M—C bonds in selected compounds there *is* appreciable shortening consistent with the π-bonding concept.

28-7 Vibrational Spectra of Metal Carbonyls

Infrared spectra have been widely used in the study of metal carbonyls since the C—O stretching frequencies give very strong sharp bands well separated from other vibrational modes of any other ligands that may also be present.

The CO molecule has a stretching frequency of 2143 cm^{-1}. Terminal CO groups in neutral metal carbonyl molecules are found in the range 2125–1850 cm^{-1}, showing the reduction in CO bond orders. Moreover, when changes are made that should increase the extent of M—C back-bonding, the CO frequencies are shifted to even lower values. Thus, if some CO groups are replaced by ligands with low or negligible back-accepting ability, those CO groups that remain must accept more $d\pi$ electrons from the metal to prevent the accumulation of negative charge on the metal atom. Hence, the frequency for $Cr(CO)_6$ is ca. 2000 cm^{-1} (exact values vary with phase and solvent) whereas, when three CO groups are replaced by amine groups that have essentially no ability to back-accept, as in $Cr(CO)_3(dien)$, dien = $NH(CH_2CH_2NH_2)_2$, there are two CO stretching modes with frequencies of ~1900 and 1760 cm^{-1}. Similarly, in $V(CO)_6^-$, where more negative charge must be taken from the metal atom, a band is found at ~1860 cm^{-1} corresponding to the one found at ~2000 cm^{-1} in $Cr(CO)_6$. Conversely, a change that would tend to inhibit the shift of electrons from metal to CO π orbitals, such as placing a positive charge on the metal, should cause the CO frequencies to rise, for example,

$$Mn(CO)_6^+ \sim 2090 \qquad Mn(dien)(CO)_3^+ \sim 2020, \sim 1900$$

$$Cr(CO)_6 \sim 2000 \qquad Cr(dien)(CO)_3 \sim 1900, \sim 1760$$

$$V(CO)_6^- \sim 1860$$

The most important use of IR spectra of CO compounds is in *structural* diagnosis, whereby bridging and terminal CO groups can be recognized.

For terminal M—CO the frequencies of C—O stretches range from 1850 to 2125 cm^{-1} but for bridging CO groups the range is from 1750 to 1850 cm^{-1}. Figure 28-4 shows how these facts may be used to infer structures. Observe that $Fe_2(CO)_9$ has strong bands in both the terminal and the bridging regions. From this alone it could be inferred that the structure must contain

Figure 28-4   The IR spectra in the CO stretching region of (*a*) solid $Fe_2(CO)_9$, and (*b*) $Os_3(CO)_{12}$ in solution. Notice the greater sharpness of the solution spectrum. The most desirable spectra are those obtained in nonpolar solvents or in the gas phase.

both types of CO groups; X-ray study shows that this is true. For $Os_3(CO)_{12}$ several structures consistent with the general rules of valence can be envisioned; some of these would have bridging CO groups, while the actual one (Fig. 28-2) does not. The IR spectrum alone [Fig. 28-4(*b*)] shows that no structure with bridging CO groups is acceptable, since there is no absorption band below $2000 \ cm^{-1}$.

In using the *positions* of CO stretching bands to infer the presence of bridging CO groups, certain conditions must be remembered. The frequencies of terminal CO stretches can be quite low if (a) there are ligands present that are good donors but poor π acceptors, or (b) there is a net negative charge on the species. In either case, back-donation to the CO groups becomes very extensive, thus increasing the M—C bond orders, decreasing the C—O bond orders, and driving the CO stretching frequencies down.

28-8   Reactions of Metal Carbonyls

The variety of reactions of the various carbonyls is so large that only a few types can be mentioned. For $Mo(CO)_6$ and $Fe(CO)_5$, Fig. 28-5 gives an indication of the extensive chemistry that any individual carbonyl typically has.

The most important general reactions of carbonyls are those in which CO groups are displaced by ligands, such as PX_3, PR_3, $P(OR)_3$, SR_2, NR_3, OR_2, RNC, and so on, or unsaturated organic molecules, such as C_6H_6 or cycloheptatriene. Derivatives of organic molecules are discussed in Chapter 29.

Another important general reaction is that with bases (OH^-, H^-, NH_2^-) leading to the carbonylate anions that are discussed in Section 28-9.

Substitution reactions may proceed by either thermal or photochemical activation. In some instances, only the photochemical reaction is practical. Generally, the photochemical process involves first expulsion of a CO group after absorption of a photon, followed by entry of the substituent into the

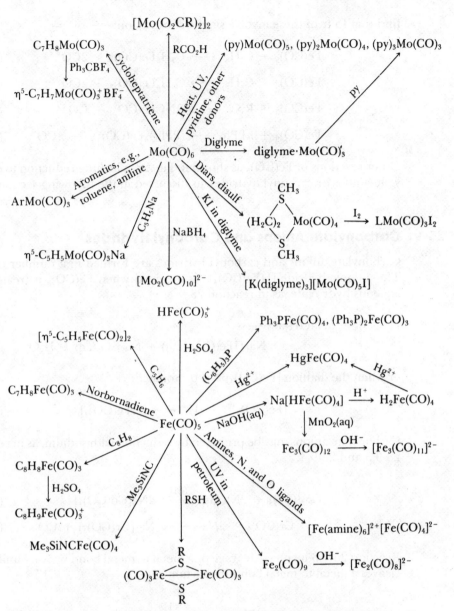

Figure 28-5 Some reactions of the carbonyls $Mo(CO)_6$ and $Fe(CO)_5$. Further discussion is given in the text.

coordination sphere. For example,

$$Cr(CO)_6 \xrightarrow[-CO]{h\nu} Cr(CO)_5 \xrightarrow{+L} Cr(CO)_5L \qquad (28\text{-}8.1)$$

The advantage offered by the photochemical route of reaction 28-8.1 is that di- and trisubstituted products can be avoided.

If we consider further the reactions of $Fe(CO)_5$ as shown in Fig. 28-5, we find that four of these involve simple substitution:

$$Fe(CO)_5 + C_7H_8 \longrightarrow C_7H_8Fe(CO)_3 + 2CO \qquad (28\text{-}8.2)$$

$$Fe(CO)_5 + C_8H_8 \longrightarrow C_8H_8Fe(CO)_3 + 2CO \qquad (28\text{-}8.3)$$

$$Fe(CO)_5 + RNC \longrightarrow RNCFe(CO)_4 + CO \qquad (28\text{-}8.4)$$

$$Fe(CO)_3 + n\,PPh_3 \longrightarrow (PPh_3)_n Fe(CO)_{5-n} + nCO \qquad (28\text{-}8.5)$$

Other reactions of $Fe(CO)_5$ as shown in Fig. 28-5 include reduction to carbonylate anions or carbonyl hydrides, as discussed in the following section.

28-9 Carbonylate Anions and Carbonyl Hydrides

Carbonylate anions and carbonyl hydrides are formed in a number of ways. The anionic hydride $[HFe(CO)_4]^-$ is obtained when $Fe(CO)_5$ is treated with aqueous hydroxide, as in reaction 28-9.1:

$$Fe(CO)_5 + 3NaOH(aq) \longrightarrow$$
$$Na[HFe(CO)_4](aq) + Na_2CO_3(aq) + H_2O \qquad (28\text{-}9.1)$$

or when the dianion $[Fe(CO)_4]^{2-}$ is protonated:

$$[Fe(CO)_4]^{2-} + H^+ \longrightarrow [HFe(CO)_4]^- \qquad (28\text{-}9.2)$$

Carbonylate anions may be prepared by reduction with sodium, as in reactions 28-9.3 and 28-9.4:

$$Co_2(CO)_8 + 2Na/Hg \xrightarrow{\text{THF}} 2Na[Co(CO)_4] \qquad (28\text{-}9.3)$$

$$Cr(CO)_6 + 2Na \longrightarrow Na_2[Cr(CO)_5] + CO \qquad (28\text{-}9.4)$$

Reaction 28-9.3 involves cleavage of a metal to metal bond by Na. Similarly, Li cleaves a metal to metal bond in reaction 28-9.5:

$$Mn_2(CO)_{10} + 2Li \xrightarrow{\text{THF}} 2Li[Mn(CO)_5] \qquad (28\text{-}9.5)$$

The cobalt tetracarbonyl anion may also be prepared by reaction 28-9.6:

$$2Co^{2+}(aq) + 11CO + 12OH^- \xrightarrow{\text{KCN(aq)}} 2[Co(CO)_4]^-$$
$$+ 3CO_3^{2-} + 6H_2O \qquad (28\text{-}9.6)$$

The stoichiometries of the simpler carbonylate anions obey the 18-electron rule (noble gas formalism). Most of them are readily oxidized by air. The alkali metal salts are soluble in water, from which they can be precipitated by large cations such as $[Ph_4As]^+$. In the presence of water and other weak acids, though, many of the carbonylate anions can be protonated to give hydrides.

An important general reaction of carbonylate anions is with halogen compounds. Thus with alkyl halides and with acyl halides we have reactions 28-9.7 and 28-9.8:

$$[Fe(CO)_4]^{2-} + RX \longrightarrow [RFe(CO)_4]^- + X^- \qquad (28\text{-}9.7)$$

$$[Fe(CO)_4]^{2-} + RC(O)Cl \longrightarrow [RC(O)Fe(CO)_4]^- + X^- \qquad (28\text{-}9.8)$$

which proceed by classic S_N2 mechanisms to give metal alkyls and metal acyls, respectively. As another example, consider the formation of a metal to carbon bond as in reaction 28-9.9:

$$Mn(CO)_5^- + ClCH_2CH{=}CH_2 = (CO)_5MnCH_2CH{=}CH_2 + Cl^- \qquad (28\text{-}9.9)$$

In addition, metal to metal bonds may be formed, as in reactions 28-9.10 and 28-9.11:

$$[Fe(CO)_4]^{2-} + 2Ph_3PAuCl \longrightarrow (Ph_3PAu)_2Fe(CO)_4 + 2Cl^- \qquad (28\text{-}9.10)$$

$$Co(CO)_4^- + Mn(CO)_5Br \longrightarrow (OC)_4CoMn(CO)_5 + Br^- \qquad (28\text{-}9.11)$$

As has already been mentioned, hydrides corresponding to carbonylate anions can be isolated. A few of the neutral ones are listed in Table 28-1C, along with their properties. These neutral carbonyl hydrides are usually rather unstable. They can be obtained by acidification of the appropriate alkali carbonylates, as in reactions 28-9.12 or 28-9.13:

$$Na[Co(CO)_4] + H^+(aq) \longrightarrow HCo(CO)_4 + Na^+(aq) \qquad (28\text{-}9.12)$$

$$Na_2[Fe(CO)_4] + 2H^+ \longrightarrow H_2Fe(CO)_4 + 2Na^+ \qquad (28\text{-}9.13)$$

They may also be obtained by reduction of metal halides as in reaction 28-9.14:

$$Fe(CO)_4I_2 \xrightarrow{\text{NaBH}_4 \text{ in THF}} H_2Fe(CO)_4 \qquad (28\text{-}9.14)$$

or by cleavage of metal to metal bonds by H_2

$$Mn_2(CO)_{10} + H_2 \xrightarrow[\text{200 °C}]{\text{200 atm}} 2HMn(CO)_5 \qquad (28\text{-}9.15)$$

$$Co_2(CO)_8 + H_2 \longrightarrow 2HCo(CO)_4 \qquad (28\text{-}9.16)$$

Reaction 28-9.17 is another route to the neutral carbonyl hydride of cobalt:

$$Co + 4CO + \tfrac{1}{2}H_2 \xrightarrow[\text{150 °C}]{\text{50 atm}} HCo(CO)_4 \qquad (28\text{-}9.17)$$

The neutral carbonyl hydrides are slightly soluble in water where they behave as acids, ionizing to give carbonylate anions, as in Eqs. 28-9.18 to 28-9.20:

$$HMn(CO)_5 = H^+ + [Mn(CO)_5]^- \qquad pK \sim 7 \qquad (28\text{-}9.18)$$

$$H_2Fe(CO)_4 = H^+ + [HFe(CO)_4]^- \qquad pK_1 \sim 4 \qquad (28\text{-}9.19)$$

$$HCo(CO)_4 = H^+ + [Co(CO)_4]^- \qquad \text{Strong acid} \qquad (28\text{-}9.20)$$

The neutral carbonyl hydrides have structures in which the hydrogen atom occupies a regular place in the coordination polyhedron, and the M—H distances are approximately equal to the values expected from the sum of the single-bond covalent radii. A good example is afforded by the structure of $HMn(CO)_5$, shown in Fig. 28-6. For purposes of electron counting, the hydrogen atom can be considered to add one electron to the $M(CO)_n$ entity to which it is attached.

In contrast to the neutral carbonyl hydrides, in the anionic hydrido carbonyls such as $[HM(CO)_5]^-$, where M = Cr or W, and the previously mentioned $[HFe(CO)_4]^-$, the hydrogen atoms have much more hydridic character. Consequently, the anionic hydrides are not proton donors, but can be hydride (H^-) donors. In this way they find application as reducing agents for alkyl halides or acid chlorides as in Eqs. 28-9.21 and 28-9.22:

$$RX + [HFe(CO)_4]^- \longrightarrow RH + [XFe(CO)_4]^- \qquad (28\text{-}9.21)$$

$$RC(O)Cl + [HCr(CO)_5]^- \longrightarrow RC(O)H + [ClCr(CO)_5]^- \qquad (28\text{-}9.22)$$

In nonpolar solvents, and in the presence of acids such as acetic acid, the

Figure 28-6 The structure of the neutral hydride $HMn(CO)_5$, showing the stereochemical activity of the hydrogen atom and the metal–hydrogen distance (which approximates the sum of the normal covalent radii).

anionic hydrides are also useful as reducing agents for aldehydes and ketones, giving alcohols as in reactions 28-9.23 and 28-9.24:

$$RC(O)H + [HCr(CO)_5]^- + HOAc \longrightarrow$$
$$RCH_2OH + [(OAc)Cr(CO)_5]^- \qquad (28\text{-}9.23)$$

$$RC(O)R' + [HCr(CO)_5]^- + HOAc \longrightarrow$$
$$RCH(OH)R' + [(OAc)Cr(CO)_5]^- \qquad (28\text{-}9.24)$$

In the presence of strong acids, or with time in the presence of weak acids, most anionic hydrido carbonyls decompose via loss of H_2.

28-10 Carbonyl Halides and Related Compounds

Carbonyl halides, $M_x(CO)_yX_z$, are known for most of the elements forming binary carbonyls and also for Pd, Pt, Au, Cu^I, and Ag^I. They are obtained either by the direct interaction of metal halides and carbon monoxide, usually at high pressure, or by the cleavage of polynuclear carbonyls by halogens:

$$Mn_2(CO)_{10} + Br_2 \xrightarrow{40\ ^\circ C} 2Mn(CO)_5Br \underset{\substack{CO \\ 150\ atm}}{\overset{\substack{in\ petrol \\ at\ 120\ ^\circ C}}{\rightleftharpoons}}$$
$$[Mn(CO)_4Br]_2 + 2CO \qquad (28\text{-}10.1)$$

$$RuI_3 + 2CO \xrightarrow{220\ ^\circ C} [Ru(CO)_2I_2]_n + \tfrac{1}{2}I_2 \qquad (28\text{-}10.2)$$

$$2PtCl_2 + 2CO \longrightarrow [Pt(CO)Cl_2]_2 \qquad (28\text{-}10.3)$$

Examples of the halides and some of their properties are listed in Table 28-2. Carbonyl halide anions are also known; they are often derived by reaction of ionic halides with metal carbonyls or substituted carbonyls:

$$M(CO)_6 + R_4N^+X^- \xrightarrow{diglyme} R_4N^+[M(CO)_5X]^- + CO$$
$$M = Cr, Mo, W \qquad (28\text{-}10.4)$$

$$Mn_2(CO)_{10} + 2R_4N^+X^- \longrightarrow (R_4N^+)_2[Mn_2(CO)_8X_2]^{2-} + 2CO \qquad (28\text{-}10.5)$$

Dimeric or polymeric carbonyl halides are invariably bridged through the halogen atoms and not by carbonyl bridges, for example, in structures 28-III and 28-IV.

28-III   28-IV

Table 28-2 Some Examples of Carbonyl Halide Complexes

Compound	Form	mp °C	Comment
$Mn(CO)_5Cl$	Pale yellow crystals	Sublimes	Loses CO at 120 °C in organic solvents; can be substituted by pyridine, and so on
$[Re(CO)_4Cl]_2$	White crystals	Decomp. >250	Halogen bridges cleavable by donor ligands or by CO (pressure)
$[Ru(CO)_2I_2]_n$	Orange powder	Stable >200	Halide bridges cleavable by ligands
$[Pt(CO)Cl_2]_2$	Yellow crystals	195; sublimes	Hydrolyzed by H_2O; PCl_3 replaces CO

The halogen bridges can be broken by numerous donor ligands such as pyridine, substituted phosphines, isocyanides, and so on, as in the following reaction:

28-V

$$(28\text{-}10.6)$$

28-VI

CARBON MONOXIDE ANALOGS

28-11 Isocyanide Complexes

An isocyanide, $R—N{\equiv}C:$, is very similar electronically to $:O{\equiv}C:$, and there are many isocyanide complexes stoichiometrically analogous to metal carbonyls. Isocyanides can occupy bridging as well as terminal positions. Examples are such crystalline air-stable compounds as red $Cr(CNPh)_6$, white

[Mn(CNCH₃)₆]I, and orange Co(CO)(NO)(CNC₇H₇)₂, all of which are soluble in benzene.

Isocyanides generally appear to be stronger σ donors than CO, and various complexes such as [Ag(CNR)₄]⁺, [Fe(CNR)₆]²⁺, and [Mn(CNR)₆]²⁺ are known where π bonding is of relatively little importance; derivatives of this type are not known for CO. However, the isocyanides are capable of extensive back-acceptance of π electrons from metal atoms in low oxidation states. This is indicated qualitatively by their ability to form compounds such as Cr(CNR)₆ and Ni(CNR)₄, analogous to the carbonyls and more quantitatively by C≡N stretching frequencies which, like CO stretching frequencies, are markedly lowered when the ligand acts as a π acid.

28-12 Dinitrogen (N₂) Complexes

The fact that CO and N₂ are isoelectronic had for years led to speculation as to the possible existence of M—NN bonds analogous to M—CO bonds, but it was only in 1965 that the first example, [Ru(NH₃)₅N₂]Cl₂, was reported. Subsequent work has shown that the [Ru(NH₃)₅N₂]²⁺ cation can be obtained in a number of ways, for example,

by reaction of N₂H₄ with aqueous RuCl₃
by reaction of NaN₃ with [Ru(NH₃)₅(H₂O)]³⁺
by reaction of N₂ with [Ru(NH₃)₅H₂O]²⁺
by reaction of RuCl₃(aq) with Zn in NH₃(aq)

Of these the direct reaction with N₂ to displace H₂O is perhaps most notable. Despite much study, no effective way of reducing coordinated N₂ to NH₃ has yet been found. However, there are several systems in which reduction of N₂ to NH₃ and/or N₂H₄ is catalyzed by low-valent metal compounds, presumably via transient M—N₂ complexes.

A *bridging* N₂ ligand, of the M-N-N-M type, is formed in the reaction

$$[Ru(NH_3)_5Cl]^{2+} \xrightarrow[N_2]{Zn/Hg} \{[Ru(NH_3)_5]_2N_2\}^{4+} \qquad (28\text{-}12.1)$$

The terminal-type N₂ ligands have strong IR bands in the range 1930–2230 cm⁻¹ (100–400 cm⁻¹ below that of free N₂, 2331 cm⁻¹) that may be used diagnostically.

The formation of N₂ complexes by direct uptake of N₂ gas at 1 atm has been observed, especially with tertiary phosphine ligands in reactions such as

$$Co(acac)_3 + 3Ph_3P + N_2 \xrightarrow{Al(iso\text{-}C_4H_9)_3} Co(H)(N_2)(Ph_3P)_3 \qquad (28\text{-}12.2)$$

$$FeCl_2 + 3PEtPh_2 + N_2 \xrightarrow{NaBH_4,\ EtOH} FeH_2(N_2)(PEtPh_2)_3 \qquad (28\text{-}12.3)$$

$$MoCl_4(PPhMe_2)_2 + N_2 + 2PPhMe_2 \xrightarrow{Na/Hg\ in\ THF}$$
$$cis\text{-}Mo(N_2)_2(PPhMe_2)_4 \qquad (28\text{-}12.4)$$

Several typical compounds containing M—NN groups have been structurally characterized. The three atom chains are essentially linear, the N—N distances are slightly longer than that in the N_2 molecule, and the M—N distances are short enough to indicate some multiple bond character.

The bonding in M—N_2 groups is similar to that in terminal M—CO groups. The same two basic components, M $\leftarrow N_2$ σ donation and M $\rightarrow N_2$ π acceptance, are involved. The major quantitative differences, which account for the lower stability of N_2 complexes, arise from small differences in the energies of the molecular orbitals of CO and N_2. It appears that N_2 is weaker than CO in both its σ-donor and π-acceptor functions, which accounts for the poor stability of N_2 complexes in general.

28-13 Thiocarbonyl Complexes

The CS molecule, unlike CO, does not exist under ordinary conditions, although it can be made in dilute gas streams by photolysis of CS_2. Nevertheless, CS can be stabilized by complexing and a few compounds are known. Thus $RhCl(PPh_3)_3$ reacts with CS_2 to give $RhCl(\eta^1\text{-}CS_2)(\eta^2\text{-}CS_2)(PPh_3)_2$, which in methanol gives *trans*-$RhCl(CS)(PPh_3)_2$.

Thiocarbonyl complexes have CS stretches in the region 1270–1360 cm^{-1}, depending on the oxidation state of the metal, charge on the complex, and the like, whereas the stretch for CS trapped in a matrix at $-190\,°C$ is at 1274 cm^{-1}. The $d\pi$–$p\pi$ bonding is similar to that for the carbonyls.

28-14 Nitrogen Monoxide Complexes

The NO molecule is similar to CO except that it contains one more electron, which occupies a π* orbital (cf. Section 3-6). Consistent with this similarity, CO and NO form many comparable complexes although, as a result of the presence of the additional electron, NO also forms a class (bent MNO) with no carbonyl analogs.

Linear, Terminal MNO Groups

We have seen that the CO group reacts with a metal atom that presents an empty σ orbital and a pair of filled $d\pi$ orbitals, as is illustrated in Fig. 28-3, to give a linear MCO grouping with a C $\rightarrow$ M σ bond and a significant degree of M$\rightarrow$C π bonding. The NO group engages in an entirely analogous interaction with a metal atom that may be considered, at least formally, to present an empty σ orbital and a pair of $d\pi$ orbitals containing only three electrons. The full set of four electrons for the M$d\pi \rightarrow \pi$*(NO) interactions is thus made up of three electrons from M and one from NO. In effect, NO contributes three electrons to the total bonding configuration under circumstances where CO contributes only two. Thus, for purposes of formal electron "bookkeeping," the ligand NO can be regarded as a three-electron donor in the same sense as the ligand CO is considered a two-electron donor. This leads to the following very useful general rules concerning stoichiometry, which may be applied without specifically allocating the difference in the number of electrons to any particular (i.e., σ or π) orbitals:

1. Compounds isoelectronic with one containing an M(CO)$_n$ grouping are

those containing $M'(CO)_{n-1}(NO)$, $M''(CO)_{n-2}(NO)_2$, and so on, where M', M'', and so on, have atomic numbers that are 1, 2, ..., and so on, less than M. Some examples are

(a) $(\eta^5\text{-}C_5H_5)Cu(CO)$, $(\eta^5\text{-}C_5H_5)Ni(NO)$;

(b) $Fe(CO)_5$, $Mn(CO)_4(NO)$; and

(c) $Ni(CO)_4$, $Co(CO)_3(NO)$, $Fe(CO)_2(NO)_2$, $Mn(CO)(NO)_3$, and $Cr(NO)_4$.

The isoelectronic and isostructural series in (c) is the longest one known. All are, like $Ni(CO)_4$, tetrahedral molecules.

2. Three CO groups can be replaced by two NO groups. Examples of pairs of compounds so related are

$$Fe(CO)_5 \qquad Fe(CO)_2(NO)_2$$
$$Mn(CO)_4NO \qquad Mn(CO)(NO)_3$$

Structural data suggest that under comparable circumstances M—CO and M—NO bonds are about equally strong, but in a chemical sense the M—N bonds appear to be stronger, since substitution reactions on mixed carbonyl–nitrosyl compounds typically result in displacement of CO in preference to NO. For example, $Co(CO)_3NO$ reacts with R_3P, X_3P, amine, and RNC ligands, invariably to yield the $Co(CO)_2(NO)L$ product.

The NO vibration frequencies for linear MNO groups substantiate the idea of extensive M to N π bonding, leading to appreciable population of NO π^* orbitals. Nitrogen monoxide has its unpaired electron in a π^* orbital; the N—O stretching frequency is 1860 cm^{-1}. For typical linear MNO groups in molecules with small or zero charge, the observed frequencies are in the range 1800–1900 cm^{-1}. This indicates the presence of approximately one electron pair shared between metal $d\pi$ and NO π^* orbitals.

Bent, Terminal MNO Groups

It has long been known that NO can form single bonds to univalent groups such as halogens and alkyl radicals, affording the bent species

Metal atoms with suitable electron configurations and partial coordination shells may bind NO in a similar way. This type of NO complex is formed when the incompletely coordinated metal ion, L_nM, would have a $t_{2g}^6 e_g^1$ configuration, thus being prepared to form one more single σ bond. The M—N—O angles are in, or near, the range 120–140°. Typical compounds are $[Co(NH_3)_5NO]Br_2$ and $IrCl_2(PPh_3)_2NO$.

Bridging NO Groups

These are less common than bridging CO groups, but well-established cases of both double and triple bridges are known. As in carbonyls, the bridging NO frequencies are at lower frequencies than terminal ones.

Bridging NO groups are also to be regarded as three-electron donors. The doubly bridging ones may be represented as

$$\ddot{\text{N}}::\ddot{\text{O}}$$

where the additional electron required to form two metal to nitrogen single bonds is supplied by one of the metal atoms.

28-15 Complexes of Group VB(15) and Group VIB(16) Ligands

Trivalent phosphorus, arsenic, antimony, and bismuth compounds, as well as divalent sulfur and selenium compounds, can give complexes with transition metals. These donors are, of course, quite strong Lewis bases and give complexes with Lewis acids such as BR_3 compounds where d orbitals are not involved. However, the donor atoms do also have empty $d\pi$ orbitals and back-acceptance into these orbitals is possible, as is shown in Fig. 28-7.

Based on IR data an extensive series of ligands involving Group VB(15) and Group VIB(16) donor atoms can be arranged in the following order of decreasing π acidity:

$$CO \sim PF_3 > PCl_3 \sim AsCl_3 \sim SbCl_3 > PCl_2(OR) > PCl_2R > PCl(OR)_2$$
$$> PClR_2 \sim P(OR)_3 > PR_3 \sim AsR_3 \sim SbR_3 \sim SR_2$$

It is noteworthy that IR spectral evidence, as well as photoelectron spectroscopy, shows that PF_3 is as good or better than CO as a π acid. It is not then surprising that PF_3 forms an extensive group of $M_x(PF_3)_y$ compounds, many of which are analogs of corresponding $M_x(CO)_y$ compounds and some of which, for example, $Pd(PF_3)_4$ and $Pt(PF_3)_4$, are more stable than their carbonyl analogs, which can be observed only at very low temperatures.

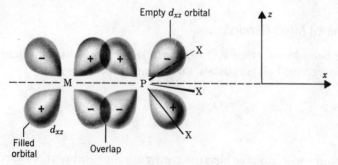

Figure 28-7 Diagram showing the π back-bonding from a filled metal d orbital to an empty phosphorus $3d$ orbital of the PX_3 ligand, taking the z axis as the M—P bond axis. A similar overlap occurs in the yz plane using the d_{yz} orbital.

The other Group VB(15) and VIB(16) ligands are all capable of replacing some CO groups, to form compounds such as $(R_3P)_3Mo(CO)_3$ or even $(R_3P)_4Mo(CO)_2$, but rarely can they replace all CO groups starting from a carbonyl. However, by special methods (such as cocondensation of metal atoms with Me_3P, or by treating metal compounds with diphosphines under strongly reducing conditions), products such as $Mo(PMe_3)_6$ and $Mo(Me_2PCH_2CH_2PMe_2)_3$ can be obtained.

28-16 Cyanide Complexes

The formation of cyanide complexes is restricted almost entirely to the transition metals of the d block and their near neighbors Zn, Cd, and Hg. This suggests that metal—CN π bonding is of importance in the stability of cyanide complexes, and there is evidence of various types to support this. However, the π-accepting tendency of CN^- is much lower than for CO, NO, or RNC. This is, of course, reasonable in view of its negative charge. CN^- is a strong σ donor so that back-bonding does not have to be invoked to explain the stability of its complexes with metals in normal (i.e., II, III) oxidation states. Nonetheless, because of the formal similarity of CN^- to CO, NO, and RNC, it is convenient to discuss its complexes in this chapter.

The majority of cyano complexes have the general formula $[M^{n+}(CN)_x]^{(x-n)-}$ and are anionic, such as $[Fe(CN)_6]^{4-}$, $[Ni(CN)_4]^{2-}$, and $[Mo(CN)_8]^{3-}$. Mixed complexes, particularly of the type $[M(CN)_5X]^{n-}$, where X may be H_2O, NH_3, CO, NO, H, or a halogen, are also well known.

Although bridging cyanide groups might be expected in analogy with those formed by CO, none has been definitely proved. However, linear bridges, M—CN—M, are well known and play an important part in the structures of many crystalline cyanides and cyano complexes. Thus AuCN, $Zn(CN)_2$, and $Cd(CN)_2$ are all polymeric with infinite chains.

The free anhydrous acids corresponding to many cyano anions can be isolated, examples being $H_3[Rh(CN)_6]$ and $H_4[Fe(CN)_6]$. These acids are different from those corresponding to many other complex ions, such as $[PtCl_6]^{2-}$ or $[BF_4]^-$, which cannot be isolated except as hydroxonium (H_3O^+) salts. They are also different from metal carbonyl hydrides in that they do not contain metal to hydrogen bonds. Instead, the hydrogen atoms are situated in hydrogen bonds between anions, that is, MCN---H---NCM.

STUDY GUIDE

Study Questions

A. Review

1. For each of the π-acceptor ligands mentioned in this chapter, state the nature of the acceptor orbital(s).

2. Write the formulas for the mononuclear metal carbonyl molecules formed by V, Cr, Fe, and Ni. Which ones satisfy the noble gas formalism?

3. Why are the simplest carbonyls of the metals Mn, Tc, Re and Co, Rh, Ir groups polynuclear?

4. Explain, with necessary orbital diagrams, how CO, which has negligible donor properties toward simple acceptors such as BF_3 can form strong bonds to transition metal atoms.

5. In what ways can CO be bound to a metal atom?

6. Discuss and explain the trend in CO stretching frequencies in the series $V(CO)_6^-$, $Cr(CO)_6$, $Mn(CO)_6^+$.

7. Draw the structures of $Fe_2(CO)_9$, $Ru_3(CO)_{12}$, and $Rh_4(CO)_{12}$.

8. Which are the only two metals to react directly with CO under conditions suitable for practical syntheses?

9. What is the general type of reaction used to prepare metal carbonyls? State the main ingredients, the function of each, and some examples.

10. How are the following compounds made? What are their principal physical characteristics?
    (a) $Fe(CO)_5$ from iron powder
    (b) $Co_2(CO)_8$ from hydrated cobalt (II) sulfate
    (c) $Cr(CO)_6$ from hydrated chromium (III) chloride
    (d) $Mn_2(CO)_{10}$ from hydrated manganese (II) chloride
    (e) $Fe_3(CO)_{12}$ from $Fe(CO)_5$

11. Explain why $Mo(py)_2(CO)_4$ has two forms, one having a single CO stretching band in the IR spectrum, the other four.

12. Give the formulas of some simple carbonylate ions and carbonyl hydrides. Do they follow the noble gas rule?

13. In a carbonyl complex with a linear OC—M—CO group, how will the CO stretching frequency change when (a) one CO is replaced by triethylamine, (b) a positive charge is put on the complex, and (c) a negative charge is put on the complex?

14. How is N_2 related to CO? Are N_2 complexes more or less stable than CO complexes? What was the first N_2 complex discovered and when?

15. Describe the bonding of NO to a metal in the case where the M—N—O chain is essentially linear; specifically contrast it with the analogous M—C—O bonding in terms of how many electrons are involved.

16. Besides linear M—N—O bonding, what other three kinds are there?

17. Explain why nitric oxide can be regarded as a three-electron donor ligand. Would you expect the stoichiometries of compounds with the following chelate ligands to be similar to those formed by NO?

Would there be any difference in the formal oxidation state of the metal, for example, in $Mn(CO)_4NO$ and $Mn(CO)_4[CH_2N(CH_3)_2]$ (shown on the right)?

18. Explain how trialkyl or aryl phosphines can bind to a metal.

19. Which PX_3 ligand is most similar in its bonding ability to CO?

20. Discuss the similarities and differences between CN^- and CO as ligands.

B. Additional Exercises

1. In order to have a vanadium carbonyl that satisfies the noble gas formalism, what would be the simplest formula? Why do you think this fails to occur?

2. It is known that in $Mn_2(CO)_{10}$ the carbonyl groups move rapidly from one manganese atom to the other. On the basis of what you find in Sections 28-3 and 28-4 suggest a plausible intermediate for this process.

3. Do you think that carbonyls of the lanthanides are likely to be stable? Whatever your answer, give reasons.

4. Write both bridged and nonbridged structures for $Mn_2(CO)_{10}$ and $Co_2(CO)_8$. The former has CO stretching bands only in the range 2044–1980 cm^{-1} while the latter has bands in the range 2071–2022 cm^{-1}, as well as two at 1860 and 1858 cm^{-1}. Which structure is indicated to be correct in each case?

5. What are the formulas of the metal carbonyls that are isoelectronic with $Cr(NO)_4$, $Mn(CO)(NO)_3$, $Mn(CO)_4NO$, $Co(NO)_3$, $Fe(CO)_2(NO)_2$?

6. Write balanced equations for the following reactions
   (a) $Mn_2(CO)_{10}$ is heated with I_2
   (b) $Mo(CO)_6$ is refluxed with KI in THF
   (c) $Fe(CO)_5$ is shaken with aqueous KOH
   (d) $Ni(CO)_4$ is treated with PCl_3
   (e) $Co_2(CO)_8$ is treated with NO in petroleum

7. What is the difference between a π-acid ligand like RNC and a ligand like C_2H_4 that forms π complexes?

8. In a linear group R_3P—M—CO, how would the CO frequency change when

$$R = F, CH_3, C_6H_5, -\!\!\bigcirc\!\!-CH_3, \text{ or } -\!\!\bigcirc\!\!-F$$

9. Why is pK_2 for $H_2Fe(CO)_4$ smaller than pK_1 by nine units? What does this tell us?

10. Put the following ligands in decreasing order of π acidity

$$CH_3CN \quad (C_2H_5)_2O \quad PCl_3 \quad As(C_6H_5)_3 \quad CH_3NC \quad Et_3N$$

11. Determine whether or not the following structures obey the 18-electron rule:
    (a) $H_2Fe(CO)_4$ (b) $V(CO)_6$ (c) $[V(CO)_6]^-$
    (d) $W(CO)_5PPh_3$ (e) $Mn(CO)_4NO$ (f) $[Cr(CO)_5]^-$
    (g) $Co(H)(N_2)(PPh_3)_3$ (h) $Mn_2(I)_2(CO)_8$ (i) $[W(CO)_5Cl]^-$
    (j) $HMn(CO)_4$ (k) $[V(CO)_5H]^{2-}$

12. Explain the relative position of the IR stretching absorptions in $[V(CO)_6]^-$ versus $Cr(CO)_6$.

13. Explain why $V(CO)_6$ is readily reduced to the monoanion.

14. Describe the bonding of a doubly bridging CO group between two metals. Use the three-centered, two-electron MO approach.

15. Use the MO approach to describe the bonding of a triply bridging CO group to three metal centers.

16. Suggest preparations of the following products:

(a) $W(CO)_5(py)$ (b) $Na[HCr(CO)_5]$

(c) $MeNCFe(CO)_4$ (d) $K[Mo(CO)_5I]$

(e) $Mo(CO)_3(py)_3$ (f) $HCo(CO)_4$

(g) $K[Co(CO)_4]$ (h) $Mn(CO)_4(I)(py)$

(i) $Mn(CO)_3(I)(py)_2$ (j) $Re(CO)_4Cl(py)$

(k) *trans*-$RhCl(CS)(PPh_3)_2$

17. Write balanced equations for each of the preparations of $[Ru(NH_3)_5N_2]^{2+}$.

18. Write balanced equations for three separate routes to the anion $[Co(CO)_4]^-$. What do you suspect is its geometry?

C.   Questions from the Literature of Inorganic Chemistry

1. Consider the paper by F. A. Cotton, D. J. Darensbourg, and B. W. S. Kolthammer, *Inorg. Chem.,* **1981**, *20,* 4440–4442.

(a) Write a balanced equation for the synthesis of the title compound. [*Note:* The PPN⁺ counterion is a large organic cation, bis(triphenylphosphine)iminium, which may be considered to be noninvolved in the essential chemistry of this system.] What is the role of the methanol reagent in this preparation?

(b) In which compounds mentioned in this paper do steric effects preclude a short M—P bond?

(c) What significant inter- or intramolecular contacts (or lack of contacts) lead the authors to propose that the M—P bond reported here is not influenced by steric effects?

(d) What mechanism for substitution has been assumed in predicting that the PMe_3 ligand in $W(CO)_5PMe_3$ should be less labile than the $P(t\text{-}Bu)_3$ ligand in $W(CO)_5P(t\text{-}Bu)_3$? Explain.

2. Consider the work by R. J. Dennenberg and D. J. Darensbourg, *Inorg. Chem.,* **1972,** *11,* 72–77.

(a) Summarize the evidence that is presented in favor of a dissociative mechanism for the substitution (decomposition) reactions reported here.

(b) Why is cleavage of a M—N bond easier than cleavage of a M—CO bond?

(c) Show with orbital overlap diagrams the π bond between M and pyridine that is responsible for the slower substitution of this unsaturated amine than of the saturated amines.

3. Consider triphenyltris(THF)chromium(III) as reported by S. I. Khan and R. Bau, *Organometallics,* **1983,** *2,* 1896–1897.

(a) Assign oxidation states to the ligands and to the metal. How many electrons should each ligand be considered to donate to chromium?

(b) What evidence is there for the $d\pi$–$p\pi$ bonding to the phenyl ligands? Show the orbitals that would be involved in such a π-bond system.

(c) The dianion $[Cr(C_6H_5)_5]^{2-}$ is mentioned. Does it satisfy the 18-electron rule?

4. Consider the hydrido pentacarbonyl of chromium as reported by M. Y. Darensbourg and J. C. Deaton, *Inorg. Chem.,* **1981,** *20,* 1644–1646.

(a) Write equations for each of the routes (outlined in the introduction), which involve the monoanion $[HCr(CO)_5]^-$. Why do these routes not serve as useful methods for isolation of $[HCr(CO)_5]^-$?

(b) Should the dimer $[(CO)_5Cr—H—Cr(CO)_5]^-$ be considered to be saturated from the standpoint of the 18-electron rule? Answer also for the monomeric $[HCr(CO)_5]^-$.

(c) Write an equation for each step in the successful synthesis, as reported here, of the tetraethylammonium salt of $[HCr(CO)_5]^-$.

5. Consider the anionic hydrido carbonyl dimer $[HFe_2(CO)_8]^-$ as reported by H. B. Chin and R. Bau, *Inorg. Chem.*, **1978**, *17*, 2314–2317.

(a) How is the structure of this anion related to that of $Fe_2(CO)_9$?

(b) What bonds in the anion should be described by the three-center, two-electron formalism?

(c) What arguments do the authors present that M—Cl—M systems should not be formulated as electron deficient (three-center, two-electron) bonds?

(d) What IR evidence suggests the presence of bridging CO ligands in this compound?

SUPPLEMENTARY READING

Abel, E. W. and Stone, F. G. A., "The Chemistry of Transition-Metal Carbonyls: Structural Considerations," *Quart. Rev.*, **1969**, *23*, 325.

Abel, E. W. and Stone, F. G. A., "The Chemistry of Transition-Metal Carbonyls: Synthesis and Reactivity," *Quart. Rev.*, **1970**, *24*, 498.

Allen, A. D., "Complexes of Dinitrogen," *Chem. Rev.*, **1973**, *73*, 11.

Braterman, P. S., *Metal Carbonyl Spectra*, Academic, New York, 1975.

Coates, G. E., Green, M. L. H., Powell, P., and Wade, K., *Principles of Organometallic Chemistry*, Chapman and Hall, London, 1977.

Darensbourg, M. Y., "Ion Pairing Effects on Transition Metal Carbonyl Anions," *Prog. Inorg. Chem.*, **1985**, *33*, 221.

Enemark, J. H. and Feltham, R. D., "Nitric Oxide Complexes," *Coord. Chem. Rev.*, **1974**, *13*, 339.

Hoffmann, R., "Theoretical Organometallic Chemistry," *Science*, **1981**, *211*, 995.

Malatesta, L. and Cenini, S., *Zerovalent Complexes of Metals*, Academic, New York, 1974.

McAuliffe, C. A., Ed., *Transition Metal Complexes of Phosphorus, Arsenic, and Antimony Ligands*, MacMillan, New York, 1973.

Pearson, A. J., *Metallo-Organic Chemistry*, Wiley-Interscience, New York, 1985.

Pearson, R. G., "The Transition-Metal-Hydrogen Bond," *Chem. Rev.*, **1985**, *85*, 41.

Singleton, E. and Oosthuizen, H. E., "Metal Isocyanide Complexes," *Advances in Organometallic Chemistry*, Vol. 22, F. G. A. Stone and R. West, Eds., Academic, New York, 1983.

Wender, I. and Pino, P., Eds., "Organic Syntheses via Metal Carbonyls," Wiley, New York, 1968.

Wilkinson, G., Stone, F. G. A., and Abel, E. W., Eds., *Comprehensive Organometallic Chemistry*, Pergamon Press, New York, 1982.

chapter 29

ORGANOMETALLIC COMPOUNDS

29-1 General Survey of Types

Organometallic compounds are those in which the *carbon* atoms of organic groups are bound to metal atoms. For example, an alkoxide such as $(C_3H_7O)_4Ti$ is not considered to be an organometallic compound because the organic group is bound to Ti by oxygen, whereas $C_6H_5Ti(OC_3H_7)_3$ is, because a metal to carbon bond is present. The term organometallic is usually rather loosely defined and compounds of elements such as boron, phosphorus, and silicon, which are at best scarcely metallic, are included in the category. A few general comments on the various types of compounds can be made first.

Ionic Compounds of Electropositive Metals. The organometallic compounds of highly electropositive metals are usually ionic, insoluble in hydrocarbon solvents, and are very reactive toward air, water, and the like. The stability and reactivity of ionic compounds are determined in part by the stability of the carbanion. Compounds containing unstable anions (e.g., $C_nH_{2n+1}^-$) are generally highly reactive and often unstable and difficult to isolate. Metal salts of carbanions whose stability is enhanced by delocalization of electron density are more stable although still quite reactive; examples are $(C_6H_5)_3C^-Na^+$ and $(C_5H_5^-)_2Ca^{2+}$.

σ-Bonded Compounds. Organometallic compounds in which the organic residue is bound to a metal atom by a normal two-electron covalent bond (albeit in some cases with appreciable ionic character) are formed by most metals of lower electropositivity and, of course, by nonmetallic elements. The normal valence rules apply in these cases, and partial substitution of halides, hydroxides, and so on, by organic groups occurs as in $(CH_3)_3SnCl$, $(CH_3)SnCl_3$, and so on. In most of these compounds, the bonding is predominantly covalent and the chemistry is organic-like, although there are many differences from carbon chemistry due to the following factors.

(a) The possibility of using higher d orbitals in, for example, SiR_4, which is not feasible in CR_4.

(b) Donor ability of alkyls or aryls with lone pairs as in PEt_3, SMe_2, and so on.

(c) Lewis acidity due to incomplete valence shells as in BR_3 or coordinative unsaturation as in ZnR_2.

(d) Effects of electronegativity differences between M—C and C—C bonds.

Transition metals may form simple alkyls or aryls but these are normally less stable than those of main group elements for reasons that we discuss later (Section 29-11). There are numerous compounds in which additional ligands such as CO or PR_3 are present.

Nonclassically Bonded Compounds. In many organometallic compounds there is a type of metal to carbon bonding that cannot be explained in terms of ionic or electron-pair σ bonds. One class comprises the alkyls of Li, Be, and Al that have *bridging* alkyl groups. Here, there is electron deficiency as in boron hydrides, and the bonding is of a similar multicenter type. A second, much larger class comprises compounds of transition metals with alkenes, alkynes, benzene, and other ring systems such as $C_5H_5^-$.

We consider first the organometallic compounds of the main group elements, including the nonclassically bonded ones, and then turn to the transition metal compounds.

29-2 Synthetic Methods

There are many ways of generating metal to carbon bonds that are useful for both nontransition and transition metals. Some of the more important ways are as follows:

1. *Direct Reactions of Metals.* The earliest synthesis, by the English chemist Sir Edward Frankland in 1845, was the interaction of Zn and an alkyl halide. Frankland was, in fact, attempting to synthesize alkyl radicals; his discovery played a decisive part in the development of modern ideas of chemical bonds. Much more useful, however, was the discovery by the French chemist, V. Grignard, of what are now called Grignard reagents by interaction of magnesium with alkyl or aryl halides in ether:

$$Mg + CH_3I \xrightarrow{\text{Ether}} CH_3MgI \qquad (29\text{-}2.1)$$

Direct interactions of alkyl or aryl halides occur also with Li, Na, K, Mg, Ca, Zn, and Cd.

2. *Use of Alkylating Agents.* The previously mentioned compounds can be utilized to make other organometallic compounds. The most important and widely used are Grignard and lithium reagents. Aluminum and mercury alkyls and certain sodium derivatives, especially $Na^+C_5H_5^-$, are also useful alkylating agents.

Most nonmetal and metal halides or halide derivatives can be alkylated in ethers, or hydrocarbon solvents, for example,

$$PCl_3 + 3C_6H_5MgCl = P(C_6H_5)_3 + 3MgCl_2 \qquad (29\text{-}2.2)$$

$$VOCl_3 + 3(CH_3)_3SiCH_2MgCl = VO(CH_2SiMe_3)_3 + 3MgCl_2 \qquad (29\text{-}2.3)$$

$$PtCl_2(PEt_3)_2 + CH_3MgCl = PtCl(CH_3)(PEt_2)_2 + MgCl_2 \qquad (29\text{-}2.4)$$

3. *Interaction of Metal or Nonmetal Hydrides with Alkenes or Alkynes.* One of the best examples for nonmetals, and one that finds wide use in synthesis, is the hydroboration shown in Eq. 29-2.5:

$$\tfrac{1}{2}B_2H_6 + 3 \;\; {>}C{=}C{<} \;\; \xrightarrow{\text{Ether}} \;\; B\!\left(\!\begin{array}{c} | \;\; | \\ C-C- \\ | \;\; | \end{array}\!\right)_3 \qquad (29\text{-}2.5)$$

Reaction 29-2.5 may be regarded as an addition across the double bond of the alkene. The intermediate trialkyl borane may be protonated as in reaction 29-2.6:

$$\left(\!\begin{array}{c} \text{H} \;\; \text{H} \\ | \;\; | \\ R-C-C- \\ | \;\; | \\ \text{H} \;\; \text{H} \end{array}\!\right)_3\!\!B \;\; \xrightarrow{H_3O^+} \;\; \begin{array}{c} \text{H} \;\; \text{H} \\ | \;\; | \\ R-C-C-H \\ | \;\; | \\ \text{H} \;\; \text{H} \end{array} + B(OH)_3 \qquad (29\text{-}2.6)$$

and the net result is hydrogenation of the original alkene. Oxidation of the trialkyl borane molecule as in Eq. 29-2.7:

$$\left(\!\begin{array}{c} \text{H} \;\; \text{H} \\ | \;\; | \\ R-C-C- \\ | \;\; | \\ \text{H} \;\; \text{H} \end{array}\!\right)_3\!\!B \;\; \xrightarrow{H_2O_2} \;\; \begin{array}{c} \text{H} \;\; \text{H} \\ | \;\; | \\ R-C-C-OH \\ | \;\; | \\ \text{H} \;\; \text{H} \end{array} + B(OH)_3 \qquad (29\text{-}2.7)$$

gives the alcohol.

For transition metals and hydride complexes, such reactions are of prime importance in that many catalytic syntheses involving transition metals (Chapter 30) have, as an early step, the reaction

$$L_nMH + \;\; {>}C{=}C{<} \;\; = \;\; L_nM-\!\begin{array}{c} \;\; \text{H} \\ | \;\; | \\ C-C- \\ | \;\; | \end{array} \qquad (29\text{-}2.8)$$

4. *Oxidative–Addition Reactions.* The so-called oxad reactions (Section 30-2), where alkyl or aryl halides are added to coordinatively unsaturated transition metal compounds generate metal–carbon bonds; for example,

$$RhCl(PPh_3)_3 + CH_3I = RhClI(CH_3)(PPh_3)_2 + PPh_3 \qquad (29\text{-}2.9)$$

5. *Insertion Reactions.* Certain "insertion" reactions (Section 30-3) may also allow the generation of bonds to carbon, for example,

$$[(CN)_5Co-Co(CN)_5]^{4-} + HC\equiv CH = \left[(CN)_5Co-\overset{H}{\underset{H}{C}}=C-Co(CN)_5 \right]^{4-}$$

$$(29\text{-}2.10)$$

$$SbCl_5 + 2HC\equiv CH = Cl_3Sb(CH=CHCl)_2 \qquad (29\text{-}2.11)$$

The reactions in Part 3 can also be regarded as "insertions" into the M—H bond.

PART A
NONTRANSITION METALS

29-3 Lithium Alkyls and Aryls

Organometallic compounds of lithium have been discussed in a preliminary fashion in Section 10-8. One of the major uses of metallic lithium, industrially and in the laboratory, is for the preparation of organolithium compounds which, in their reactions, generally resemble Grignard reagents, although the lithium reagents are usually more reactive. Organolithium compounds are prepared by interaction of the metal with an organic halide, usually the chloride, in benzene or petroleum. Ethers can be used as solvents, but they are attacked slowly by the lithium compounds. Examples of typical preparations include reaction with ethyl chloride as in Eq. 29-3.1:

$$C_2H_5Cl + 2Li \longrightarrow C_2H_5Li + LiCl \qquad (29\text{-}3.1)$$

metal–hydrogen exchange as in Eq. 29-3.2:

$$C_4H_9Li + \quad Fe \quad = \quad Fe \quad + C_4H_{10} \qquad (29\text{-}3.2) \quad \cdot$$

metal–halogen exchange as in Eq. 29-3.3:

$$C_4H_9Li + \quad \qquad = \quad \qquad + C_4H_9Br \qquad (29\text{-}3.3)$$

and metal–metal exchange as in Eq. 29-3.4:

$$2Li + R_2Hg \longrightarrow 2RLi + Hg \qquad (29\text{-}3.4)$$

Butyllithium in hexane, benzene, or ethers is commonly used for such reactions. Methyllithium is also prepared by exchange through the interaction of C_4H_9Li and CH_3I in hexane at low temperatures, whence it precipitates as insoluble white crystals.

Organolithium compounds all react rapidly with oxygen, being usually spontaneously flammable in air, with liquid water, and with water vapor. However, lithium bromide and iodide form solid complexes of stoichiometry $RLi(LiX)_{1-6}$ with the alkyls, and these solids are stable in air.

Organolithium compounds are among the very few alkali metal compounds that have properties—solubility in hydrocarbons or other nonpolar liquids and high volatility—typical of covalent substances. They are generally liquids or low-melting solids. Molecular association is an important feature of the alkyls in both crystals and solutions. Thus in methyllithium (Fig. 29-1) the Li atoms are at the corners of a tetrahedron with the alkyl groups centered over the facial planes. The CH_3 group is symmetrically bound to three Li atoms, and this alkyl bridge bonding is of the electron-deficient multicenter type (Section 3-7). Aggregate formation is due principally to the Li—C—Li rather than to Li—Li bonding interactions.

Figure 29-1 The structure of $(CH_3Li)_4$ showing the tetrahedral Li_4 unit with the methyl groups located symmetrically above each face of the tetrahedron. [Adapted from E. Weiss and E. A. C. Lucken, *J. Organomet. Chem.*, **1964,** *2*, 197.] See also Fig. 10-4.

In solutions the nature of the polymerized species depends on the solvent, the steric nature of the organic radical, and temperature. In hydrocarbons MeLi, EtLi, PrLi, and some others are hexamers, but *tert*-butyllithium, which presumably is too bulky, is only tetrameric. In ethers or amines solvated tetramers are formed. There are no aggregates smaller than tetramers.

However, when chelating ditertiary amines, notably tetramethylethylenediamine (TMED), $Me_2NCH_2CH_2NMe_2$, are used, comparatively stable monomeric alkyllithium complexes are obtained. The alkyls and aryls also form complexes with other metal alkyls such as those of Mg, Cd, and Zn. For example,

$$2LiC_6H_5 + Mg(C_6H_5)_2 = Li_2[Mg(C_6H_5)_4] \qquad (29\text{-}3.5)$$

It is not surprising that there are wide variations in the comparative reactivities of Li alkyls depending on the differences in aggregation and ion-pair interactions. An example is benzyllithium, which is monomeric in THF and reacts with a given substrate more than 10^4 times as fast as the tetrameric methyllithium. The monomeric TMED complexes mentioned previously are also very much more reactive than the corresponding aggregated alkyls. Alkyllithiums can polylithiate acetylenes, acetonitrile, and other compounds; thus, $CH_3C \equiv CH$ gives Li_4C_3, which can be regarded as a derivative of C_3^{4-}.

Reactions of lithium alkyls are generally considered to be carbanionic in nature. Lithium alkyls are widely employed as stereospecific catalysts for the polymerization of alkenes, notably isoprene, which gives up to 90% of 1,4-*cis*-polyisoprene; numerous other reactions with alkenes have been studied. The TMED complexes again are especially active: not only will they polymerize ethylene but they will even metallate benzene and aromatic compounds, as well as reacting with hydrogen at 1 atm to give LiH and alkane.

29-4 Organosodium and Organopotassium Compounds

These compounds have been discussed in Section 10-8 and are all essentially ionic and not soluble to any appreciable extent in hydrocarbons. They are exceedingly reactive, sensitive to air, and are hydrolyzed vigorously by water.

Most important are the sodium compounds from acidic hydrocarbons such as cyclopentadiene, indene, acetylenes, and the like. These are obtained by reaction of the hydrocarbon with metallic sodium or sodium dispersed in THF or DMF.

29-5 Magnesium

The organic compounds of Ca, Sr, and Ba are highly ionic and reactive and are not useful, but the magnesium compounds are probably the most widely used of all organometallic compounds; they are used very extensively in organic chemistry, as well as in the synthesis of alkyl and aryl compounds of other elements. They are of the types RMgX (the Grignard reagents) and MgR_2. The former are made by direct interaction of the metal with an organic halide, RX, in a suitable solvent, usually an ether such as diethyl ether or THF. The reaction is normally most rapid with iodides (RI) and iodine may be used as an initiator. For most purposes, RMgX reagents are used *in situ*. The species MgR_2 are best made by the dry reaction

$$HgR_2 + Mg(\text{excess}) \longrightarrow Hg + MgR_2 \qquad (29\text{-}5.1)$$

The dialkyl or diaryl is then extracted with an organic solvent. Both RMgX, as solvates, and R_2Mg are reactive, being sensitive to oxidation by air and to hydrolysis by water.

The nature of Grignard reagents *in solution* is complex and depends on the nature of the alkyl and halide groups and on the solvent, concentration, and temperature. Generally, the equilibria involved are of the type:

$$RMg\diamondsuit{X}{X}MgR \rightleftharpoons 2RMgX \rightleftharpoons R_2Mg + MgX_2 \qquad (29\text{-}5.2)$$

Solvation (not shown) occurs and association is predominantly by halide rather than by carbon bridges, except for methyl compounds where bridging by CH_3 groups may occur.

In dilute solutions and in more strongly donor solvents the monomeric species normally predominate; but in diethyl ether at concentrations greater than 0.1 M association gives linear or cyclic polymers. For crystalline Grignard reagents both of the structures $RMgX \cdot nS$ where, n, the number of solvent molecules, S, depends on the nature of R, and $R(S)Mg(\mu\text{-}X)_2Mg(S)R$ have been found. The Mg atom is usually tetrahedrally coordinated.

Zinc and *cadmium* compounds are similar to those of magnesium but differ in their reactivities. The lower alkyls of zinc are liquids spontaneously flammable in air. They react vigorously with water.

29-6 Mercury

A vast number of organomercury compounds are known, some of which have useful physiological properties. They are of the types RHgX and R_2Hg. They are commonly made by the interaction of $HgCl_2$ and RMgX, but Hg—C bonds can also be made in other ways, to be discussed.

The *RHgX compounds* are crystalline solids. When X can form covalent bonds to mercury, for example, Cl, Br, I, CN, SCN, or OH, the compound is a covalent nonpolar substance more soluble in organic liquids than in water. When X is SO_4^{2-} or NO_3^-, the substance is saltlike and presumably quite ionic, for instance, $[RHg]^+[NO_3]^-$.

The *dialkyls and diaryls* are nonpolar, volatile, toxic, colorless liquids, or low-melting solids. They are unaffected by air or water, presumably because of the low polarity of the Hg—C bond and the low affinity of mercury for oxygen. However, they are photochemically and thermally unstable, as would be expected from the low bond strengths $(50–200 \text{ kJ mol}^{-1})$. In the dark, mercury compounds can be kept for months. The decomposition generally proceeds by homolysis of the Hg—C bond and free radical reactions.

All RHgX and R_2Hg molecules have linear bonds. The principal utility of dialkyl- and diarylmercury compounds, and a very valuable one, is in the preparation of other organometallic compounds by *interchange* reactions. For example,

$$\tfrac{n}{2}\,R_2Hg \,+\, M \longrightarrow R_nM \,+\, \tfrac{n}{2}\,Hg \qquad (29\text{-}6.1)$$

This reaction proceeds essentially to completion with the Li and Ca groups, and with Zn, Al, Ga, Sn, Pb, Sb, Bi, Se, and Te, but with In, Tl, and Cd reversible equilibria are established. Partial alkylation of reactive halides can be achieved, for example,

$$AsCl_3 \,+\, Et_2Hg \longrightarrow EtHgCl \,+\, EtAsCl_2 \qquad (29\text{-}6.2)$$

Mercury released to the environment, as metal, for example, by losses from electrolytic cells used for NaOH and Cl_2 production, or as compounds such as alkylmercury seed dressings or fungicides, constitutes a serious hazard. This is a result of biological methylation to give highly toxic $(CH_3)_2Hg$ or CH_3Hg^+. Models for vitamin B_{12} such as methylcobaloximes (Section 31-8), which have Co—CH_3 bonds, will transfer the CH_3 to Hg^{2+}. There are a number of microorganisms that can perform the same function, possibly by similar routes.

Mercuration and Oxomercuration

An important reaction for the formation of Hg—C bonds, and one that can be adapted to the synthesis of a wide variety of organic compounds, is the addition of mercuric salts, notably the acetate, trifluoroacetate, or nitrate to unsaturated compounds.

Mercuration of aromatic compounds occurs as follows:

$$+ \; CH_3CO_2H \qquad (29\text{-}6.3)$$

Mercuric salts also react with alkenes in a reversible reaction

$$(29\text{-}6.4)$$

The reversibility is readily shown by using $Hg(OCOCF_3)_2$, since the latter is soluble in nonpolar solvents; the equilibrium constants for the reaction 29-

6.4 can be measured. In most instances, the reactions must be carried out in an alcohol or other protic medium, where further reaction with the solvent occurs. The reaction is then called *oxomercuration*. For example,

$$\text{>C=C<} + Hg(OCOCH_3)_2 + C_2H_5OH$$

$$\downarrow$$

$$\begin{array}{c} C_2H_5O \\ \text{—C—C—} \\ HgOCOCH_3 \end{array} + CH_3CO_2H \qquad (29\text{-}6.5)$$

The evidence that HgX_2 adds across the double bond is usually indirect, often, by observing the products on hydrolysis, for example,

$$CH_2{=}CH_2 + Hg(NO_3)_2 \xrightarrow{\ OH^-\ } HOCH_2CH_2Hg^+ + 2NO_3^- \quad (29\text{-}6.6)$$

In these reactions, *mercurinium ions* of the type like structures 29-I and 29-II are believed to be intermediates. In $FSO_3H{-}SbF_5{-}SO_2$ at $-70\,^\circ C$ long-lived mercurinium

$$\begin{array}{cc} Hg^{2+} & \overset{\displaystyle X}{\underset{\displaystyle\vert}{Hg^+}} \\ \text{>C—C<} & \text{>C—C<} \\ \text{29-I} & \text{29-II} \end{array}$$

ions have been obtained by reactions such as

$$CH_3OCH_2CH_2HgCl \xrightarrow{\ H^+\ } CH_3OH_2^+ + CH_2CH_2Hg^{2+} + HCl \quad (29\text{-}6.7)$$

$$\bigcirc\!\!| + Hg(OCOCF_3)_2 \xrightarrow{\ H^+\ } \overset{\displaystyle\bigcirc}{}\!\!\!\text{Hg}^{2+} \qquad (29\text{-}6.8)$$

This type of addition has been used for the synthesis of alcohols, ethers, and amines from alkenes and other unsaturated substances. The additions of HgX_2 are carried out in water, alcohols, or acetonitrile, respectively. The mercury is removed from the intermediate by reduction with sodium borohydride. An example is

$$\bigcirc \xrightarrow[\text{H}_2\text{O, THF}]{Hg(OCOCH_3)_2} \overset{HgOCOCH_3}{\bigcirc}\!\!\!\!\underset{OH}{} \xrightarrow{NaBH_4} \overset{H}{\bigcirc}\!\!\!\!\underset{OH}{} \qquad (29\text{-}6.9)$$

29-7 Boron

There is a very extensive chemistry of organoboron compounds.

The *trialkyl-* and *triarylborons* are made from the halides by lithium or Grignard reagents, and by hydroboration. The lower alkyls inflame in air, but the aryls are stable. Like other BX_3 compounds alkylborons behave as Lewis acids giving adducts, for example, $R_3B \cdot NR_3$. Furthermore, when boron halides are treated with four equivalents of alkylating agent, the trialkyl or triaryl gives an anion BR_4^-. The most important compound is *sodium tetraphenylborate*, $Na[B(C_6H_5)_4]$. This is soluble in water and is stable in weakly acid solution; it gives insoluble precipitates with larger cations such as K^+, Rb^+, or Me_4N^+, that are suitable for gravimetric analysis. There are also di- and monoalkyl compounds such as R_2BX or RBX_2 where X may be a halogen, OH, H, and so on.

29-8 Aluminum

The alkyls of Al are of great importance because of their industrial use as catalysts for the polymerization of ethylene and propylene (Section 30-10). They are also widely used as reducing and alkylating agents for transition metal complexes.

The alkyls may be prepared by the reactions:

$$2Al + 3R_2Hg \longrightarrow 2R_3Al \text{ or } [R_3Al]_2 + 3Hg \qquad (29\text{-}8.1)$$

$$RMgCl + AlCl_3 \longrightarrow RAlCl_2, \ R_2AlCl, \ R_3Al \qquad (29\text{-}8.2)$$

More direct methods suitable for large-scale use are

$$AlH_3 + 3C_nH_{2n} \longrightarrow Al(C_nH_{2n+1})_3 \qquad (29\text{-}8.3)$$

$$LiAlH_4 + 4C_nH_{2n} \longrightarrow Li[Al(C_nH_{2n+1})_4] \qquad (29\text{-}8.4)$$

Although $(AlH_3)_n$ cannot be made by direct interaction of Al and H_2, nevertheless, in the presence of aluminum alkyl, the following reaction to give the dialkyl hydride can occur:

$$Al + \tfrac{3}{2}H_2 + 2AlR_3 \longrightarrow 3AlR_2H \qquad (29\text{-}8.5)$$

This hydride will then react with olefins:

$$AlR_2H + C_nH_{2n} \longrightarrow AlR_2(C_nH_{2n+1}) \qquad (29\text{-}8.6)$$

Thus the direct interaction of Al, H_2, and olefin can be used to give either the dialkyl hydrides or the trialkyls.

Other technically important compounds are the "sesquichlorides" such as $Me_3Al_2Cl_3$ or $Et_3Al_2Cl_3$. These compounds can be made by direct interaction of Al or Mg—Al alloy with the alkyl chloride.

The aluminum lower alkyls are reactive liquids, inflaming in air and exploding with water. All other derivatives are similarly sensitive to air and

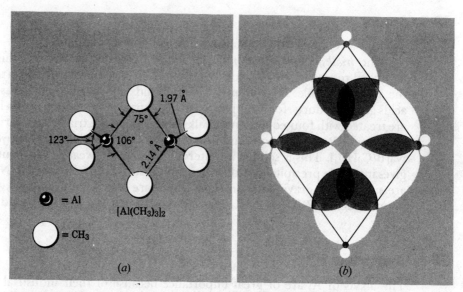

Figure 29-2 (*a*) The structure of $Al_2(CH_3)_6$. (*b*) The orbital overlap in the plane of the Al—C—Al bridge bonds.

moisture though not all are spontaneously flammable. Certain aluminum alkyls form reasonably stable dimers. The structure of trimethylaluminum is shown in Fig. 29-2(*a*). The alkyl bridge is formed by multicenter bonding, that is, Al—C—Al, (*3c–2e*) bonds (Section 3-7). Each Al atom supplies an sp^3 hybrid orbital and so does the C atom. The bonding situation is shown in Fig. 29-2(*b*). A similar description holds true for bridging in $[Be(CH_3)_2]_n$, which is a linear polymer, each Be atom being tetrahedral.

There is no simple explanation why boron trialkyls do not dimerize in a similar way, especially since hydrogen bridges are very important in the boranes (Sections 3-7 and 12-5). The coordinative unsaturation of Al alkyls also means that they behave as Lewis acids, giving adducts such as R_3AlNR_3 or anionic species like $Li[AlEt_4]$. In this respect all of the coordinatively unsaturated alkyls of Group IIIB(13) and Group IIB(12) elements are similar.

29-9 Silicon, Ge, Sn, and Pb

There is an extensive chemistry of the Group IVB(14) elements bound to carbon. Some of the compounds, notably silicon—oxygen polymers and alkyltin and alkyllead compounds, are of commercial importance; germanium compounds have no uses.

Essentially all the compounds are of the tetravalent elements. In the divalent state the trimethylsilylmethyl derivatives, $M[CH(SiMe_3)_2]_2$, are the only well-established compounds with σ bonds. Other tin compounds that might appear to contain Sn^{II} are linear or cyclic polymers of Sn^{IV}.

For all four elements the compounds can generally be designated $R_{4-n}MX_n$, where R is an alkyl or aryl and X can be H, Cl, O, COR′, OR′, NR'_2, SR′,

$Mn(CO)_5$, $W(CO)_3(\eta^5\text{-}C_5H_5)$, and so on. The elements can also be incorporated into heterocyclic rings of various types.

For a given class of compound, those with C—Si and C—Ge bonds have higher thermal stability and lower reactivity than those with bonds to Sn and Pb. In catenated compounds, similarly, Si—Si and Ge—Ge bonds are more stable and less reactive than Sn—Sn and Pb—Pb bonds. For example, Si_2Me_6 is very stable, but Pb_2Me_6 blackens in air and decomposes rapidly in CCl_4 although it is fairly stable in benzene.

The bonds to carbon are usually made via interaction of Li, Hg, or Al alkyls or RMgX and the Group IVB(14) halide, but there are some special synthetic methods noted in the following sections.

Silicon

The organometallic compounds of Si and Ge are very similar in their properties.

Silicon—carbon bond energies are less than those of C—C bonds but are still quite high, in the region 250–335 kJ mol^{-1}. The tetraalkyls and tetraaryls are hence thermally quite stable; $Si(C_6H_5)_4$, for example, boils unchanged at 530 °C.

The chemical reactivity of Si—C bonds is generally greater than that of C—C bonds because (a) the greater polarity of the bond, $Si^{\delta+}$—$C^{\delta-}$, allows easier nucleophilic attack on Si and electrophilic attack on C than for C—C compounds, and (b) displacement reactions at silicon are facilitated by its ability to form five-coordinate transition states by utilization of d orbitals.

Alkyl- and Arylsilicon Halides

These halides are of special importance because of their hydrolytic reactions. They may be obtained by normal Grignard procedures from $SiCl_4$ or, in the case of the methyl derivatives, by the *Rochow process* in which methyl chloride is passed over heated, copper-activated silicon:

$$CH_3Cl + Si(Cu) \longrightarrow (CH_3)_nSiCl_{4-n} \qquad (29\text{-}9.1)$$

The halides are liquids that are readily hydrolyzed by water, usually in an inert solvent. The silanol intermediates R_3SiOH, $R_2Si(OH)_2$, and $RSi(OH)_3$ can sometimes be isolated, but the diols and triols usually condense under the hydrolysis conditions to *siloxanes* that have Si—O—Si bonds. The exact nature of the products depends on the hydrolysis conditions, and linear, cyclic, and complex cross-linked polymers of varying molecular weights can be obtained. They are often referred to as *silicones;* the commercial polymers usually have R = CH_3, but other groups may be incorporated for special purposes.

Controlled hydrolysis of the alkyl halides in suitable ratios can give products of particular physical characteristics. The polymers may be liquids, rubbers, or solids, which have in general high thermal stability, high dielectric strength, and resistance to oxidation and chemical attack.

Examples of simple siloxanes are $Ph_3SiOSiPh_3$ and the cyclic trimer or tetramer $(Et_2SiO)_{3(or\ 4)}$; linear polymers contain $-SiR_2-O-SiR_2-O-$ chains, whereas the cross-linked sheets have the basic unit

$$-O-\overset{\displaystyle R}{\underset{\displaystyle O}{\overset{|}{\underset{|}{Si}}}}-O-$$

Tin

Where the compounds of tin differ from those of Si and Ge, they do so mainly because of a greater tendency of Sn^{IV} to show coordination numbers higher than four and because of ionization to give cationic species.

Trialkyltin compounds, R_3SnX, are always associated in the solid by anion bridging (structures 29-III and 29-IV). The coordination of the tin atom is close to tbp with planar $Sn(Me)_3$ groups. In water the perchlorate and some other compounds ionize to give cationic species, for example, $[Me_3Sn(H_2O)_2]^+$.

29-III   29-IV

Dialkyltin compounds, R_2SnX_2, have a behavior similar to that of the trialkyl compounds. Thus the fluoride, Me_2SnF_2, is again polymeric, with bridging F atoms, but Sn is octahedral and the Me—Sn—Me group is linear. However, the chloride and bromide have low melting points (90 and 74 °C) and are essentially molecular compounds. The halides also give conducting solutions in water, and the aqua ion has the linear C—Sn—C group characteristic of the dialkyl species (cf. the linear species Me_2Hg, Me_2Tl^+, Me_2Cd, Me_2Pb^{2+}), probably with four water molecules completing octahedral coordination. The linearity in these species appears to result from maximizing of *s* character in the bonding orbitals of the metal atoms. Organotin *hydrides* are useful reducing agents in organic chemistry and can add to alkenes by free radical reactions to generate other organotin compounds.

Organotin compounds have a number of uses in marine antifouling paints, fungicides, wood preserving, and as catalysts for curing silicone and epoxy resins.

Lead

The most important compounds of lead are $(CH_3)_4Pb$ and $(C_2H_5)_4Pb$, which are made in huge quantities for use as antiknock agents in gasoline. The environmental increase in lead is largely due to the burning of leaded gasolines, and their use is being phased out in the USA and elsewhere.

The commercial synthesis is the interaction of a sodium–lead alloy with CH_3Cl or C_2H_5Cl in an autoclave at 87 to 100 °C, without solvent for C_2H_5Cl but in toluene at a higher temperature for CH_3Cl. The reaction is complicated and not fully understood, and only a quarter of the lead appears in the desired product:

$$4NaPb + 4RCl \longrightarrow R_4Pb + 3Pb + 4NaCl \qquad (29\text{-}9.2)$$

The required recycling of the lead is disadvantageous and electrolytic procedures have been developed.

The lower alkyls are nonpolar highly toxic liquids. The tetramethyllead decomposes around 200 °C and the tetraethyllead around 110 °C by free radical processes.

29-10 Phosphorus, As, Sb, and Bi

There is an extensive chemistry of organometallic compounds, especially of phosphorus and arsenic. This was developed largely because of the physiological properties of these compounds. Thus, one of the first chemotherapeutic agents, salvarsan, which was discovered by P. Ehrlich, led to a wide study of arylarsenic compounds.

The so-called "organophosphorus" compounds that have anticholinesterase activity and are widely used as insecticides do *not* contain P—C bonds, but are P^V derivatives such as phosphates or thionates. For example, parathion is $(EtO)_2P(S)(OC_6H_4NO_2)$.

Most of the genuine organometallic derivatives are compounds with only three or four bonds to the central atom, although a few R_5M compounds are known. The simplest synthesis is the reaction

$$(O)MX_3 + 3RMgX \longrightarrow (O)MR_3 + 3MgX_2 \qquad (29\text{-}10.1)$$

Trimethylphosphine is spontaneously flammable in air, but the higher trialkyls are oxidized more slowly. The R_3MO compounds, which may be obtained from the oxo halides as shown in Eq. 29-10.1 or by oxidation of the corresponding R_3M compounds, are all very stable. The trialkyl- or alkylarylphosphines are usually liquids with an unpleasant odor. The triarylphosphines are white crystalline solids reasonably stable in air. Tertiary phosphines, arsines, and stibines are all good π-acid ligands for d-group transition metals (Section 28-15). The oxides, R_3MO, also form many complexes, but they function as simple donors. Trialkyl- and triarylphosphines, -arsines, and -stibines generally react with alkyl and aryl halides to form quaternary salts:

$$R_3M + R'X \longrightarrow [R_3R'M]^+X^- \qquad (29\text{-}10.2)$$

The tetraphenylphosphonium and tetraphenylarsonium ions are useful for precipitating large anions such as ReO_4^-, ClO_4^-, and complex anions of metals.

An important phosphonium compound is obtained by the reaction

$$PH_3 + 4HCHO + HCl(aq) = [P(CH_2OH)_4]^+Cl^- \qquad (29\text{-}10.3)$$

It is a white crystalline solid, soluble in water, and is used in the flameproofing of fabrics.

Triphenylphosphine, as well as being an important ligand, is utilized in the Wittig reaction for olefin synthesis. This reaction involves the formation of alkylidenetriphenylphosphoranes from the action of butyllithium or other base on the quaternary halide, for example,

$$[(C_6H_5)_3PCH_3]^+Br^- \xrightarrow{\textit{n-Butyllithium}} (C_6H_5)_3P{=}CH_2 \qquad (29\text{-}10.4)$$

This intermediate reacts very rapidly with aldehydes and ketones to give zwitterionic compounds (structure 29-V), which eliminate triphenylphosphine oxides under mild conditions to give olefins (structure 29-VI):

$$+ (C_6H_5)_3PO \qquad (29\text{-}10.5)$$

Alkylidenephosphoranes such as $Me_3P{=}CH_2$, $Et_3P{=}CH_2$, $Me_2EtP{=}CH_2$, and $Et_3P{=}CHMe$, are all colorless liquids, stable for long periods in an inert atmosphere.

PART B
TRANSITION METALS

For transition metals, σ-bonded alkyls or aryls are stable only under special circumstances. Unstable or labile species with σ bonds to carbon are of great significance particularly in catalytic reactions of alkenes and alkanes induced by transition metals or metal complexes. Transition metal to carbon σ bonds also exist in nature in Vitamin B_{12} derivatives (Section 31-8).

The unique characteristics of d orbitals allow the binding to metal atoms of unsaturated hydrocarbons and other molecules. The bonding is nonclassical and the metal complexes of alkenes, alkynes, arenes, and the like, have no counterparts elsewhere in chemistry.

29-11 Transition Metal to Carbon σ Bonds

Although the compound $[(CH_3)_3PtI]_4$, which has a structure based on a cube with Pt and I atoms at alternate corners and each Pt bound to three CH_3 groups, was made in 1909 by Pope and Peachy, attempts to prepare compounds such as $(C_2H_5)_3Fe$ by reactions of Grignard reagents with metal halides failed. Although evidence indicated that alkyls were present in solution at low temperatures, complicated decomposition and coupling reactions occurred at ambient temperatures.

Over 30 years ago it was found that, provided other ligands such as the η^5-cyclopentadienyl group described later in this chapter, or those of the π-acid type (Chapter 28) were present, alkyl compounds could be isolated; one example is $CH_3Mn(CO)_5$. It now appears that the principal reason for the stability of these compounds is that the coordination sites required for decomposition reactions to proceed are blocked. The main reason for the instability of most binary alkyls or aryls is that they are coordinatively unsaturated, and there are easy pathways for thermodynamically possible decomposition reactions to occur. Possible decomposition pathways include homolysis of the M—C bond, which generates free radicals, as well as the transfer of a hydrogen atom from carbon to the metal. A particularly common reaction is the transfer from the β carbon of the alkyl chain (Eq. 29-11.1)

$$M—CH_2—CH_2—R \rightleftharpoons \left[\begin{array}{c} H \\ | \\ M \longleftarrow \begin{array}{c} CHR \\ \| \\ CH_2 \end{array} \end{array} \right] \longrightarrow$$

$$MH + CHR{=}CH_2 \qquad (29\text{-}11.1)$$

resulting in the elimination of olefin and formation of an M—H bond. The reverse of this reaction, that is, the formation of alkyls by addition of olefins to M—H bonds (cf. Section 30-6) is of very great importance in catalytic reactions discussed in the next chapter. Once the hydrogen atom has been transferred to the metal, further reaction can occur to give the metal and hydrogen, or the hydrogen can be transferred to the alkene to form alkane. Thus it has been shown that the copper alkyl, $(Bu_3P)CuCH_2C(Me)_2Ph$, decomposes largely by a free radical pathway but that the similar alkyl, $(Bu_3P)CuCH_2CH_2CH_2CH_3$, decomposes by a nonradical pathway involving Cu—H bond formation. The difference is that the latter, but not the former, has a hydrogen atom on the second, β-carbon atom.

There are a number of reasonably thermally stable alkyls that cannot undergo the β-hydride-transfer, alkene-elimination reaction. These have groups

Table 29-1　Some Binary Transition Metal Alkyls

Compound	Properties
$Ti(CH_2Ph)_4$	Red crystals, mp 70 °C; tetrahedral
$VO(CH_2SiMe_3)_3$	Yellow needles, mp 75 °C; has V=O bond
$Cr(1\text{-norbornyl})_4$	Red-brown crystals; tetrahedral; d^2 paramagnetic
$Mo_2(CH_2SiMe_3)_6$	Yellow plates, decomp. 135 °C; has Mo≡Mo bond
$Re(CH_3)_6$	Green crystals; octahedral; d^1 paramagnetic

such as $-CH_2C_6H_5$, $-CH_2SiMe_3$, $-CH_2CMe_3$, $-CH_2\overset{+}{P}Me_3$, and 1-norbornyl (structure 29-VII).

M

29-VII

Although hydrogen transfer from an α-carbon atom to produce a hydrido carbene intermediate as the first step in decomposition:

$$M-CHRR' \longrightarrow M=CRR' \qquad (29\text{-}11.2)$$

is possible, this is evidently less favorable than the β transfer and is rarely observed. Methylmetal compounds, such as $(CH_3)_4Ti$, or the $[(CH_3)_3PtI]_4$ already mentioned, are accordingly much more stable than the homologous ethylmetal compounds. However, even $Ti(CH_3)_4$ decomposes at ca. $-80°C$, but on addition of ligands such as bipyridine, which leads to coordinative saturation as in $Ti(bipy)(CH_3)_4$, a substantial increase in thermal stability results. This shows again the necessity of having coordination sites on the metal available in order to allow decomposition reactions to proceed. Another striking example of this principle is that substitution-inert complexes (Section 6-5) of Cr^{III}, Co^{III}, and Rh^{III} may have M—C bonds even when H_2O or NH_3 are ligands; one example is $[Rh(NH_3)_5C_2H_5]^{2+}$. Particularly important are the cobalt complexes of the vitamin B_{12} type and their synthetic analogs discussed in Chapter 31. One example is the dimethylglyoxime complex (structure 29-VIII).

29-VIII

Some representative examples of alkyls are given in Table 29-1.

29-12 Alkene Complexes

About 1830, W. C. Zeise, a Danish pharmacist, characterized compounds that had stoichiometries $PtCl_2C_2H_4$ and $K[PtCl_3C_2H_4]$. Although these were the first organometallic derivatives of transition metals to be prepared, their true nature was fully established only around 1953.

Ethylene and most other alkenes can be bound to transition metals in a wide variety of complexes. The structures of two such complexes are shown in Fig. 29-3. The fact that the plane of the olefin, and the C=C axis are perpendicular to one of the expected bond directions from the central metal atom is of key significance. In addition, the expected line of a bond orbital from the metal atom strikes the C=C bond at its midpoint.

The most useful description of the bonding in alkene complexes is illustrated in Fig. 29-4. The bonding consists of two interdependent components: (a) overlap of the π-electron density of the alkene with a σ-type acceptor orbital on the metal atom; and (b) a "back-bond" resulting from flow of electron density from filled metal d_{xz} or other $d\pi-p\pi$ hybrid orbitals into the π^*-*antibonding* orbital on the carbon atoms. It is thus similar to that discussed for the bonding of CO and other π-acid ligands (Chapter 28) and implies the retention of appreciable "double-bond" character in the olefin. Of course, the donation of π-bonding electrons to the metal σ orbital and the introduction of electrons into the π^*-antibonding orbital both weaken the π bonding in the olefin, and in every case except the anion of Zeise's salt there is significant lengthening of the olefin C—C bond. There appears to be some correlation between lengthening of the bond and the electron-withdrawing power of the substituents of the olefin. This is exemplified by the structures shown in Fig. 29-3 where the $C_2(CN)_4$ complex has a C—C bond about as long as a normal single bond.

In the extreme of a very long C—C distance the bonding could be formulated as a kind of metallocyclopropane ring, involving two $(2c-2e)$ M—C bonds and a C—C single bond. In Fig. 29-3(b) the bond angles at the two olefin

(a) (b)

Figure 29-3 The structures of two monoalkene complexes. (a) The $[PtCl_3C_2H_4]^-$ anion of Zeise's salt. (b) The molecule $(Ph_3P)_2(CO)(Br)Ir[C_2(CN)_4]$, with phenyl groups of the triphenylphosphine ligands omitted for clarity. The monoalkene $C_2(CN)_4$ is tetracyanoethylene.

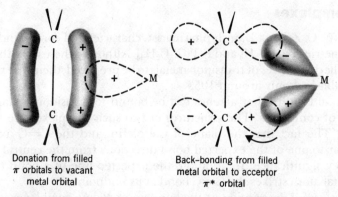

Donation from filled
π orbitals to vacant
metal orbital

Back-bonding from filled
metal orbital to acceptor
π* orbital

Figure 29-4   Diagrams showing the MO view of the alkene–
metal bonding. (*a*) The donation of π-electron density from
the alkene to the metal. (*b*) The donation of π-electron
density from the metal to the alkene.

carbon atoms are consistent with this view. This representation of the bonding
and the MO description are complementary, and there is a smooth gradation
of one description into the other.

Alkenes with unconjugated double bonds can form independent linkages
to a metal atom. Two representative complexes, of 1,5-cyclooctadiene and
norbornadiene, are structures 29-IX and 29-X, respectively. Three unconjugated double bonds may be coordinated to one metal atom as in the *trans, trans,
trans*-cyclododecatriene complex (structure 29-XI).

29-IX

Fe(CO)$_3$
29-X

29-XI

When two or more *conjugated* double bonds are engaged in bonding to a
metal atom the interactions become more complex, though qualitatively the
two types of basic, synergic components are involved. Buta-1,3-diene is an
important case and shows why it is an oversimplification to treat the bonding
as simply collections of separate monoolefin–metal interactions.

Two extreme formal representations of the bonding of a buta-1,3-diene
group to a metal atom are shown in Fig. 29-5. The degree to which individual
structures approach either of these extremes can be judged by the lengths of
the C—C bonds. A short–long–short pattern is indicative of Fig. 29-5(*a*) while
a long–short–long pattern is indicative of Fig. 29-5(*b*). In no case has a pronounced short–long–short pattern been established and the actual variation
seems to lie between approximate equality of all three bond lengths and the
long–short–long pattern.

Figure 29-5 Two extreme formal representations of the bonding of a *cis*-buta-1,3-diene group to a metal atom. Part (*a*) implies that there are two substantially independent monoolefin–metal interactions, while (*b*) depicts σ bonds to carbon atoms 1 and 4 coupled with an alkene–metal interaction at carbon atoms 3 and 2.

From a purely *formal* point of view each double bond in any olefin can be considered as a two-electron donor. If we have a polyolefin involved, the metal atom usually reacts so as to complete its normal coordination. For example, both $Mo(CO)_6$ and $Fe(CO)_5$ react with cyclohepta-1,3,5-triene to give structures 29-XII and 29-XIII, respectively. In structure 29-XIII there is one uncoordinated double bond.

$Mo(CO)_3$

29-XII

$Fe(CO)_3$

29-XIII

Cyclooctatetraene with four essentially unconjugated double bonds can bind in several ways depending on the metal system. With $PtCl_2$, it uses its 1- and 5-olefinic linkages, as in structure 29-XIV, and with $Fe(CO)_3$, which has a predilection for binding 1,3-diolefins, it is bound as in structure 29-XV.

29-XIV

29-XV

Synthesis

Olefin complexes are usually synthesized by interaction of metal carbonyls, halides, or occasionally other complexes with the olefin. Some representative examples are

$$Mo(CO)_6 + C_7H_8 \xrightarrow{\text{reflux}} Mo(CO)_3C_7H_8 + 3CO \qquad (29\text{-}12.1)$$

$$RhCl_3(aq) + C_2H_4 \xrightarrow{\text{25 °C in ethanol}} [(C_2H_4)_2RhCl]_2 \qquad (29\text{-}12.2)$$

Some of the earliest studies were made with the Ag^+ ion and in solutions we have equilibria of the type

$$Ag^+(aq) + \text{olefin} = [Ag \text{ olefin}]^+ \qquad (29\text{-}12.3)$$

The interaction of hydrocarbons with Ag^+ ions sometimes gives crystalline precipitates that are useful for purification of the olefin. Thus cyclooctatetraene or bicyclo-2,5-heptadiene, when shaken with aqueous silver perchlorate (or nitrate), give white crystals of stoichiometry olefin·$AgClO_4$ or 2 olefin·$AgClO_4$, depending on the conditions. Benzene also gives crystalline complexes with $AgNO_3$, $AgClO_4$, or $AgBF_4$. In $[C_6H_6 \cdot Ag]^+ ClO_4^-$ the metal ion is asymmetrically located with respect to the ring.

29-XVI

1-4-*Tetrahapto*,1,3,5-Cyclooctatrienetricarbonylruthenium

29-XVII

(*pentahapto*cyclopentadienyl)(1-3-*trihapto*cycloheptatrienyl)carbonyliron

29-XVIII

$(\eta^5\text{-}C_5H_5)_2(\eta^1\text{-}C_5H_5)_2Ti$

Figure 29-6 Illustrations of the *hapto* notation. Structure 29-XVI contains an η^4 ligand. Structure 29-XVII contains both an η^3 and an η^5 ligand. Structure 29-XVIII contains two η^5 and two η^1 cyclopentadienyl ligands.

29-13 Notation and Electron Counting in Alkene and Related Complexes

In addition to alkene complexes, there are more complex systems (such as the allyls to be discussed in Section 29-16) in which delocalized π electrons are bound to metals. Some systematic notation is required to designate the number of carbon atoms that are bound to the metal. This is done by use of the term *hapto-* (from the Greek, to fasten). Prefixes designate the number of carbon atoms that are fastened to the metal: *trihapto-, tetrahapto-, pentahapto-,* and so on. An equivalent designation uses the Greek η, with superscripts: η^3, η^4, η^5, and so on. Structures 29-XVI, 29-XVII, and 29-XVIII in Fig. 29-6 should help to make clear the use of the notation.

Electron Counting Rules as Applied to Alkene Complexes

We take the convention as stated previously that each double bond in a neutral olefin is a two-electron donor. The following cases are representative.

$[PtCl_3C_2H_4]^-$, Fig. 29-3(a):

Pt(II)		8 electrons
Cl^-	$2 \times 3 =$	6 electrons
C_2H_4	$2 \times 1 =$	2 electrons
		Total = 16 electrons

$Fe(CO)_3(C_7H_8)$, structure 29-X:

Fe		8 electrons
Norbornadiene	$2 \times 2 =$	4 electrons
CO	$2 \times 3 =$	6 electrons
		Total = 18 electrons

Ni (cyclododecatriene), structure 29-XI:

Ni		10 electrons
Cyclododecatriene	$2 \times 3 =$	6 electrons
		Total = 16 electrons

$Cr(CO)_3(\eta^6$-cyclohepta-1,3,5-triene), structure 29-XII:

Cr		6 electrons
η^6-C_7H_8	$2 \times 3 =$	6 electrons
CO	$2 \times 3 =$	6 electrons
		Total = 18 electrons

Fe(CO)₃(η⁴-cyclohepta-1,3,5-triene),
structure 29-XIII:

Fe		8 electrons
η^4-C_7H_8	$2 \times 2 =$	4 electrons
CO	$2 \times 3 =$	6 electrons

Total = 18 electrons

29-14 Other π-Donor Ligands; Delocalized Carbocyclic Groups

In 1951 a compound of formula $(C_5H_5)_2Fe$ was reported and was subsequently shown to have a unique "sandwich" structure (29-XIX) in which the metal lies between two planar cyclopentadienyl rings. Many η^5-C_5H_5 compounds are now known. Some have only one η^5-C_5H_5 ring as in structure 29-XX, others have two rings but with these at an angle as in structure 29-XXI.

29-XIX   29-XX   29-XXI

Other symmetric ring systems now known to form complexes are C_3Ph_3, C_4H_4, C_6H_6, C_7H_7, and C_8H_8. There is a formalism of describing these ring systems as if they assume the charge required to achieve an aromatic electron configuration. The "magic numbers" for aromaticity are 2, 6, and 10 so that these carbocycles can be written as:

The charges may be used in assigning formal oxidation numbers to the metal atoms in the complexes. Thus $(\eta^5$-$C_5H_5)_2Fe$ can be regarded as formed from the cyclopentadienide ion $C_5H_5^-$ and Fe^{2+} so that the compound contains Fe^{II}. In the benzene compound $C_6H_6Cr(CO)_3$ chromium has the formal oxidation state 0 as in $Cr(CO)_6$.

Examples of carbocyclic complexes are structures 29-XXII to 29-XXV.

29-XXII   29-XXIII   29-XXIV   29-XXV

Cyclopentadienyls

Cyclopentadiene is a weak acid ($pK_a \sim 20$) and with strong bases forms the cyclopentadienide ion $C_5H_5^-$. The general method for synthesizing metal complexes is the reaction of this ion with a metal halide or other complex, for example,

$$C_5H_6 + Na \xrightarrow{\text{THF}} C_5H_5^- + Na^+ + \tfrac{1}{2}H_2 \quad \text{(main reaction)} \quad (29\text{-}14.1)$$

$$2C_5H_5^- + NiCl_2 \xrightarrow{\text{THF}} (\eta^5\text{-}C_5H_5)_2Ni + 2Cl^- \quad\quad (29\text{-}14.2)$$

Two other methods are (a) the use of C_5H_5Tl, which is insoluble in water, stable, and easily stored:

$$C_5H_6 + TlOH \xrightarrow{\text{H}_2\text{O}} C_5H_5Tl\downarrow + H_2O \quad\quad (29\text{-}14.3)$$

$$FeCl_2 + 2TlC_5H_5 \xrightarrow{\text{THF}} 2TlCl + (\eta^5\text{-}C_5H_5)_2Fe \quad\quad (29\text{-}14.4)$$

and (b), the use of a strong organic base as a proton acceptor,

$$2C_5H_6 + CoCl_2 + 2Et_2NH \xrightarrow[\text{amine}]{\text{in excess}}$$

$$(\eta^5\text{-}C_5H_5)_2Co + 2Et_2NH_2Cl \quad (29\text{-}14.5)$$

Since the C_5H_5 anion acts as a uninegative ligand, the dicyclopentadienyl compounds are of the type $(\eta^5\text{-}C_5H_5)_2MX_{n-2}$ where the oxidation state of the metal, M, is n and X is a uninegative ion. When $n = 2$ we obtain neutral molecules like $(\eta^5\text{-}C_5H_5)_2Fe^{II}$. When $n = 3$, we may obtain a cation like $[(\eta^5\text{-}C_5H_5)_2Co^{III}]^+$ or, when $n = 4$, a halide like $(\eta^5\text{-}C_5H_5)_2Ti^{IV}Cl_2$. Some typical η^5-cyclopentadienyl compounds are given in Table 29-2. The C—C distance and bond order in $\eta^5\text{-}C_5H_5$ rings are similar to C—C distances in benzene. For two compounds, $(\eta^5\text{-}C_5H_5)_2Fe$, which has been given the trivial name *ferrocene*, and $(\eta^5\text{-}C_5H_5)Mn(CO)_3$ or *cymantrene*, aromatic-like reactions can be carried out. These compounds will survive the reaction conditions, but other $\eta^5\text{-}C_5H_5$

Table 29-2   Some Di-η^5-cyclopentadienyl Metal Compounds[a]

Compound	Appearance; mp,°C	Unpaired Electrons	Other Properties
$(\eta^5\text{-}C_5H_5)_2Fe$	Orange crystals; 174	0	Oxidized by $Ag^+(aq)$ or dilute HNO_3 to blue cation $\eta^5\text{-}Cp_2Fe^+$. Stable thermally to >500 °C
$(\eta^5\text{-}C_5H_5)_2Cr$	Scarlet crystals; 173	2	Very air sensitive
$(\eta^5\text{-}C_5H_5)_2Co^+$	Yellow ion and salts	0	Forms numerous salts and a stable strong base (absorbs CO_2 from air); thermally stable to ~400 °C
$(\eta^5\text{-}C_5H_5)_2TiCl_2$	Bright red crystals; 230	0	C_6H_5Li gives $\eta^5\text{-}Cp_2Ti(C_6H_5)_2$; reducible to $\eta^5\text{-}Cp_2TiCl$
$(\eta^5\text{-}C_5H_5)_2WH_2$	Yellow crystals; 163	0	Moderately stable in air, soluble benzene, and so on; soluble in acids giving $\eta^5\text{-}Cp_2WH_3^+$ ion

[a]$Cp = C_5H_5$. Note that many substituted derivatives are known and that pentamethyl cyclopentadienyls (*Cp) have been especially well studied. Their properties sometimes differ from Cp analogs, *e.g.* Cp_2Mn is high spin when dilute, whereas *Cp_2Mn is low spin.

compounds are decomposed. Typical reactions are Friedel–Crafts acylation, metallation by butyllithium, sulfonation, and so on. Indeed, there is an extensive "organic chemistry" of these molecules.

The bonding in $\eta^5\text{-}C_5H_5$ complexes is well described by an MO approach involving overlap of metal *d* orbitals (principally the d_{z^2} orbital, but also the d_{xz} and d_{yz} orbitals) with various π molecular orbitals of the cyclopentadienyl rings. For instance, if the *z* axis passes through the ring centers and the metal atom, then a bonding π molecular orbital of each cyclopentadienyl ring overlaps well with the corresponding lobe of the d_{z^2} orbital. In this fashion, bonding between the central metal atom and the "π-cloud" of each cyclopentadienyl ring is established.

In the compounds with only one $\eta^5\text{-}C_5H_5$ ring, the lobes of the *d* orbitals not involved in bonding to the ring can overlap with suitable orbitals in other ligands such as CO, NO, R_3P, and so on. Observe that only in the neutral compounds and $(\eta^5\text{-}C_5H_5)_2M^+$ are the rings parallel; in other compounds such as structure 29-XXI the rings are at an angle.

Benzenoid–Metal Complexes

Of other carbocycles, those containing benzene and substituted benzenes are the most important. Curiously, the first $(\eta^6\text{-}C_6H_6)M$ compounds were prepared as long ago as 1919, but their true identities were recognized only in 1954. A series of chromium compounds was obtained by F. Hein in 1919 from the reaction of $CrCl_3$ with C_6H_5MgBr; they were formulated as "polyphenylchromium" compounds, namely, $(C_6H_5)_nCr^{0,1+}$ where n = 2, 3, or 4. They actually contain "sandwich"-bonded C_6H_6 and C_6H_5—C_6H_5 groups as, for example, in structure 29-XXVI.

29-XXVI   29-XXVII

The prototype neutral compound, *dibenzenechromium*, $(C_6H_6)_2Cr$ (structure 29-XXVII), has also been obtained from the Grignard reaction of $CrCl_3$. A more effective method applicable to other metals is the direct interaction of an aromatic hydrocarbon and a metal halide in the presence of Al powder as a reducing agent and halogen acceptor plus $AlCl_3$ as a Friedel–Crafts-type activator. Although the neutral species are formed directly in the case of chromium, the usual procedure is to hydrolyze the reaction mixture with dilute acid that gives the cations $(C_6H_6)_2Cr^+$, (mesitylene)$_2Ru^{2+}$, and so on. These cations may then be reduced to the neutral molecules.

Dibenzenechromium, which forms dark brown crystals, is much more sensitive to air than is ferrocene, with which it is isoelectronic; it does not survive the reaction conditions of aromatic substitution. As with the η^5-C_5H_5 compounds complexes with only one arene ring can be prepared:

$$C_6H_5CH_3 + Mo(CO)_6 \xrightarrow{\text{reflux}} C_6H_5CH_3Mo(CO)_3 + 3CO \quad (29\text{-}14.6)$$

$$C_6H_6 + Mn(CO)_5Cl + AlCl_3 \longrightarrow [C_6H_6Mn(CO)_3]^+[AlCl_4]^- \quad (29\text{-}14.7)$$

The cyclooctatetraenyl ion, $C_8H_8^{2-}$, forms similar sandwich compounds with actinides, for example, $(\eta^8$-$C_8H_8)_2U^{IV}$ (structure 29-XXV). It appears that f orbitals are involved in the bonding here.

29-15 Alkyne Complexes

In acetylenes there are *two* π bonds at 90° to each other and both can be bound to a metal as in structure 29-XXVIII. The Co atoms and the acetylene carbon atoms form a distorted tetrahedron, and the C_6H_5 (or other groups) on the acetylene are bent away as shown.

29-XXVIII

There are also complexes where the alkyne is coordinated to only one metal atom and serves simply as the equivalent of an olefin or carbon monoxide ligand. Thus we have the reactions:

$$+ RC{\equiv}CR \xrightarrow{UV} \qquad \text{where } R = CF_3 \text{ or } Ph$$

$$\text{Mn(CO)}_3 \qquad \text{(OC)}_2\text{Mn} \tag{29-15.1}$$

$$\text{PtCl}_4{}^{2-} + t\text{-BuC}{\equiv}C\,t\text{-Bu} \longrightarrow \tag{29-15.2}$$

A third way of bonding, notably in Pt, Pd, and Ir complexes is that shown in Fig. 29-7. In these the C—C stretching frequency is lowered considerably, to the range 1750–1770 cm^{-1}, indicative of a C—C double bond. The C—C bond length of 1.32 Å is consistent with this view, as is the large distortion from linearity.

Finally, many important reactions of acetylenes, especially with metal car-

Figure 29-7
The structure of $(Ph_3P)_2Pt(PhC_2Ph)$, in which diphenylacetylene is most simply formulated as a divalent, bidentate ligand.

bonyls, involve incorporation of the acetylenes into rings, thus producing species with new organic ligands bound to the metals. Some examples are the following:

$$Fe(CO)_5 + 2C_2H_2 \longrightarrow \underset{Fe(CO)_3}{\boxed{}}=O \quad + \quad \boxed{} \tag{29-15.3}$$

$$(\eta^5\text{-}C_5H_5)Co(CO)_2 + 2R_2C_2(R = CH_3 \text{ or } CF_3) \longrightarrow \boxed{} \tag{29-15.4}$$

$$Fe(CO)_5 + 2C_2(CH_3)_2 \xrightarrow{h\nu} \boxed{} \tag{29-15.5}$$

29-16 Allyl Complexes

The allyl group $CH_2{=}CH{=}CH_2$ can be bound to metals in a delocalized (*trihapto*) fashion and can be considered to behave as a three-electron donor ligand. A representative structure is shown in Fig. 29-8. The allyl group can also be bound by a σ bond and transformation between σ or η^1 allyls and π or η^3 allyls may be quite facile:

$$\underset{\sigma \text{ or } \eta^1\text{-Allyl}}{M \overset{\overset{\textstyle H_2}{C}}{\underset{\underset{\textstyle H_2}{C}}{\diagdown}}\overset{}{\underset{}{CH}}} \rightleftharpoons \underset{\pi \text{ or } \eta^3\text{-Allyl}}{M{-}{\cdots}\overset{\overset{\textstyle H_2}{C}}{\underset{\underset{\textstyle H_2}{C}}{\diagup}}CH} \tag{29-16.1}$$

Allyl complexes may be obtained from allyl Grignard reagents or from allyl chloride as in the reactions:

$$NiCl_2 + 2C_3H_5MgBr \xrightarrow[-10\ ^\circ C]{\text{Ether}} \boxed{}Ni + 2MgX_2 \tag{29-16.2}$$

$$\text{Na}^+ \left[\underset{\text{Mo(CO)}_3}{\bigcirc} \right]^- + \text{C}_3\text{H}_5\text{Cl} \longrightarrow$$

$$\underset{\substack{\text{Mo(CO)}_3 \\ \text{H}_2\text{C} \\ \text{CH}=\text{CH}_2}}{\bigcirc} \xrightarrow[\text{UV}]{\Delta \text{ or}} \underset{\substack{\text{Mo} \\ \text{C } \text{ C}}}{\bigcirc} \qquad (29\text{-}16.3)$$

They can also be obtained by protonation of butadiene complexes, for example,

$$(29\text{-}16.4)$$

Allyl complexes play an important role in many catalytic reactions, particularly those involving conjugated alkenes.

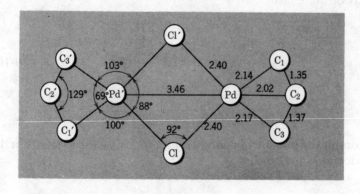

(a)

(b)

Figure 29-8   Structure of the allylpalladium(II) chloride dimer (*a*) side view and (*b*) top view. [Reprinted by permission from W. E. Oberhansli and L. F. Dahl, *J. Organomet. Chem.*, **1965**, *3*, 43.]

29-17 Carbene and Alkylidene Complexes

Although carbenes, $:CR_2$, are short lived in the free state, many organic reactions proceed by way of carbene intermediates. An increasing number of compounds are known in which carbenes are "stabilized" by binding to a transition metal. A carbene could be regarded as a two-electron donor comparable to CO, since there is a lone pair of electrons present on what is formally a divalent carbon atom. This view is depicted in structure 29-XXIX. An alternative view is that there is a metal to carbon double bond (similar to a $C=C$ double bond), as in structure 29-XXX.

$$M \longleftarrow :CR_2 \qquad M=CR_2$$
$$\text{29-XXIX} \qquad \text{29-XXX}$$

Indeed there is evidence to support both formal types of bonding, since there exist two main classes of carbene complexes: one where the metal is in a formally low oxidation state (structure 29-XXIX), the other where the metal is in a high oxidation state (structure 29-XXX). The compounds with metals in low oxidation states are properly called **carbene complexes,** and they are sometimes referred to as Fischer-type complexes after their discoverer, E. O. Fischer. General methods of synthesis involve attack of nucleophilic reagents on coordinated CO or RNC, followed by an electrophilic attack, as shown in the two steps of Eq. 29-17.1:

$$Cr(CO)_6 + LiR = Li^+ \left[(OC)_5CrC\begin{smallmatrix} O \\ \\ R \end{smallmatrix} \right]^- \xrightarrow{R_3'O^+} (OC)_5CrC\begin{smallmatrix} OR' \\ \\ R \end{smallmatrix} \qquad (29\text{-}17.1)$$

Carbene complexes can also be formed by cleavage of a $C=C$ double bond in certain electron-rich alkenes, as in reaction 29-17.2:

$$(29\text{-}17.2)$$

Structural studies of chromium(0) compounds such as those shown in structures 29-XXXI and 29-XXXII:

29-XXXI   29-XXXII

show that the M—CXY skeleton is always planar, while the M—C distances indicate some $d\pi$–$p\pi$ bonding to the carbene carbon, as in the bonding of π-acid ligands such as CO.

Complexes of the second type, where the metal is in a high oxidation state (i.e., structure 29-XXX), are properly termed **alkylidene complexes.** They are sometimes also called Schrock-type complexes, after their discoverer, R. R. Schrock. These are commonly obtained by deprotonation reactions of alkyl groups, as in reaction 29-17.3:

$$(\eta\text{-}C_5H_5)_2Ta(CH_3)_3 \xrightarrow{Ph_3C^+BF_4^-} (\eta\text{-}C_5H_5)_2Ta(CH_3)_2^+$$

$$\downarrow \text{NaOCH}_3 \qquad \qquad (29\text{-}17.3)$$

$$(\eta\text{-}C_5H_5)_2Ta\underset{CH_2}{\overset{CH_3}{\diagdown}}$$

The tantalum(V) product of reaction 29-17.3 provides a unique comparison of a metal to carbon single bond (2.246 Å) and a metal to carbon double bond (2.026 Å).

Alkylidene complexes are known to be intermediates in a number of organic reactions that are catalyzed by transition metal complexes, especially the alkene metathesis reaction. This involves exchange of groups on an alkene, as shown generally in reaction 29-17.4:

$$
\begin{array}{c}
RCH{=}CH_2 \\
+ \\
RCH{=}CH_2
\end{array}
\longrightarrow
\begin{array}{c}
RCH \\
\| \\
RCH
\end{array}
+
\begin{array}{c}
CH_2 \\
\| \\
CH_2
\end{array}
\qquad (29\text{-}17.4)
$$

Alkene metathesis is catalyzed by Mo, W, and Re oxohalides in the presence of an alkylating agent, and is considered to proceed by way of the sequence shown in Eq. 29-17.5:

$$
\underset{B}{\overset{A}{>}}C{=}M +
\underset{D}{\overset{C}{>}}\!\!=\!\!\underset{F}{\overset{E}{<}}
\rightleftharpoons
\begin{array}{c}
B \\
A{-}\!\!\!-{-}M \\
C{-}\!\!\!-{-}E \\
D\;F
\end{array}
\longrightarrow
\underset{C\quad D}{\overset{A\quad B}{>\!\!<}} +
\underset{E\quad F}{\overset{M}{<}}
\qquad (29\text{-}17.5)
$$

where there is a metallacyclic intermediate.

The decomposition of certain metal alkyl compounds can also give alkylidene complexes by α-hydrogen transfer as in Eq. 29-17.6:

$$
\overset{\displaystyle H}{\underset{\displaystyle |}{}}
M{-}CH_3 \longrightarrow M{=}CH_2 \qquad (29\text{-}17.6)
$$

The chemical reactivities of carbene and alkylidene complexes differ considerably. In carbene complexes the carbon bound to the metal is electrophilic, and it is readily attacked by nucleophiles as in Eq. 29-17.7:

$$(CO)_5\overset{\delta-}{Cr} \longleftarrow \overset{\delta+}{:C}\overset{OCH_3}{\underset{CH_3}{\diagdown}} \quad = \quad (CO)_5Cr \longleftarrow \left| \right|\begin{matrix} CH_3O \diagdown \diagup CH_3 \\ C \\ C \\ N \\ R \end{matrix} \qquad (29\text{-}17.7)$$

By contrast, the carbon atom bound to the metal in alkylidenes is nucleophilic.

29-18 Carbyne and Alkylidyne Complexes

These have M—CR groupings, and, in the same way as carbenes, the metals fall into two classes: those in either high or low oxidation states. **Carbyne compounds** can be regarded as derived from the four-electron donor CR. The metal —C—C groups are usually linear or nearly so. Carbyne compounds can be obtained from carbene compounds, for example, by reaction 29-18.1:

$$(CO)_4(Me_3P)Cr^0 \leftarrow C\overset{OMe}{\underset{Me}{\diagdown}} \quad \xrightarrow[\text{pentane}]{BX_3}$$

$$(CO)_3(Me_3P)XCr^I{-}CMe + CO + BX_2OMe \qquad (29\text{-}18.1)$$

Alkylidyne compounds of metals in high oxidation states can be formulated with M≡C triple bonds. They can be obtained by deprotonation of alkylidenes as in reaction 29-18.2:

$$(Me_3CCH_2)_3Ta^V{=}C\overset{H}{\underset{CMe_3}{\diagup}} \quad \xrightarrow{BuLi} \quad Li[(Me_3CCH_2)_3Ta^V{\equiv}CCMe_3] \qquad (29\text{-}18.2)$$

Some remarkable compounds have been made that have single, double, and triple MC bonds, for example, the tungsten(VI) complex shown in structure 29-XXXIII:

$$Me_3CCH_2{-}W\overset{PMe_3}{\underset{PMe_3}{\overset{\displaystyle =CHCMe_3}{\underset{\displaystyle \equiv CCMe_3}{\big|}}}}$$

29-XXXIII

The analogy between acetylenes (RC≡CR) and alkylidynes (LM≡CR) suggested to F. G. A. Stone that similar behavior towards other transition metal complexes could be expected. This concept has led to a wide variety of metal cluster compounds of the type shown in structure 29-XXXIV:

$$ML_x$$

$$L_nM \cdots \cdots ML_m$$

$$R-C$$

29-XXXIV

The latter can be compared with the acetylene complex shown in structure 29-XXVIII, which has a Co_2C_2 core. The alkylidyne-derived complexes (structure 29-XXXIV) have M_3C cores.

STUDY GUIDE

Scope and Purpose

This chapter is an indispensable prerequisite to the study of Chapter 30. It is also a natural continuation of topics covered in earlier chapters.

Although organometallic chemistry is a subarea of both inorganic and organic chemistry, it is such a large field that it could be considered a full-fledged branch of chemistry in itself. It draws on both inorganic and organic chemistry; yet, the whole is greater than the sum of the parts.

We have covered in this one chapter only some of the salient points. Familiar as well as new and novel types of structures are encountered, and some new concepts of bonding, structure, and the like are presented. Each type of structure and each class of substance deserves careful study.

We have somewhat relaxed the normal expectation concerning the need for full, completely balanced chemical equations. This is done in some cases for clarity, and in other cases because the nature of all the products, is not clearly established.

Study Questions

A. Review

1. Give a definition of an organometallic compound.
2. What are the three broad classes of organometallic compounds? Cite an example of each.
3. Describe at least three important general methods for preparing organometallic compounds.
4. What is the most characteristic structural feature of lithium alkyls?
5. Why are the tetramethylethylenediamine complexes of the lithium alkyls more reactive than the alkyls themselves?
6. What is a formula for a Grignard reagent and how are Grignard reagents prepared? What is the other general type of organomagnesium compound?

7. What sorts of species are believed actually to exist, in equilibrium, in a Grignard reagent in diethyl ether solution?

8. Give an example of a metal interchange reaction involving an organomercury compound.

9. Indicate with sketches the structures of the following:

$$LiCH_3 \qquad MgCH_3Br[O(C_2H_5)_2]_2 \qquad Hg(CH_3)_2 \qquad Al(CH_3)_3 \qquad (CH_3)_3SnF$$

10. Write an equation illustrating each of the terms: hydroboration reaction, mercuration, oxymercuration.

11. How would you prepare each of the following $NaBPh_4$ (from BCl_3); cyclopropylmercury bromide (from mercury); diethylzinc (from zinc); trimethylaluminum (from aluminum)?

12. What are siloxanes? Silicones? How are they made?

13. What is an alkylidenetriphenylphosphorane (Wittig reagent)? How are they made and what are they used for?

14. Why is $Ti(bipy)(CH_3)_4$ much more thermally stable than $Ti(CH_3)_4$?

15. Explain mechanistically why transition metal alkyls that have a β hydrogen atom are usually unstable, whereas analogous compounds in which the alkyls do not have β-hydrogen atoms generally are stable.

16. Besides β-hydrogen transfer, what is another important mode of decomposition of some metal alkyls?

17. Describe the structure of the anion, $[PtCl_3C_2H_4]^-$, in Zeise's salt, emphasizing the significant features on which an understanding of the metal–olefin bonding must be based.

18. Show with drawings the two important types of orbital overlap that explain the metal–olefin bonding in $[PtCl_3C_2H_4]^-$.

19. Show with drawings the expected structures of the following cyclooctatetraene (COT) complexes $(COT)Cr(CO)_3$, $(COT)Fe(CO)_3$, $(COT)PtCl_2$.

20. Give the formal names for the following:

21. Write equations for a two-step preparation of $(\eta^5\text{-}C_5H_5)_2Ni$ from C_5H_6, Na, and $NiCl_2$.

22. List the five symmetric ring systems that are known to form carbocyclic complexes of the type $[(RC)_n]ML_x$.

23. Enumerate the differences between (a) carbenes and alkylidenes and (b) carbynes and alkylidynes.

24. State two ways of obtaining η^3-allyl complexes.

25. Show how carbene complexes can be obtained from metal carbonyls.

B. Additional Exercises

1. What are mercurinium ions and what part do they play in oxomercuration reactions?

2. Describe the bonding in (a) dimethylberyllium, and (b) trimethylaluminum in terms of multicenter bonds.

3. Discuss the mechanism of the synthesis of alkenes from aldehydes or ketones by use of the Wittig reaction.

4. Explain the following observations

   (a) Although the M—C force constants and presumably bond strengths are comparable, $PbMe_4$ begins to decompose by radical formation at ca. 200 °C, while $TiMe_4$ is unstable above -80 °C.

   (b) Alkyl halides, $R'X$, react with phosphate esters, $P(OR)_3$, to give dialkylphosphonates, $O{=}P(OR)_2R'$ and RX.

   (c) The compound $(CH_3)_2PBH_2$ is trimeric and is extraordinarily stable and inert.

   (d) At -75 °C the proton resonance spectrum of trimethylaluminum shows two resonances in the ratio $2:1$ but at 25 °C only one peak at an average position is found.

5. Consider the interaction of a hydrido species L_nMH with hex-1-ene in benzene solution at 25 °C.

   (a) Why and how are *cis*- and *trans*-hex-2-enes formed?

   (b) If L_nMD was used, where would the deuterium finish up?

6. Assuming H transfer from CH_3 to metal is a plausible first step in decomposition of a methyl compound, write a mechanism for decomposition of $Ti(CH_3)_4$ in petroleum solution.

7. The interaction of $Na_2Fe(CO)_4$ with $(CH_3)_2NCH_2I$ gives the carbene complex $(CO)_4FeCHN(CH_3)_2$. Write a plausible reaction sequence.

8. The interaction of $(\eta^5\text{-}C_5H_5)_2Co^+$ salts with sodium borohydride as H^- source gives a red diamagnetic hydrocarbon-soluble product, $C_{10}H_{11}Co$. This has no band in the IR around 2000 cm^{-1} and the nmr spectrum is quite complex. The interaction of $(\eta^5\text{-}C_5H_5)_2Co$ with CH_3I gives $(\eta^5\text{-}C_5H_5)_2CoI$ and $C_{11}H_{13}Co$. Explain these reactions.

9. Compare the bonding of C_2H_4 and O_2 in the compounds $(Ph_3P)_2Pt(O_2)$ and $(Ph_3P)_2Pt(C_2H_4)$.

10. Compare the bond distances in structures 29-XXXI and 29-XXXII with the sum of the appropriate single-bond covalent radii to determine the extent of π bonding to each of the three substituents of these carbene ligands. Draw pictures representing the π-bond network about a planar carbene carbon.

11. Apply the 18-electron formalism to the reactant and product of reaction 29-16.4, and give the *hapto* notation that is appropriate for each organic ligand.

12. Apply the 18-electron formalism to each of the five compounds found in Table 29-2.

13. Draw the structure of each of the substances found in reactions 29-12.1 and 29-12.2.

14. Explain why the cyclohepta-1,3,5-triene ligand is *hexahapto* towards the $Cr(CO)_3$ fragment but only *tetrahapto* towards the $Fe(CO)_3$ fragment.

15. Would you expect Zeise's salt to add other ligands readily? Explain.

16. Why are there two different Al—C bond lengths in Al_2Me_6?

17. Suggest a synthesis for:

    (a) $Na[BEt_4]$ (b) $Li[AlEt_4]$ (c) $EtMgBr$ (d) PEt_3

C. Questions from the Literature of Inorganic Chemistry

1. Consider the two olefin complexes of iron(0) as reported by M. V. R. Strainer and J. Takats, *Inorg. Chem.*, **1982**, *21*, 4044–4049.

(a) Of the two ligands DEF and DEM, which is the stronger π acceptor? Support your conclusion with data from the article.

(b) Apply the 18-electron formalism to the title compounds.

(c) Why do olefins prefer the equatorial position in five-coordinate complexes such as these?

(d) Arrange the ligands CO, DEM, DEF, and PPh_3 in order of π acidity as found in these five-coordinate complexes. Justify your order based on data found in this article.

2. Consider the alkyne complexes of tantalum reported by G. Smith, R. R. Schrock, M. R. Churchill, and W. Y. Youngs, *Inorg. Chem.*, **1981**, *20*, 387–393.

(a) Write balanced chemical equations for the preparations of the four alkyne complexes reported here.

(b) Apply the 18-electron formalism to the two complexes $Ta(\eta^5-C_5Me_5)(cyclooctene)(Cl)_2$ and $Ta(\eta^5-C_5Me_5)(PhC\equiv CPh)(Cl)_2$.

(c) Why do you suppose the two-electron donor alkenes are readily replaced by the four-electron donor alkynes in these Ta compounds?

3. Consider the η^2-alkyne ligands found in the report by F. W. B. Einstein, K. G. Tyers, and D. Sutton, *Organometallics*, **1985**, *4*, 489–493.

(a) Apply the 18-electron formalism to Compounds *1a* and *1b* of this paper.

(b) Enumerate the differences between this diphenylacetylene ligand and the one featured in the article of Question 2. What accounts for the differences between a four-electron donor alkyne and a two-electron donor alkyne ligand?

4. Consider the alkyl–alkenyl–alkynylboranes of H. C. Brown, D. Basavaiah, and N. G. Bhat, *Organometallics*, **1983**, *2*, 1468–1470.

(a) Write a balanced chemical equation for each step in the synthesis of compound *4a*, starting with compound *3a*, ethylbromoborane·SMe_2.

(b) Describe each step in (a) as either hydroboration, methanolysis, nucleophilic displacement, or adduct formation.

SUPPLEMENTARY READING

Alper, H., *Transition Metal Organometallics in Organic Synthesis*, Vol. 2, Academic, New York, 1978.

Atwood, J. D., *Inorganic and Organometallic Reaction Mechanisms*, Brooks/Cole, Monterey, CA, 1985.

Baker, R., "Pi-Allyl Complexes in Organic Synthesis," *Chem. Rev.*, **1973**, *73*, 487.

Becker, E. I. and Tsutsui, M., *Organometallic Reactions,*, Vols. 1–4, Wiley-Interscience, New York, 1970–1972.

Coates, G. E., Green, M. L. H., Powell, P., and Wade, K., *Principles of Organometallic Chemistry*, Chapman and Hall, London, 1977.

Collman, J. P. and Hegedus, L. S., *Principles and Applications of Organotransition Metal Chemistry*, University Science Books, Mill Valley, CA, 1980.

Davies, S. G., *Organotransition Metal Chemistry, Applications to Organic Synthesis*, Pergamon Press, New York, 1982.

Dotz, K. H., et al., *Transition Metal Carbene Complexes*, Verlag Chemie, Weinheim, 1983.

Haiduc, I., and Zuckermann, J. J., *Basic Organometallic Chemistry*, Walter de Gruyter, New York, 1985.

Hartley, F. R., and Patai, S., Eds., *The Chemistry of the Metal–Carbon Bond,* Vol. 3, Wiley, New York, 1985.

Herberhold, M., *Metal Pi Complexes,* Elsevier, New York, 1972.

Kosolapoff, G. M. and Maier, L., *Organophosphorus Compounds,* Wiley, New York, 1972.

Lukehart, C. M., *Fundamental Transition Metal Organometallic Chemistry,* Brooks/Cole, Monterey, CA, 1985.

Matteson, D. S., *Organometallic Reaction Mechanisms of the Nontransition Elements,* Academic, New York, 1974.

Mole, T. and Jeffery, E. A., *Organoaluminum Compounds,* Elsevier, New York, 1972.

Pearson, A. J., *Metallo-Organic Chemistry,* Wiley-Interscience, New York, 1985.

Sawyer, A. K., *Organotin Compounds,* Vols. 1–3, Dekker, New York, 1974.

Wakefield, B. J., *Organolithium Compounds,* Pergamon Press, New York, 1974.

Wilkinson, G., Stone, F. G. A., and Abel, E. W., Eds., *Comprehensive Organometallic Chemistry,* Pergamon Press, New York, 1982.

Yamamoto, A., *Organotransition Metal Chemistry,* Wiley-Interscience, New York, 1986.

chapter 30

STOICHIOMETRIC AND CATALYTIC REACTIONS OF ORGANOMETALLIC COMPOUNDS

The production of most bulk organic chemicals including gasoline and fuel oils ultimately rests on the abundance of oil, natural gas, and coal. Most of the processes used to convert these raw materials into useful products depend on catalytic reactions involving transition metals. Heterogeneous processes where one or more metals (with other additives) are supported on zeolites, alumina, silica, or graphite are most commonly used. This is especially true where vast quantities of materials are involved, as in the processing and reforming of petroleums. Heterogeneous catalysis has the advantage that the catalyst can often operate at high temperatures and that the catalyst is readily separated from feed stock and products. There are also some disadvantages such as mass transfer problems in solids, limited variability, lack of high selectivity, and the fact that only a small part of the metal content may be in "active sites." Homogeneous catalysis in solution has advantages in that high activities are possible and that alteration of electronic and steric factors through ligand substitution may allow for design of high selectivity. The disadvantages of homogeneous catalysis are that such systems are commonly decomposed at high temperatures, and most important, that there can be serious problems in separating feedstocks, products, and catalysts. Nevertheless, a number of important commercial homogeneous catalyic processes are in use. Among the most important are the hydroformylation of alkenes, the Monsanto acetic acid process, and the Wacker process for making acetaldehyde from ethylene. Homogeneous reactions can also provide a greater insight into the mechanisms of catalyzed reactions since they are more amenable to study, especially by spectroscopic methods.

Before we discuss specific catalytic reactions, we must consider a number of stoichiometric ones that are important themselves, as well as for their relevance to catalysis. Although the principles discussed in this chapter have some applicability to heterogeneous catalysis, we shall not discuss these processes.

STOICHIOMETRIC REACTIONS

30-1 Coordinative Unsaturation

If two substances A and B are to react at the central metal of a complex in solution, then there must be vacant sites for their coordination to the metal. In heterogeneous reactions, the surface atoms of metals and metal oxides, halides, and so on, are necessarily coordinatively unsaturated. In solution, even intrinsically coordinatively unsaturated complexes such as square-planar d^8 systems are solvated, and coordinated solvent molecules will have to be replaced by reacting molecules, as in Eq. 30-1.1:

$$
\begin{array}{c}
\text{Solvent} \\
\text{L}_1\diagdown \ \big| \ \diagup\text{L}_3 \\
\diagup\text{M}\diagdown \\
\text{L}_2 \ \ \big| \ \ \text{L}_4 \\
\text{Solvent}
\end{array}
+ A + B \longrightarrow
\begin{array}{c}
\text{A} \\
\text{L}_1\diagdown \ \big| \ \diagup\text{L}_3 \\
\diagup\text{M}\diagdown \\
\text{L}_2 \ \ \big| \ \ \text{L}_4 \\
\text{B}
\end{array}
+ 2 \text{ Solvent} \qquad (30\text{-}1.1)
$$

In five- or six-coordinated metal complexes, coordination sites must be made available, either by thermal or photochemical dissociation of one or more ligands. For example, up to two phosphine ligands can be dissociated in the Rh complex of Eq. 30-1.2:

$$
\text{RhH(CO)(PPh}_3)_3 \underset{+\text{PPh}_3}{\overset{-\text{PPh}_3}{\rightleftharpoons}} \text{RhH(CO)(PPh}_3)_2 \underset{+\text{PPh}_3}{\overset{-\text{PPh}_3}{\rightleftharpoons}} \text{RhH(CO)(PPh}_3) \qquad (30\text{-}1.2)
$$

allowing the Rh complex to be useful as a catalyst at 25 °C. The iridium analog, namely, $\text{IrH(CO)(PPh}_3)_3$, is not useful as a catalyst unless the dissociation of ligands (a slow process at 25 °C) is induced by heat or UV light.

The ready substitution of ligands that is necessary for catalytic activity may also be prompted by a change of oxidation state at the metal, as in the oxidative–addition reactions discussed in the next section.

30-2 Metal Atoms as Centers of Acid–Base Behavior in Complexes

Protonation and Lewis Base Behavior of Metals

In electron-rich complexes, the metal may have substantial electron density located on it and, consequently, may be attacked by protons or other electrophilic reagents. An example is the bis(cyclopentadienyl)rhenium hydride, which may be protonated as in Eq. 30-2.1:

$$
(\eta^5\text{-C}_5\text{H}_5)_2\text{HRe} + \text{H}^+ \rightleftharpoons (\eta^5\text{-C}_5\text{H}_5)_2\text{H}_2\text{Re}^+ \qquad (30\text{-}2.1)
$$

and has a pK_b comparable to that of ammonia. Many carbonyl, phosphine, or phosphite complexes may be protonated, some examples being reactions 30-

STOICHIOMETRIC AND CATALYTIC REACTIONS OF ORGANOMETALLIC COMPOUNDS

The production of most bulk organic chemicals including gasoline and fuel oils ultimately rests on the abundance of oil, natural gas, and coal. Most of the processes used to convert these raw materials into useful products depend on catalytic reactions involving transition metals. Heterogeneous processes where one or more metals (with other additives) are supported on zeolites, alumina, silica, or graphite are most commonly used. This is especially true where vast quantities of materials are involved, as in the processing and reforming of petroleums. Heterogeneous catalysis has the advantage that the catalyst can often operate at high temperatures and that the catalyst is readily separated from feed stock and products. There are also some disadvantages such as mass transfer problems in solids, limited variability, lack of high selectivity, and the fact that only a small part of the metal content may be in "active sites." Homogeneous catalysis in solution has advantages in that high activities are possible and that alteration of electronic and steric factors through ligand substitution may allow for design of high selectivity. The disadvantages of homogeneous catalysis are that such systems are commonly decomposed at high temperatures, and most important, that there can be serious problems in separating feedstocks, products, and catalysts. Nevertheless, a number of important commercial homogeneous catalyic processes are in use. Among the most important are the hydroformylation of alkenes, the Monsanto acetic acid process, and the Wacker process for making acetaldehyde from ethylene. Homogeneous reactions can also provide a greater insight into the mechanisms of catalyzed reactions since they are more amenable to study, especially by spectroscopic methods.

Before we discuss specific catalytic reactions, we must consider a number of stoichiometric ones that are important themselves, as well as for their relevance to catalysis. Although the principles discussed in this chapter have some applicability to heterogeneous catalysis, we shall not discuss these processes.

STOICHIOMETRIC REACTIONS

30-1   Coordinative Unsaturation

If two substances A and B are to react at the central metal of a complex in solution, then there must be vacant sites for their coordination to the metal. In heterogeneous reactions, the surface atoms of metals and metal oxides, halides, and so on, are necessarily coordinatively unsaturated. In solution, even intrinsically coordinatively unsaturated complexes such as square-planar d^8 systems are solvated, and coordinated solvent molecules will have to be replaced by reacting molecules, as in Eq. 30-1.1:

$$\begin{array}{c} \text{Solvent} \\ L_1 \cdots \overset{|}{\underset{|}{M}} \cdots L_3 \\ L_2 \diagup \quad \diagdown L_4 \\ \text{Solvent} \end{array} + A + B \longrightarrow \begin{array}{c} A \\ L_1 \cdots \overset{|}{\underset{|}{M}} \cdots L_3 \\ L_2 \diagup \quad \diagdown L_4 \\ B \end{array} + 2\,\text{Solvent} \qquad (30\text{-}1.1)$$

In five- or six-coordinated metal complexes, coordination sites must be made available, either by thermal or photochemical dissociation of one or more ligands. For example, up to two phosphine ligands can be dissociated in the Rh complex of Eq. 30-1.2:

$$RhH(CO)(PPh_3)_3 \underset{+PPh_3}{\overset{-PPh_3}{\rightleftharpoons}} RhH(CO)(PPh_3)_2 \underset{+PPh_3}{\overset{-PPh_3}{\rightleftharpoons}} RhH(CO)(PPh_3) \quad (30\text{-}1.2)$$

allowing the Rh complex to be useful as a catalyst at 25 °C. The iridium analog, namely, $IrH(CO)(PPh_3)_3$, is not useful as a catalyst unless the dissociation of ligands (a slow process at 25 °C) is induced by heat or UV light.

The ready substitution of ligands that is necessary for catalytic activity may also be prompted by a change of oxidation state at the metal, as in the oxidative–addition reactions discussed in the next section.

30-2   Metal Atoms as Centers of Acid–Base Behavior in Complexes

Protonation and Lewis Base Behavior of Metals

In electron-rich complexes, the metal may have substantial electron density located on it and, consequently, may be attacked by protons or other electrophilic reagents. An example is the bis(cyclopentadienyl)rhenium hydride, which may be protonated as in Eq. 30-2.1:

$$(\eta^5\text{-}C_5H_5)_2HRe + H^+ \rightleftharpoons (\eta^5\text{-}C_5H_5)_2H_2Re^+ \qquad (30\text{-}2.1)$$

and has a pK_b comparable to that of ammonia. Many carbonyl, phosphine, or phosphite complexes may be protonated, some examples being reactions 30-

2.2 to 30-2.5:

$$Fe(CO)_5 + H^+ \rightleftharpoons FeH(CO)_5^+ \tag{30-2.2}$$

$$Ni[P(OEt)_3]_4 + H^+ \rightleftharpoons NiH[P(OEt)_3]_4^+ \tag{30-2.3}$$

$$Ru(CO)_3(PPh_3)_2 + H^+ \rightleftharpoons [RuH(CO)_3(PPh_3)_2]^+ \tag{30-2.4}$$

$$Os_3(CO)_{12} + H^+ \rightleftharpoons [HOs_3(CO)_{12}]^+ \tag{30-2.5}$$

The protonation of carbonylate anions (Section 28-9) may similarly be regarded as addition of H^+ to the electron-rich metal center, as in reaction 30-2.6:

$$Mn(CO)_5^- + H^+ \rightleftharpoons HMn(CO)_5 \tag{30-2.6}$$

The Oxidative Addition Reaction

Coordinatively unsaturated compounds, whether transition metal or not, can generally add neutral or anionic nucleophiles. Such reactions are simple additions, and two examples are given in Eqs. 30-2.7 and 30-2.8:

$$PF_5 + F^- \rightleftharpoons PF_6^- \tag{30-2.7}$$

$$TiCl_4 + 2OPCl_3 \rightleftharpoons TiCl_4(OPCl_3)_2 \tag{30-2.8}$$

Even when the metal is formally electron-rich, coordinatively unsaturated complexes may still readily add nucleophiles. Consider reactions 30-2.9 and 30-2.10:

$$trans\text{-}IrCl(CO)(PPh_3)_2 + CO \rightleftharpoons IrCl(CO)_2(PPh_3)_2 \tag{30-2.9}$$

$$[PdCl_4]^{2-} + Cl^- \rightleftharpoons [PdCl_5]^{3-} \tag{30-2.10}$$

A special circumstance arises when addition of a ligand is accompanied by oxidation of the metal. The oxidative addition reaction may be written generally as in Eq. 30-2.11:

$$L_nM + XY \longrightarrow L_n(X)(Y)M \tag{30-2.11}$$

It is a reaction in which the formal oxidation state of the metal increases by two. Also, the formal oxidation state of the ligand is reduced upon addition, often with cleavage of an intraligand bond.

For an oxidative addition reaction to proceed, we must have (a) nonbonding electron density on the metal, (b) two vacant coordination sites on the reacting complex, L_nM (in order to allow formation of two new bonds to X and Y), and (c) a metal with stable oxidation states separated by two units.

Many reactions of even nonmetal compounds may be regarded as oxidative additions. Consider, for example, the oxidative addition reactions of the halogens represented in Eqs. 30-2.12 to 30-2.14:

$$(CH_3)_2S + I_2 \rightleftharpoons (CH_3)_2SI_2 \tag{30-2.12}$$

$$PF_3 + F_2 \rightleftharpoons PF_5 \tag{30-2.13}$$

$$SnCl_2 + Cl_2 \rightleftharpoons SnCl_4 \tag{30-2.14}$$

Formally, at least, we consider that the zero-valent halogens have oxidized the central atoms in these reactions, and that they are coordinated in the products as halide (X^-) groups. For transition metals, the most common oxidative addition reactions involve complexes of the metals with d^8 and d^{10} electron configurations, notably Fe^0, Ru^0, Os^0; Rh^I, Ir^I; Ni^0, Pd^0, Pt^0; and Pd^{II} and Pt^{II}. An especially well-studied complex is the square-planar *trans*-IrCl(CO)(PPh$_3$)$_2$, which undergoes reactions such as Eq. 30-2.15:

$$\textit{trans-}Ir^ICl(CO)(PPh_3)_2 + HCl \rightleftharpoons Ir^{III}HCl_2(CO)(PPh_3)_2 \tag{30-2.15}$$

It should be noted that in oxidative additions of molecules such as H_2, HCl, or Cl_2, two new bonds to the metal are made, and the X—Y bond is broken. However, molecules that contain multiple bonds may be added oxidatively to a metal complex without cleavage. In such cases, three-membered rings are formed with the metal. Two examples of this are reactions 30-2.16 and 30-2.17:

$$(30-2.16)$$

$$Pt(PPh_3)_4 + (CF_3)_2CO \longrightarrow \quad + 2PPh_3 \tag{30-2.17}$$

The latter reaction also provides an example of the situation where the most stable coordination number in the oxidized state would be exceeded, so that expulsion of ligands (in this case two PPh$_3$) attends the process.

In Table 30-1 we list the types of molecules that are known to add oxidatively to a complex in at least one instance.

Oxidative addition reactions can be regarded as equilibria of the type shown in reaction 30-2.18:

$$L_nM^n + XY \rightleftharpoons L_nM^{n+2}XY \tag{30-2.18}$$

Whether the equilibrium lies on the reduced-metal or the oxidized-metal side depends very critically on (a) the nature of the metal and its ligands, (b) the nature of the addend XY and of the M—X and M—Y bonds so formed, and

Table 30-1 Some Substances that Can Be Added
to Complexes in Oxidative–Addition Reactions

Atoms Become Separated	Atoms Remain Connected
H_2	O_2
HX (X = Cl, Br, I, CN, RCO_2, ClO_4)	SO_2
H_2S, C_6H_5SH	CF_2=CF_2, $(CN)_2C$=$C(CN)_2$
RX ⎫	RC≡CR'
RCOX ⎬ R = Me, Ph, CF_3, and so on	RNCS
RSO_2X ⎭	RNCO
R_3SnX ⎫ X = Cl, Br, I	RN=C=NR'
R_3SiX ⎭	$RCON_3$
Cl_3SiH	R_2C=C=O
Ph_3PAuCl	CS_2
HgX_2, CH_3HgX (X = Cl, Br, I)	$(CF_3)_2CO$, $(CF_3)_2CS$, CF_3CN
C_6H_6	

(c) the medium in which the reaction is conducted. When the molecule XY
adds without severance of X from Y, the two new bonds to the metal are
necessarily in cis positions. When X and Y are separated by addition to the
metal, the product may be one of several isomers with cis or trans MX and MY
groups, as shown in Eq. 30-2.19:

$$
\begin{array}{c}
\underset{L_2}{\overset{L_1}{\diagdown}}M\underset{L_3}{\overset{L_4}{\diagup}} \;+\; XY \\[2mm]
\downarrow \\[2mm]
\end{array}
$$

(30-2.19)

$$
\underset{Y}{\overset{X}{\mid}}\;L_1\!-\!M\!-\!L_4\;L_2\;L_3 \qquad \underset{L_4}{\overset{X}{\mid}}\;L_1\!-\!M\!-\!Y\;L_2\;L_3 \qquad \underset{L_3}{\overset{X}{\mid}}\;L_1\!-\!M\!-\!Y\;L_2\;L_4 \qquad \text{and so on}
$$

The final product will be the isomer or mixture of isomers that is the most
stable thermodynamically under the reaction conditions. The ligands, solvent,
temperature, pressure, and the like will have a decisive influence on this.
Consequently, the nature of the final product does not necessarily give a guide
to the initial product of the addition, since isomerization of the initial product
may occur under the conditions of the addition.

Mechanisms of Oxidative-Addition Reactions

Studies indicate that the following types of pathways are possible:

1. A purely *ionic mechanism* is favored by a polar medium. In polar media,
HCl or HBr would be dissociated, and protonation of a square complex would
first produce a five-coordinate intermediate:

$$MXL_3 + H^+(\text{solvated}) \longrightarrow MHXL_3^+ \qquad (30\text{-}2.20)$$

Intramolecular isomerization followed by coordination of X^- would then give the final product:

$$MHXL_3^+ + Cl^-(\text{solvated}) \longrightarrow MHClXL_3 \qquad (30\text{-}2.21)$$

2. In an S_N2 attack of the type common in organic chemistry, the transition metal complex attacks an alkyl halide, as in reactions 30-2.22 and 30-2.23:

$$L_nM: \overset{\frown}{\ } CR^1R^2R^3X \longrightarrow L_nM^{\delta+}\text{----}\underset{\underset{R^3}{|}}{\overset{R^1 \quad R^2}{C}}\text{----}X^{\delta-} \qquad (30\text{-}2.22)$$

$$L_nMX(CR^1R^2R^3) \longleftarrow [L_nM\text{---}CR^1R^2R^3]^+ + X^- \qquad (30\text{-}2.23)$$

It is RX that is added.

3. Several oxidative addition reactions are *free radical* in nature and can be initiated by free radical sources such as peroxides.

4. Under nonpolar conditions, particularly with molecules that have little or no polarity—such as hydrogen or oxygen—*one step, concerted processes* give products with the new bonds formed cis to one another as in Eq. 30-2.24:

$$(30\text{-}2.24)$$

Notice that the filled nonbonding d orbitals of the metal in reaction 30-2.24 have the proper symmetry to populate (i.e., reduce) the antibonding orbital of X—Y.

Consider the following observations:

1. When solid *trans*-IrCl(CO)(PPh$_3$)$_2$ reacts with HCl gas, the product has H and Cl in cis positions.

2. The addition of HCl or HBr to *trans*-IrCl(CO)(PPh$_3$)$_2$ in nonpolar solvents such as benzene also gives cis-addition products. If wet or polar solvents (such as DMF) are used, the addition products are cis and trans mixtures.

The concerted mechanism seems appropriate for the reactions in nonpolar media, and the ionic mechanism in polar media.

The fact that many of the d^8 complexes react with molecular hydrogen might seem surprising in light of the high energy (ca. 450 kJ mol^{-1}) of the H—H bond. The attack on the hydrogen molecule probably places electron density from the metal into the σ-antibonding MO of the hydrogen, helping to weaken the H—H bond. Homolysis of the H—H bond results. This mechanism implies initial coordination of molecular hydrogen to the metal and indeed some complexes of this type are now characterized, for example, *trans*-$(R_3P)_2(CO)_3W(H_2)$. It has even been possible by nmr to detect the following series of steps in certain cases:

$$L_nM \underset{-H_2}{\overset{+H_2}{\rightleftharpoons}} L_nM(H_2) \rightleftharpoons L_nM\overset{H}{\underset{H}{\diagdown}} \qquad (30\text{-}2.25)$$

An alternate mechanism, that operates in other cases, is heterolytic cleavage of the H—H bond by base-promoted removal of H^+ as in Eq. 30-2.26:

$$RuCl_2(PPh_3)_3 + H_2 + Et_3N \longrightarrow RuHCl(PPh_3)_3 + Et_3NH^+Cl^- \qquad (30\text{-}2.26)$$

30-3 Migration of Atoms or Groups from Metal to Ligand: The Insertion Reaction

"Insertion" is a broadly applicable description of a reaction in which any atom or group is inserted between two other atoms initially bound together. In the general case Eq. 30-3.1:

$$L_nM{-}X + YZ \longrightarrow L_nM{-}(YZ){-}X \qquad (30\text{-}3.1)$$

the group YZ is inserted into the M—X bond. Some representative examples are given in reactions 30-3.2 to 30-3.6:

$$R_3SnNR_2 + CO_2 \longrightarrow R_3SnOC(O)NR_2 \qquad (30\text{-}3.2)$$

$$Ti(NR_2)_4 + 4CS_2 \longrightarrow Ti(S_2CNR_2)_4 \qquad (30\text{-}3.3)$$

$$R_3PbR' + SO_2 \longrightarrow R_3PbOS(O)R' \qquad (30\text{-}3.4)$$

$$[(NH_3)_5RhH]^{2+} + O_2 \longrightarrow [(NH_3)_5RhO_2H]^{2+} \qquad (30\text{-}3.5)$$

$$(CO)_5MnCH_3 + CO \longrightarrow (CO)_5MnCOCH_3 \qquad (30\text{-}3.6)$$

For transition metals, detailed studies have been made on the insertion of CO and SO_2 into metal to carbon bonds. Insertions of CO_2 into M—H and M—O bonds are also known. We shall consider only insertions of CO into M—C bonds.

Mechanistic studies using ^{14}CO-labeled $CH_3Mn(CO)_5$ have shown that (a) the CO molecule that becomes the acyl ligand is *not* derived from the external CO, but is one that was already coordinated to the metal atom; that (b) the incoming CO is added cis to the acyl group as in Eq. 30-3.7:

$$(30\text{-}3.7)$$

and that (c) the conversion of the alkyl ligand into the acyl ligand can be promoted by the addition of ligands other than CO, for instance excess PPh_3, as in reaction 30-3.8:

$$\underset{\substack{\text{Mn}}}{\overset{\substack{CH_3}}{\text{(OC)}}} + PPh_3 \longrightarrow \underset{\substack{\text{Mn}}}{\overset{\substack{Ph_3P \quad C-CH_3}}{\text{(OC)}}} \qquad (30\text{-}3.8)$$

Kinetic studies of such insertion reactions show that the first step involves an equilibrium between the octahedral alkyl and a five-coordinate acyl intermediate:

$$CH_3Mn(CO)_5 \rightleftharpoons CH_3COMn(CO)_4 \qquad (30\text{-}3.9)$$

The in-coming ligand (whether CO, PPh_3, or the like) then adds to the five-coordinate intermediate as in reaction 30-3.10:

$$CH_3COMn(CO)_4 + L \longrightarrow CH_3COMn(CO)_4L \qquad (30\text{-}3.10)$$

The insertion of CO is thus best considered to be an alkyl migration to a coordinated carbon monoxide. The migration is to a cis CO ligand and probably proceeds through a three-centered transition state as in reaction 30-3.11:

$$\underset{\substack{\text{M—CO}}}{\overset{\substack{R_3\\C}}{|}} \longrightarrow \underset{\substack{\text{M----CO}}}{\overset{\substack{R_3\\C}}{}} \longrightarrow \text{M—C}\underset{\substack{O}}{\overset{\substack{CR_3}}{}} \qquad (30\text{-}3.11)$$

Since five-coordinate species can undergo intramolecular rearrangements, more than one isomer of the final product *may* be formed.

Multiple insertions may occur under certain circumstances. Consider reaction 30-3.12:

$$WMe_6 + 9CO \longrightarrow W(CO)_6 + 3Me_2CO \qquad (30\text{-}3.12)$$

which involves initial transfer to give an acetyl ligand, followed by methyl migration to give acetone.

One further important example that can be regarded as an insertion is reaction 30-3.13:

$$M\text{—H} + CH_2{=}CH_2 = M\text{—}CH_2CH_3 \qquad (30\text{-}3.13)$$

which will be discussed in Section 30-6.

30-4 Reactions of Coordinated Ligands

Nucleophilic Attack at Coordinated Ligands

This is a broadly general type of reaction of which there are numerous examples involving nucleophiles such as OH^-, RO^-, RCO_2^-, N_3^-, and NR_3, and so on. Ligands that are generally susceptible to attack by nucleophiles include CO, NO, RCN, RNC, alkenes, and so on. It is not always apparent that attack on the ligand is direct, as prior coordination of the nucleophile to the metal center may occur. Then the reactions should be regarded as intramolecular transfers.

Examples long known to involve reaction directly at the ligand are attack of OH^- at coordinated NO

$$[Fe(CN)_5NO]^{2-} + OH^- \xrightarrow{\text{Slow}} \left[Fe(CN)_5N\overset{\displaystyle O}{\underset{\displaystyle OH}{<}} \right]^{3-}$$

$$\Big\downarrow \text{Fast} \;\; OH^-$$

$$[Fe(CN)_5NO_2]^{4-} + H_2O$$

(30-4.1)

and attack of OH^- at coordinated CO

$$Fe(CO)_5 + OH^- \longrightarrow \left[(CO)_4Fe-C\overset{\displaystyle O}{\underset{\displaystyle OH}{<}} \right]^-$$

$$\Big\downarrow OH^-$$

$$(CO)_4FeH^- + HCO_3^-$$

(30-4.2)

The attack of alkoxide ions RO^- on CO gives the M—C(O)OR group as in Eq. 30-4.3:

$$[Ir(CO)_3(PPh_3)_2]^+ \underset{H^+}{\overset{CH_3O^-}{\rightleftharpoons}} Ir(CO)_2(\overset{\displaystyle O}{\overset{\displaystyle \|}{C}}OCH_3)(PPh_3)_2$$

(30-4.3)

Such reactions are important in the catalyzed syntheses of carboxylic acids and esters from alkenes, CO, and water or alcohols.

Coordinated carbon monoxide can also be attacked by lithium alkyls as in reaction 30-4.4:

$$LiCH_3 + W(CO)_6 \longrightarrow Li^+[(CO)_5W-C(O)CH_3]^-$$

(30-4.4)

Alkene and dienyl complexes are also attacked by nucleophiles as in reaction 30-4.5:

$$(30\text{-}4.5)$$

Isocyanide complexes, on the other hand, are attacked by alcohols to form "carbene" complexes, as in Eq. 30-4.6:

$$(Et_3P)Cl_2PtCNPh + EtOH \longrightarrow (Et_3P)Cl_2Pt{=}C{\overset{OEt}{\underset{NHPh}{}}} \qquad (30\text{-}4.6)$$

Attack Involving Hydride Ion

Reduction by H^- of certain η^5-C_5H_5 rings produces η^4-cyclopentadiene ligands as in reaction 30-4.7 while hydride reduction of η^6-C_6H_6 (arene) ligands gives

$$(30\text{-}4.7)$$

η^5-cyclohexadienyls:

$$[C_6H_6Mn(CO)_3]^+ + H^- \longrightarrow \qquad (30\text{-}4.8)$$

Hydride transfer also occurs with certain complex alkyls, where conversion into an olefin complex as in Eq. 30-4.9 can be achieved by abstraction from the alkyl ligand of H^-, using triphenylmethyl tetrafluoroborate.

$$\eta^5\text{-}C_5H_5(CO)_2Fe\text{---}CHRCH_2R'$$

$$BH_4^- \Updownarrow Ph_3C^+BF_4^-$$

$$(30\text{-}4.9)$$

Intramolecular Hydrogen Transfer

A special case of transfer reactions is one in which a hydrogen atom is initially transferred to the metal giving an intermediate hydride ligand. Such reactions are especially important for triarylphosphines and triarylphosphites. An example is reaction 30-4.10:

$$(30\text{-}4.10)$$

Such reactions are termed ortho- or cyclometallations.

30-5 Reactions of Coordinated Molecular Oxygen

We observed previously that molecular oxygen can add to certain metal complexes without full cleavage of the O—O bond, and that there is some correlation between O—O distances in the O_2 ligands and the reversibility with which the O_2 complex is formed. In the extreme case, full oxidative–addition of O_2 gives the O_2^{2-} ligand with long O—O distances in the ligand. Less severe oxidation upon addition leads to reversible adduct formation as in hemoglobin.

Coordinated oxygen may be more reactive than free oxygen because of the O—O bond weakening that accompanies even weak addition to metals. Thus coordinated O_2 may be attacked more successfully. The mechanisms of attack on coordinated oxygen are poorly understood, but in many cases free radicals are involved. However, for some phosphine complexes, the reaction proceeds through peroxo intermediates that may be isolated. An example is the platinum peroxocarbonate of reaction 30-5.1:

$$(30\text{-}5.1)$$

The mechanism of oxidation of SO_2 by the oxygen complex $IrCl(CO)(O_2)$-$(PPh_3)_2$ to give a sulfato complex

$$(30\text{-}5.2)$$

has been studied with an ^{18}O tracer.

CATALYTIC REACTIONS

The term catalyst requires careful use. The term—meaning a substance added to accelerate a reaction—may have some application in heterogeneous systems. In such systems, where, for example, a gas mixture is passed over a solid catalyst, the solid catalyst may be recovered unchanged. Homogeneous catalytic systems, however, proceed in solution by way of a series of linked chemical reactions involving different metal complexes at each point in the process. What one adds initially to the reaction mixture is quickly engaged in a number of reactions and equilibria. The concept of one particular species being "the catalyst" then has no validity. Instead, one speaks in terms of intermediates involved in the various steps of a catalytic cycle.

The catalytic cycles to be described all involve the same sorts of changes in oxidation state and coordination number that have been delineated for stoichiometric reactions in the preceding sections. In the catalytic systems, however, the metal complex is returned to its original state at the end of one cycle.

30-6 Isomerization

Many transition metal complexes, especially those of the Group VIIIA(8)–VIIIA(10) metals, promote double-bond migration (isomerization) in alkenes. The products are the thermodynamically most stable isomeric mixtures. Thus 1-alkenes give mixtures of cis and trans 2-alkenes. This reaction is characteristic for many transition metal hydrido complexes; the isomerization involves transfer of H from the transition metal hydride to a coordinated alkene, giving a metal–alkyl complex. In addition many complexes that do not have M—H bonds, for example, $(Et_3P)_2NiCl_2$, will catalyze the isomerization of alkenes provided a source of hydride (such as molecular hydrogen) is present.

The first step in the catalytic cycle must be the coordination of the alkene:

$$L_nMH + RCH{=}CH_2 \rightleftharpoons L_nMH(RCH{=}CH_2) \qquad (30\text{-}6.1)$$

Reaction 30-6.1 is followed by hydride transfer to form an alkyl ligand:

$$(30\text{-}6.2)$$

Reaction 30-6.2, in the reverse direction, has already been identified as the primary route for the decomposition of many alkyls. (The reverse of reaction 30-6.2 is termed β elimination; the alkene is eliminated from the metal alkyl by transfer to the metal of a hydrogen from the β carbon of the alkyl ligand.) Thus we expect that Eq. 30-6.2 is readily reversible, and that there should be a scrambling of all hydrogen atoms during the catalytic process. When fluoroolefins are used as in reaction 30-6.3:

$$RhH(CO)(PPh_3)_3 + C_2F_4 \longrightarrow Rh(CF_2CF_2H)(CO)(PPh_3)_2 + PPh_3 \qquad (30\text{-}6.3)$$

stable metal alkyls are obtained, and it can be demonstrated that the hydride of the original metal complex is attached to the β carbon of the alkyl ligand. This is required if the four-centered transition state of reaction 30-6.2 is involved.

With alkenes other than ethylene, there is the possibility of addition of M—H across the double bond in either Markovnikov or anti-Markovnikov fashion. Thus we may have reactions 30-6.4 or 30-6.5.

$$
\left[\begin{array}{c} \text{H} \quad\quad \text{H} \\ L_nM \cdots\cdots C \\ C \quad\quad CH_2R \\ \text{H} \quad\quad \text{H} \end{array} \right] \rightleftharpoons \begin{array}{c} \text{H} \quad\quad \text{H} \\ L_nM \quad\quad C \\ C \quad\quad CH_2R \\ \text{H} \quad\quad \text{H} \end{array} \tag{30-6.4}
$$

(A)

$$ L_nMH + RCH_2CH{=}CH_2 $$

$$
\left[\begin{array}{c} \text{H} \quad\quad \text{H} \\ L_nM \cdots\cdots C \\ C \quad\quad \text{H} \\ \text{H} \quad\quad CH_2R \end{array} \right] \rightleftharpoons \begin{array}{c} \text{H} \quad\quad \text{H} \\ L_nM \quad\quad C \\ C \quad\quad \text{H} \\ \text{H} \quad\quad CH_2R \end{array} \tag{30-6.5}
$$

aMar = anti-Markovnikov   (B)
Mar = Markovnikov

In the anti-Markovnikov addition Eq. 30-6.4, the hydrogen atom is transferred from the metal to the β carbon of the chain, giving the primary alkyl derivative (A). The reverse of Eq. 30-6.4 requires β elimination from compound A. Since only one carbon is positioned β to the metal, the original olefin must reform upon reversal of reaction 30-6.4. Observe, however, that because of free rotation about C—C bonds, the same hydrogen need not be eliminated with the olefin as was given to the olefin in making the alkyl ligand of compound A. Thus in anti-Markovnikov addition there may be scrambling of hydrogen atoms at the β position, but not isomerization of the alkene. On the other hand, there are two possibilities for β elimination from the secondary alkyl derivative B that is formed by Markovnikov addition as in reaction 30-6.5. If the H atom is β eliminated from the CH_3 group of compound B, the original alkene is reformed. If the H atom is β eliminated from the methylene carbon of the CH_2R group in compound B, then a 2-alkene is reformed. Thus isomerization may occur through initial Markovnikov addition of the metal hydride across the alkene, and it should be noted that either cis or trans 2-alkenes, or both, may be formed.

30-7 Hydrogenation

The fact that molecular hydrogen reacts with many substances at room temperature has allowed the design of useful catalysts for the reduction by H_2 of unsaturated compounds such as alkenes or alkynes. The most successful catalytic cycles use complexes such as $RhCl(PPh_3)_3$ in benzene or ethanol–benzene solution. The rates of hydrogenation depend on the nature of the groups at the site of reduction, and selectivity is, therefore, possible. In reaction 30-7.1,

$$\text{(30-7.1)}$$

for example only one of two C=C double bonds is actually reduced. Furthermore, in contrast to heterogeneous catalysis, where scattering of hydrogen (traced by use of D_2) throughout the molecule usually results, homogeneous catalysis leads to discrete addition of H_2 (D_2) to one C=C site.

The mechanism of hydrogenations using $RhCl(PPh_3)_3$ appears to involve the cycle shown in Fig. 30-1 where P = PPh_3.

There are a number of similar catalytic systems that can reduce not only

C=C and C≡C groups but also $>$C=O, —N=N—, and —CH=N—.

Another catalytic system for reductions employs $RhCl_3(py)_3$ in DMF plus $NaBH_4$.

One of the most important developments has been the use of optically active phosphine ligands to achieve highly selective hydrogenation of prochiral unsaturated compounds. Rhodium cationic complexes of the type

Figure 30-1 A mechanism for the catalytic hydrogenation of an alkene. Clockwise from the top left: oxidative addition of H_2 to form the dihydride, A; dissociation of a phosphine ligand to give a free coordination site for alkene addition, giving the alkene complex, B; insertion of the alkene ligand into the M—H bond to give an alkyl ligand, C; reductive elimination of the alkane and regeneration of the catalyst precursor, D. (P = PPh_3)

[RhLL(solvent)]$^+$ (where LL is a chelating phosphine ligand) are the most commonly used. A wide variety of ligands, LL, with chirality at carbon or phosphorus have been investigated, one important example being (+ or −)-2,3-O-isopropylidene-2,3-dihydroxy-1,4-bis(diphenylphosphino)butane, usually called (+ or −)DIOP, shown in structure 30-I:

30-I

The most important application has been the synthesis of the chiral drug L-DOPA (dihydroxyphenylalanine, used in the treatment of Parkinson's disease) by the Monsanto Company. Prochiral compounds of the type R′CH=C(NHR$_2$)CO$_2$H can be reduced to chiral amino acids, and the optical purity may be > 95%.

It is important to note that, unlike the catalytic cycle shown in Fig. 30-1 using monodentate phospine ligands, with catalytic systems involving chelating phosphine ligands, a complex with substrate forms first. It is then that oxidative–addition of H$_2$ takes place. The enantiomeric selectivity arises from preferential complexation of the prochiral substrate at the metal containing the chiral LL. In some cases intermediate complexes can be characterized by ^{31}P nmr spectra; one example is shown in structure 30-II:

30-II

the rhodium complex of α-benzamidocinnamic acid. Two stereoisomers, differing in the configuration at the bound olefin, exist in a 10:1 ratio at room temperature.

30-8 Other Catalyzed Additions to Alkenes

There are two addition reactions of alkenes that are commercially important. These are the hydrosilylation and the hydrocyanation reactions.

Hydrosilylation of Alkenes

The hydrosilylation of alkenes is similar to hydrogenation except that H and SiR$_3$ from a silane, R$_3$SiH, are added across the double bond as in reaction 30-

8.1:

$$RCH=CH_2 + HSiR_3 \longrightarrow RCH_2CH_2SiR_3 \qquad (30-8.1)$$

The commercial process uses hexachloroplatinic acid as the catalyst, but phosphine complexes of cobalt, rhodium, palladium, or nickel may also be used. The ready addition of silanes to *trans*-IrCl(CO)(PPh$_3$)$_2$ as in reaction 30-8.2:

$$IrCl(CO)(PPh_3)_2 + R_3SiH \longrightarrow IrHCl(CO)(PPh_3)_2SiR_3 \qquad (30-8.2)$$

suggests that the first step in hydrosilylations is oxidative–addition of the Si—H group to the metal center. In the case of reaction 30-8.2 the product is coordinatively saturated; there is no further available site at the metal center, and the process ends here. In the actual catalytic systems, there must be a further coordination site available, because the next step is addition of the M—H group across the double bond of the alkene to form an alkyl group. Reductive elimination of the newly formed alkyl with the SiR$_3$ group yields the product and regenerates the catalyst.

Hydrocyanation of Alkenes

The DuPont Company has patented a process using nickel phosphite complexes for the addition of HCN to alkenes. The process also employs Lewis acid co-catalyst and yields high percentages of adiponitrile, an important nylon precursor. The process works because HCN, although only a weak acid, adds oxidatively to nickel phosphite compounds, NiL$_4$, as in Eq. 30-8.3:

$$NiL_4 + HCN = NiH(CN)L_2 + 2L \qquad (30-8.3)$$

Likely further steps in the catalytic cycle include addition of the olefin as in reaction 30-8.4:

$$NiH(CN)L_2 + RCH=CH_2 \longrightarrow (RCH=CH_2)NiH(CN)L_2 \qquad (30-8.4)$$

insertion of the olefinic ligand into the Ni—H bond to form an alkyl ligand:

$$(RCH=CH_2)NiH(CN)L_2 \longrightarrow RCH_2CH_2—Ni(CN)L_2 \qquad (30-8.5)$$

reductive elimination of the nitrile as in Eq. 30-8.6:

$$RCH_2CH_2—Ni(CN)L_2 \longrightarrow RCH_2CH_2CN + NiL_2 \qquad (30-8.6)$$

and, finally, regeneration of the active catalytic species by oxidative–addition of a second equivalent of HCN, as in reaction 30-8.7:

$$NiL_2 + HCN \longrightarrow NiH(CN)L_2 \qquad (30-8.7)$$

This proposal provides a good example of the general requirement that such a catalyst readily undergo additions, oxidative–additions, and reductive eliminations—the same sequence that is apparently involved in the hydrosilylations.

30-9 Hydroformylation

The hydroformylation reaction is the addition of H_2 and CO (or formally of H and the formyl group, HCO) to an alkene, usually a terminal, or 1-alkene, as in reaction 30-9.1:

$$RCH{=}CH_2 + H_2 + CO \longrightarrow RCH_2CH_2CHO \qquad (30\text{-}9.1)$$

The aldehyde product may be further reduced under the reaction conditions to an alcohol, as in reaction 30-9.2:

$$RCH_2CH_2CHO + H_2 \longrightarrow RCH_2CH_2CH_2OH \qquad (30\text{-}9.2)$$

Originally, cobalt compounds were used as catalysts at temperatures of ca. 150 °C and > 200-atm pressure, and some 3 million tons/yr of alcohols, usually C_7–C_9, have been produced in this way. The original processes gave mixtures of straight- and branched-chain products in the ratio of ca. 3:1, but considerable effort has been made to improve the yield of the straight-chain products. The processes employing cobalt catalysts also gave, undesirably, reduction of the feedstock alkenes to alkanes.

Extensive information is available on the catalytic cycle employing

Figure 30-2 A catalytic cycle for the hydroformylation of alkenes using triphenylphosphine complexes. The configurations of the complexes are not known with certainty. The equilibria involving F and G are "nonproductive."

$RhH(CO)(PPh_3)_3$, which is active even at 25 °C and 1-atm pressure. In addition, the rhodium catalyst produces only an aldehyde, making it ideally suited to study. On use of high concentrations of PPh_3, high yields of linear aldehydes can be obtained, and little of the alkene reactant is lost as the simple alkane reduction products. The reaction cycle is shown in Fig. 30-2. The initial step is addition of the alkene to $RhH(CO)_2(PPh_3)_2$ (compound A in Fig. 30-2), followed by insertion of the olefinic ligand into the Rh—H bond to give the alkyl complex, B. The latter then undergoes migratory insertion of CO into the Rh—C bond to give the acyl derivative, C. Oxidative–addition of H_2 then gives the dihydrido acyl, D. It is this last step, the only one involving a change in oxidation state for the Rh, that is most likely the rate-determining step in the cycle. The final steps are reductive elimination of the aldehyde to give E and reformation of A by addition of CO.

The high PPh_3 concentrations that are essential in providing high yields (> 95%) of linear aldehydes are probably required to suppress dissociative formation of monophosphine species, and thus to force the attack of olefin on bis(phosphine) species such as compound A. The bis(phosphine) complexes favor anti-Markovnikov addition to the olefin, and thereby lead to linear aldehydes.

30-10 Ziegler–Natta Polymerization

Hydrocarbon solutions of $TiCl_4$ in the presence of triethylaluminum, polymerize ethylene at 1-atm pressure. An extension of this Ziegler–Natta polymerization of ethylene is the copolymerization of styrene, butadiene, and a third component (usually dicyclopentadiene or 1,4-hexadiene) to give synthetic rubbers. Vanadyl halides instead of titanium halides are then the preferred catalysts.

The Ziegler–Natta system is heterogeneous, and the active species is a fibrous form of $TiCl_3$ that is formed *in situ* from $TiCl_4$ and $AlEt_3$. Preformed $TiCl_3$ may also be used. During the course of the polymerization, many different alkyl groups become available, and it appears that a second role of the

Figure 30-3 Steps in the Ziegler–Natta, $TiCl_3$-catalyzed polymerization of ethylene.

aluminum species, in addition to that of forming $TiCl_3$, is replacement of a chloride at the $TiCl_3$ surface by an alkyl group. Thus the catalytic process as in Fig. 30-3 begins with addition of ethylene to the vacant coordination site of a surface-Ti. The alkyl group is transferred to the coordinated ethylene, another ethylene is bound to the newly created vacant coordination site, and the process of polymerization continues.

30-11 Palladium-Catalyzed Oxidations

It was long known that ethylene compounds of palladium, for example, $[(C_2H_4)PdCl_2]_2$, are rapidly decomposed in aqueous solution to form acetaldehyde (an oxidized product of ethylene) and Pd metal, according to the stoichiometry of reaction 30-11.1:

$$C_2H_4 + PdCl_2 + H_2O \longrightarrow CH_3CHO + Pd + 2HCl \quad (30\text{-}11.1)$$

The conversion of this stoichiometric reaction into a catalytic one (the Wacker process) required the linking together of reaction 30-11.1 with the following known reactions:

$$Pd + 2CuCl_2 \longrightarrow PdCl_2 + 2CuCl \quad (30\text{-}11.2)$$

$$2CuCl + 2HCl + \tfrac{1}{2}O_2 \longrightarrow 2CuCl_2 + H_2O \quad (30\text{-}11.3)$$

The sum of reactions 30-11.1, 30-11.2, and 30-11.3 is the desired oxidation of ethylene, reaction 30-11.4:

$$C_2H_4 + \tfrac{1}{2}O_2 \longrightarrow CH_3CHO \quad (30\text{-}11.4)$$

The catalytic oxidation of ethylene by Pd^{II}–Cu^{II} chloride solutions is essentially quantitative, and only low Pd concentrations are required.

Since the reaction proceeds in Pd^{II} solutions with a chloride concentration $> 0.2\ M$, the metal is most likely present as $[PdCl_4]^{2-}$. Reactions 30-11.5 and 30-11.6 then occur:

$$[PdCl_4]^{2-} + C_2H_4 \rightleftharpoons [PdCl_3(C_2H_4)]^- + Cl^- \quad \text{(fast)} \quad (30\text{-}11.5)$$

$$[PdCl_3(C_2H_4)]^- + H_2O \rightleftharpoons [PdCl_2(H_2O)(C_2H_4)] + Cl^- \quad (30\text{-}11.6)$$

The neutral product of reaction 30-11.6 is attacked nucleophilically by water giving the hydroxy–alkyl ligand shown in structure 30-III:

$$\left[\begin{array}{c} Cl \diagdown \diagup CH_2CH_2OH \\ Pd \\ Cl \diagup \diagdown OH_2 \end{array} \right]^-$$

30-III

which eventually leads to products by the sequence shown in reactions 30-11.7 and 30-11.8:

$$\left[\begin{array}{c} Cl \\ Cl \end{array} Pd \begin{array}{c} H \quad H \\ C \\ C \\ H \quad OH \\ OH_2 \end{array}\right]^{-} \xrightarrow{-H_2O} \left[\begin{array}{c} Cl \\ Cl \end{array} Pd \begin{array}{c} H \quad H \\ C \\ C-H \\ H \quad OH \end{array}\right] \qquad (30\text{-}11.7)$$

$$CH_3CHO + H^+ \longleftarrow CH_3CHOH^+ + Pd^0 + 2Cl^- \qquad (30\text{-}11.8)$$

The mechanism for the required reoxidation of Pd metal by Cu(II) chloro complexes (reaction 30-11.2) is not well understood, but inner sphere electron transfer by chloro bridges is probably involved.

The reactivity of palladium complexes in other systems has been extensively studied, and there now are many catalytic processes involving alkenes, arenes, CO, acetylenes, and the like. Extensions of the Wacker process using media other than water are known; thus in acetic acid, vinyl acetate is obtained, while in alcohols, vinyl ethers are obtained. Also with alkenes other than ethylene, ketones may be obtained. Propene, for example, gives acetone.

30-12 Catalytic Reactions of Carbon Monoxide

We have already considered the hydroformylation reaction, an addition of H_2 and CO to alkenes. There are other important reactions involving CO, two of which we consider here.

Acetic Acid Synthesis

Acetic acid can be made by carbonylation of methanol. Originally, a high temperature and high pressure reaction using cobalt iodide was used. The Monsanto Chemical Company, however, has introduced a process using rhodium that operates under milder conditions: ca. 180 °C, 40 atm. The key to this reaction (and to other carbonylations-e.g., of methyl acetate to give acetic anhydride) involves the use of methyl iodide, which can oxidatively add to Rh^I as in Fig. 30-4. Carbon monoxide insertion gives an acyl intermediate that undergoes reductive elimination of acetyl iodide, $H_3C-\overset{\displaystyle O}{\overset{\|}{C}}-I$. Hydrolysis of the latter by water in the aqueous–methanol feed then gives acetic acid and HI, as in reaction 30-12.1:

$$H_3C-\overset{\displaystyle O}{\overset{\|}{C}}-I + H_2O \longrightarrow CH_3CO_2H + HI \qquad (30\text{-}12.1)$$

CH_3I

(1)

$$\begin{bmatrix} I-Rh-CO \\ I \end{bmatrix}^- \quad CO$$

(2)

$$\begin{bmatrix} I-Rh-CH_3 \\ I \quad C \\ O \end{bmatrix}^-$$

$$CH_3C \overset{O}{\underset{I}{\diagdown}}$$

(4)

$$\begin{bmatrix} I \\ I-Rh-C \overset{O}{\diagdown} \\ I \quad C \quad CH_3 \\ O \end{bmatrix}$$

(3)

$$\begin{bmatrix} I \\ I-Rh \overset{CO}{\diagdown} \\ I \quad C \overset{O}{\diagdown} \\ CH_3 \end{bmatrix}^-$$

CO

Figure 30-4 Catalytic cycle for the synthesis of acetic acid from methanol. The steps are (1) oxidative–addition of CH_3I, (2) migratory insertion of CO, (3) addition of CO, and (4) reductive elimination of $H_3C-\overset{\overset{\displaystyle O}{\|}}{C}-I$. Subsequent hydrolysis of $H_3C-\overset{\overset{\displaystyle O}{\|}}{C}-I$ gives CH_3CO_2H.

HI then reacts with methanol to regenerate methyl iodide, as in reaction 30-12.2:

$$HI + CH_3OH \longrightarrow CH_3I + H_2O + I^- \qquad (30\text{-}12.2)$$

In absence of water and in presence of lithium acetate, carbonylations of methanol or methyl acetate gives acetic anhydride *via.* the reaction

$$CH_3C(O)I + CO_2Me^- \longrightarrow CH_3C(O)O_2CMe \qquad (30\text{-}12.3)$$

The cycle is similar to that in Figure 30-4.

Fischer–Tropsch Reactions

These reactions were discovered by F. Fischer and H. Tropsch in Germany, in the late 1920s. The reactions make use of iron or other oxide catalysts to reduce CO by hydrogen, giving hydrocarbons, the simplest representative reaction being Eq. 30-12.4:

$$CO + 3H_2 \longrightarrow CH_4 + H_2O \tag{30-12.4}$$

Under selected conditions, petroleum or fuel oils can be made. The process is not very economical, even with very cheap coal as a source of feedstock synthesis gas, but is operated commercially in South Africa. A much more important reaction is methanol synthesis, reaction 30-12.5:

$$CO + 2H_2 \longrightarrow CH_3OH \qquad \Delta H° = -92 \text{ kJ mol}^{-1} \tag{30-12.5}$$

which may be accomplished by using heterogeneous, copper-promoted, zinc oxide catalysts at 250 °C and 50 atm. This process provides a means of using methane waste gases from oil wells by oxidation to synthesis gas as in Eq. 30-12.6:

$$CH_4 + H_2O \longrightarrow CO + 3H_2 \tag{30-12.6}$$

followed by conversion to methanol by reaction 30-12.5. The methanol can then be converted to acetic acid and acetic anhydride as discussed previously, bringing the formerly wasted methane usefully into the petrochemicals market.

It is possible to make other alcohols directly from CO and H_2, notably ethylene glycol by use of homogeneous rhodium catalysts. Such processes are, however, not yet economical.

Finally, it should be noted that the water–gas shift reaction, Eq. 30-12.7:

$$CO + H_2O = CO_2 + H_2 \tag{30-12.7}$$

can be catalyzed both heterogeneously and homogeneously. The reaction is used to remove CO from synthesis gas, thereby increasing the amount of H_2 that is available for ammonia synthesis, as was mentioned in Section 9-1.

STUDY GUIDE

Study Questions

A. Review

1. What is meant by a coordinatively unsaturated species? Give two examples, and explain how these species may arise in solutions beginning with coordinatively saturated ones.

2. Define the term oxidative addition (oxad) reaction. What conditions must be met for such a reaction to occur? What is the reverse of such a reaction called?

3. Draw plausible structures for the reaction products of $IrCl(CO)(PR_3)_2$ with H_2, CH_3I, PhNCS, CF_3CN, $(CF_3)_2CO$, O_2.

4. How can one account for the low activation energy for oxidative–addition of H_2 with its very strong H—H bond?

5. What is an insertion reaction? Give two real examples.

6. Describe the actual pathway for the reaction of PEt_3 with $CH_3Mn(CO)_5$ to give $CH_3COMn(CO)_4PEt_3$.

7. Complete the following equations and show with diagrams the structures of the principal products:

   (a) $Ru(CO)_3(PPh_3)_2 + HBF_4 \longrightarrow$

   (b) $Ir(CO)_3(PPh_3)_2^+ + CH_3O^- \longrightarrow$

   (c) $W(CO)_6 \xrightarrow{\text{LiCH}_3} [A] \xrightarrow{\text{Me}_3O^+} [B]$

   (d) $[Fe(CN)_5NO]^{2-} + 2\,OH^- \longrightarrow$

   (e) $ReCl_4(NCCH_3) + 2\,PhNH_2 \longrightarrow$

8. Show the steps by which a hydrido complex can cause isomerization of 1-alkenes to 2-alkenes? Is this generally stereospecific?

9. Write a balanced equation showing the overall (net) reaction in each of the following processes: hydroformylation; hydrosilylation; the Ziegler–Natta process; the Wacker process for synthesis of acetaldehyde.

10. Outline the main steps by which Ziegler–Natta polymerization proceeds.

11. Outline the mechanism of the Wacker process.

B. Additional Exercises

1. Write a plausible mechanism for the reaction of $Ti(NEt_2)_4$ with CS_2 to give $Ti(S_2CNEt_2)_4$.

2. Give a plausible catalytic cycle to account for the conversion of ethylene to propionaldehyde employing $RhH(CO)(PPh_3)_3$ as the catalyst.

3. Suggest a catalytic cycle to account for the action of

$$[Rh(PEtPh_2)_2(CH_3OH)_2]^+PF_6^-$$

in methanol as a catalyst for hydrogenation of but-1-ene by H_2 at 25 °C and 1-atm pressure.

4. The complex $Ni[P(OEt)_3]_4$ in acidic solution is used in the synthesis of hexa-1,4-diene from ethylene and butadiene. Suggest a plausible catalytic cycle.

5. $Ni[P(OEt)_3]_4$ is also used to catalyze the process

$$CH_2{=}CH{-}CH{=}CH_2 + HCN \longrightarrow NC(CH_2)_4CN$$

Again, suggest a sensible sequence of steps.

6. Suggest a mechanism for the following so-called 1,3-insertion reaction.

$$(\eta^5\text{-}C_5H_5)(CO)_2Fe{-}\overset{1}{C}H_2\overset{2}{C}{\equiv}\overset{3}{C}\overset{4}{C}H_3 + SO_2$$

7. It has been proved that the alkyl group retains its configuration when CO insertion to produce the acyl occurs for $(\eta^5\text{-}C_5H_5)(CO)_2Fe{-}CHD{-}CHD{-}C(CH_3)_3$. Propose a mechanism that accounts for this.

8. Write a mechanism for the conversion of butadiene to *trans-trans-trans*-cyclo-dodecatriene, using a Ni⁰ species.

9. RhH(CO)(PR₃)₃ in benzene under pressure of ethylene reacts with benzoyl chloride to give propiophenone, PhC(O)C₂H₅. Suggest a mechanism.

10. A catalytic process for making propionic acid from acetic acid has been developed. It uses HI, H₂, CO, and H₂O as stoichiometric reagents and a patented Ru(CO)ₓI_y compound as catalyst. HI and H₂O are regenerated by the full catalytic process. Plausible steps in the catalytic cycle include (a) oxidative–addition of

$$H_3C-\overset{\overset{\textstyle O}{\|}}{C}-I$$; (b) addition of H₂ to Ru, and migration to give an α-hydroxyethyl ligand; (c) hydrogenation of the latter, with elimination of water to give an ethyl ligand; (d) insertion of CO to give an acyl ligand; and (e) hydrolysis to propionic acid. Write out the catalytic cycle in the style of Fig. 30-4.

11. The complex [η⁵-C₅H₅Re(CO)₂NO]⁺ can be reduced using NaBH₄ in THF–water mixtures giving first a formyl complex, second a hydroxymethyl complex, and third a methyl complex. Draw structures of the four compounds, apply the 18-electron formalism to each, and discuss the relevance of these reactions to our understanding of Fischer–Tropsch chemistry.

C.   Problems from the Literature of Inorganic Chemistry

1. Consider the report (of a Rh catalyst for olefin hydrogenation) by C. O'Connor and G. Wilkinson, *J. Chem. Soc. (A)*, **1968**, 2665–2671.

   (a) Prepare sketches of each rhodium compound in the hydrogenation cycle proposed here.

   (b) Describe (addition, oxidative–addition, reductive elimination, etc.) each step in the process.

   (c) Enumerate the data or reasoning favoring each structure in (a) and each step in (b).

   (d) Why, according to the authors, is hydrogenation with this catalyst only possible, apparently, for terminal olefins of the formula RHC=CH₂?

2. Read the paper on reductions using CO + H₂O in place of H₂ by H. Kang, C. H. Mauldin, T. Cole, W. Slegeir, K. Cann, and R. Pettit, *J. Am. Chem. Soc.*, **1977**, *99*, 8323–8325.

   (a) Propose reactions and mechanisms for the formation from CO, H₂O and Fe(CO)₅ of HFe(CO)₄⁻, H₂Fe(CO)₄, and H₂.

   (b) Propose a mechanism for the pH-dependent reduction (actually hydroformylation) of ethylene to propanol. How do the authors account for the pH dependence?

   (c) Explain how Fe(CO)₅ serves as a catalyst for the water–gas shift reaction.

3. Consider the study reported by E. L. Muetterties and P. L. Watson, *J. Am. Chem. Soc.*, **1976**, *98*, 4665–4667.

   (a) Write balanced equations for two separate preparations of the hydrogen adduct, or dihydride, H₂Co[P(OMe)₃]₄⁺.

   (b) Draw the structure of the dihydride in (a). What data indicate a predominantly cis arrangement of the two (formally) H⁻ ligands? What is the difference between a "dihydrogen adduct" and a "dihydride"?

   (c) What experiments suggest that reductive elimination of H₂ from the dihydride in (a) is a unimolecular process?

   (d) How has reductive elimination of CH₄ been studied here? How does CH₄ elimination compare with H₂ elimination?

4. Consider the paper by E. M. Hyde and B. L. Shaw, *J. Chem. Soc. Dalton Trans.*, **1975**, 765–767.

   (a) Enumerate the differences between oxidative–addition of H_2 and CH_3I to *trans*-$[IrX(CO)L_2]$ complexes in general.

   (b) How were rate constants obtained in this study for the addition of H_2 to $IrCl(CO)(PR_3)_2$ complexes?

   (c) How does H_2 addition to $[IrCl(CO)(PMe_2Ph)_2]$ compare with H_2 addition to $[IrCl(CO)\{PMe_2(C_6H_4OMe)_2\}_2]$?

   (d) How does CH_3I oxidative–addition compare with H_2 oxidative–addition towards both of the complexes in (c)?

   (e) What mechanistic interpretation do the authors give for the differences noted in (c) and (d)?

5. Consider the paper by K. L. Brown, G. R. Clark, C. E. L. Headford, K. Mardson, and W. R. Roper, *J. Am. Chem. Soc.*, **1979**, *101*, 503–505.

   (a) Apply the 18-electron formalism to explain the various preparations and reactions of this η^2-formyl complex of Os^0.

   (b) The "hydrido-formyl" $Os(CHO)H(CO)_2(PPh_3)_2$ eliminates H_2, while the "chloroformyl" $Os(CHO)Cl(CO)_2(PPh_3)_2$ eliminates CO, not HCl. Why? Explain.

6. Read the article by C. P. Casey, M. W. Meszaros, S. M. Neuman, I. G. Cesa, and K. J. Haller, *Organometallics*, **1985**, *4*, 143–149.

   (a) Compare the syntheses and structures of the analogous acetyl and formyl complexes as reported here.

   (bv) Apply the 18-electron formalism to each reactant and product in your answer to (a).

   (c) What does a comparison of these two structures seem to indicate about the reason why CO insertion into a M—C bond occurs more readily than CO insertion into a M—H bond?

SUPPLEMENTARY READING

Alper, H., Ed., *Transition Metal Organometallics in Organic Synthesis*, Vol. 1, 1976, Vol. 2, 1978, Academic, New York.

Collman, J. P. and Hegedus, L. S., *Principles and Applications of Organotransition Metal Chemistry*, University Science Books, Mill Valley, CA, 1980.

Gates, B. C., Katzer, J. R., and Schuit, G. C. A., *Chemistry of Catalytic Processes*, McGraw-Hill, New York, 1979.

James, B. R., *Homogeneous Hydrogenation*, Wiley-Interscience, New York, 1973.

Kochi, J. K., *Organometallic Mechanisms and Catalysis*, Academic, New York, 1978.

Masters, C., *Homogeneous Transition Metal Catalysis, A Gentle Art*, Chapman and Hall, London, 1981.

Parshall, G. W., *Homogeneous Catalysis*, Wiley-Interscience, New York, 1980.

Tolman, C. A., "The 16- and 18-Electron Rule in Organometallic Chemistry and Homogeneous Catalysis," *Chem. Soc. Rev.*, **1972**, *11*, 337.

Wilkinson, G., Abel, E. W., and Stone, F. G. A., Eds., *Comprehensive Organometallic Chemistry*, Pergamon Press, New York, 1982.

Yamamoto, A., *Organotransition Metal Chemistry*, Wiley-Interscience, New York, 1986.

chapter 31

BIOINORGANIC CHEMISTRY

31-1 Overview

Biochemistry is not merely an elaboration of organic chemistry. The chemistry of life involves, in essential and indispensible ways, at least 25 elements. In addition to the "organic" elements C, H, N, and O, there are 9 other elements that are required in relatively large quantities, and called, therefore, **macronutrients.** These are Na, K, Mg, Ca, S, P, Cl, Si, and Fe. There are also many other elements, **micronutrients,** that are required in small amounts by at least some forms of life: V, Cr, Mn, Co, Ni, Cu, Zn, Mo, W, Se, F, and I. As research activity intensifies, and as instrumental methods of analysis and detection become more sophisticated and more sensitive, it is likely that other elements will be added to the list of micronutrients. The elements Cr, Ni, W, and Se have been added only within the last few years.

The metallic elements play a variety of roles in biochemistry. Several of the most important roles are the following:

1. *Regulatory action* is exercised by Na^+, K^+, Mg^{2+}, and Ca^{2+}. The flux of these ions through cell membranes and other boundary layers sends signals that turn metabolic reactions on and off.

2. *The structural role* of calcium in bones and teeth is well known, but many proteins owe their structural integrity to the presence of metal ions that tie together and make rigid certain portions of these large molecules, portions that would otherwise be only loosely linked. Metal ions particularly known to do this are Ca^{2+} and Zn^{2+}.

3. An enormous amount of *electron transfer* chemistry goes on in biological systems, and nearly all of it depends critically on metal-containing electron transfer agents. These include cytochromes (Fe), ferridoxins (Fe), and a number of copper-containing "blue proteins" such as azurin, plastocyanin, and stellacyanin.

4. *Metalloenzymes or metallocoenzymes* are involved in a great deal of enzymatic activity, which depends on the presence of metal ions at the active site of the enzyme or in a key coenzyme. Of the latter, the best known is vitamin B_{12}, which contains cobalt. Important metalloenzymes include carboxypeptidase (Zn), alcohol dehydrogenase (Zn), superoxide dismutase (Cu, Zn), urease (Ni), and cytochrome P-450 (Fe).

5. All aerobic forms of life depend on *oxygen carriers*, molecules that carry oxygen from the point of intake (such as the lungs) to tissues where O_2 is used

in oxidative processes that generate energy. There are three major types of oxygen carriers, and all of them contain metal ions that provide the actual binding sites for the O_2 molecules. These are

Hemoglobins (Fe), found in all mammals.
Hemerythins (Fe), found in various marine invertebrates.
Hemocyanins (Cu), found in arthropods and molluscs.

Each of these roles will be discussed in this chapter.

31-2 The Role of Model Systems

Because of the size and complexity of most biochemical molecules and processes, it is often advantageous to find smaller and simpler models upon which controlled experiments can be more easily performed, and with which hypotheses can be tested. Bioinorganic chemistry has been an especially fruitful area for the use of model systems, particularly where transition metals are involved. Of course it is not always possible to find or develop suitable models, and it can be dangerously misleading should overly simplistic models be used naively. Even in the best of circumstances, a model can give only a partial view of how the real system works. If these limitations are recognized, the model system approach can provide valuable guidance to eventual study of the real systems.

The broad and detailed knowledge that we have of coordination chemistry sets the stage for an understanding of the role of metal ions in biological systems. Fundamental principles and generalizations about the behavior of metal complexes are valid whether the metal is coordinated by some relatively simple set of man-made ligands or by a gigantic protein molecule, where the coordinating groups are often carboxyl oxygen atoms, thiol sulfur atoms, or amine nitrogen atoms. Moreover, the optical spectra, magnetic moments, and epr spectra of transition metal ions afford the same powerful methods of study as when applied to the simpler complexes. Thus we have methods for checking the models against the real systems.

Throughout this chapter we shall frequently refer to model systems that have played a role in understanding real bioinorganic systems. Among these are iron–porphyrin compounds relevant to the understanding of hemoglobin, myoglobin, cytochromes, and enzyme P-450; models for hemerythrin; the cobaloxime model for vitamin B_{12}; iron–sulfur cluster compounds as models for ferredoxins; and a number of copper complexes that serve as models for a variety of copper-containing enzymes.

31-3 The Alkali and Alkaline Earth Metals

The elements Na, K, Mg, and Ca are ubiquitous in living systems and play an assortment of vital roles. Inorganic chemists who were interested in coordination chemistry used to have a tendency to regard these elements as relatively uninteresting. Nothing could be further from the truth if one is seeking an understanding of life processes.

Sodium and Potassium

Sodium and potassium ion concentrations and the balance (or ratio) of their concentrations in various parts of an organism are controlled by a number of special complexing agents. These generally are **cavitands,** that is macrocyclic molecules with polar interior groups for binding the ions and nonpolar (hydrophobic) exterior groups that enable the cavitands to carry the Na^+ or K^+ ions across cell boundaries. An example is the cyclic dodecapeptide **valino-mycin,** shown as structure 31-I, and in Chapter 10 as structure 10-III.

$$\left(-O-\overset{\overset{\displaystyle CH(CH_3)_2}{|}}{\underset{\underset{\displaystyle H}{|}}{C}}-\overset{\overset{\displaystyle}{\|}}{\underset{\underset{\displaystyle O}{\|}}{C}}-\overset{\overset{\displaystyle}{|}}{\underset{\underset{\displaystyle H}{|}}{N}}-\overset{\overset{\displaystyle CH(CH_3)_2}{|}}{\underset{\underset{\displaystyle H}{|}}{C}}-\overset{\overset{\displaystyle}{\|}}{\underset{\underset{\displaystyle O}{\|}}{C}}-O-\overset{\overset{\displaystyle CH_3}{|}}{\underset{\underset{\displaystyle H}{|}}{C}}-\overset{\overset{\displaystyle}{\|}}{\underset{\underset{\displaystyle O}{\|}}{C}}-\overset{\overset{\displaystyle}{|}}{\underset{\underset{\displaystyle H}{|}}{N}}-\overset{\overset{\displaystyle CH(CH_3)_2}{|}}{\underset{\underset{\displaystyle H}{|}}{C}}-\overset{\overset{\displaystyle}{\|}}{\underset{\underset{\displaystyle O}{\|}}{C}}- \right)_3$$

31-I

The Na^+ concentration within animal cells has to be kept about 10 times lower than that in the extracellular fluids, whereas an opposite **gradient** (by a factor of 30) must be maintained for the K^+ ion. The maintenance of these balances requires energy. and when such balances are abruptly changed, electrical potentials responsible for the transmission of nerve impulses are created.

Calcium

Calcium serves in a staggering variety of roles, the most obvious being in the structural materials such as teeth, bones, shells, and a number of other less well-known calcium-rich deposits. It is important to note that none of these calciferous biological materials is an inert "mineral." Bone, for example, though consisting largely of calcium carbonate and phosphate, is continually being deposited and reabsorbed, and it acts as a buffer for body Ca^{2+} and phosphate ions, as controlled by hormonal action. The form of calcium phosphate that occurs in bone and teeth has the same composition as the mineral apatite, $Ca_{10}(PO_4)_6X_2$, where X represents F, Cl, or OH, or a mixture of these.

Calcium is essential to the action of extracellular enzymes, and it participates in many regulatory processes. It is generally complexed by the side-chain carboxyl groups of proteins, with additional bonding sometimes to peptide carbonyl groups and hydroxyl groups.

Magnesium

Magnesium, because of its high charge–radius ratio and consequent strong hydration {as $[Mg(H_2O)_6]^{2+}$}, plays biological roles that are very different from those of calcium. One of its major roles is as a counterion to the negatively charged $ROPO_3H^-$ groups in nucleotides and polynucleotides. Sometimes it approaches the phosphate anions as $[Mg(H_2O)_6]^{2+}$, but it is also found as $[Mg(H_2O)_5]^{2+}$ or $[Mg(H_2O)_4]^{2+}$ with one or two phosphate oxygen atoms, respectively, completing its first coordination sphere. The magnesium ion helps to stabilize the three-dimensional structure of ribonucleic acid (RNA) and deoxyribonucleic acid (DNA) and is thus crucial to the proper functioning of the genetic machinery of the cell. Also, adenosine diphosphate (ADP) and adenosine triphosphate (ATP—shown in structure 31-II) exist mainly as 1:1 complexes with the magnesium ion. Magnesium also has a unique role in the plant kingdom as the central atom of chlorophyll, which will be discussed in the next section.

31-II

31-4 Metalloporphyrins

One of the most important ways in which metal ions are involved is in complexes with a type of macrocyclic ligand called a *porphyrin*. Porphyrins are derivatives of *porphine*. They differ in the arrangement of substituents around the periphery. The porphine molecule is shown in Fig. 31-1(a), and the two most important metal complexes of porphyrins, *chlorophyll* and *heme*, are shown in Fig. 31-1(b) and (c). In the complexes the inner hydrogen atoms have been displaced by the metal ions.

Chlorophyll

There are several very similar but not identical chlorophyll molecules. Green plants contain two and various algae contain others. Notice that in Fig. 31-1(b) the basic porphin system has been modified in two ways. In pyrrole ring IV, one of the double bonds has been trans-hydrogenated, and a cyclopentanone ring has been fused to the side of pyrrole ring III. Nevertheless, the fundamental properties of the porphin system are retained.

Photosynthesis is a complex sequence of processes in which solar energy is first absorbed and ultimately—in a series of redox reactions, some of which proceed in the dark—used to drive the overall endothermic process of com-

Figure 31-1 (*a*) The prototype porphine molecule. (*b*) One of the chlorophyll molecules. (*c*) The heme group.

bining water and carbon dioxide to give glucose; molecular oxygen is released simultaneously:

$$6CO_2 + 6H_2O = C_6H_{12}O_6 + 6O_2 \qquad (31\text{-}4.1)$$

The function of the chlorophyll molecules in the chloroplast is to absorb photons in the red part of the visible spectrum (near 700 nm) and pass this energy of excitation on to other species in the reaction chain. The ability to absorb the light is due basically to the conjugated polyene structure of the porphine ring system. The role of the magnesium ion is, at least, twofold. (1) It helps to make the entire molecule rigid so that energy is not too easily lost thermally, that is, degraded to molecular vibrations. (2) It enhances the rate at which the shortlived singlet excited state initially formed by photon absorption is transformed into the corresponding triplet state, which has a longer lifetime and thus can transfer its excitation energy into the redox chain.

At an early stage of the electron transfer sequence that leads ultimately to the release of molecular oxygen, a manganese complex, of unknown composition, undergoes reversible redox reactions. At still other stages, iron-containing substances, called cytochromes and ferredoxins, and a copper-containing substance, called plastocyanin, also participate. Thus, photosynthesis requires the participation of complexes of no less than four metallic elements.

Heme Proteins

Iron is certainly the most widespread of the heavy or transition metals in living systems. Its compounds participate in a variety of activities. The two main functions of iron-containing materials are (1) transport of oxygen, and (2) mediation in electron transfer chains. So much iron is required for these purposes that there is also a chemical system to store and transport iron. We turn first to compounds in which the iron is present as heme, the porphyrin complex depicted in Fig. 31-1(c). The heme group functions in all cases in intimate association with a protein molecule. The chief heme proteins are

1. Hemoglobins
2. Myoglobins
3. Cytochromes, including a special type, P-450
4. Enzymes such as catalase and peroxidase

Hemoglobin and Myoglobin

These are closely related. Hemoglobin has a molecular weight of 64,500 and consists of four subunits, each containing one heme group. Myoglobin is very similar to one of the subunits of hemoglobin, one of which is shown in Fig. 31-2. Hemoglobin has two functions. (1) It binds oxygen molecules to its iron atoms and transports them from the lungs to muscles where they are delivered to myoglobin molecules. These store the oxygen until it is required for metabolic action. (2) The hemoglobin then uses certain amino groups to bind carbon dioxide and carry it back to the lungs.

The heme group is attached to the protein in both hemoglobin and myoglobin through a coordinated histidine–nitrogen atom, F8, shown in Fig. 31-2. The position trans to the histidine–nitrogen atom is occupied by a water molecule in the deoxy species or O_2 in the oxygenated species. The structure of the Fe—O_2 grouping is still uncertain, but changes in the oxidation state of iron and the introduction of O_2 (and other ligands) cause important changes in the structure of heme, as we describe here.

Hemoglobin is not simply a passive container for oxygen but an intricate molecular machine. This may be appreciated by comparing its affinity for O_2 to that of myoglobin. For myoglobin (Mb) we have the following simple equilibrium:

$$\text{Mb} + O_2 = \text{MbO}_2 \qquad K = \frac{[\text{MbO}_2]}{[\text{Mb}][O_2]} \qquad (31\text{-}4.2)$$

If f represents the fraction of myoglobin molecules bearing oxygen and P represents the equilibrium partial pressure of oxygen, then

$$K = \frac{f}{(1-f)P} \qquad \text{and} \qquad f = \frac{KP}{1 + KP} \qquad (31\text{-}4.3)$$

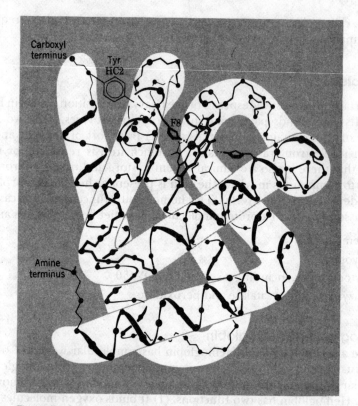

Figure 31-2 A representation of one of the four subunits of hemoglobin. The continuous black band represents the peptide chain and the various sections of the helix. Dots on the helical chain represent α-carbon atoms. The heme group is near the top of the diagram (just to the right of center), with the iron atom represented as a large dot. The coordinated histidine is labeled F8, meaning the 8th residue of the F helix. (This diagram was adapted from one kindly provided by M. Perutz.)

This is the equation for the hyperbolic curve labeled Mb in Fig. 31-3. Hemoglobin with its four subunits has more complex behavior; it approximately follows the equation

$$f = \frac{KP^n}{1 + KP^n} \qquad n \approx 2.8 \tag{31-4.4}$$

where the exact value of n depends on pH. Thus, for hemoglobin (Hb) the oxygen-binding curves are sigmoidal as is shown in Fig. 31-3. The fact that n exceeds unity can be ascribed physically to the fact that attachment of O_2 to one heme group increases the binding constant for the next O_2, which in turn increases the constant for the next one, and so on.

Although Hb is about as good an O_2 binder as Mb at high O_2 pressure, it is much poorer at the lower pressures prevailing in muscle and, hence, passes

Figure 31-3 The oxygen-binding curves for myoglobin (Mb) and hemoglobin (Hb), showing also the pH dependence for the latter.

on its oxygen to the Mb as required. Moreover, the need for O_2 will be greatest in tissues that have already consumed oxygen and simultaneously have produced CO_2. The CO_2 lowers the pH, thus causing the Hb to release even more oxygen to the Mb. The pH-sensitivity (called the Bohr effect), as well as the progressive increase of the O_2 binding constants in Hb, is due to interactions between the subunits; Mb behaves more simply because it consists of only one unit. It is clear that each of the two is essential in the complete oxygen-transport process. Carbon monoxide, PF_3, and a few other substances are toxic because they become bound to the iron atoms of Hb more strongly than O_2; their effect is one of competitive inhibition.

The way in which interactions between the four subunits in Hb give rise to both the cooperativity in oxygen binding and to the Bohr effect (pH dependence), both of which are so essential to the role played by Hb is now partly understood. The mechanism is very intricate, but one essential feature depends directly on the coordination chemistry involved. Deoxyhemoglobin has a high-spin distribution of electrons, with one electron occupying the $d_{x^2-y^2}$ orbital that points directly toward the four porphyrin nitrogen atoms. The presence of this electron in effect increases the radius of the iron atom in these directions by repelling the lone-pair electrons of the nitrogen atoms. The result is that the iron atom actually lies about 0.7 to 0.8 Å out of the plane of these nitrogen atoms, in order that it not be in too close contact with them. The iron atom is also coordinated by a nitrogen atom on the imidazole ring of the amino acid histidine, labeled F8 in Fig. 31-2. Thus the iron atom in deoxyhemoglobin has square-pyramidal coordination, as is shown in Fig. 31-4(a).

When an oxygen molecule becomes bound to the iron atom, it occupies a position opposite to the imidazole–nitrogen atom. The presence of this sixth ligand alters the strength of the ligand field, and the iron atom goes into a low-spin state, in which the six d electrons occupy the d_{xy}, d_{yz}, and d_{zx} orbitals. The

Figure 31-4 (*a*) The five-coordinate, high-spin
Fe^{II} in deoxyhemoglobin. (*b*) The six-coordinate,
low-spin iron in oxyhemoglobin, showing the distance that the side-chain histidine residue F8 has
moved upon oxygenation.

$d_{x^2-y^2}$ orbital is then empty and the previous effect of an electron occupying
this orbital in repelling the porphyrin nitrogen atoms vanishes. The iron atom
is thus able to slip into the center of an approximately planar porphyrin ring
and an essentially octahedral complex is formed, as shown in Fig. 31-4(*b*).

As the iron atom moves, it pulls the imidazole side chain of histidine F8
with it, thus moving that ring about 0.75 Å. This shift is then transmitted to
other parts of the protein chain to which F8 belongs and, in particular, a large
movement of the phenolic side chain of tyrosine HC2 is produced. From here
various shifts of atoms in the neighboring subunit are caused, and these shifts
influence the oxygen-binding capability of the heme group in that subunit.
Thus the movement of the iron atom of the heme group in one subunit of

Fe—O—O   Linear

Fe   Side-on

Fe—O   Bent

Figure 31-5 Three conceivable O_2–iron bonding geometries for hemoglobin or myoglobin.

hemoglobin acts as a kind of "trigger," which sets into motion extensive structural changes in other subunits.

One of the interesting problems about oxygen binding by hemoglobin concerns the structure of the Fe–O_2 grouping. Three possibilities are shown in Fig. 31-5. The linear geometry has no precedent and is least probable. The side-on arrangement is found in some simple O_2 complexes involving other metals, such as $(PPh_3)_2ClIrO_2$, but is very unlikely for hemoglobin. The bent chain appears most probable, since O_2 is isoelectronic with NO^+, and since the latter forms complexes with bent Co^{III}—N—O chains. Also, there is one fairly good model compound, an iron(II)porphyrin complex of O_2, in which the bent arrangement has been found.

Hemoglobin Modeling

The ability of the heme in hemoglobin or myoglobin to bind an O_2 molecule and later release it without the iron atom becoming permanently oxidized to the iron(III) state is obviously essential to the functioning of these oxygen carriers. This remarkable ability has been taken for granted in the preceding discussion, but it merits further discussion. It is the reversibility of the hemoglobin and myoglobin reactions with O_2 that must be matched by any useful model.

Early attempts to employ simple Fe^{II}–porphyrin complexes, or even free heme itself, plus an aromatic amine molecule (to take the place of the histidine F8) were not successful. On exposing such a "model" to O_2, oxidation (rather than oxygenation) occurred promptly and irreversibly. Oxygen was absorbed, but not released. The reason for this is now understood: Dioxygen reacts to produce an O-bridged dinuclear complex of iron(III), as in Eq. 31-4.5:

$$2(\text{Amine})\text{Fe} + \tfrac{1}{2}O_2 \longrightarrow (\text{Amine})\text{Fe}—O—\text{Fe}(\text{Amine}) \quad (31\text{-}4.5)$$

In hemoglobin and myoglobin, the bulk of the protein surrounding the heme unit assures that each heme unit remains isolated. To have an effective model, something must be added to the simple iron–porphyrin to accomplish this same degree of bulk. The two ways in which this has been done are represented schematically in Fig. 31-6 and then more realistically in Fig. 31-7. Model com-

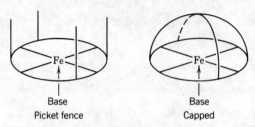

Base
Picket fence

Base
Capped

Figure 31-6 Schematic representations of two ways in which hemelike models may be modified to preclude dimerization via. μ–O bridging.

pounds such as those shown in Fig. 31-7 do engage in reversible oxygen binding, quite similar to the behavior of myoglobin. In the two examples shown in Fig. 31-7, a suitable amine (such as pyridine) is bound on the unprotected side, and the O_2 molecule then enters either between the "pickets" or under the "cap," where it is bound end-on to the iron atom.

Other Heme Proteins

It is a fascinating fact that heme, the iron–porphyrin complex shown in Fig. 31-1(*c*), functions in Nature for a number of other tasks in addition to carrying oxygen. We shall not go into any of these in detail, but they should at least be mentioned since inorganic chemists have contributed to our understanding of all of them, both through research on the natural materials themselves, and through fabrication and study of model systems.

Cytochromes. These are found in both plants and animals, serving as electron carriers. They accept an electron from a slightly better reducing agent and pass it on to a slightly better oxidizing agent. In the cytochromes, the heme iron is coordinated by a nitrogen atom of an imidazole ring on one side of the porphyrin plane, and it is coordinated on the other side of the porphyrin plane by the sulfur atom of a methionine residue from a different part of the protein backbone. Thus the potential oxygen-carrying capacity of the heme in cytochromes is blocked.

Cytochrome P-450 Enzyme. This is a special type of cytochrome that functions as an enzyme by catalyzing the oxidation of C—H bonds to C—OH groups, as well as a number of other oxidations. A key step is the formation of a FeO intermediate containing either iron(IV) or iron(V).

Catalases. These heme proteins catalyze the decomposition of peroxides according to Eq. 31-4.6:

$$2H_2O_2 \longrightarrow 2H_2O + O_2 \qquad (31\text{-}4.6)$$

Peroxidases. These catalyze the oxidation of numerous compounds by hydrogen peroxide or by organic peroxides, ROOH.

Figure 31-7 Actual examples of (a) the "picket fence" and (b) the "capped" types of heme models.

31-5   Iron–Sulfur Proteins

These are proteins that contain strongly bound, functional iron atoms, but not porphyrins. The iron atoms are bound by sulfur atoms. These proteins all participate in electron transfer sequences.

Rubredoxins

These are found in anaerobic bacteria where they are believed to participate in biological redox reactions. They are relatively low-molecular weight proteins (ca. 6000), and they usually contain only one iron atom. In the best character-ized one, from the bacterium *C. Pasturianum,* the iron atom, which is normally in the III oxidation state, is surrounded by a distorted tetrahedron of cysteinyl sulfur atoms. Fe—S distances range from 2.24 to 2.33 Å, and the S—Fe—S angles from 104 to 114°. A schematic representation of this is given in Fig. 31-8. When the Fe^{III} is reduced to Fe^{II}, there is a slight (0.05 Å) increase in the Fe—S distances, but the essentially tetrahedral coordination is maintained. Mössbauer spectroscopy has shown that the iron is in the high-spin condition in both oxidation states. Inorganic chemists have prepared and studied $[Fe(SR)_4]^{2-}$ and $[Fe(SR)_4]^{-}$ complexes as models to help understand the properties of the rubredoxins.

Ferredoxins and High-Potential Iron Proteins

These are also relatively small proteins (6000–12,000) that contain iron–sulfur redox centers that are held in place by bonds from cysteine sulfur atoms to iron. The difference from rubredoxin is that here the redox centers are clusters of two, three, or four iron atoms, each with an equal number of sulfur atoms (so-called inorganic sulfur). In each case, an approximate tetrahedron of sulfur atoms is completed about each iron atom by the sulfur atoms of cysteine resi-dues of the peptide.

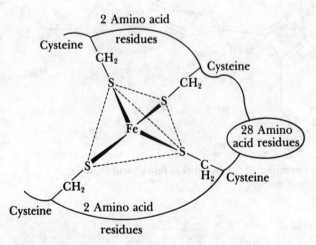

Figure 31-8   The location of the iron atom in the rubre-doxin molecule.

The two-iron cluster, complete with its attached cysteine sulfur atoms, can be described as two FeS_4 sharing an edge. In a convenient notation, the two iron clusters can be represented as $[2Fe–2S]^{n+}$. They have relatively simple behavior. Their normal state is $[2Fe–2S]^{2+}$ (meaning that both iron atoms are iron(III)), but they can be reduced at potentials similar to that of the standard H^+/H_2 electrode (i.e., -0.0 V on the hydrogen scale) to $[2Fe–2S]^+$.

Several kinds of spectroscopic evidence indicate that in the reduced $[2Fe–2S]^+$ cluster, the added electron is localized on one iron atom, so that one Fe^{II} and one Fe^{III} are present. In the $[2Fe–2S]^{2+}$ cluster, the Fe–Fe distance is only 2.72 Å, and the two formally high-spin (d^5) iron atoms have their magnetic moments so strongly coupled antiferromagnetically that the cluster is diamagnetic. Upon reduction to give $[2Fe–2S]^+$, this coupling persists, and the $[2Fe–2S]^+$ cluster has only one unpaired electron. This has been very helpful, since it means that esr detection of the reduced cluster is quite easy.

The four-iron clusters $[4Fe–4S]^{n+}$ appear to be more common than the two-iron clusters mentioned previously, and they have more complex behavior. In biological systems they have three oxidation levels, giving them charges of $+3$, $+2$, or $+1$. In any given system, though, only one pair of these charge types is employed. For those systems called *ferredoxins* (abbreviated Fd), the normally isolated substance contains a diamagnetic $[4Fe–4S]^{2+}$ cluster; this can be reversibly reduced at about 0.0 V (vs the hydrogen electrode) to give $[4Fe–4S]^+$, which has one unpaired electron. These four-iron ferredoxins obviously behave much like the ferredoxins that contain two-iron clusters.

For the systems called *high-potential iron–sulfur proteins* (abbreviated HiPIP), the operative redox couple, at about $+0.75$ V (vs the hydrogen electrode), is between the clusters $[4Fe–4S]^{3+}$ and $[4Fe–4S]^{2+}$. The redox behavior of both Fd's and HiPIPs is summarized in reaction 31-5.1:

$$[4Fe–4S]^{3+} \underset{-e^-}{\overset{+e^-}{\rightleftarrows}} [4Fe–4S]^{2+} \underset{-e^-}{\overset{+e^-}{\rightleftarrows}} [4Fe–4S]^+ \qquad (31\text{-}5.1)$$

$$\begin{array}{ccc} S = \tfrac{1}{2} & S = 0 & S = \tfrac{1}{2} \\ \sim +350\text{ mV} & & \sim -400\text{ mV} \\ \text{HiPIP couple} & & \text{Fd couple} \end{array}$$

where the redox potentials are given in millivolts (mV) against the standard calomel electrode, the usual practice in the research literature.

Let us now emphasize a very important point, for which there is not yet a generally accepted explanation. Both HiPIP and Fd are normally isolated with the $[4Fe–4S]^{2+}$ cluster. For Fd, a reversible, one-electron reduction occurs at -400 mV, but reversible oxidation to the $3+$ level has never been accomplished. For HiPIPs, conversely, reversible one-electron oxidation occurs readily, but reduction can be achieved only under forcing conditions having no relevance to the biological situation. Unquestionably, however, the $[4Fe–4S]^{2+}$ clusters in the two types of compounds are the same. What, then, causes the marked difference in their redox behavior?

Two hypotheses are under consideration. One focuses on the number of hydrogen bonds from surrounding protein NH groups to cysteinyl sulfur atoms. There appear to be about twice as many of these for a Fd than for a HiPIP; thus reduction (the introduction of negative charge) would be preferred for a Fd. A second hypothesis is that oxidation and reduction of the $[4Fe-4S]^{2+}$ cluster lead to different sorts of structural deformations, and that the protein conformations about the cluster in Fd's and HiPIPs differ so as to favor the reductively induced changes in the Fd case and the oxidatively induced ones in the HiPIP case. This is a fascinating question which will, no doubt, be resolved as better structural data are obtained and, perhaps, as model systems become better characterized.

The study of ferredoxin and HiPIP biochemistry provides a classic example of how inorganic chemists can use model systems to investigate complex biological processes. It has been possible to synthesize compounds containing $[Fe_4S_4(SR)_4]^{x-}$ anions that are very similar in many aspects (especially structural ones) to the $[4Fe-4S]^{n+}$ clusters that are bonded to the four cysteinyl sulfur atoms of the peptide chain. It is even possible, by treating ferredoxins with solutions of mercaptides, RS^-, to extract the $[4Fe-4S]^{2+}$ clusters from the protein and capture them as $[Fe_4S_4(SR)_4]^{2-}$ anions.

The three-iron clusters are at present poorly understood. There is direct X-ray evidence in at least one case for the occurrence of such a cluster in a crystalline ferredoxin, and evidence is accumulating that they occur in others. However, their biological significance is still being debated, and it may be that at least in some cases they are not present *in vivo*, but arise during isolation procedures, perhaps by degradation of $[4Fe-4S]^{n+}$ clusters.

31-6 Hemerythrin

In a number of marine worms, there exists a different solution to the oxygen carrying problem. Again, the active metal is iron, but the rest of the picture is quite different: no porphyrin ligand is involved, and two iron atoms are required to bind one molecule of O_2. The full details of how the active site of a hemerythrin actually works are still uncertain, but there is good evidence (not conclusive, however) that the process goes according to the scheme shown in Fig. 31-9.

The two-iron active site has the iron atoms connected by three bridging groups, two of which are carboxyl anions from the side chains of glutamic acid-58 and aspartic acid-106. The other bridging ligand is either O^{2-} or OH^-, but probably OH^-. All of the remaining ligands (which complete an octahedron about one iron atom and a type of 5-coordination about the other iron atom) are imidazole nitrogen atoms from histidine residues. The possibility that a

31-III

Figure 31-9   A possible description of the mode of oxygen binding by hemerythrin.

sixth ligand (very weakly held) may be present at the second iron atom cannot be entirely ruled out.

Spectroscopic evidence shows that the oxygen is definitely bound in a peroxo form, with the two oxygen atoms not equivalent. It is virtually certain that it occupies the position shown in Fig. 31-9(b), but the finer details, such as the OO—H · · · O hydrogen bond, are speculative.

To develop a better understanding of the interactions between the two iron atoms in the active site of hemerythrins, several model systems, of the type shown in structure 31-III, have been synthesized. In these models, the bridging carboxyl groups are derived from acetic acid, and the nitrogen atoms are supplied by tridentate triammines whose conformations cause them naturally to occupy three mutually cis positions.

31-7   Iron Supply and Transport

Iron metabolism requires provision for storing and transporting iron. In humans and in many other higher animals the storage materials are *ferritin* and *hemosiderin.* These are present in liver, spleen, and bone marrow. Ferritin is a water soluble, crystalline substance consisting of a roughly spherical protein sheath, of ~75-Å inside diameter and ~120-Å outside diameter, which in turn is built up of ~20 subunits. Within this sheath is a micelle of colloidal Fe_2O_3—H_2O—phosphate. Up to 23% of the dry weight may be iron; the protein portion alone, called apoferritin, is stable, crystallizes, and has a molecular weight of about 450,000. Hemosiderin contains larger proportions of the hy-

(a)

(b)

Figure 31-10   (a) A typical ferrichrome. (b) Typical structure of an acyclic ferrioxamine.

drous metal oxide, but its constitution is variable and ill-defined in comparison with that of ferritin.

Transferrin is a protein that binds iron(III) very strongly and transports it from ferritin to red blood cells and vice versa. Iron passes between ferritin and transferrin as Fe^{2+}, but the details of the redox process are obscure.

In microorganisms, iron is transported by substances called *ferrichromes* and *ferrioxamines*. The former are trihydroxamic acids in which the three hydroxamate groups are on three side chains of a cyclic hexapeptide. The latter have the three hydroxamate groups as part of the peptide chain, which may be cyclic or acyclic. Typical structures are shown in Fig. 31-10.

The importance of these compounds derives from their exceptional ability to chelate iron(III) and then pass through cell membranes, thus carrying iron from inorganic sources, such as $Fe_2O_3 \cdot xH_2O$, to points of need in the cells.

31-8 The Bioinorganic Chemistry of Cobalt: Vitamin B₁₂

The best-known biological function of cobalt is its intimate involvement in the coenzymes related to vitamin B_{12}, the structure of which is shown in Fig. 31-11. This structure is not as overwhelming as it might seem at first glance. It consists of four principal components:

1. A cobalt atom.
2. A macrocyclic ligand called the *corrin* ring, which bears various substituents. The essential corrin ring system is shown in bold lines. It resembles the porphine ring, but differs in various ways, notably in the absence of one methine ($=CH-$) bridge between a pair of pyrrole rings.
3. A complex organic portion consisting of a phosphate group, a sugar, and an organic base, the latter being coordinated to the cobalt atom.
4. A sixth ligand may be coordinated to the cobalt atom. This ligand can be varied, and when the cobalt atom is reduced to the oxidation state +1, it is evidently absent.

The entire entity shown in Fig. 31-11, but neglecting the ligand X, is called cobalamin.

The term vitamin B_{12} refers to cyanocobalamin, which has cobalt in the +3 oxidation state and CN^- as the ligand X. The cyanide ligand is introduced during the isolation procedure and is not present in any active form of the vitamin. In the biological system, the ligand, X, is likely to be H_2O much of the time, but another possibility, which has been identified by actual isolation of the complex, is the 5'-deoxyadenosyl radical, as shown in Fig. 31-12. The particular coenzyme in which this is found was the first organometallic compound to be observed in a living system.

The B_{12} coenzymes act in concert with a number of enzymes, but the best studied systems involve the dioldehydrases, where reactions such as Eq. 31-8.1 are catalyzed:

$$RCHOHCH_2OH \longrightarrow RCH_2CHO + H_2O \qquad (R = CH_3 \text{ or } H) \qquad (31\text{-}8.1)$$

Figure 31-11 The structure of cobalamin. The corrin ring is shown in heavy lines.

From studies of the nonenzymic chemistry of B_{12} coenzymes and of model systems noted below, a body of knowledge about fundamental B_{12} chemistry has been built up. Some of this chemistry undoubtedly plays a role in its activities as a coenzyme. The cobalamins can be reduced in neutral or alkaline solution to give cobalt(II) and cobalt(I) species, often called B_{12r} and B_{12s} respectively. The latter is a powerful reducing agent, decomposing water to give hydrogen and B_{12r}. These reductions can apparently be carried out *in vivo* by

Figure 31-12 The 5′-deoxyadenosyl group that may constitute the ligand X in Fig. 31-11.

reduced ferredoxin. When cyano- or hydroxocobalamin is reduced, the ligand (CN^- or OH^-) is lost, and the resulting five-coordinate cobalt(I) species reacts with ATP in the presence of a suitable enzyme to generate the B_{12} coenzyme.

In nonenzymic systems, rapid reaction of B_{12s} occurs with alkyl halides, acetylenes, and the like, as shown in reactions 31-8.2 to 31-8.4, where [Cb] represents the cobalamin group. Methylcobalamin has an extensive chemistry,

$$
\begin{array}{ll}
\xrightarrow{\text{HC}\equiv\text{CH}} \quad
\begin{matrix} \text{CH}=\text{CH}_2 \\ | \\ [\text{Cb}] \end{matrix}
& (31\text{-}8.2) \\[2em]
B_{12s} \xrightarrow{\text{RBr}} \quad
\begin{matrix} \text{R} \\ | \\ [\text{Cb}^+]\text{Br}^- \end{matrix}
& (31\text{-}8.3) \\[2em]
\xrightarrow{\text{BrCN}} \quad
\begin{matrix} \text{CN} \\ | \\ [\text{Cb}^+]\text{Br}^- \text{(cyanocobalamin, B}_{12}) \end{matrix}
& (31\text{-}8.4)
\end{array}
$$

some of which is involved in the metabolism of methane-producing bacteria. It transfers CH_3 groups to Hg^{II}, Tl^{III}, Pt^{II}, and Au^I. It is, evidently, in this way that certain bacteria accomplish their unfortunate feat of converting relatively harmless elemental mercury, which collects in sea or lake bottoms, into the exceeding toxic methylmercury ion, CH_3Hg^+.

A number of models for vitamin B_{12} have been synthesized and studied. The best known are the bis(dimethylglyoximato) complexes, an example of which is shown in Fig. 31-13. This and other models have as their essential feature a planar tetradentate ligand with amido-type nitrogen atoms. Many of these quite successfully model the reducibility to the cobalt(I) state, as well as the formation and reactions of the key cobalt–carbon bonds.

Figure 31-13 A cobaloxime, or bis(dimethylglyoximato)cobalt complex, which is a model for cyanocobalamin, vitamin B_{12}.

It is interesting that cobalt porphyrins are not very good models for B_{12} since they cannot be reduced to the cobalt(I) state under conditions where vitamin B_{12s} is obtained. This inability of the porphyrin ligand to stabilize the cobalt(I) species may be a reason why the corrin ring system was evolved.

31-9   Metalloenzymes

Enzymes are large protein molecules so built that they can bind at least one reactant (called the substrate) and catalyze an important biochemical reaction. They are extremely efficient as catalysts, typically causing rates to increase 10^6 times or more compared to the uncatalyzed rate. They are also usually highly specific, catalyzing only one, or a few reactions, rather than all those of a given class.

Some enzymes incorporate one or more metal atoms in their normal structure. The metal ion does not merely participate during the time that the enzyme–substrate complex exists, but is a permanent part of the enzyme. The metal atom, or at least one of the metal atoms when two or more are present, occurs at or very near to the active site (the locus of the bound, reacting substrate) and plays a role in the activity of the enzyme. Such enzymes are called *metalloenzymes,* and at least 80 have been identified.

The following metals are most often found in metalloenzymes, especially the last three: Mo, Ca, Mn, Fe, Cu, and Zn. Although Co^{2+} can often be made to replace Zn^{2+} in zinc metalloenzymes, with retention or even enhancement of activity, the actual presence of Co^{2+} in the native enzymes is rare.

Zinc Metalloenzymes

No less than 25 of these are known. Two of the most important, or at least best studied, are the following:

Carbonic anhydrase (MW = 30,000; 1 Zn):

This enzyme occurs in red blood cells and catalyzes the dehydration of the bicarbonate ion and the hydration of CO_2 according to reaction 31-9.1:

$$OH^- + CO_2 = HCO_3^- \tag{31-9.1}$$

These reactions would otherwise proceed too slowly to be compatible with physiological requirements.

Carboxypeptidase (MW = 34,300; 1 Zn):

This enzyme in the pancreas of mammals catalyzes the hydrolysis of the peptide bound at the carboxyl end of a peptide chain, as in reaction 31-9.2:

$$—R''CH—CONH—CHR'—CONH—CHRCO_2^- + H_2O \longrightarrow$$
$$—R''CH—CONH—CHR'—CO_2^- + H_3N^+CHRCO_2^- \tag{31-9.2}$$

Figure 31-14 (*a*) A proposed mode of binding of the substrate in carboxypeptidase. The substrate is shown in heavy type and lines. The curved line schematically defines the "surface" of the enzyme molecule. (*b*) A possible first step in the mechanism, wherein a carboxyl side chain attacks the carbonyl carbon atom, forming an anhydride. (*c*) Subsequent steps in the proposed mechanism, including hydrolysis of the intermediate anhydride and dissociation of the products from the active site.

The enzyme has a particular preference for substrates in which the side chain, R, is aromatic, that is, $-CH_2C_6H_5$ or $-CH_2C_6H_4OH$.

The structure and mechanism of action of carboxypeptidase have been partly elucidated. The zinc ion is bound in a distorted tetrahedral environment, with two histidine nitrogen atoms, one glutamate carboxyl oxygen atom, and a water molecule as ligands. The binding of the substrate probably occurs as is shown in Fig. 31-14(a). Notice that the carbonyl oxygen atom of the peptide linkage that is to be broken has replaced the water molecule in the coordination sphere of the zinc ion.

The key step in a possible, but speculative, mechanism is shown in Fig. 31-14(b). Once the peptide bond has been broken with formation of the acid anhydride, rapid hydrolysis of the anhydride would occur, as in Fig. 31-14(c). The products would then vacate the active site, leaving it ready to bind another molecule of substrate and repeat the cycle.

Copper Metalloenzymes

More than 20 of these have been isolated, but in no case is structure or function well understood. The copper enzymes are mostly oxidases, that is, enzymes that catalyze oxidations. Examples are (1) *Ascorbic acid oxidase* (MW = 140,000; 8 Cu), which is widely distributed in plants and microorganisms. It catalyzes oxidation of ascorbic acid (vitamin C) to dehydroascorbic acid. (2) *Cytochrome oxidase*, the terminal electron acceptor in the oxidative pathway of cell mitochondria. This enzyme also contains heme. (3) Various *tyrosinases*, which catalyze the formation of pigments (melanins) in a host of plants and animals.

In many lower animals, such as crabs and snails, the oxygen-carrying molecule is a copper-containing protein *hemocyanin*, which despite the name, contains no heme group. The hemocyanins represent the third system in Nature (besides hemoglobins and hemerythrins) for oxygen carrying from the point of intake to those tissues where O_2 is required. Like hemoglobin, hemocyanins have many subunits in the complete molecule and, therefore, exhibit cooperativity in O_2 binding. The active sites consist of two copper atoms (ca. 3.8 Å apart) that jointly bind one O_2 molecule. The way they do this apparently involves the conversion of the colorless $Cu^I \ldots Cu^I$ deoxy center to a peroxide-bridged $Cu^{II}-O-O-Cu^{II}$, which is bright blue.

31-10 Nitrogen Fixation

Elemental nitrogen, N_2, is relatively unreactive. In order to "fix" nitrogen, that is, make nitrogen react with other substances to produce nitrogen compounds, it is generally necessary to use energy-rich conditions. High temperatures or electrical discharges can supply the necessary activation energy. However, primitive bacteria and some blue-green algae can fix nitrogen under mild conditions, that is, ambient temperature and pressure. Metalloenzymes play a key role in this process.

Bacterial Nitrogenase Systems

Our more detailed information about nitrogen fixation comes mainly from studies of free-living soil bacteria. These can be cultured in the laboratory and essential components isolated and purified. Biological nitrogen fixation is a reductive process. An important fact, established using $^{15}N_2$, is that the first recognizable product is always NH_3. Apparently all intermediates remain bound to the enzyme system.

It has been known since 1930 that molybdenum is essential for bacterial nitrogen fixation, since this function can be turned off and on by removing and then restoring molybdenum to the environment. Magnesium and iron are also essential.

In 1960 the first active cell-free extracts were prepared, and since then, *nitrogenases*, as the enzymes are called, have been obtained in fairly pure condition from several bacteria. In each case the nitrogenase can be separated

Figure 31-15 Typical Fe—S—Mo cluster systems that have been prepared as models for the nitrogenase iron–molybdenum cofactor. (*a*) A double cubane complex containing two $MoFe_3S_4$ cubane units bridged through their Mo atoms by three thiolate groups. (*b*) A simple iron–thiomolybdate complex. (*c*) A bridged double cubane. (*d*) The product of the reaction of excess catechol with the trianionic form of (*c*). The benzene ring of the third chelating catechol ligand on the right-most iron is omitted for clarity.

into two proteins, one with molecular weight of about 220,000 and the other around 60,000. Neither of these proteins is separately active, but on mixing them activity is obtained immediately. The first protein contains one or two molybdenum atoms and 30 atoms each of iron and sulfur, suggesting that the metals may be coordinated by sulfur. The second, smaller protein of nitrogenase contains one [4Fe–4S] cluster, but no molybdenum.

There has been much speculation about the roles played by these components of nitrogenase. The generally accepted idea is that the molybdenum atom or atoms bind the dinitrogen, and that the iron atoms participate in one or more redox chains that supply the electrons needed to reduce N_2. When the system operates *in vitro,* it requires considerable amounts of ATP, and ca. 440 kJ of free energy are dissipated per mole of N_2 fixed. This is puzzling, since the actual overall reaction, shown in Eq. 31-10.1

$$N_2(g) + 3H_2(g) = 2NH_3(g) \qquad \Delta H^0_{298} = -46 \text{ kJ mol}^{-1} \qquad (31\text{-}10.1)$$

is only slightly exothermic. The nitrogenase system can even more efficiently reduce acetylene (exclusively to ethylene), and this constitutes a convenient assay of nitrogenase activity.

It has been possible to isolate a relatively small molecule (MW = 1000–1500), called the iron–molybdenum cofactor, which contains 6–8 iron atoms and 8–10 "inorganic" sulfide groups per molybdenum atom. Extended X-ray absorption fine structure (EXAFS) studies have indicated that these are all combined into some kind of large cluster in which molybdenum and iron atoms have three to four sulfur atoms as nearest neighbors. This has led to the preparation of a number of Mo—Fe—S cluster molecules in the hope of modeling the natural system. Typical models are shown in Fig. 31-15.

STUDY GUIDE

Scope and Purpose

We have sketched some important inorganic aspects of the chemistry of life. This has been an area of great recent interest among researchers, and new understandings develop so frequently, that the reader should expect to consult recent journal articles for more up-to-date information. Continued study in the references provided under "Supplementary Reading" is highly encouraged.

The major message of this chapter is that the chemistry of life involves more than 20 elements besides those traditionally treated in organic chemistry. Though these other elements tend to have limited roles, life processes require them just as surely as they require proteins, carbohydrates, and lipids.

Study Questions

A. Review

1. Name four transition metals and two nontransition metals that play important roles in biological processes.

2. Draw the structure of porphine and explain how the structures of heme and chlorophyll are related to it.

3. What role does the magnesium ion play in the functioning of chlorophyll?

4. What constitutes a heme protein? Name three of them.

5. What are the functions of hemoglobin and myoglobin? What are the principal similarities in their structures?

6. What changes occur in the heme groups of hemoglobin on going from deoxy- to oxyhemoglobin?

7. What is the structure of the redox center of HiPIP and of the 4-Fe and 8-Fe ferredoxins?

8. What functions do ferrichromes and ferrioxamines have? What are their chief chemical features?

9. State the main components of cobalamin. How do B_{12}, B_{12r}, and B_{12s} differ?

10. What role does the zinc ion play in the action of carboxypeptidase?

11. What is the principal reaction of nitrogenase?

12. List the ways in which the cobaloximes resemble cobalamin.

C. Questions from the Literature of Inorganic Chemistry

1. Consider the paper by J. Halpern, "Mechanisms of Coenzyme B_{12}-Dependent Rearrangements," *Science*, **1985**, *227*, 869.

    (a) What is the significance of the observation that reactions involving the coenzyme B_{12} give scrambling of the methylene hydrogens from the 5'-deoxyadenosine of the coenzyme with the hydrogen atom involved in the migration [e.g., eq. (1)] at the substrate?

    (b) Through what various spin states does the cobalt atom of the coenzyme B_{12} progress during the operation of the mechanism shown in Fig. 2 of this article? What is the difference in the number of *d* electrons on B_{12} and B_{12r}?

    (c) What factors are said to influence the critical cobalt–carbon bond dissociation energies?

    (d) What features do the "DH" and the "saloph" cobalt complex model systems have in common with the coenzyme B_{12}?

    (e) What analogy does the author draw between the reversible cobalt–carbon bond dissociation of coenzyme B_{12} and the reversible binding of dioxygen as in Eqs. 23 and 24?

2. Consider the extensive work by J. P. Collman and students, represented by the following paper, and the references therein: J. P. Collman, J. I. Brauman, B. I. Iverson, J. L. Sessler, R. M. Morris, and Q. H. Gibson, *J. Am. Chem. Soc.*, **1983**, *105*, 3052.

    (a) What are the main similarities and differences, structurally, between the "picket fence" and "pocket" porphyrins that are described in this article?

    (b) How is solvation thought to reduce affinities for O_2 of the unprotected iron(II) porphyrins?

    (c) What advantages in O_2 binding do the "picket fence" and "pocket" porphyrins have over those iron(II) porphyrins that are "unprotected" from solvation effects?

    (d) How do the O_2 and CO affinities of the "picket fence" porphyrins compare with those of the "pocket" porphyrins?

(e) What geometries for the M—O_2 and M—CO groups seem to make sense in explaining the observations in (d)?

3. Consider the work by J. Chatt on nitrogen fixation analogs: J. Chatt, A. J. Pearman, and R. L. Richards, *J. Chem. Soc. Dalton Trans.*, **1977**, 1852.

(a) The N_2 complexes reported here are protonated to give ammonia. How is this reaction of interest to the molybdenum nitrogenase systems?

(b) In other studies mentioned in the introduction to this paper, other complexes were protonated to give not ammonia, but intermediate reduction products. Enumerate the findings concerning the formation of diazenido, diazine, and hydrazido ligands.

(c) What is the difference between protonation of the N_2 ligand in complexes containing two bidentate dppe ligands and protonation of N_2 ligand in complexes containing four monodentate PMe_2Ph ligands? What bonding arguments do the authors present to account for these differences?

(d) At what stage do the authors propose a splitting of the N—N bond? When is this likely to occur in the overall stepwise process that is proposed?

(e) How is the oxidation state of the metal at the end of reaction sequence (5) different from the oxidation state that is likely in the enzymic system? How do the authors propose that the enzyme avoids this high an oxidation state?

SUPPLEMENTARY READING

Brill, A. S., *Transition Metals in Biochemistry*, Springer-Verlag, Berlin, 1977.

Chatt, J., Dilworth, J. R., and Richards, R. L., "Recent Advances in the Chemistry of Nitrogen Fixation," *Chem. Rev.*, **1978**, *78*, 589.

Dickerson, R. E. and Geis, I., *The Structure and Action of Proteins*, Harper & Row, New York, 1969.

Dickerson, R. E. and Geis, I., *Hemoglobin: Structure, Function, Evolution, and Pathology*, Benjamin/Cummings, Menlo Park, CA, 1983.

Eichhorn, G. L., Ed., *Inorganic Biochemistry*, Elsevier, New York, 1973.

Eichhorn, G. L. and Marzilli, L. G., *Advances in Inorganic Biochemistry*, Vols. 1–6, Elsevier, New York.

Harrison, P. M., Ed., *Metalloproteins*, Parts 1 and 2, MacMillan, New York, 1985.

Henderson, R. A., Leigh, G. J., and Pickett, C. J., "The Chemistry of Nitrogen Fixation and Models for the Reactions of Nitrogenase," *Adv. Inorg. Chem. Radiochem.*, **1983**, *27*, 197.

Hughes, M. N., *The Inorganic Chemistry of Biological Processes*, Wiley-Interscience, New York, 1981.

McMillan, D. R., Ed., "Bioinorganic Chemistry—The State of the Art," *J. Chem. Educ.*, **1985**, *62*, 916–1011. An excellent series of articles.

Niederhoffer, E. C., Timmons, J. H., and Martell, A. E., "Thermodynamics of Oxygen Binding in Natural and Synthetic Dioxygen Complexes," *Chem. Rev.*, **1984**, *84*, 137–203.

Ochiai, E. I., *Bioinorganic Chemistry*, Allyn and Bacon, Boston, 1977.

Peisach, J., Aisen, P., and Blumberg, W. E., Eds., *The Biochemistry of Copper*, Academic, New York, 1966.

Postgate, B., Ed., *The Chemistry and Biochemistry of Nitrogen Fixation*, Plenum, New York, 1971.

Pratt, J. M., "The B_{12}-Dependent Isomerase Enzymes; How the Protein Controls the Active Site," *Chem. Soc. Rev.*, **1985,** *14*, 161.

Stiefel, E. I. and Cramer, S. P., "Chemistry and Biology of the Iron–Molybdenum Cofactor of Nitrogenase," in *Molybdenum Enzymes*, T. G. Spiro, Ed., Wiley-Interscience, New York, 1985.

Vallee, B. L. and Wacker, W. E. C., "Metalloproteins," Vol. V, *The Enzymes*, H. Neurath, Ed., Academic, New York, 1970.

glossary *

Absorbance (n). The $\log_{10}$ of the ratio I_0/I, where I_0 is the intensity of incident light and I is the intensity of the transmitted light. It is usually denoted A and is equal to the unitless quantity in Beer's Law: $A = \epsilon cd$, where ϵ is the molar absorptivity, c is the concentration, and d is the path length.

Absorption (n). The process by which the intensity of radiation is reduced as it passes through a material.

Absorptivity, molar (n). The constant ϵ (in units $L\,mol^{-1}\,cm^{-1}$) in Beer's Law: $A = \epsilon cd$. It is also called the extinction coefficient.

Acid–base reaction (n). (a) According to the definition of Brønsted–Lowry, the neutralization of a proton donor by a proton acceptor; (b) according to the definition of Lewis, the formation of an adduct between an electron-pair donor and an electron-pair acceptor; (c) according to the Lux–Flood definition, the reaction of an oxide ion acceptor with an oxide ion donor.

Actinide elements (n). The elements ^{90}Th through ^{103}Lr, which follow actinium, ^{89}Ac.

Activated complex (n). That arrangement of atoms, groups, molecules, or ions that has the highest free energy along the reaction coordinate (free energy profile) for a reaction. This is also known as the transition state and corresponds to the minimum free energy that must be possessed by the reactive ensemble in order to consummate the reaction.

Addition reaction (n). A reaction in which a group, molecule, or ion combines with another. Common examples are additions across a multiple bond and addition to an atom that is able to undergo coordination sphere expansion (an increase in occupancy). This is the converse of elimination.

Adduct (n). The product of the addition of a Lewis acid to a Lewis base.

Adiabatic (adj). Without heat transfer.

Adsorption (n). The adhering or retention of a substance (usually a gas, liquid, or a mixture of these) on the surface of a material.

Alloy (n). A solid solution of two or more metals.

Allotrope (n). One of the two or more distinct forms or structures adopted by an element, for example, O_2 and O_3.

Alum (n). An ionic sulfate containing a trivalent cation (nominally Al^{3+}) and any of a number of monovalent cations such as K^+. This class of substances is named after the parent potassium alum, $KAl(SO_4)_2(H_2O)_{12}$, and may contain practically any combination of monovalent and trivalent cations.

Amalgam (n). An alloy of a metal with mercury.

Amorphous (adj). Having a random or disordered arrangement in the solid state, that is, the antithesis of crystalline.

Amphoteric (adj). Capable of reacting either as an acid or as a base. |

*n = noun, adj = adjective, v = verb.

688

Angular momentum (n). A property associated with angular motion, equal to the product of angular velocity (ω) and the moment of inertia (mr).

Angular wave function (n). That portion of the total wave function $\Psi(r, \Theta, \phi) = R(r)\Theta(\theta)\Phi(\phi)$ that is factorable from $R(r)$, namely, $\Theta(\theta)\Phi(\phi)$.

Anhydride, acidic (n). An oxide that reacts with water to form an acid. Acidic anhydrides are usually nonmetal oxides such as SO_3, P_2O_5, and so on. Thus acidic anhydrides are acids with water removed.

Anhydride, basic (n). An oxide of a metal that reacts with water to give an aqueous hydroxide, or that reacts with protic acids to give aqueous metal salts. These can sometimes be formed by thorough dehydration of hydrous oxides or hydroxides.

Anhydrous (adj). Lacking water.

Antibonding orbital (n). A molecular orbital at higher energy than the orbitals from which it was formed, resulting from negative overlap of atomic orbitals, and having less electron density (or electron probability) between the nuclei than would be true of the simple sum of the electron densities from the combining orbitals of the separate atoms.

Aqua ion (n). A metal ion that is exclusively coordinated by a given number of water molecules. (This is sometimes spelled aquo.)

Autooxidation (n). The apparently spontaneous oxidation of a substance that is exposed to the atmosphere, hence, oxidation by gaseous dioxygen.

Azimuthal quantum number (n). The orbital angular momentum quantum number $\ell = 0, 1, 2, \ldots, (n - 1)$.

Bidentate (adj). Twice-attached; used to describe a ligand.

Bond, covalent (n). The strong attractive force that holds together atoms within a molecule or complex ion, and that arises between a pair of bonded atoms through the sharing of a pair of electrons, one electron of the pair being contributed by each atom.

Bond, coordinate covalent (also called a dative bond) (n). A covalent bond in which both electrons originate from the same atom. This type of bond arises from the addition of a Lewis base to a Lewis acid. It is the electron-pair donor-acceptor bond of an adduct.

Bond, ionic (n). A bond consisting of the electrostatic attraction between a cation and an anion.

Bond, polar covalent (n). An electron-pair or covalent bond in which the electron density is not distributed equally or shared evenly between the two atoms because of a difference in electronegativity. The electron density in the bond is shifted (polarized) towards the more electronegative atom.

Bonding orbital (n). A molecular orbital at lower energy than the orbitals from which is was formed, resulting from positive overlap of orbitals from separate atoms, and having more electron density (or electron probability) between the nuclei than would be true of the simple sum of the electron densities from the combining orbitals of the separate nuclei.

Borate (n). A compound containing polynuclear oxo anions of boron, which are ring or chain polymeric anions containing planar BO_3 or tetrahedral BO_4 units. Also, neutral borate esters that may be considered to be derived from boric acid.

Borax (n). The sodium salt of the ring anion "$[B_4O_7]$," of composition $Na_2B_4O_7 \cdot 10H_2O$, more properly written $Na_2[B_4O_5(OH)_4] \cdot 8H_2O$ since the tetraborate dianion is dihydrated and contains four B—OH groups.

Brass (n). Any of the alloys variously composed of copper and zinc, sometimes also containing small amounts of other constituents, often tin or lead.

Bronze (n). Any of the alloys composed of at least 88% copper, tin (8–10%), and sometimes zinc.

Calcination (n). Strong heating of a material (usually an ore) in a furnace to achieve some desired decomposition or change, *i.e.,* of calcium carbonate to give calcium oxide and carbon dioxide.

Canonical form (n). One of the contributing resonance structures of a substance.

Carbonyl (n). A compound containing a CO group.

Catalyst (n). A substance that increases the rate (lowers the activation barrier) of attainment of equilibrium, and that, ideally, can be recovered at the end of the reaction.

Catenation (n). The self-linking of an element in its compounds; the forming of chains.

Center of inversion (n). A symmetry element (point) in a structure through which inversion [changing every location $(+x, +y, +z)$ to $(-x, -y, -z)$] leaves the structure indistinguishable from the original.

Center of symmetry (n). Another term for center of inversion.

Chalcogen (n). An element of Group VIB(16), *i.e.,* O, S, Se, Te, Po.

Chelate (n). A ligand that is able to bond to a central metal atom simultaneously through more than one donor atom.

Chirality (n). The nonsuperimpossibility of an object and its mirror image.

Clathrate (n). A solid in which are trapped one or more substances (usually gases or volatile liquids) within various interstices of the structure. These are not compounds with definite and fixed compositions, although there are limiting compositions in which all the interstices appropriate for holding the trapped substance are occupied.

Coke (n). A porous residue of carbon and mineral ash that is obtained from furnaces where coal is heated in a deficiency or absence of oxygen to drive off volatile materials.

Colloidal system (n). A dispersion of one substance within another such that one (the colloid) is uniformly distributed throughout the other (the dispersing medium) in a manner that is intermediate between a true solution and a suspension. The colloidal particle sizes may vary from 10 to 10,000 Å, and although they are too small to be seen with the unaided eye, they can be illuminated with a beam of light.

Combustion (n). Any reaction that is sufficiently exothermic so as to be self-sustaining; usually used for reactions with O_2.

Conformation (n). One of the various arrangements of atoms in a molecule or complex ion, based on differences in angle(s) of rotation about single bonds.

Conformer (n). One of a number of conformational isomers or rotamers.

Conjugate acid–base pair (n). Substances related to one another by proton transfer.

Corundum (n). The hard, α-form of Al_2O_3, containing aluminum ions in two-thirds of the octahedral holes in a hexagonally close-packed array of oxide ions.

Coulomb (n). The SI unit of charge, that of an electron being $1.6021892 \times 10^{-19}$ Coulombs.

Cryolite (n). The mineral Na_3AlF_6 which, as the melt, finds application as a medium for the electrolytic production of aluminum from bauxite.

Crystalline (adj). Having a regular and continuous three-dimensional arrangement of atoms in the solid state.

Cyclization reaction (n). A reaction that leads to the formation of rings.

Dative bond (n). See Bond, coordinate covalent.

Degenerate orbitals (n). Orbitals having the same energy.

Delta bond (n). A bond formed from the face-to-face overlap of d orbitals from separate atoms, such that the internuclear axis coincides with the intersection of the two nodal planes that divide the electron density of the bond.

Diastereomers (n). Isomers that are individually chiral, but that are not mirror images of one another.

Diastereotopic (n). Leading to diastereomers.

Dielectric constant (n). The constant, k, in the equation for the force, f, between two unit charges, q, separated by a distance, r: $f = q^2/kr^2$.

Diffusion (n). A movement of molecules (or particles) throughout a solvent (or within a mixture) so as to make the system uniform or homogeneous.

Disproportionation reaction (n). Self-reaction of one substance simultaneously to give two or more dissimilar substances.

Ductile (adj). Able to be drawn to a longer length without breaking.

Effective nuclear charge (n). That portion of the total nuclear charge that is experienced by a given electron. It is equal to the total, or formal nuclear charge, less the amount by which other electrons shield the given electron from the nucleus.

Effusion (n). The escape of a gas through a small hole in its container.

Elastomer (n). A macromolecular substance that can be stretched to at least twice its unstressed length and will return on release to nearly its original length. The elastic character of rubber is improved through vulcanization.

Electronegativity (n). The ability of an atom in a molecule to attract electrons to itself.

Electron affinity (n). The energy that is released when an electron is added to the valence shell of an atom. It is the negative of the electron attachment enthalpy, ΔH_{EA}.

Electron configuration (n). A listing of the electrons of an atom or ion according to their distribution within the various available orbitals.

Electron spin (n). The characteristic angular momentum associated with an electron, and that is independent of orbital angular momentum or motion.

Electron transfer reaction (n). An oxidation–reduction reaction in which electrons pass from one reactant to another.

Elimination reaction (n). A reaction in which a group, molecule, or ion is separated from another. Examples are dehydrohalogenations, and eliminations from metal centers that are able to undergo coordination number reduction (a decrease in occupancy). This is the converse of an addition reaction.

Emulsion (n). A type of colloidal mixture or system.

Enantiomer (n). Enantiomorph.

Enantiomorph (n). One of a pair of optical isomers, that is, one of a pair of chiral isomers, each of which is a nonsuperimposable mirror image of the other.

Enantiotopic (adj). Leading to enantiomorphs.

Enclosure surface (n). A boundary representation of an orbital such that some arbitrary fraction (usually large) of total electron density is distributed between the surface and the origin.

Eutectic system (n). A solid solution, all the components of which melt at a single temperature. Thus in eutectic systems, at the eutectic temperature and composition, all components of the mixture are simultaneously engaged in separate solid–liquid equilibria without changing the composition of the eutectic mixture.

Exchange reaction (n). A reaction in which two atoms, ions, or groups switch places either between two different molecules or ions (intermolecular exchange) or within the same molecule or ion (intramolecular exchange).

Fixation (n). Any process by which otherwise inert dinitrogen is combined with other elements, most notably of dinitrogen to give ammonia.

Fluorescence (n). The emission, immediately following excitation, of electromagnetic radiation (at longer wavelength than that necessary to accomplish the excitation) from a substance in an excited electronic state. The electronic process that accounts for the release of the electromagnetic radiation is characteristically a spin-allowed process. This and phosphorescence together constitute the general behavior known as luminescence.

Flux (n). An additive that aids in the fusion of a material, and that often imparts to the melt a resistance to oxide formation.

Frequency (n). In any periodic motion, the number of cycles completed in a unit of time, *i.e.*, cycles per second, or s^{-1}. In electromagnetic radiation, frequency ν (in s^{-1}) equals the speed c (cm s^{-1}) divided by the wavelength λ (cm), or $\nu = c/\lambda$.

Friedel–Crafts reaction (n). A reaction catalyzed by Al_2Cl_6 and resulting in the condensation of alkyl or aryl halides with benzene or its derivatives, and in which an alkyl (R) or acyl (RCO) group is substituted for a hydrogen atom of the aromatic ring to give, respectively, an alkyl or a ketone.

Fusion (n). Melting.

Galvanized (adj). Coated with zinc, either by dipping in molten zinc (hot dipping), sherardizing (rolling in powdered zinc at ca. 300°C), or electrodeposition.

Gas hydrate (n). A clathrate compound in which water is the host (a pentagonal dodecahedral arrangement of water molecules being common) and gases are trapped.

Geometrical isomers (n). Molecules or complex ions having the same empirical formulae, and the same atomic linkages, but differing in the spatial orientation of like groups.

Glass (n). An amorphous solid (prepared from a supercooled liquid) in which there is the same type of arrangement as in the liquid but without appreciable translational energy. A glass should be regarded as a metastable material because the corresponding crystalline material would have a lower free energy, but the glassy structure cannot rearrange to the preferred crystalline lattice. One normally thinks of the silica glasses but, technically, even metals may form glasses.

Grignard reagent (n). An organomagnesium halide, of formal composition RMgX, usually prepared in anhydrous ether solution and used to transfer R groups.

Group orbitals (n). Linear combinations of orbitals from separate atoms and conforming to molecular geometry so that, as a group, they can overlap with orbitals of other groups or atoms, leading to bonding.

Halogen (n). An element of Group VIIB(17), *i.e.*, F, Cl, Br, I, and At.

Hapto (adj). A prefix used (in conjunction with a designation mono-, di-, tri-, tetra-, penta-, hexa-, etc.) to specify the number of atoms within a ligand that are attached to a metal.

Heterogeneous (adj). Consisting of dissimilar components (antonym: homogeneous).

Heterolysis (n). Cleavage of an electron-pair bond in an unsymmetrical fashion so that one atom of the pair retains both electrons of the bond.

Heterolytic (adj). Leading to or pertaining to heterolysis.

Homogeneous (adj). Having uniform composition, structure, and properties throughout (antonym: heterogeneous).

Homologous (adj). Consisting of the same general class, but differing by the addition of various numbers of some common unit, *i.e.*, the homologous series of alkanes built up of CH_2 units.

Homolysis (n). Cleavage of an electron-pair bond symmetrically so as to allow each atom of the pair to retain one electron.

Homolytic (adj). Leading to or pertaining to homolysis.

Hybrid orbital (n). A combination of two or more atomic orbitals of like energy on the same atom.

Hydrated (adj). Containing in the crystalline form a distinct, fixed, and reproducible number of water molecules incorporated into the crystal structure, *e.g.*, $CuSO_4 \cdot 5H_2O$ or $CoCl_2 \cdot 6H_2O$.

Hydrolysis (n). A decomposition with water, the hydrogen and hydroxyl of which are found in separate products of the reaction. A more general definition—any reaction with water—is sometimes also used.

Hydrolytic (adj). Involving hydrolysis.

Hydrous (adj). Generally containing water, but not in the distinct, fixed, and reproducible proportions typical of a hydrated substance. Examples: A hydrous metal oxide, $MO \cdot nH_2O$ as opposed to a distinct hydroxide, $M(OH)_2$.

I_a. The associative interchange mechanism of ligand substitution.

I_d. The dissociative interchange mechanism of ligand substitution.

Inert (adj). Slow to react, and, in particular, having a half-life for reaction of a minute or longer.

Insertion reaction (n). The interposition of a new molecule, group, or ion between atoms in a structure such that the added molecule, group, or ion separates the two parts of the structure that were formerly bonded together.

Intermediate (n). A structure that occurs along the reaction pathway and that has a lower free energy than the two transition states that bracket it. Also, a precursor to some desired product. These are generally postulated rather than actually isolable.

Inversion center. See center of inversion.

Inversion reaction (n). A change of the chirality at a single center of chirality.

Ion pair (n). A set of oppositely charged ions that are associated by electrostatic forces.

Isoelectronic (adj). Having the same electron configuration.

Isomer (n). One of two or more substances that are structurally and physically different but which have the same elemental composition.

Isomerization reaction (n). A conversion of one isomer into another.

Isomorphous (adj). Having the same shape, form, or structure; generally said of crystals.

Isostructural (adj). Having the same structure.

Isotope (n). One of two or more forms of an atom, all of which have the same atomic number (*i.e.*, the same number of protons), but which differ in the number of neutrons in the nucleus of the atom. The atomic mass and the mass number of the various isotopes of an element are different.

Jahn–Teller Effect (n). The requirement that a nonlinear molecule with degenerate orbitals must undergo a structural change in order to lift the degeneracy; in other words, the requirement that molecules adopt geometries that do not lead to a degeneracy in valence-level orbitals.

Kieselguhr (n). Infusorial or diatomaceous earth, which is a fine powder used as an absorbent or clarifying agent. In its most useful form it is a soft, white, porous powder, mostly of hydrated silica.

Labile (adj). Quick to react, in particular having a half-life for reaction of less than a minute.

Lanthanides (n). The elements ^{58}Ce to ^{71}Lu, which follow lanthanum, ^{57}La.

Ligand (n). A molecule, group, or ion that bonds to a metal atom or ion.

Ligand field (n). The electrostatic field created by a set of ligands arranged in some particular geometry about a metal.

Lime (n). Calcium oxide.

Limestone (n). Naturally occurring calcium carbonate.

Luminescence (n). Either fluorescence or phosphorescence.

Malleable (adj). Extensible or deformable in all dimensions, without loss in character, by hammering or rolling.

Magnesite (n). The mineral $MgCO_3$.

Magnetite (n). The mineral Fe_3O_4 or lodestone.

Metallic (adj). Having the properties of a metal—luster (surface sheen), high thermal conductivity, and high electrical conductivity. Malleability and ductility also characterize the many metals.

Metalloid (n). An element that exhibits some metallic characteristics together with some nonmetallic ones; examples are Ge and Te.

Metathesis (n). An exchange of comparable groups, such that two compounds form two new ones.

Mineral (n). A naturally occurring inorganic substance, which has a characteristic elemental composition and structure, and which is found in pure crystalline form, or in a composite rock in the earth's crust.

Moderator (n). A substance that reduces the speed of neutrons created in nuclear fusion reactors.

Molar absorptivity. See absorptivity, molar.

Molecular sieves (n). Sodium or calcium aluminosilicates with porous cavities generally 3–4 Å in size, which are able to discriminate among substances based on molecular sizes.

Momentum (n). Classically, the product of mass and velocity.

Multiplicity, spin (n). For an ensemble of electrons, the spin multiplicity equals the quantity $(2S + 1)$, where S is the spin quantum number.

Node (n). A point, line, or surface where electron density is zero, caused by a change in the sign of the wave function for the electron. Also, in stationary waves, a point, line, or surface at which there is no displacement.

Nonbonding (adj). Neither bonding nor antibonding.

Nuclear reaction (n). A reaction that changes the atomic number or mass number of an atom.

Occupancy (n). A spatial designation for an atom in a molecule or complex ion. When an atom A resides in a molecule AB_xE_y, with x being the number of other atoms B bound to A, and y being the number of lone pairs of electrons (E) at atom A, the occupancy at A is $x + y$.

Octet (n). A set of eight.

Octet rule (n). A rule whose application is limited to elements of the first short period, stating that a set of eight electrons (as various combinations of shared and lone electrons) at an atom in its compounds is most stable.

Olefin (n). A substance containing a C=C double bond.

Oleum (n). Fuming sulfuric acid; 100% H_2SO_4 containing some dissolved SO_3.

Oligomer (n). A polymer made up of only a few (usually less than four) monomers.

Optical activity (n). The ability of a substance to rotate the plane of plane-polarized light, and a characteristic property of individual enantiomorphs or chiral substances.

Optical isomerism (n). The isomerism associated with chirality.

Orbit (n). The path followed by the electron in Bohr's theory of the hydrogen atom, characterized by the quantity r, the distance from the nucleus of the electron.

Orbital (n). The space-dependent (time-independent) portion of the wave function for an electron in an atom, molecule, or ion.

Ore (n). A natural inorganic material from which important metals or nonmetals may be extracted.

Oxidation (n). A loss of electrons, corresponding to an increase in oxidation state.

Oxidizing agent (n). A substance that causes oxidation, and which is, as a consequence, reduced.

Oxo process (n). The general catalytic reaction of olefins with carbon monoxide and molecular hydrogen to give, variously, alcohols, aldehydes, *etc.*

Oxy acid (n). A protic acid containing an element combined with oxygen; the ionizable hydrogen atoms are attached to O atoms.

Passivation (of metals) (n). A treatment that renders the metal surface inert, and which usually results from the action of strong oxidizing agents.

Pauli exclusion principle. A postulate that no single atom may possess two electrons that have the same four quantum numbers.

Perovskite (n). The mineral $CaTiO_3$, a mixed-metal oxide.

Phosphorescence (n). The delayed emission of electromagnetic radiation from a substance in an excited electronic state. As in fluorescence, the emitted wavelength is longer than that necessary to accomplish the excitation. Phosphorescence is different in that the emission is delayed because the electronic process that accounts for the emission is a spin-forbidden process by the rules of quantum mechanics. Phosphorescence and fluorescence together constitute the general behavior known as luminescence.

Pi bond or π bond (n). A bond formed from side-to-side overlap of p or d orbitals from separate atoms, such that the internuclear axis lies in a single nodal plane that divides the electron density of the bond.

Polar (adj). Having a full or partial separation of opposite electrical charges by some distance.

Polar coordinates (n). A coordinate system employing a length r and two angles Θ and ϕ for representing the location of a point in space. The location of a point in space by the Cartesian coordinate system (x, y, z) is related to its location by the polar coordinate system as follows: $x = r \sin\Theta \cos\phi$, $y = r \sin\Theta \sin\phi$, $z = r \cos\Theta$.

Polarizable (adj). Able to be induced to have polar character.

Polarizability (n). The ease with which polar character can be induced. Technically this is the size of the electric dipole moment that is induced by a given electric field.

Polymorphic (adj). Having multiple shapes, forms, or structures (said normally of crystalline solids).

Polyphosphate (n). A condensed phosphate containing P—O—P linkages, an example being diphosphate, $[O_3P-O-PO_3]^{4-}$. The general formula is $[P_nO_{3n+1}]^{(n+2)-}$.

Precursor (n). An intermediate preceding the desired product.

Promoted catalyst (n). A catalyst that has been altered so as to increase its activity.

Pyrolysis (n). Breaking down by heat.

Pyrophoric (n). Spontaneously flammable in air.

Quantum (n). The indivisible or most elementary amount of electromagnetic radiation. One quantum is involved per electron in electronic transitions in atoms and the like.

Amounts (intensities) of electromagnetic radiation are restricted to integral numbers of the quantum. The energy of a particular quantum is given by Planck's equation $E = h\nu$, where ν is frequency (in cycles s^{-1}) and h is Planck's constant (in erg s^{-1}).

Quartz (n). The most stable and most dense of the normal crystalline forms of SiO_2.

Quicklime (n). Calcium oxide.

Quicksilver (n). Mercury.

Racemic (adj). Containing equal amounts of each of a pair of enantiomorphs such that the mixture is not optically active, although both enantiomorphs are individually chiral.

Racemization (n). Production of a mixture that is racemic, through an interconversion among enantiomorphs.

Radial wave function (n). That portion of the total wave function $\Psi(r, \Theta, \phi)$ that is dependent only upon r, the radial distance from the nucleus.

Rare earth element. See lanthanides.

Rearrangement (n). A change in geometry.

Reducing agent (n). A substance that causes reduction, and which is, as a consequence, oxidized.

Reduction (n). A gain of electrons, corresponding to a decrease in oxidation state.

Rock (n). A hard and compacted aggregate of various minerals, sometimes having a uniform and characteristic composition, *e.g.*, marble, but often being visibly heterogeneous (*e.g.*, granite).

Rutile (n). One of the mineral forms of titanium dioxide.

S$_N$1 (adj). Nucleophilic substitution that has a unimolecular rate-determining step.

S$_N$2 (adj). Nucleophilic substitution that has a bimolecular rate-determining step.

Saturated (adj). Having sufficient electrons to allow two-center, two-electron single bonds throughout.

Selection rule (n). A statement about the quantum mechanical allowedness of a process.

Sequester (v). To draw aside, remove, or bind up a substance so as to influence its freedom of movement or independent action; the process by which a polydentate ligand can surround a metal ion and render it unreactive.

Silane (n). A hydride of silicon, *e.g.*, SiH_4, or in general, Si_nH_{2n+2}.

Silica (n). SiO_2, which, in its most stable crystalline form is quartz, but which exists in numerous other variations including, but not limited to, (a) other crystalline materials formed from quartz by the aid of fluxes (e.g., tridymite, cristobalite, keatite, *etc.*), (b) amorphous solids, (c) hydrated silicas including aqueous colloidal systems (sols and gels), (d) silica glass, and (e) biogenic silicas such as diatomaceous earth.

Silica gel (n). A solid network of spherical colloidal silica particles.

Silica sol (n). A colloidal suspension of amorphous silica in water.

Silicates (n). Compounds containing polynuclear oxoanions of silicon that contain SiO_4 tetrahedra, which are variously linked to give chain, ring, sheet, cage, or framework structures.

Silicone (n). A linear or chain polymer containing —R_2Si—O—SiR_2—O— repeating units, sometimes cross-linked by $RSiO_3$ units.

Sigma bond (n). A bond formed by the end-to-end overlap of orbitals from separate atoms, such that there is no nodal plane that includes the internuclear axis.

Solvation (n). An association with solvent.

Solvolysis (n). A reaction with solvent; when the solvent is water, it is called hydrolysis.

Sphalerite (n). Zinc blende, the denser or β-form of ZnS, the α-form being wurtzite.

Spin angular momentum. See angular momentum, spin.

Steam reforming (n). A thermal and catalyzed degradation in the presence of steam.

Symmetry (n). The property of having two or more identical parts that are related to each other by rotation, reflection, or inversion.

Symmetry, center of. See center of inversion.

Tautomer (n). One of a set of isomers that are readily interconverted by rearrangements of atoms.

Tautomerism (n). The occurrence of tautomers.

Tautomerization (n). The (usually reversible) interconversion of tautomers.

Transition state (n). The point (on the reaction profile for a chemical reaction) at which the activated complex has been reached.

Unsaturated (adj). (a) Having one or more multiple bonds formed by electrons that might also be used to bond to additional atoms, to achieve saturation. (b) Any compound containing an atom that may yet add more groups, *i.e.*, that may undergo an increase in coordination number or occupancy is said to be coordinatively unsaturated.

Valence (n). The capacity of an atom to form bonds to other atoms.

Viscosity (n). Resistance to flow.

Volatile (adj). Easily vaporized.

Vulcanization (n). Irreversible treatment of a rubber compound so that the substance is made less plastic and more elastic. The process is accomplished by certain chemical changes, such as an increase in the extent of cross linking, often by sulfur atoms, in the rubber compound.

Wave number (n). The reciprocal of wavelength, generally stated in units of reciprocal centimeters (cm^{-1}). It can be used as a unit of energy because, according to Planck, $E = h\nu = hc/\lambda$.

Wurtzite (n). The less dense α-form of ZnS, the other form being sphalerite.

Zinc blende. See sphalerite.

Zeolites (n). Framework aluminosilicates that contain cavities, into which ions and molecules of various sizes are more or less free to move, and be retained.

index

Printed and Bound by KIN KEONG PRINTING CO. PTE. LTD. - Republic of Singapore.

PHYSICAL AND CHEMICAL CONSTANTS

Avogadro's number $\quad N_A = 6.022045 \times 10^{23}$ mol^{-1}

Electron charge $\quad e = 4.8030 \times 10^{-10}$ abs esu
$\quad = 1.6021892 \times 10^{-19}$ C

Electron mass $\quad m_e = 9.1091 \times 10^{-31}$ kg
$\quad = 5.4860 \times 10^{-4}$ amu
$\quad = 0.5110$ MeV

Proton mass $\quad m_p = 1.6726485 \times 10^{-27}$ kg
$\quad = 1.007276470$ amu

Gas constant $\quad R = 8.31441$ J mol^{-1} K^{-1}
$\quad = 1.9872$ cal mol^{-1} K^{-1}
$\quad = 0.08206$ L atm mol^{-1} K^{-1}

Ice point $\quad = 273.15$ K

Molar volume $\quad = 22.414 \times 10^3$ cm^3 mol^{-1}
$\quad = 2.2414 \times 10^{-2}$ m^3 mol^{-1}

Planck's constant $\quad h = 6.626176 \times 10^{-34}$ J s
$\quad = 6.626176 \times 10^{-27}$ erg s

Boltzmann's constant $\quad k = 1.380662 \times 10^{-23}$ J K^{-1}

Rydberg constant $\quad \Re = 1.097373177 \times 10^{-7}$ m^{-1}

Faraday's constant $\quad \mathcal{F} = 9.648670 \times 10^4$ C mol^{-1}

Speed of light $\quad c = 2.99792458 \times 10^8$ m s^{-1}

Bohr radius $\quad a_0 = 0.52917706 \times 10^{-10}$ m

Other numbers $\quad \pi = 3.14159$
$\quad e = 2.7183$
$\quad \ln 10 = 2.3026$

CONVERSION FACTORS

1 cal $\quad = 4.184$ joules (J)

1 eV/molecule $\quad = 96.485$ kJ mol^{-1}
$\quad = 23.061$ kcal mol^{-1}

1 kcal mol^{-1} $\quad = 349.76$ cm^{-1}
$\quad = 0.0433$ eV

1 kJ mol^{-1} $\quad = 83.54$ cm^{-1}

1 wave number (cm^{-1}) $\quad = 2.8591 \times 10^{-3}$ kcal mol^{-1}

1 erg $\quad = 2.390 \times 10^{-11}$ kcal

1 centimeter (cm) $\quad = 10^8$ Å
$\quad = 10^7$ nm

1 picometer (pm) $\quad = 10^{-2}$ Å

1 nanometer (nm) $\quad = 10$ Å